THE EARTH-SPACE SCIENCES

The New Laidlaw Science Program

MODERN SCIENCE, LEVEL ONE

MODERN SCIENCE, LEVEL TWO

MODERN SCIENCE, LEVEL THREE

MODERN SCIENCE, LEVEL FOUR

MODERN SCIENCE, LEVEL FIVE

MODERN SCIENCE, LEVEL SIX

THE BIOLOGICAL SCIENCES   THE EARTH-SPACE SCIENCES

THE PHYSICAL SCIENCES

THE EARTH-SPACE

SCIENCES

Investigating Man's Environment

DR. ALBERT R. HIBBS
Senior Staff Scientist
Jet Propulsion Laboratory
California Institute of Technology

DR. ALBERT F. EISS
Learning Systems Consultant
West Georgia Educational Service System

LAIDLAW BROTHERS · PUBLISHERS
A Division of Doubleday & Company, Inc.

RIVER FOREST, ILLINOIS
Palo Alto, California   Dallas, Texas   Atlanta, Georgia   Toronto, Canada

ACKNOWLEDGMENTS

The cover was designed by Donald C. Meighan.

The illustrations for THE EARTH-SPACE SCIENCES were drawn by Donald C. Meighan, Donald T. Pitcher, Frank Larocco, and Paul Hazelrigg.

The photographs were supplied through the courtesy and cooperation of many individuals and organizations. Appreciation is expressed particularly to Environmental Science Services Administration (ESSA), Jet Propulsion Laboratory (JPL), Mount Wilson and Palomar Observatories, and National Aeronautics and Space Administration (NASA). Credit is given with each photograph on the page where it appears, except on pages 2, 3, 227, 238, 267, and 370. Credits for photographs on page 2 are as follows. *Top row, left to right:* Zentrale Farbbild Agentur; Zentrale Farbbild Agentur; Harry Engels from National Audubon Society; De Wys, Inc. *Lower left:* Zentrale Farbbild Agentur. *Middle row, left to right:* Zentrale Farbbild Agentur; ESSA. *Bottom row, left to right:* De Wys, Inc.; Authenticated News International. Credits for photographs on page 3 are as follows. *Left:* NASA. *Right, top to bottom:* NASA; Zentrale Farbbild Agentur. Credits for photographs on page 227 are as follows. *Far right, top to bottom:* L. H. Sharp; De Wys, Inc.; L. H. Sharp; Zentrale Farbbild Agentur. Credits for photographs on page 238 are as follows. *Left, top to bottom:* Alaska Pictorial Service; Alaska Pictorial Service; U. S. Department of the Interior, Geological Survey. *Right, top to bottom:* U. S. Department of the Interior, Geological Survey; U. S. Army Photograph. Credits for photographs on page 267 are as follows. *Left top and right middle:* Carl E. Östman. *All others:* Grant Heilman. Credits for photographs on page 370 are as follows. *Left, top and bottom:* G. R. Roberts. *Right, top to bottom:* Steve and Delores McCutcheon, Alaska Pictorial Service; Jerome Wyckoff.

The photograph on page 51 was reproduced by kind permission of The Royal Society, London. Color photographs credited to Mount Wilson and Palomar Observatories on pages 18, 54, 66, 79 *right,* 82, 83, 107, and 130; Copyright © by California Institute of Technology and Carnegie Institution of Washington.

TO THE STUDENT

In some ways, the earth would be quite different if it were not for the presence of living things. Therefore, in any study of the earth, living things must be mentioned. Some evidence indicates that living things have changed through the ages. But how the changes occurred and how the changes should be interpreted are questions that are still to be answered. In this book, some theories about these changes are mentioned. As you study, keep in mind that these are theories, not facts. Science will continue to work for final answers.

CONTENTS

NASA

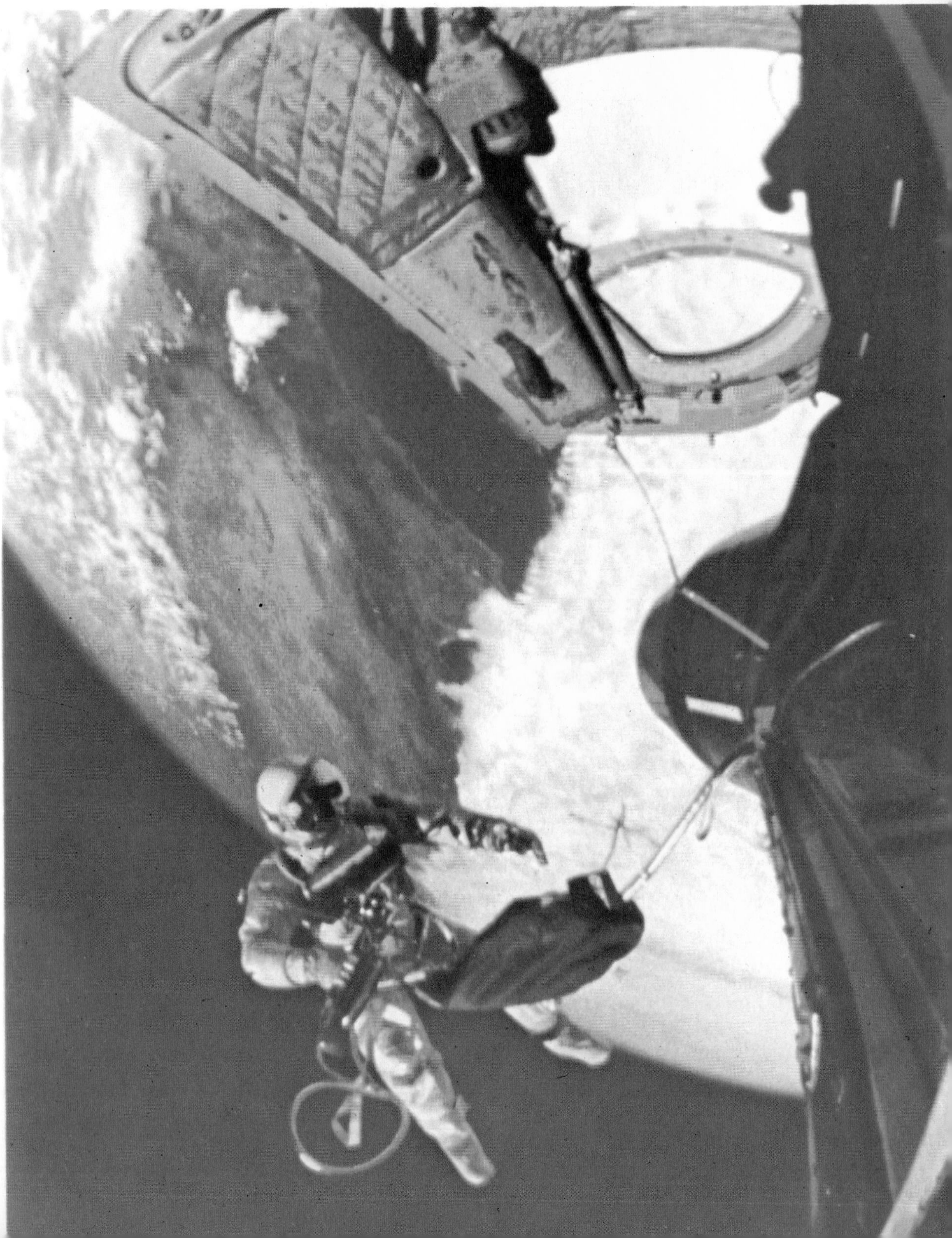

UNIT 1

MAN, SCIENCE, EARTH, AND SPACE

Chapters

1. The Importance of Studying Our Environment
2. How Scientists Study the Earth and Space

There are probably several reasons why you are taking a course in earth and space science. A desire to understand more about your environment should be among these reasons. If this is so, you have a trait very characteristic of humans. You are curious. You want to see for yourself what is going on in the world and, even more important, you probably want to know why things happen as they do.

There is much you can learn about your environment by carefully observing, measuring, and recording what is going on right now. For instance, you might find it is fun to determine and then record the weather conditions as they vary from day to day. Activities like this are not just for enjoyment. They are often useful and important. For example, you might be able to report your findings to a local radio or TV station. Then your observations would contribute to the weather report for your area.

In every field of science, observing and recording are essential. However, scientists usually want to do more than just reconstruct the past. Being able to predict and control the changes in our environment is the final goal. Before this control is realized, however, there must be a great deal of work done in gathering and classifying information. Then the interpretation of the data can result in the discovery of cause and effect relationships. A knowledge of these relationships may in turn lead to ways to control the things which happen in our environment.

The importance of our environment is emphasized in this unit. The differences in the way each type of scientist views the environment are also discussed.

◄ An astronaut "walks" in space to further explore a part of our environment.

CHAPTER 1

The earth as it appears from a distance of 22,300 miles in space.

The Importance of Studying Our Environment

The boundaries of a person's environment change as his age changes. Usually the more mature a person gets, the more aware of his environment he becomes. Aren't you aware of a much larger part of your environment now than you were three or four years ago?

But a person's age is not the only factor that determines the limits of his environment. When was the last time you read about or heard about some new project for the exploration of the earth or of space near the earth? Do you see how these explorations can have an effect upon your environment? Even though they may not increase the physical size of our surroundings, the information obtained will undoubtedly increase our understanding and awareness of our environment.

As you read this chapter you will learn some of the reasons why scientists think it is important that we take a good, close look at our earth and space environment. Perhaps you may have some additional reasons for learning about the earth and space.

1. Why Study the Earth

Our home. Where do you live? Not your address—but where do you *really* live? Do you live on a plain or on the side of a hill? Do you live in a valley with a river close by? Can you see mountains from your school? How far away is the ocean or a lake?

If you live where the land is flat, you know that somewhere there are mountains miles high. Why aren't they closer to you? If you live in the rolling hills, you know that somewhere in the country there is a broad desert of sand stretching off into the distance with only a few dry bushes between you and the horizon. If you live near the ocean, you know that the shore might be a sandy beach in one place and a rocky cliff somewhere else. Why are there such differences?

How did this earth take on so many different shapes? Why is it flat in some places and hilly in others? What caused mountains to be formed where they are—or for that matter, what caused them to be formed at all?

Land forms. Little by little, every year, the earth itself changes. Somewhere on the earth, volcanoes are shooting clouds of smoke and ash into the air and pouring lava down their sides to cover the ground around them. Earthquakes shake the land—sometimes here, sometimes there—and always after an earthquake, the form of the surface is a little bit different.

Sometime you may find a rock which has the mark of an ancient snail shell clearly visible. How long ago did that snail live, and what other creatures lived beside him? Or perhaps you'll pick up a piece of rock with a rough and bubbly surface. Such a rock probably came from some volcano that poured out its lava where you now stand. How long ago was that? Will it happen again?

All of the changes which take place on the surface of the earth do not originate within the earth. There are some changes which are brought about by surface forces. For example,

Figure 1-1. Earthquakes cause change at the earth's surface, as illustrated in the picture on the left. Rivers also cause change—by washing away soil from one place and depositing it in another. Which type of change do you think occurs most rapidly?

all of the rivers and streams that flow through your state are constantly carrying mud and water down their courses—however far they have to go—to the ocean. What happens when all the dirt is washed away? How is the balance kept between the water that the river carries away and the rainfall that replenishes its source?

Materials you will need: eroded slope, ruler

Find a bare slope containing gullies an inch or two wide where running water has carried away part of the soil. Such slopes can frequently be found around new buildings and new road construction. Measure the width and depth of a gully. After a rainstorm, again measure the width and depth of the same gully. Is there a difference in the measurements taken before and after the rainstorm? If so, what does this difference indicate? What measurements could be made in order to determine the volume of the gully?

The atmosphere. The atmosphere is a vast storehouse of energy. Forces more powerful than those developed by any bomb man has ever made can be observed in the weather changes that take place every day. Usually no harm comes when energy is released in the gentle spring rain, but what about the fury of a hurricane or the destruction caused by a tornado? What makes a rainstorm turn into a thunderstorm or into a hurricane? What causes the weather to be clear one day and stormy the next?

In our part of the world, the summers are warmer than the winters. But one summer is hotter than another, and in some winters the storms are so bad that they become legendary

MONKMEYER

Figure 1-2. Studying the atmosphere and attempting to predict its changes accurately require information from all parts of the world. This weather station in the Arctic is the northernmost one in the world. The information obtained from this station and others in a world-wide network of surface stations is supplemented by data from weather satellites.

Figure 1-3. Because of the extreme conditions of pressure and darkness, many features and conditions below the surface of the ocean are difficult to observe. Thus, studying the ocean often requires some very special equipment. Bathyscaphs such as *Trieste* (shown here) and its successor *Trieste II* are capable of going to the deepest parts of the ocean. In 1960, *Trieste* set a world record by going to a depth of 35,800 feet in the Marianas Trench in the Pacific Ocean. During the elevatorlike descents of this strange-looking craft, scientists are able to observe their surroundings from within the white sphere.

WIDE WORLD PHOTOS

—for example, the great blizzards of 1886 and 1887 in the Great Plains of the United States. Thousands of years ago a large part of our country was covered with ice the year-round. Now, only the peaks of high mountains are covered with snow all year. Why do these changes and differences exist? Why doesn't the "weather machine" of the earth work more steadily?

You have probably noticed that each of the observations made about the earth has led to a series of questions. These are just some of the questions that have caused men to study the earth as long as there has been a recorded history of man. These studies have produced some answers, but each answer that is worked out simply opens up new avenues of investigation with more questions to be answered.

The ocean. As if the mysteries of the atmosphere and the land forms of the earth were not enough, the ocean compounds the situation by posing an almost uncountable number of additional problems. Much of our knowledge of the ocean is revealed through the study of fish unlucky enough to find their way into our nets. Of course, we can learn by other means. We can measure how deep the water is, and we can put down thermometers on long cables to measure the temperatures of the deep ocean waters. We can track the surface currents and measure the tides. But sometimes the currents and tides are as confusing as the weather. And down beneath the surface are other currents which we scarcely know about. They are like vast rivers moving across the ocean floor, carrying rocks and mud from one place to another, carving and changing the contour of the ocean bottom. This is the same ocean bottom that may one day be dry land—even as much of the land we walk on now was once the bottom of the sea.

We study the land, the ocean, and the air because, taken together, they are the earth, and the earth is where we live. We want to know about where we live. We want to know how our earth came to be the way it is. We want to know what makes it change, and what changes are likely to take place next.

2. Why Study Space

Our home in space. Just as we live on the earth, so we live in space. The vacuum of space beyond the thin layer of our atmosphere is a dangerous place for man to live—even with the protection of a space suit. Nevertheless, the space through which we move is part of our home, part of our environment.

The nearness of space. Actually, space is a comparatively nearby part of our environment when judged in terms of distance alone. The exact edge of space—the place where we might say the atmosphere ends and space begins—cannot be drawn precisely. However, we might say that space begins about 100 miles above the surface of the earth. How many places that you know of are 100 miles or more away from you? How far is the next reasonably large city, for example? You may have traveled much more than 100 miles on your last vacation and not thought the distance very great.

As you probably know, all the people in the world do not use the same units of measurement. In many parts of the world, the *kilometer* (kil′ ə mē′tər) is the unit used for describing distance. One kilometer does not represent as great a distance as one mile. In fact, a distance of one mile is about 1.6 kilometers. Thus, 100 miles is about the same as 160 kilometers.

Space travel. One reason why we study space is the fact that it, like the earth, is where we live. But a second reason is that now, for the first time in history, man is actually traveling through space beyond the limits of the earth's atmosphere. Ever since man has looked at the moon and stars, he has been making up stories about them. Many of the stories include fantasies about actual travel to these distant bodies. And now, we are building equipment to actually make these incredible journeys.

Figure 1-4. An artist's conception of a space station of the future. Perhaps space stations will be used as stopover points in future trips through space, just as way stations or posthouses were stopover points for early travelers on the continents.

NASA

The Earth

7,900 miles

The Solar System

7,400,000,000 miles

The Milky Way Galaxy
590,000,000,000,000,000 miles

Figure 1-5. The earth seems huge to us. However, it is a mere speck in the vastness of the solar system. The solar system is an even smaller speck in our Milky Way Galaxy. And our immense galaxy is but one of billions in a universe of incredible size.

What we now know (or think we know) about space and the other planets and moons will guide us in planning our first explorations of the solar system. However, we are bound to make some unexpected discoveries which will show that some of our present ideas are wrong. When this happens, we will have to admit the error and use the new discoveries as the basis for revising our theories.

But remember, even though many things have already been accomplished, these feats of landing on and exploring bodies other than our earth will not be easy. The reason is that although space is near, at least in terms of miles alone, it is far in terms of the effort required to get there. No automobile engine would ever carry you on a drive to space. To put you and your spacecraft into an orbit a few hundred miles above the earth takes an enormous amount of energy compared to the amount needed to move you and your car the same distance over the hills and mountains of the earth's surface.

The vastness of space. Beyond the interest in studying our space environment as the place where we live, and beyond the excitement of understanding or participating in the program of space exploration, there lies a deeper reason for studying space. The earth is a planet, moving in its course around the sun. But our planet is only one of many objects which are in such orbits. There are eight other planets— some are bigger and some are smaller. There are comets, asteroids, dust particles, and meteoroids which also make their way around the sun. Some of these smaller bodies actually strike the earth as our orbital path crosses theirs.

The sun, the huge, glowing center of the whole revolving family called the solar system, is only one of a group of billions of stars, half of which are bigger than our sun. This group is our own galaxy, which we have named the Milky Way Galaxy. It is a flat, disklike collection of stars which appears to us, as we look out at it from our position inside it, to be a milky band stretched across the night sky. The band is made up of so many stars that they actually seem to blend together into one continuous ribbon of faint light. But the billions

Figure 1-6. The galaxy NGC 598 is a huge collection of stars and gas clouds. Although this galaxy cannot be seen with the naked eye because of its great distance from us, it can be photographed. This picture of NGC 598 is from a photograph taken through a large telescope. Astronomers estimate that it takes light two million years to travel from this galaxy to the earth.

of stars that make up the faint ribbon of light are all in our own galaxy. Beyond the limits of our galaxy there are countless other galaxies. The galaxies are sprinkled through the vastness of space all about us. Just as stars exist in huge systems called galaxies, galaxies seem to be associated in groups of some kind.

There even appear to be larger units—clusters of groups of galaxies—stretching out so far that they are more distant than we can see even with our best telescopes. Some galaxies are so far away that it takes their light (traveling 186,000 miles per second) more than 2,000,000,000 (2×10^9) years to reach us. There are other objects (scientists are not sure what they are) which are thought to be at least three times farther away than the most distant galaxies we have observed. These ob-

jects were discovered by using radio telescopes —a new addition to the list of tools used in astronomy.

Think of what you see when looking into the sky in the daytime and in the nighttime. Can you see farther into space in the daytime or nighttime? Explain.

If we imagine a model of our galaxy in which the earth is represented by a grain of salt, then the mass of all the stars in our Milky Way Galaxy would correspond to enough salt to fill the Empire State Building. And, of course, there are millions and millions of other galaxies within the range of our telescopes and probably many more beyond the limits of our observation.

DO IT YOURSELF

Make a list

Put today's date at the top of a sheet of paper. Then list all the kinds of space objects you know about. Keep the sheet of paper. Whenever you learn of a new space object, record the date and add the name of the new object to your list. Also write a brief description of the new object. Watch the list grow. Notice how you use the words in your study of earth and space science.

Our place in space. The earth is but a speck of dust in a vast and mighty universe. And yet, it is a very important speck of dust to us. Our relation to the rest of the universe cannot be measured merely in terms of mass, volume, and position. There must be more. Where did we come from? Do other stars have planets revolving about them? If so, are any of them like the earth? Might these planets be inhabited by intelligent creatures?

These questions lead to a much deeper reason for studying space—to better understand our own position in it, a tiny but important speck in a vast collection of other specks. Somehow in the study of these relations, we might be able to figure out how this planet which we live on came to be. A better understanding of the origin of our earth might lead to a better understanding of the life which covers its surface.

We study space because, like the earth, it is our home, and we wish to know (1) how we came to live here, and (2) what our true relationship is to the rest of the universe.

3. Why Study the Earth and Space Together

Earth—unique but not independent. The various forces which shape the earth seem to have their origin in the various portions of the earth itself. The forces of the wind and water which move across its surface seem to come from the atmosphere itself. The eruption of volcanoes and the outpouring of lava seem to be releasing energy from some mysterious heat engine in the center of the earth. The adjustment of imbalances in the weight of rocks and of dirt as they are redistributed over the earth causes earthquakes which produce disastrous forces. And yet, all of these earthly forces have had their origin somewhere else. The vast mechanism of the weather machine—which creates the winds and the rains, gives rise to the rivers and their erosion of the land, and pushes waves against the shoreline—is driven by the sun. The energy from deep within the earth's center, some of which is released through volcanoes or as earthquakes, probably is the result of the breaking up of the atomic nuclei of certain elements. These elements were part of the earth when it was formed about 4,000,000,000 (4×10^9) years ago. These elements are *radioactive* (rā'di ō ak'tiv), which means that they are constantly

INTERNATIONAL VISUAL AIDS CENTER

Figure 1-7. Great amounts of energy are released from the earth's interior when a volcano erupts. What is the source of this energy? Theories about this energy have been proposed, but, as yet, no definite answer to the question has been found.

changing because the nuclei of the atoms in them are breaking up. Energy is released in the process.

Radioactive minerals are changing because their atomic nuclei are breaking up. What do you think becomes of an atom when its nucleus breaks apart? Do you suppose it all changes into energy? Is anything left? How fast, do you think, do these changes take place?

The earth is a planet. The earth was collected out of space in some unknown way from a mixture of those same chemical elements that make up the sun and the most distant stars. It is as much a part of space as a child is part of its parents.

Each member of your family has individual characteristics. The earth—as a member of the space family—has its own individual characteristics. For example, although the earth resembles its planetary brothers in many ways, it has an atmosphere that is quite unique. Why it has this unique atmosphere is not known, but some very interesting theories about the causes are being widely discussed.

Because the earth is so much a part of the space in which it moves, we assume that the laws that man has formulated in his earth-bound laboratories (such as the law of gravity) are universal laws. That is, they will accurately describe the nature of things on the moon or anywhere else in the universe just as they do on earth. So if we ever understand the origin, history, and present condition of the earth we will also have a better understanding of the origin, history, and present condition of the rest of the universe.

Extending our knowledge. We are already using our knowledge of the earth, which we have gained by on-the-spot exploration, to build theories about the possible nature of the moon and planets. As firsthand knowledge of these other bodies becomes available, we can use this new knowledge to improve our theories about the earth.

For example, many scientists believe that the earth has a core composed of molten iron. They think the earth is large enough to have retained enough of the heat generated by the radioactive elements it contains to heat up its interior until the rocks melted. The iron, being more dense, then settled into the center. If we extend this theory and the reasoning which lies behind it to the other planets, we would guess that Venus might be similarly constructed. But probably Mars, and even more probably the moon, would never have become so hot. Consequently, they would have no liquid core—iron or otherwise. Detailed examination of the moon and other planets will provide data to either substantiate or disprove this theory.

Figure 1-8. This picture of the earth's interior is based on present knowledge. As studies of the earth and space yield more information, the picture may have to be changed.

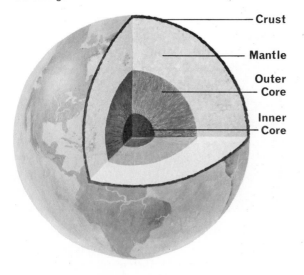

Crust

Mantle

Outer Core

Inner Core

THE EARTH'S STRUCTURE

20

At the same time, there are other scientists who think that the core of the earth is not iron at all. Instead they believe it to be composed of rock, similar to that nearer the surface. The only difference is that the vast pressure of the earth's interior has squeezed the rock into a particularly dense mineral form. This form is unlike anything seen on the surface of the earth, and unlike anything which can be produced with our comparatively limited laboratory equipment.

Theories about the structure of the earth do vary. A theory proposed by a scientist who believes the earth's core is iron will differ from a theory proposed by a scientist who thinks the earth's core is rock. Such uncertainty about the exact nature of the earth's core leads to uncertainty concerning the earth's magnetic field. The earth's magnetic field is, in some ways, related to the position of the land forms on the earth's surface, so even the land forms are related to the nature of the earth's core. You can see that extending our knowledge of the earth's core will lead to a better understanding of several other features of the earth. But how can we determine which theory of the earth's core—the iron theory or the rock theory—is correct? A firsthand examination of some of the other objects in the solar system would aid in that determination. Making such an examination would be a good illustration of how we extend our knowledge by studying space. We not only learn a great deal about space and the other objects in space, but we also add to our knowledge of our own planet.

The interdependence of earth and space. All of this—the nature and history of the earth's core and the magnetic field which may (or may not) be associated with it—is simply one small detail in the overall study of the earth. And yet, a scientist studying this detail will quickly find himself studying questions of the history and origin of the solar system and the stars themselves. So it is with other questions of the earth or of space. The scientist who studies the earth is continually asking questions about the nature of the other parts of the universe. In the same manner, the scientist who studies space must refer to the earth for examples and evidence of natural occurrences. After all, the earth is still the only planet we can observe directly. Our planet earth is, therefore, our most convenient source of information.

In science there are many examples of two fields which are linked together by common problems and common methods of scientific research. For instance, a knowledge of chemistry is essential for the study of biology. Terms such as biochemistry have come into use because many biologists must use the same methods and equipment for their studies that the chemist uses. A growing list of names such as biophysics, physical chemistry, geochemistry, and astrophysics indicates that the various fields of science are more related than they are unrelated.

But earth science and space science are linked together in a particularly close and natural way. It is not just convenient to study the earth and space together. It is essential. Consider the research now being carried out in space. The information gained in some space projects has added to our knowledge of the earth as well as to our knowledge of space. Weather satellites, for example, have advanced man's knowledge of the movements of weather conditions to a world-wide scale. Also, observations of the orbits of man-made satellites have yielded information concerning the shape and mass of the earth. Thus, information about the earth can be gained through space studies and vice versa. The earth and space are studied together because that is the way they are in nature.

Checking Your Knowledge

IMPORTANT IDEAS

1. Our environment on earth includes the land, the atmosphere, and the oceans.

2. We study the earth so we can reconstruct the past and predict (maybe even control) events in the future.

3. Only the thin blanket of our atmosphere separates us from our space environment.

4. We assume that scientific laws are as valid in space as they are on earth.

5. Space travel will enable scientists to verify or disprove some theories of the solar system now held by scientists.

6. The universe, as we know it now, is incredibly vast.

USING NEW WORDS

The list below contains words used in the study of the earth and space. You may already be familiar with these words and their meanings. If not, you should become acquainted with them, because an understanding of the words used is essential to learning about the earth and space.

kilometer	lava	blizzard
galaxy	meteoroid	solar system
tornado	atmosphere	hurricane
volcano	earthquake	magnetic field
universe	radioactive	thunderstorm
orbit	asteroid	planet

1. List on your paper, in separate columns, those words related to the study of space, of the weather, and of the earth.

2. Explain the differences between a hurricane, a tornado, and a blizzard.

3. Write a description of the relationship between lava and volcano.

4. Which words name objects or regions found in space?

TEST YOURSELF

Study the test below. On your paper, write the numerals *1-10*. After each numeral write the correct response to that part of the test with the corresponding numeral.

1. When the size of our sun is compared with the sizes of the other stars in the galaxy, our sun is (*one of the largest, about average, one of the smallest*).

2. Our sun is larger than any other object in (*the universe, the Milky Way Galaxy, the solar system*).

3. Of the objects in space named (*an asteroid, the North Star, a large planet, a comet*), which one would not be found in the solar system?

4. Of the objects in space named, the one which is farthest from the earth is (*the nearest star, the nearest planet, the nearest galaxy, the nearest meteoroid*).

5. Of the following list of space objects, the largest one is (*the moon, the sun, the Milky Way Galaxy*).

6. Just as the earth is part of the solar system, our sun is part of a large system of stars called ____.

7. The speed at which light travels through space is ____ miles per second. This speed is equivalent to a speed of ____ kilometers per second.

8. Melted rock is very often associated with an active volcano. The name which has been given to the melted rock flowing from a volcano is ____.

9. If an element gives off heat and other kinds of energy because the nuclei of its atoms are breaking up, that element is said to be ____.

10. Moving air or water wears away the soil. This process is called ____.

Extending Your Knowledge

QUESTIONS TO EXPLORE

1. What features would you look for in a space suit if you were planning a space trip?

2. A pencil mark is about 1/20 of an inch wide (if your pencil is pretty dull!). What radius would you use to draw a circle representing the earth if the pencil line represented the 100-mile thick atmosphere? HINT: Use 4,000 miles as the earth's radius.

3. In the text it is stated that according to one theory, the moon would not have a molten core such as the earth is believed to have. On the basis of what you learned in this chapter, how would you explain this difference in structure?

4. In this chapter the terms *weather machine* and *heat engine* are used. Are these real machines? If so, what are these machines like? If not, what do the terms mean?

5. Suppose that you were asked to testify before a government space committee considering the space budget for the next fiscal year. What arguments could you give for continuing our program of space exploration? For discontinuing it? For changing it?

6. The earth has several features which the other planets in the solar system do not. List some of the features that make the earth unique among the planets.

SOME THINGS TO DO

1. Prepare a skit (for use at a science club meeting or as a presentation to the class) to illustrate the steps taken by man in accumulating his knowledge of the solar system. This is an activity for a small group rather than for an individual.

2. Using magnets, the ends of which are marked N and S, find out which poles of a magnet attract each other. Then find out how one of the magnets will align itself if it is free to swing—that is, if you use the magnet as a compass needle. Which way does the pole marked N point? If you were going to label the north magnetic pole of the earth, would you use an N or an S?

3. Use reference materials to find the meaning of astrology. Is astrology a science? Find out what connection, if any, exists between astronomy and astrology.

4. List the changes in your community you have observed in your lifetime. How many of these are man-made? Are man-made changes or natural changes more commonly observed? Which are more permanent?

CHALLENGES IN SCIENCE

1. Most scientists think that the interior of the earth is very hot. What evidence is there to support this belief? What are some theories which would account for a very high temperature at the earth's center?

2. Certain things are believed to be the same everywhere in the universe. For instance, the speed of light, the law of universal gravitation, and the equivalence of matter and energy ($E = mc^2$). Suppose we suddenly discovered that light does not travel at the same speed everywhere in space, that the law of gravitation is not universally true, and that $E = mc^2$ is a correct statement only for situations within the Milky Way Galaxy. How would these discoveries affect the field of earth and space science?

3. Using a grain of sand to represent our sun, figure out how far away you would place another grain of sand to represent the nearest star. What would be the diameter of a "galaxy" of grains of sand? NOTE: You will have to determine the diameter of an average grain of sand. How can you do this?

GENERAL ELECTRIC COMPANY

Specialists put final touches on a weather satellite.

CHAPTER 2

How Scientists Study the Earth and Space

Have you ever noticed that when a group of people perform together, whether it is a football team, a combo, the cast of a play, or a pit crew at an automobile race, each person in the group does something different? In spite of the differences in the things individuals are doing, the group as a whole is working toward a common goal. The group is working as a team.

Putting together an accurate description of the earth and space also requires teamwork. Because of the many types of problems encountered, and many other factors, one person cannot do a satisfactory job of securing and interpreting all the data necessary for a study of the earth and space. Thus, different people have concentrated their efforts in particular fields of earth and space science.

In your study of this chapter, you will find out what these different fields are, how the scientists work in each field, and, most important, how all of the efforts of these scientists go together to give a more accurate and meaningful description of the earth and space. Do you think that you would be interested in becoming a part of the team involved in the exploration of earth and space?

1. Fields of Study in the Earth and Space Sciences

The need for specialization. The scientists who study the earth and space, like all other scientists, are trying to better understand the way things happen. Of course, if a scientist tried to study and understand every one of the natural phenomena on earth and in space in one lifetime, he would have a hopeless task. As a scientist learns more and more about the general workings of nature, he becomes interested in certain special problems. In fact, even the title, "The Earth-Space Sciences" is a label which indicates only certain branches of science, although at first it seems as if it should include everything in the universe.

Thus, when a scientist says he studies the earth, he usually does not mean to include the living things on the earth. Instead, he usually is referring to the earth's rocks and soils, the *lithosphere* (lith′ə sfir); the waters of the earth, the *hydrosphere* (hī′drə sfir); and the gases which surround the earth, the *atmosphere* (at′mə sfir).

Fields of study overlap. It is not possible to make hard and fast rules about what is or is not included in some particular field of science. In general, the scientists who study the earth are not primarily concerned with living things. Nevertheless, they cannot ignore the effects living things have on the earth and its parts. For example, a scientist involved in the study of the atmosphere would very quickly encounter the theory that green plants, through the process of photosynthesis, have produced and continue to maintain the present amount of free oxygen in our atmosphere. Another scientist involved in the study of sedimentary rocks would find himself concerned with the way limestone forms. In the formation of limestone, the shells of millions and millions of tiny sea animals pile up on the ocean floor. They become cemented together to form layers of limestone. In some places these layers are hundreds of feet thick. Although the study of the earth is mainly concerned with things that are not alive, the activities of living things, including man himself, must be taken into account by those scientists who study the earth.

How do the scientists who study space define their subject? Some of them say that everything outside the atmosphere of the earth is in their field of study. Of course, they have difficulty in deciding exactly where the atmosphere of the earth ends. Some of these scientists have undertaken as their specialty the study of this

AUTHENTICATED NEWS INTERNATIONAL

Figure 2-1. A team of researchers obtains a sample of sediment from the bottom of one of the Great Lakes. The study of such samples is but one of many different types of research being carried on in the various fields of earth science.

very problem—namely, what is the nature and behavior of the outer edge of the earth's atmosphere?

Space is said to begin where the atmosphere ends. How would you define "where the atmosphere ends"?

There are many objects in space. There are many phenomena taking place in space. No one scientist could possibly study them all. Thus, scientists specialize in particular fields of study. Some scientists specialize in the study of stars. Others are particularly concerned with the planets. Still others try to learn the nature of the gases that exist in space between the stars and the possible kinds of magnetic fields which may affect this interstellar region of space.

Sometimes scientists have to study things which do not seem to be related at the time

Figure 2-2. Samples of the earth's crust can be examined in a laboratory. But no material from deep within the earth—and only small samples from objects in space—have been brought into a laboratory.

they are studied. As an example, consider cosmic rays and galaxies. Before interacting with our atmosphere, cosmic rays are the tiny nuclei or central cores of atoms. A galaxy is the largest object we can observe. Would you believe that a study of cosmic rays would lead to investigations of galaxies? A description of how it happened follows.

For many years physicists have been studying the behavior of cosmic rays. It has been discovered that cosmic rays originate somewhere in space. When the tiny particles called cosmic rays enter the earth's atmosphere, they have an extremely high velocity and, therefore, they have a great deal of energy. Even using the most powerful particle accelerators (atom smashers) available, scientists cannot give as much energy to tiny subatomic particles as that which cosmic rays have when they enter the earth's atmosphere. The source of these cosmic rays is still a mystery, but there is evidence that the origin of cosmic rays must be somewhere within the galaxies of stars. No other object could contain the huge sources of energy needed to accelerate these cosmic particles in their flight through space. For this reason, physicists who are concerned with the nature and origin of cosmic rays find themselves studying the nature and structure of galaxies.

Making observations. The scientists who study space have a very special problem. They seldom get a chance to touch the objects they are studying or to bring them into a laboratory for examination. A *geologist* (ji ol′ə jist) can bring a rock into his laboratory. There he can crush the rock, dissolve it in acid, or conduct any other test he knows of in order to find out what elements are present as well as how much of each element is present. Through careful analysis of rock samples, he gains a better understanding of the nature of the mountain range where he found the rocks. He might also

Figure 2-3. Looking through a telescope is not the only way to study a star. Scientists must use many other instruments to analyze the light from a star.

ZENTRALE FARBILD AGENTUR

DE WYS, INC.

Figure 2-4. An astronomy teacher uses diagrams to explain Kepler's laws. These important laws concerning satellite orbits were derived by combining observations and reasoning.

gain some knowledge of how the mountain range is related to the countryside around it.

Using reasoning. A scientist studying a star cannot use direct observation, since he has no way of bringing parts of the star to his laboratory for analysis. Instead, to determine what kind of gases are in the star's atmosphere, he uses instruments to analyze the light which shines from the outer surface of the star. If he wishes to propose a theory about the makeup of the interior of the star, he must make his hypothesis by using a process of reasoning. That is, the proposed hypothesis is the result of inferences made on the basis of observations.

Although the geologist has a certain advantage over the astronomer in being able to observe materials of the earth directly, the advantage is limited. The geologist can look only so far down into the earth. Even the deepest holes he has been able to drill provide samples of the rock from only a few miles beneath the surface. The center of the earth is almost 4,000 miles farther down. The geologist, too, must rely on inferences based on observation to re-

late the things he can test and measure to the vast volume of the earth which is beyond his reach.

Combining observations and reasoning. In the study of the earth and space, measurements must be combined with reasoning in order to gain the sort of understanding which the scientist seeks. In his search for an understanding of natural phenomena, a scientist hypothesizes as to why things occur as they do. The hypothesis is not just a wild guess. It is based on evidence. The scientist who makes the hypothesis, along with many other scientists, will use a combination of reasoning and observation in testing and retesting the hypothesis to be sure that it agrees with the general laws of science and with all the observations that have been made.

For example, how does a star begin, and how does it grow? How long will a star last, and what happens to it as it grows older? Some scientists have worked out theories to describe the evolution of a star, but, of course, it is impossible to check these theories directly. We have no time machine to alter time by the billions of years that would be needed to see whether or not a star goes through the various steps that fit the theory. Except for the sun we cannot get close enough to any star to measure directly any of the characteristics, such as size, which the theory of stellar evolution describes.

Nevertheless, scientists still check the theories. The laws of physics, which can be tested in earth-based laboratories, describe the way matter and energy are related. As far as we

can tell, these rules apply throughout the universe. Therefore, we can apply mathematics and the laws of physics in determining the characteristics of a distant star.

By combining scientific observations, the general laws of nature as discovered in our laboratories, and the mathematics needed to organize our thinking, we can relate the nature and history of distant stars to the nature and history of many of the things we see around us every day.

2. Astronomers and Astrophysicists

Scientists who study space. The scientists who study the objects in space and the phenomena taking place in space are *astronomers* (ə stron′ə merz) and *astrophysicists* (as′trō fiz′ə sists). Although these names stand for two different kinds of scientists, it is difficult to make a sharp distinction between the roles played by each of them.

The distinction is not based on what is studied, for both the astronomer and the astrophysicist have the same general subject of study—that is, the nature of space and the objects in space. The difference between the two kinds of scientists lies mainly in the type of understanding each seeks to gain. But there is another difference—a difference in their

CALIFORNIA INSTITUTE OF TECHNOLOGY

Figure 2-5. Astronomers who study stars and galaxies get most of their information by studying the spectra of these objects. Shown below are some spectra obtained from various light sources. Spectrum 5 is the sun's spectrum. The picture on the left is of Dr. Maarten Schmidt of the Mt. Wilson and Palomar Observatories. He is examining a small photographic plate of a spectrum. A microscope, such as the one shown, is used to make a detailed analysis of such small spectra.

LOWELL OBSERVATORY PHOTOGRAPH

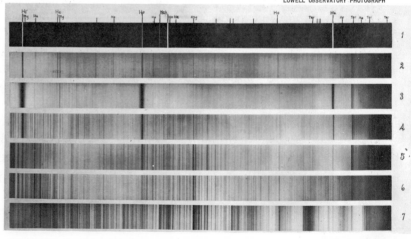

methods—as you shall see in the following paragraphs.

Astronomers. An astronomer is a person who studies the appearance and movements of objects in space. He measures the orbits of the planets and their moons. As precisely and accurately as possible, he determines the positions and colors of stars, and—for stars of particular interest—he makes a detailed analysis of the light coming from them.

The astronomer is highly trained in the use of a telescope. He knows how to set up and operate a *spectrometer* (spek trom'ə tər)—an instrument used to separate light into a band of colors called a *spectrum*. Measurement of the wave length of each of the colors of light present can then be made. This information can be used to tell which chemical elements are present in the star being observed. The information can also be used to tell something about the motion of the star. An astronomer, in order to take measurements which are of particular interest to him, may well design his own equipment.

An astronomer studying other galaxies is able to determine their brightness and position by taking photographs of the galaxies. Using a large telescope, he focuses the dim light from a faraway galaxy onto photographic film, and allows the film to be exposed to that light for a long period of time. Using this technique, along with the correct type of film, he obtains photographs of distant galaxies—galaxies much too faint to be seen directly with his own eyes, even when using a telescope.

Astrophysicists. An astrophysicist is concerned with the makeup of stars and galaxies. Much of his work is theoretical. He makes use of the observations of the astronomer to determine what elements exist in various stars, as well as the relative amounts of each element. It is the astrophysicist who formulates and then tries to substantiate or disprove the theories concerning the birth, development, and final death of a star.

The astrophysicist is skilled in the use of mathematics. He uses mathematics just as the astronomer uses his telescope. The astrophysicist works with the fundamental laws of physics, such as the law of universal gravitation, just as the astronomer works with the rules which control the operation of his spectrometer. Thus, mathematics and physics are the basic tools of the astrophysicist.

The astrophysicist also writes down a theoretical description of the characteristics of the materials of space. He works to make sure that his descriptions do not disagree with the things that scientists already know about physics and about space. He carefully checks his theories against the observations and measurements made by astronomers. He even extends his theories to the things the astronomers cannot see. For example, astrophysicists attempt to describe the various magnetic fields that are thought to exist within and between the galaxies. They even try to determine the nature of stars which exploded billions of years ago, the only remnants of which may be the cosmic rays which speed through space, some to strike the surface of the earth.

3. Geologists, Geochemists, and Geophysicists

Scientists who study the earth. The word *geology* (ji ol'ə ji) means the study of the earth. For many years, all the scientists who took part in this study were called geologists. But, in more recent times, the field of earth science has expanded so greatly that geologists

GRANT HEILMAN

Figure 2-6. Coal (left) and diamond (below) are two materials composed of the same element—carbon. However, the arrangement of the carbon atoms in coal differs from that in diamond. Because of this difference in arrangement, the physical properties of coal are very different from those of diamond.

WARD'S NATURAL SCIENCE ESTABLISHMENT, INC.

find themselves specializing in separate fields of study within geology. Today there are many different classifications for the men and women who study the earth. These classifications include geochemists, geophysicists, seismologists, glaciologists, petroleum geologists, and still others. But of all these fields, the most widely studied areas are *geology, geochemistry,* and *geophysics.*

Geologists. The geologist can claim to be carrying on the work of the first scientists who studied the earth. Like the astronomer, he is concerned with the way things look and how they behave. He measures the positions of various kinds of rock. He carefully identifies the rocks themselves, noting the kinds of minerals which occur in them. The atoms in rocks arrange themselves in various orders, many

of them being beautiful crystals. Two rocks which look different may be composed of the same elements. The rocks look different because the atoms have arranged themselves into different crystal structures. Thus, geologists must look not only at what chemicals are in the rocks, but also at how these chemicals are combined and how the atoms are arranged. This is the study of minerals, or *mineralogy* (min′ə ral′ə ji).

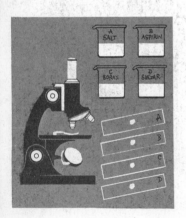

FIND OUT BY TRYING

Materials you will need: a microscope, microscope slides, solutions of salt, sugar, aspirin, borax, or any other substance you wish to examine

Place a drop of one of the solutions on a microscope slide. Allow the solution to evaporate. Examine with the microscope any material remaining on the slide. Is the material a shapeless mass or is there evidence of crystals? Repeat with other solutions. Can you notice any difference in the residue of one solution when compared with the residue from another solution? If there are differences, could the differences be used to identify the substances?

The geologist is trained to recognize different kinds of rocks quite quickly and seldom needs to carry a rock back to the laboratory to decide what it is. He is trained to make maps and to use them to trace out the locations of mineral deposits or the flow of a field of lava.

When a geologist is studying a particular portion of the earth, he walks over it, noting the position of the different kinds of rocks he finds. Using these observations he seeks to determine the sequence of events which might have happened to make that portion of the earth look the way it does.

On the side of a cliff, for example, the geologist may find a rock with fossils in it which indicate that the area was once the bottom of an ocean. He recognizes the straight lines in the rock as corresponding to the layers of mud and sea shells which gradually piled up to form this rock. But now the layers are not level. They are tilted, and he measures the angle of the tilt. Running through a crack in this rock is a thin vein of quartz, which he knows was formed in a different way: by melt-ing and then cooling. He begins to understand the history of the cliff and the history of that portion of the lithosphere of which the cliff is a part.

The cliff may be beside the bank of a stream. If so, he can figure out how much soil the water in that stream must have carried away in order to dig the channel through which it now runs. After he has accumulated enough information, the geologist may be able to write the story of this portion of the surface of the earth.

Rivers constantly carry soil and rock particles to the ocean. What reasons can you give to explain why all the soil and rock particles are not now in the ocean?

GRANT HEILMAN

Figure 2-8. An experienced geologist can often learn a great deal about the past history of a place by studying a land form such as this cliff composed of various layers of rock.

Figure 2-7. The Grand Canyon is more than just a beautiful sight. By studying the position and composition of the exposed layers of rock, geologists can reconstruct some of the history of the region.

AUTHENTICATED NEWS INTERNATIONAL

Geochemists. The *geochemist* (jē'ō kem' ist) studies the chemical composition of the materials in the earth's crust. He examines the mineral specimens which the geologist brings back to the laboratory. But he wants to do more than simply recognize them and tell the difference between one and another. He wants to find answers to the following questions: How were those minerals formed? How hot was the volcano from which this particular bit of lava came? Why do some portions of the surface of the earth have more iron in them than others?

Although some elements, such as silicon and oxygen, are quite common in all of the earth's rocks, some other elements are very rare. The distribution of the elements in the lithosphere poses many questions which the geologist wishes to be able to answer. Two basic questions are these: In what manner were the elements distributed between one portion of the earth and the next? How does the presence of rare elements affect the nature of the minerals in which they occur?

The geochemist must be very skillful in the use of laboratory equipment. He must devise ways of measuring the abundance of elements which make up less than one millionth of the sample with which he is dealing. He must figure out how different minerals were formed, what kind of pressures must have been placed on the rock, and what the temperatures were when a particular crystal was formed.

Many years ago, Leonardo da Vinci, an early scientist with many abilities, said that the secrets of nature lie in her details. The geochemist is seeking out these secrets in the minute details of the chemistry of the earth's rocks and soil.

Geophysicists. The *geophysicist* (jē'ō fiz'ə sist) seeks to understand the earth's internal structure. He wants to know the cause of volcanoes and why there are earthquakes. For

Figure 2-9. These men are studying a record which represents movements of the earth's crust. Such records reveal features of the earth's subsurface structure which have never been seen.

example, he attempts to figure out the temperature deep within the earth's interior, thousands of miles below the surface.

Like the astrophysicist, the geophysicist uses observations, mathematics, and the natural laws derived in the laboratory in his attempt to understand the structure of a part of the earth or, perhaps, the earth as a whole. He tries to figure out the history of the earth—how it was formed, and what forces have modified it to its present appearance. He would like to know where mountains come from, and why new mountain ranges are being built in one place while in another place old mountains are being worn away.

Different approaches to a problem. The geologist, the geochemist, and the geophysicist could quite possibly find themselves cooperating in order to solve a problem. In some cases, the problem may also be one for the astronomer and the astrophysicist. Suppose a geologist, on a walk across the desert, found a *meteorite* (mē′ti ə rīt). In spite of the fact that it might look like an ordinary rock to most people, the geologist would very likely recognize it for what it was—a piece of matter which had reached the earth from outer space. The geochemist might determine that the minerals in this meteorite are different from anything ever seen in earthly rock. Some of the *trace elements* (chemical elements usually present in only very minute amounts) in the meteorite would probably be present in greater abundance than is typical for rocks of the

earth. The geophysicist might try to describe the kind of planet or asteroid that broke up to produce this particular rock. But determining the nature and position of asteroids and planets is a problem for the astronomer. Furthermore, determining the forces in space which might cause such a body to break up into a mass of rocklike meteoroids is a problem for the astrophysicist.

Each of these scientists will have his portion of theory to add to the story of the meteorite, and each one must rely upon the others to help determine if his portion of the theory is correct. Of course, each of these scientists must also be ready to admit that the theory as a whole, or his part of it, could be wrong, for the origin of meteorites is still a mystery.

4. Meteorologists and Oceanologists

Meteorologists. The study of the weather is the science of *meteorology* (mē′ti ə rol′ə ji). It is the meteorologist's job to figure out the behavior of the ocean of air which covers the surface of the earth. He knows many of the laws of science which govern the behavior of the atmosphere, but his problem is to figure out how to apply these rules.

He realizes that the atmosphere operates on a "budget" of energy. The main "income" of energy is from the direct rays of the sun. The "expense" of energy is also in the form of radiation, but mostly of a different sort. Between the time the energy is absorbed from the sun and radiated back into space, it is used in several ways. Some of the energy is used to evaporate water. This energy is given back to the atmosphere when the water vapor condenses into rain. The return of this energy to the atmosphere may happen many miles from where it was originally absorbed. Some of the incoming energy heats the soil or the atmos-

phere itself, causing currents and winds in the atmosphere. Eventually, however, the energy is radiated back into space so that, over a long period of time, the income and outflow of energy tend to be equal.

If income is compared to outflow for short periods, a month or two for example, we usually find that income does not equal outflow. As you probably guessed, in the summer more energy is coming in than is leaving. The excess energy is warming up the soil and the atmosphere. In winter more energy is leaving than is coming in. Thus, some of the energy used for evaporation of water and producing air currents is coming from the earth and from the air itself, causing a general lowering of the temperature.

The earth receives only a very tiny fraction of the total energy radiated by the sun. What happens to the rest of the sun's energy?

All the exchanges of energy must fit into the framework of the laws of conservation of energy. Also, the motions of the air must be such that they can be described by Newton's laws of motion. You can see that the task of understanding and predicting the weather is one of almost overwhelming complexity.

It is the job of the meteorologist to try to explain this complexity. Using special theories which allow him to apply his mathematical skills, he hopes not only to keep abreast of the changes in the weather; he also seeks ways to predict it. Perhaps as the meteorologist's understanding of the atmosphere increases, we will one day be able to control the weather. But when we look at all the complications which are now in the way of simply predicting it, controlling the weather seems to be a very distant goal.

Oceanology—studying the ocean. The atmosphere is not the only part of the earth which carries heat from one place to another. The surface waters of the oceans absorb heat

Figure 2-10. Meteorologists use complex equipment, such as computers and radar, in order to accurately predict and report atmospheric conditions at various places throughout the world.

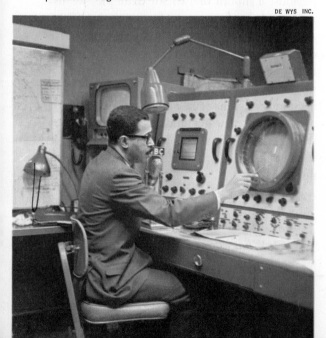

from the sun's rays. Near the equator the more direct rays result in warmer water. This additional heat is carried by the ocean currents to the colder regions farther north or farther south. Along the way, the waters exchange the heat back and forth with the air above them, and then, if clouds should form, some heat from the sun is reflected back into space. In a short time, as these conditions change, the behavior of the atmosphere—or what we usually call the weather—also changes.

You can see how the meteorologist and the *oceanologist* (ō'shən ol'ə jist) often find themselves working hand in hand. Either directly or indirectly, many of the important surface currents in the ocean are driven by the wind; therefore, they are a result of the weather. The ocean currents in turn carry heat to the different places of the earth and, in doing so, help to control the weather. The ocean currents also carry minerals from one point to another, and the deep currents of the ocean erode the ocean bottom, moving vast slides of mud and ooze down the slopes of undersea mountains.

Just as the laws of physics can describe the behavior of the atmosphere, so do they describe the behavior of the ocean. But the ocean is so complex that knowledge of these fundamental laws is only a beginning. Furthermore, the oceanologist has a special problem that the meteorologist does not have. The oceanologist can see only the top of the sea. Although he knows that the bottom is crossed with ridges and canyons and covered with mountain ranges, some of them steeper and more rugged than those on the dry land surface, he cannot see these features. Yet these formations on the ocean floor control many of the currents that he is studying. Like other scientists, the oceanologist must be a skillful mathematician, and also be well trained in the use of special measuring devices.

Figure 2-11. The ocean is a challenge to scientists. In addition to its size, many of its features are unseen from the surface. In the picture at the left, an instrument is being readied for lowering into the ocean. The picture above is of scientists recording data they have collected about the oceans of air and water about them.

There are weather stations all over the world, some of them completely automatic, which relay weather information by radio to a central meteorological station for analysis. The oceanologist has many fewer stations to tell him the condition of the sea, and he certainly has a much greater difficulty in mapping the sea bottom. He must use *sonar*—a method of sending sound signals to the bottom of the sea and listening for their echo—in order to map the ocean floor.

A special problem for meteorologists and oceanologists. Astronomers and geologists are usually concerned with things which take place over hundreds of millions or even billions of years. However, meteorologists and oceanologists are looking at changes which take place within a few months or a few days, sometimes within a few minutes. The astronomer can photograph again a galaxy he looked at years before, and so check the theories of the astrophysicist. The geologist can bring back another rock from the same mountain he visited years before, but the oceanologist and meteorologist find that their subjects of study have changed before they even had a chance to work out their latest theory. Understanding these changes and trying to keep up with them is one of the greatest challenges to scientists in these fields.

5. Engineers and Technicians

The engineer's role. You may not have a clear understanding of the term engineer. Is an engineer just another type of scientist? Or do engineers have an altogether different kind of job? An engineer must have a knowledge and understanding of the basic scientific laws. Also, he usually works with scientists, but he is not a scientist in the true sense. While the scientist is a discoverer, finding new knowledge and formulating theories to explain his observations, the role of the engineer is more like that of a builder. The scientist uncovers new knowledge, and the engineer puts the knowledge to work.

As scientists and engineers work together, the result is an ever-widening spiral in which increased knowledge leads to improvements in instruments and techniques. These, in turn, lead to further increases in knowledge. For example, scientists discovered the electron and formulated theories which described its behavior. Using this knowledge, engineers were able to produce "electron guns" capable of producing streams of fast-moving electrons. Scientists then used these electron guns for further studies of electrons. They discovered the effect that electric and magnetic fields have on electron streams, or cathode rays as they are sometimes called. Engineers have used the knowledge of these effects in producing more sophisticated cathode ray tubes, such as oscilloscopes and television tubes. Thus, the spiral of more knowledge leading to better instruments which give increased knowledge keeps widening.

In addition, the by-products of these combined endeavors are often valuable. In working with electrons, for example, scientists needed more complete vacuums, so the engineers devised ways to produce them. The knowledge that was gained about producing vacuums has, in turn, benefited many other areas of science and industry.

An example of teamwork. Engineers need to know the basic laws of science. In addition, they need to understand what the scientist wants to accomplish. Consider the flight of the space probe called *Mariner IV*. This complex space vehicle was launched by huge rockets, it was tracked by radar, and its path was precisely controlled from the earth. Two hundred twenty-eight days later, after the spacecraft had traveled more than 325,000,000 (3.25×10^8) miles in a curved path to reach Mars, television cameras took pictures and relayed information back 134,000,000 (1.34×10^8) miles through space to the earth so that the pictures could be reconstructed. This was an astonishing achievement.

Who did the job? The answer is that it was a combined effort of scientists and engineers. Accomplishments such as this cannot be carried out unless scientists have provided the foundation for them. For example, the laws of mechanics which were required in order to predict the launching and the path of the space vehicle had been formulated. The theory of radio transmission—for relaying information back and forth from the earth to the spacecraft—was well developed. These and many other principles provided the scientific basis for the project. But it was the engineers' job to put all the elements together into a workable piece of equipment.

Technicians. Technicians are also important members of the team that is working together to learn more about the earth and about space. The job of a technician is to use and maintain the equipment designed by scientists and put together by engineers. A technician does not need to worry about why the equipment works as it does. Nor does he try to interpret the results obtained. His concern is to keep the equipment working and to get from the apparatus the information it was designed to obtain.

Cooperation in science. Did you realize that there were so many people adding information and knowledge to the description of our environment? Although these people have different interests and training, use different tools and instruments, and observe and measure various things, each person has a role in the large task of studying the earth and space. Maybe as you learn more about what others have found out and what their interpretations are, you will find something of particular interest to you. Perhaps you too will be able to add to the increasing knowledge of our earth and space environment.

Checking Your Knowledge

1. Scientists specialize because the scope of earth and space science is too broad to be studied completely by one person.

2. There are no distinct separations between the different areas of science. In fact, there is much overlapping of information, ideas, and methods.

3. Scientists combine direct observation, reasoning, and mathematical analysis in making discoveries and forming theories to explain natural phenomena.

4. As far as we can tell, the basic principles of science which are valid on the earth are also valid everywhere else in the universe—even in the most distant galaxies.

5. Engineers and scientists are mutually interdependent even though their roles are not the same.

USING NEW WORDS

Study the nine groups of words below. The words within each group may be alike in some ways and different in some ways. On your paper, write two brief statements about each group of words. Use the letters *a* through *i* to identify the group of words about which each statement is written. In one statement tell how the words in the group are alike in their meaning. In another statement tell the differences in meaning between the words in the group.

   a. star — cosmic ray — planet
   b. rock — mineral — crystal
   c. telescope — spectrometer
   d. astronomer — astrophysicist
   e. geophysicist — astrophysicist
   f. geologist — geochemist
   g. meteorologist — oceanologist
   h. scientist — engineer — technician
   i. meteorite — meteoroid

TEST YOURSELF

Study the test below. On your paper, write the numerals *1-10*. After each numeral write the correct response to that part of the test with the corresponding numeral.

1. A ＿＿ is a scientist who studies the chemical composition of the various materials found on the earth.

2. The type of scientist most likely to use a telescope is the ＿＿.

3. The device which aids in determining the contour of the ocean floor by sending out sound waves and detecting the reflected waves is called ＿＿.

4. Cosmic rays are very tiny particles having (*great, small*) amounts of energy.

5. Each branch of science is (*related, unrelated*) to the other fields of science.

6. Tycho Brahe made and recorded very precise determinations of the positions of many stars. Tycho Brahe was (*an astrophysicist, an astronomer, a geologist*).

7. There is a theory that the pressure of a star's atmosphere affects the spectrum of the star. Formulating and attempting to check such a theory is the type of work most likely to be done by an (*astrophysicist, astronomer, engineer*).

8. "Project Mohole," an attempt to drill a hole completely through the crust of the earth at a point about 3 miles under the ocean's surface, has created many problems for (*engineers, geologists, geophysicists*).

9. Reconstructing the history of the Grand Canyon by examining the many exposed layers of rock requires a (*geologist, geophysicist, meteorologist*).

10. Operating the controls which regulate the flow of oil in a pipeline is the job of (*a geologist, an engineer, a technician*).

Extending Your Knowledge

1. If you were assigned the task of planning an expedition to explore Mars, what types of scientists would you select to make the trip? Give your reasons for including each type of scientist in the expedition and tell what each individual scientist would do.

2. What is the relationship between science and engineering? Explain why they are interdependent.

3. In the next twenty years, do you think there will be more or less demand for technicians and engineers? Give reasons for your answer. Do you think the technicians and engineers of the future will be more specialized or less specialized than they are today? Why do you think so?

4. Why is it necessary for you to have more education than your grandfather had?

5. Suppose you evaporated a one-cubic-foot sample of ocean water and found that the sample contained 2.25 pounds of solid material. How many pounds of solid material would there be in a cubic mile of sea water of the same composition?

SOME THINGS TO DO

1. Select an occupation related to earth and space science and describe (a) the type and amount of education you would need to qualify for this occupation, (b) what type of work you would be expected to do, and (c) why you do or do not think you would like to work at this occupation.

2. Describe the differences between the instruments that Copernicus used in studying astronomy and the instruments that astronomers use today.

3. If you can get a sample of ocean water, find out how much residue is left when a measured amount of water is evaporated. What would be the weight of the solid materials dissolved in a cubic mile of ocean water like your sample?

4. Visit an earth scientist or a space scientist who works in your community. For example, you might interview the meteorologist at your local airport, a scientist concerned with air pollution, a consulting geologist, or perhaps a hydrologist who is concerned with water pollution. After your interview, make a report to your class on what you have learned.

CHALLENGES IN SCIENCE

1. Many astronomical observations can be made without the use of telescopes. For example, the moon appears to be much larger when it is near the horizon than when it is high in the sky. Is it larger because it is nearer? Is it larger because of an effect of the atmosphere? Or is it just an illusion that it is larger? Devise a simple experiment to determine answers to these questions.

2. How would you determine how much solid material a nearby river or stream carries away during a 24-hour period? What measurements will you need to make? If you multiply the number of pounds carried away in one day by the number of days in a year, will the product be the number of pounds carried away in one year? What are some reasons to believe that your answer is not exact? (Another way to ask this question would be to say, "What are the sources of error in this experiment?") In what ways could you compensate for errors?

3. Explain why fossils are not usually found in volcanic rocks. Then try to think of some peculiar circumstances in which fossil remains might be embedded and preserved in volcanic material.

BREAKTHROUGHS IN SCIENCE

From July, 1, 1957 to December 31, 1958, the largest, most concerted scientific endeavor in history took place. It was called the International Geophysical Year (IGY). IGY represents a significant milepost in man's study of the earth. The scope and depth of this unprecedented exploration of our environment can be better understood by noting a few statistics. More than 10,000 scientists from 66 nations participated in the study. Approximately 2,000 stations for observing natural phenomena were established throughout the world.

The reason for this concerted effort was man's need for a more complete knowledge of his environment. This need has two important facets. First, man's intellectual curiosity needs to be satisfied. From the earliest times, history is a record of man's desire to have a more profound understanding of the earth and the universe. Second, a more complete knowledge of our environment can lead to an increased ability to control the forces within and around the earth.

IGY studies were essentially divided into three categories. (1) A study of the earth's structure and interior was made. This study called for the skills of the seismologists, geologists, geochemists, and geophysicists. (2) A study of the earth's atmosphere and hydrosphere was also undertaken. Meteorologists, glaciologists, and oceanologists carried out this portion of the work. (3) The physics of the upper atmosphere was investigated. This investigation of how particles and radiations from the sun and stars interact with the outer edge of our atmosphere was carried out by physicists, astrophysicists, and astronomers. Of course, a great many engineers and technicians were necessary to design and operate the equipment used in all of these studies.

IGY studies resulted in the collection of a great deal of data. To make this data readily available to anyone who wanted to use it, three world data centers were established: one in Russia, one in western Europe, and one in the United States. Each center received a complete set of all basic data.

Analysis of the data will be a continuing process. Some data are immediately useful, such as in weather forecasting. Other data simply add to our knowledge of the earth. For example, dramatic increases in man's knowledge of the contour of the ocean's floor have resulted from IGY. Such knowledge may have no immediate value, but because it helps to lay the foundation for future explorations, knowledge of the ocean's floor may eventually be of great practical value.

One important outcome of the IGY is that it points out the enormity of the task of learning about our earth and space environment. This task is more than one person, or even the people of one nation, can accomplish.

The idea of combining the resources—intellectual and material—of all the peoples of the world represents a breakthrough in man's scientific endeavors. The accomplishments of IGY are a giant stride toward the goal of a more complete understanding of our earth-space environment.

REVIEWING UNIT ONE

SUMMARY

1. Our earth is a space platform with only a thin layer of atmosphere separating us from the space environment.

2. We study the earth so that we may reconstruct its history and predict its future.

3. The universe is so vast that it is very difficult—if not impossible—to comprehend it as a whole.

4. It is believed that the basic laws of science are as valid in space as they are on earth, so what is learned in our laboratories can be applied to things which are being observed in space.

5. Now that man is beginning to leave the earth in his space travels, he is discovering how much there is yet to learn about the earth and space.

6. The scope of earth and space science is so great that scientists specialize in certain fields of study rather than attempting to be expert in all fields of earth and space science.

7. Some important fields of study in earth and space science are astronomy, astrophysics, geology, geochemistry, geophysics, meteorology, and oceanology.

8. Engineers and technicians are closely associated with scientific studies in all fields of science.

QUESTIONS TO DISCUSS

1. Most people believe that within our solar system, life exists only on the earth. What are some reasons for believing this? For not believing it?

2. Compare the exploratory work in space today with the work of the explorers in the 15th and 16th centuries. Compare or contrast (a) objectives, (b) dangers, (c) value of outcomes, and (d) costs.

UNIT TEST

Study the test below. On your paper, write the numerals *1-20*. After each numeral, write the letter of the correct response to the corresponding part of the test. In *1-10*, the correct response is obtained by matching the type of scientist in *List A* with the topic most familiar to him in *List B*.

List A

(a) oceanologist   (f) geophysicist
(b) mathematician   (g) mineralogist
(c) astronomer   (h) meteorologist
(d) astrophysicist   (i) seismologist
(e) geologist   (j) glaciologist

List B

1. distribution and size of galaxies
2. ocean floor and ocean currents
3. large number of tornadoes in Kansas
4. identification of rock layers
5. the Alaskan earthquake of 1964
6. using numbers and symbols
7. crystal structures in granite
8. principal features of Antarctica
9. production of energy in the sun
10. temperatures within the earth

In *11-20*, the correct response is to classify each statement as either (a) incorrect, (b) a fact, (c) a law, or (d) a theory.

11. The earth is 4½ billion years old.
12. A galaxy contains billions of stars.
13. A deep dust layer covers the moon.
14. The sun is 93 million miles away.
15. Billions of galaxies exist in space.
16. Life exists in outer space.
17. Scientists can explain everything.
18. The earth's surface constantly changes.
19. The sun revolves about the earth.
20. All objects in the universe attract each other.

ENRICHING YOUR SCIENCE EXPERIENCES

INVESTIGATIONS TO CARRY OUT

1. Find as much information as you can concerning the earth's atmosphere. Has it always been composed of the same elements? Why does it not contain any significant amounts of hydrogen and helium? Where did the oxygen come from? Will the composition of the atmosphere change in the future?

2. See if the salinity (salt content) of water has any effect on its freezing point. Place different amounts of salt in several samples of water and place them in your freezer. Have one sample without salt. Check their temperatures every ten minutes. Does the presence of salt affect the freezing point? If so, how does the amount of salt affect the freezing point? How can you use the information you collect in explaining why the oceans near the poles are only partly frozen, although the water temperature is below 32°F?

3. Sir Charles Lyell, Gerard Kuiper, and Andrija Mohorovičić are men who have contributed to the study of the earth and space. Find out what their chief contributions have been and whether or not their theories are still accepted today.

4. Obtain a Geiger counter from your school or from local Civil Defense officials. A Geiger counter is used to detect the presence of radioactive materials and cosmic rays. See if you can find any common objects or substances in which there is a detectable amount of radioactivity.

Using a material you have found to be radioactive, devise and conduct some experiments to find out any effects of changing the distance between the radioactive material and the Geiger counter. Find out any effects of placing a sheet of paper between the source of radiation and the counter. Try two or more sheets, a sheet of aluminum foil, glass, iron, plastic. Do heavy materials or light materials seem to screen out the radiation more effectively? What materials are used as shields against radiation around nuclear reactors where the radiation is very intense? Can shields be made which will effectively stop cosmic rays? Why is it necessary to know more about shielding today than it was 50 years ago?

ADDITIONAL READING IN SCIENCE

Barnett, Lincoln, *The Universe and Dr. Einstein*. 2nd rev. ed. Evanston, Ill., Harper and Row, 1957. 127 pp.

Haggerty, James J., *Man's Conquest of Space*. Englewood Cliffs, N.J., Scholastic Book Services, 1966. 125 pp.

Holden, A., and Singer, P., *Crystals and Crystal Growing*. Garden City, New York, Doubleday, 1959. 320 pp.

Newman, James R., *Science and Sensibility*. New York, Simon and Schuster, 1961. Vol. I, 372 pp.; Vol. II, 309 pp.

Rapport, S., and Wright, H., eds., *The Crust of the Earth*. New York, The New American Library, 1955. 224 pp.

AUSTRALIAN NEWS AND INFORMATION BUREAU

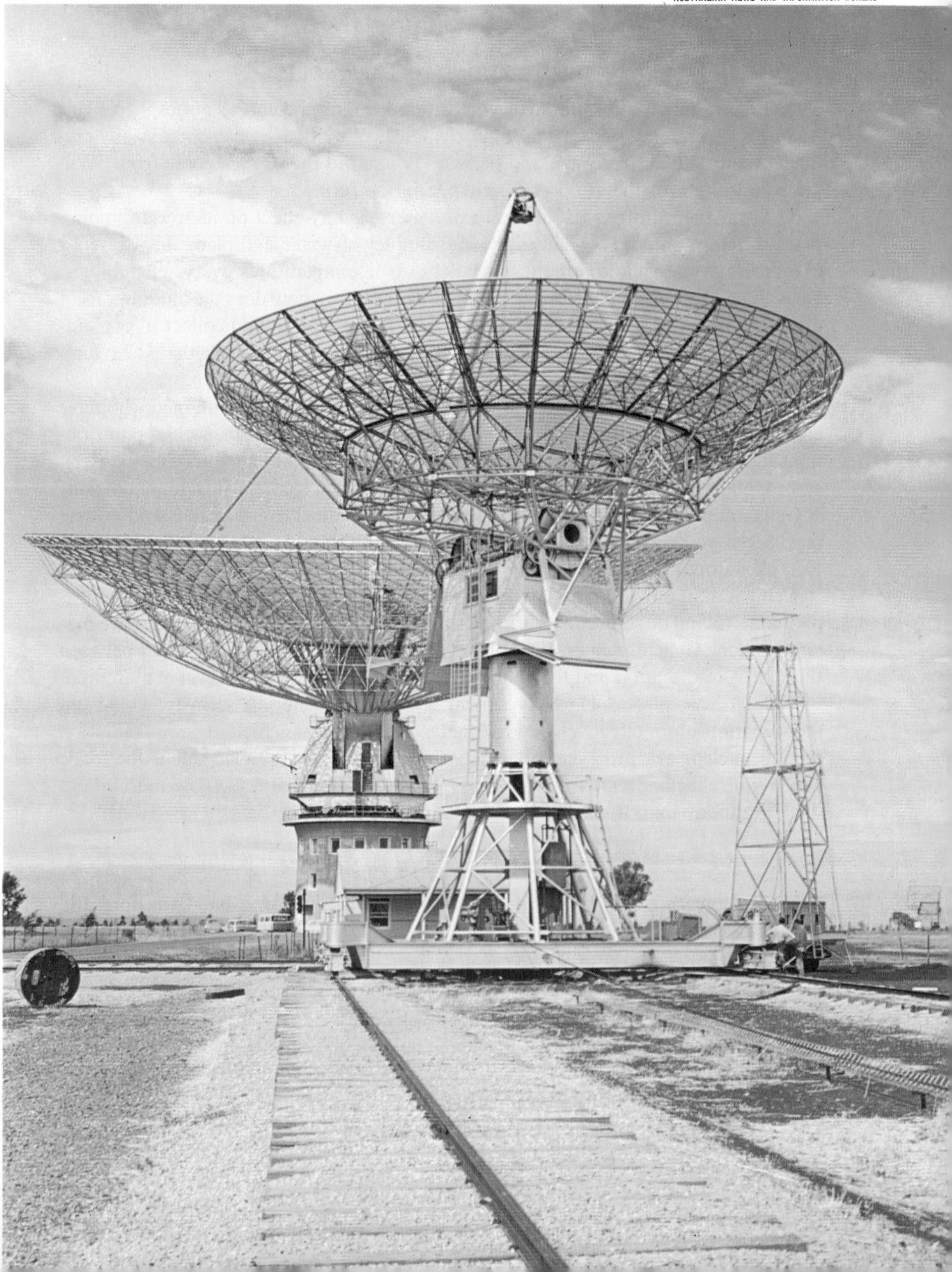

UNIT 2

THE UNIVERSE

What answer would you give if someone asked you, "What is the universe?" You might say, "The universe includes everything there is," or "It is everything and all things." These are good answers, but they provide limited information. They do not tell much about the materials of the universe. What are the materials which make up the universe? How are these materials distributed? How can we find out about these materials?

Practically all of the information we receive from the rest of the universe comes to us in the light and radio waves that reach us from space. By analyzing these radiations on the basis of what has been learned in earthbound laboratories, scientists have gathered a great amount of information about the universe as a whole.

As you study this unit, you will discover many interesting and surprising things about the universe. However, these things themselves are not the important kind of knowledge to be gained through your study. Learning how scientists have discovered what is known about the materials which make up the universe is the most important outcome of studying UNIT 2. There is another important aspect of your study of this unit. You will see how man's knowledge of his environment has been used as the basis for theories concerning the origin and evolution of the stars and galaxies of the universe. Moreover, you will learn that there are many unsolved problems still confronting the scientists who are studying the universe.

◄ Radio telescopes are important tools for studying the universe.

PHOTOGRAPH FROM THE MOUNT WILSON AND PALOMAR OBSERVATORIES

The 200-inch reflector at Mt. Palomar.

CHAPTER 3

The Sky—Our Window
to the Universe

Man's concept of the universe is constantly changing. Some changes, such as those resulting from a more accurate measurement of the distance to the moon, seem minor. Other changes are major. For example, man's realization that the sun is the center of the solar system represented a major change in his concept of the universe. Usually, the changes in man's concept of the universe—whether they are major or minor—are based on new discoveries in astronomy.

As you read and study this chapter, you will find out what man has been able to discover about the universe through his use of simple naked-eye observations. You will discover how the telescope and other instruments have increased the range and accuracy of man's observations. You will also be introduced to the present concept of a universe of galaxies. Perhaps you will find answers to some of the things you have wondered about. Undoubtedly, as you find answers, you will also find other questions arising. Don't hesitate to ask them. Try to find answers through investigating, observing, reading, and reasoning. It is through asking questions and then finding answers to his questions that man has come to his present understanding of the universe. But you must also be ready to learn that some of your questions have no answers, at least not at the present time.

1. Naked-Eye Observations

The heavenly show. When we are in a place where the air is particularly clear—perhaps on a mountain or in a desert—the night sky is rich with stars. If you live in the city, where the stars shine dimly through the haze of the night sky, a trip to the country or a visit to a planetarium will enable you to experience a view of the night sky without the interference caused by smog and bright lights. The beauty of this heavenly show has inspired poetry and legend. This ageless beauty may also help to account for the fact that astronomy is the oldest of sciences.

The early scientists were greatly interested in astronomy. In fact, they spent a great deal more time discussing the laws of the heavens and the reasons for the patterns of motion which they observed there than they did discussing the earth on which they stood. Perhaps they spent so much time discussing and studying the heavens because the stars (except for a few "wanderers") presented a regular and permanent pattern of motion. These early scientists believed that their studies would lead to a simple explanation for this pattern. In contrast, the wide variety of land forms, the sea with its constantly changing surface, and the atmosphere with its shifting clouds and storms made any patterns upon the earth so confusing as to baffle attempts at a simple explanation.

Even today, scientists find themselves applying simple, broad generalizations to describe their observations of the distant stars. Yet, in their seemingly hopeless attempts to predict such close-hand events as the weather, scientists are groping with very complex and detailed rules and formulas.

Of course, we have learned a great deal about the universe and its starry inhabitants. As new and bigger telescopes are used to obtain more and more information, our explanations of stellar phenomena become more and more complicated. Some of the reasons for this complication are evident, even for observations made without a telescope, because now our eyes can be guided by knowledge which the early astronomers did not have.

We now know that the thousands of points of light which we call stars are really gigantic spheres of hot gas. At least half of those we see are bigger than our sun. We know that, in some cases, what appears to be a single point of light is really a whole cluster of stars. These clusters are too far from us for our eyes to see the individual stars. We know also that the "wanderers" in the sky are solid planets revolving about the sun. They shine not with their own light, but by the reflected light of the sun, just as our own moon does. We know the planets are comparatively close to us, while the stars are extremely far away. But suppose for now that we imagine we do not know all of these things. Try to imagine how the sky and its mysteries seemed to the early astronomers.

Figure 3-1. A special type of projector sends out many beams of light to produce the appearance of the sky on the domed ceiling of this planetarium.

ADLER PLANETARIUM AND ASTRONOMICAL MUSEUM

Figure 3-2. Movements of the stars in the southern sky would cause "star trails," such as these, on photographic film exposed for an hour or more.

Early observations. Certainly, the early stargazers noticed the regularity of the patterns and motions of the stars. Night after night the stars appear in the same positions, relative to one another in the sky. As the hours go by, the stars slowly move across the sky, just as the sun does in the daytime. All night long various stars rise in the east. As we watch, they gradually move across the sky and set in the west. We now know that this apparent motion of the stars is caused by the earth turning on its axis once a day. As we are carried around by the rotating earth, we are given a panoramic view of the sky. At

Figure 3-3. This map can be used to locate and identify certain stars in the sky. To use the map, hold it in front of you with the current month at the top. Then, as you face north at 9:00 P.M., stars near the bottom of the map are stars near the horizon. Stars near the top are high in the sky.

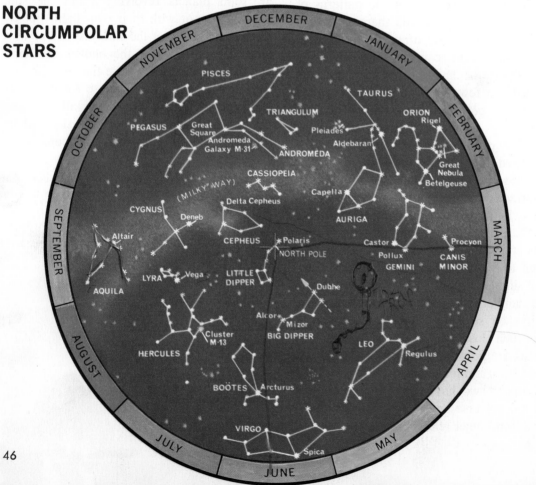

NORTH CIRCUMPOLAR STARS

night our view is of the stars, twinkling brightly in contrast to the black sky. But as the earth continues to turn, we come to a point where we begin to see the light of the sun. Then the light of the stars is lost in the flood of sunlight, and the stars are not seen in the daytime sky.

The early astronomers, clinging to the idea that the earth was the center of the universe, explained the apparent motion of the stars and sun in a different way. They believed that the stars were points of light mounted in a huge sphere which turned about the earth once a day. These astronomers thought that

as they stood still beneath and watched, the sphere with its lights moved about them.

In addition to observing a definite pattern in the motion of the stars, the early stargazers observed the uneven distribution of stars in the sky. Even a casual observation reveals that the stars are not evenly distributed about the sky. Instead, the stars seem to be in various patterns or designs. Also, it is obvious that some stars are brighter than others. The different positions and the different brightnesses are so arranged that stars seem to be in various groups. Many of these groupings of stars, or *constellations,* were given names by

Figure 3-4. This star map can be used to locate and identify those stars which are visible from the Southern Hemisphere. To use this map, you would follow the same procedure that is outlined in Figure 3-3, except you should face south instead of north.

SOUTH CIRCUMPOLAR STARS

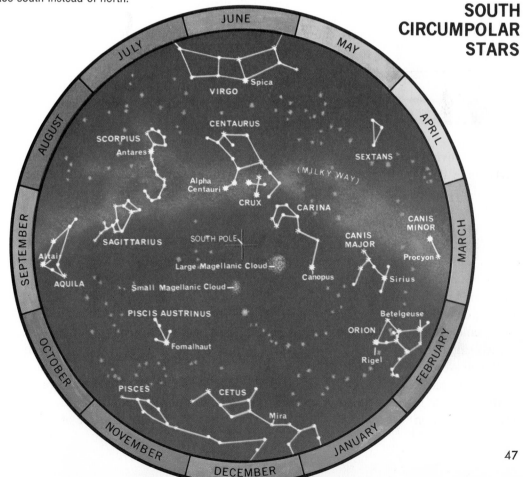

the astronomers of ancient times. On most star maps, such as the ones given on pages 46 and 47, the brightest stars in a particular constellation are shown connected by lines. The star maps help you to locate individual stars and to recognize these stars night after night. If we do enough stargazing, the constellations and the brighter stars in them get to be like old friends whom we can easily recognize and call by name.

FIND OUT BY TRYING

Materials you will need: camera, film, clock

Carry out this investigation on a moonless night in a place where there is little light from cars, street lights, or yard lights. Place the camera on the ground or on a very firm, steady support. (Any movement of the camera during exposure will spoil the photographs.) Aim the camera directly at the pole star. Set the focus at infinity and open the diaphragm as wide as possible. Take several photographs using time exposures. Vary the exposure time from 15 minutes to several hours. Describe the photographs you obtain. Do curved lines appear in the photographs? If so, compare the lines in several different photographs. Do the lines in the photographs made during a short exposure differ from those made during a longer exposure? If so, what do you think caused the differences? What figure would be formed by each of the curved lines if the lines were continued? How long an exposure would be necessary to form the figure? With this information how would you determine the rate of the earth's rotation in number of rotations per day? Degrees per day? Degrees per hour? Miles per hour (for your particular location)?

The "moving" constellations. If you were to observe the sky so much that you could recognize the brighter stars and call them by name, you would probably have noticed a variation in the moving pattern of stars. If so, you would have noticed, as the early astronomers did, that the constellations do not appear in exactly the same place in the sky at the same time each night. They appear in the same positions relative to each other, but the whole pattern of the stars seems to be shifted slightly from one night to the next.

If you were to keep a record of the position of a particular group of stars at a particular time in the evening—for example, the constellation *Cassiopeia* (kas'i ə pē'ə) at 9:00 P.M.—you would find this constellation very nearly overhead on the first of December. As the nights passed by, Cassiopeia would be a little farther to the west each night. Thus, in the spring if you were to face the pole star *Polaris*, the constellation Cassiopeia would be to the left, in the northwest part of the sky, instead of overhead. By summer, Cassiopeia would have swung down to a position between the pole star and the horizon. In fact, Cassiopeia would be so near the horizon that it would probably be invisible on a slightly hazy night. By late summer, Cassiopeia would have moved around so that at 9:00 P.M. it would be to the right of the pole star, in the eastern part of the sky. Then at

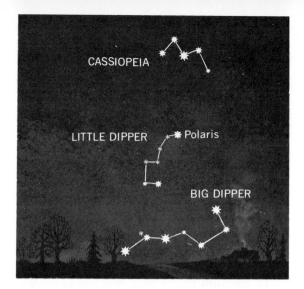

Figure 3-5. The position of the constellation Cassiopeia as it would be viewed in the night sky on December 1 at 9:00 P.M.

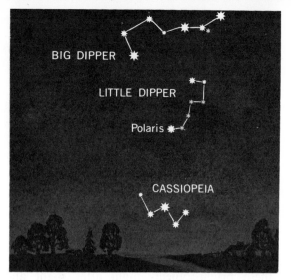

Figure 3-6. The position of the constellation Cassiopeia as it would be viewed in the night sky at 9:00 P.M. six months later, on June 1.

9:00 P.M. on the first of December, a year later than your initial observation, Cassiopeia would again be overhead.

To early astronomers, still clinging to the belief that the earth was at the center of the universe, this motion of the constellations presented quite a mystery. In order to account for the motion, they gave the "celestial sphere"—in which they believed the stars to be embedded—a special kind of motion. The early astronomers reasoned that the sphere made one complete rotation—plus a little more—each day. The extra amount of rotation carried the star pattern a little bit more to the west each night. They believed that after a year had gone by, the celestial sphere had made one extra revolution.

We now know that this continuing change in the positions of the constellations in the sky night after night—a change which brings all of the stars around in a full circle once each year—results from the motion of the earth about the sun. The earth's motion on its own axis, combined with its motion about the sun, causes the pattern of the stars to rotate not just 360 degrees each day (which

would be one complete rotation), but 360.986 degrees. By accumulating an extra 0.986 degrees of rotation each day, the pattern of the stars rotates an extra 360 degrees, or one complete turn, each year

Either of these explanations, the earth turning on its axis or the celestial sphere turning about the earth, can account for the apparent motion of the stars in the sky. Thus we can appreciate how the early astronomers might have arrived at their conclusion. Just by looking at the stars, it is impossible to say for certain that they are not points of light shining in some gigantic sphere that is spinning slowly around a centrally located and stationary earth. We now know that the stars are quite far away and located at various distances extending farther and farther out into the universe. However, there is no way to detect the differences in distances without a telescope. So, we can understand why the ancients thought of the stars as all equally distant from the earth.

The "wanderers." Among the constant patterns of the stars move five objects which appear to be bright stars. If you were to watch

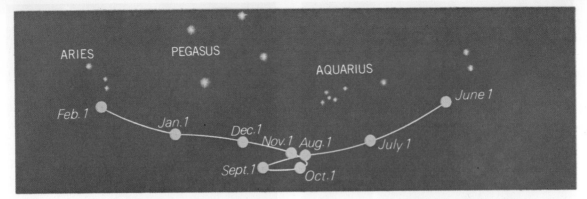

Figure 3-7. Mars usually appears to move eastward through the pattern of stars. At intervals, however, the apparent motion is reversed. Such motion, which causes a loop in the planet's apparent path, is called retrograde motion.

these bright objects night after night and keep a record of their positions in the star pattern, you would find they follow a most unusual course. The motion of each of these objects is not always regular and smooth. Sometimes the path of one or another of these objects seems to double back on itself and then loop around to start forward again. This is called *retrograde* (ret'rə grād) *motion.* As an example of this type of motion, a diagram of the path of Mars, relative to the distant stars, is shown in *Figure 3-7.*

The retrograde motion of these objects baffled the early astronomers. They called these wayward objects *planets,* a Greek word which means "wanderers." That there could be planets which moved among the stars did not conflict with their ideas about the universe nor with their conviction that the earth was at its center. If only these planets moved across the sky in a nice, smooth course at a constant speed, all would have been well with the theories. But of course they did not. Do you think you would be able to devise a theory to explain this strange planetary motion if you were firmly convinced ahead of time that the earth was at the center of all things? Of course, it would be possible to say, "Well, that's just the way it is." But this would explain nothing.

In addition to the idea that the earth was the center of all things, the early scientists had another restriction which they forced upon themselves and their theories. They believed that circles and spheres were the only perfect shapes. Therefore, every object in the heavens—being perfect—would have to be spherical in shape and move in a perfectly circular path. The observed motions of the planets did not conform to these ideas, and thus were exceedingly troublesome to explain.

The sun and the moon. As the early sky watchers viewed the heavens, they certainly observed the two brightest objects in the sky—the sun and the moon. To the early astronomers these objects were much better behaved as far as orbits were concerned. Both the sun and the moon appear to move around the earth in orbits that are nearly perfect circles. These apparently circular orbits fitted right in with the early beliefs of a central earth and the "perfect" heavenly objects. Careful measurements have since revealed that the orbit of the moon is slightly elliptical instead of perfectly circular. But even before this complication arose, the early scientists had difficulty in explaining certain aspects of the moon's appearance.

When you have seen a new moon in the sky just after the glow of evening has faded, you have probably noticed that the bright crescent is not the only part of the moon which you can see. There is a very faint light coming from the rest of the moon. The early astronomers also noticed this faint light. Perhaps you know what this light is, but the early astronomers did not. One of their theories was that the moon was somewhat *translucent* (trans lü′sənt)—that is, some light could pass through the moon. They believed that some sunlight passed through the moon, giving a slight glow even to its dark side.

How would you explain the faint glow observed outside the crescent of a new moon?

Limitations of naked-eye observations. Many of the early astronomers were skilled observers, and through their observations these astronomers learned a great deal about the universe. And yet, without the discovery of telescopes, there is much that would have remained a mystery. We can easily understand why many of the theories developed by the early astronomers now seem primitive and foolish. When we consider the evidence they had and the beliefs which were part of their culture, we realize these men were very clever. As a matter of fact, Johannes Kepler —the scientist who finally became convinced that the planets move in ellipses, and not in circles—did so on the basis of observations that were made without a telescope. Also, another scientist, Nicolaus Copernicus, using information obtained without a telescope, figured out that the sun had to be the center of the solar system. It is difficult to realize the genius required to make these important discoveries on the basis of such limited data.

In the earth and space sciences, our position today is really not much different from that of the early astronomers. Although our knowledge and understanding of the universe have been extended a great deal, we are still faced with baffling phenomena. We are still beset by a nagging belief that, as the data to be gathered in future years finally come to be understood, some of our more cherished theories will undoubtedly turn out to be wrong and have to be discarded.

2. The View with a Telescope

A closer look. The beauty of the night sky is certainly a memorable sight. As we gaze at the panorama of the sky, we cannot help wishing we could get closer to the objects there so we could examine them in more detail.

Man did find a way to examine the heavens in more detail, and he found how he could do it without having to leave the earth. The details of this important event are not known. However, we do know that in about 1605 the telescope was invented. Within a short time telescopes were being used in various places in Europe to observe the heavens.

Figure 3-8. Newton built this reflecting telescope in 1668. It was the first telescope having a mirror rather than a lens to focus the incoming light.

JOHN R. FREEMAN & CO., LONDON

Figure 3-9. This picture shows four photographs of the planet Venus. Although the photographs were taken at various times over a 17-year period, the magnification is the same in each photo. How would you explain the fact that Venus seems to get larger as it approaches the crescent phase?

LOWELL OBSERVATORY PHOTOGRAPH

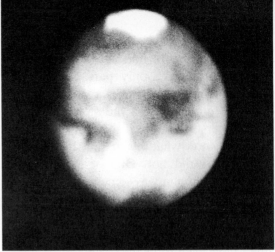

PHOTOGRAPH FROM THE MOUNT WILSON AND PALOMAR OBSERVATORIES

Figure 3-10. The planet Mars, because of its mysterious surface markings, has been the subject of much controversy among astronomers.

The planets. The planets were among the first objects to be studied with the telescope, and the planets are indeed fascinating to observe. What appear to be bright stars when viewed with the naked eye, suddenly take on size and shape in the telescope.

Venus is the brightest of the planets. As it travels around the sun, we can observe that Venus has phases, just as the moon does. Sometimes it is a crescent, and sometimes it is full, as *Figure 3-9* shows. No matter what phase we see, however, Venus appears as a featureless white object. Its cloudy atmosphere is all we can see of the planet.

Mars is considerably smaller and not as bright as Venus. However, Mars does have some features we can look at. In *Figure 3-10,* for example, you can see the white region, which is one of the two polar caps on Mars. Jupiter, too, has some interesting features. (*Figure 3-11.*) Colored bands, which are presumed to be clouds in the planet's atmosphere, and the large red spot are interesting to observe—although the reasons for their presence are not known. In addition, Jupiter has a set of moons. Four of these moons can

Figure 3-11. Jupiter is the largest planet in the solar system. Even with a very small telescope you can observe Jupiter and some of its moons.

Figure 3-12. The set of rings around Saturn makes this planet especially interesting to observe. Are there any other planets with similar rings?

be observed by using a small telescope. By using larger telescopes, a total of twelve moons revolving about Jupiter have been discovered.

Saturn is the most distant of the planets which can be seen without a telescope. Saturn takes on an even greater fascination when viewed with the telescope. In addition to the famous set of rings shown in *Figure 3-12,* Saturn has ten moons. The telescope enables us to see three more planets out beyond Saturn. These planets—Uranus, Neptune, and Pluto—are invisible to the unaided eye.

The stars. To our disappointment, the stars are still only points of light, even when seen with the aid of a telescope. The spherical shape of the stars cannot be distinguished, nor can their diameter be measured.

In spite of these limitations, there are definite advantages· to be gained by using the telescope to observe the stars. First of all, we see many more stars everywhere we look. Second, we notice that certain points of light, each of which appeared to be a single star before, now appear as clusters of stars. The stars in the cluster appear close together but

still with enough distance between that we can distinguish them as separate stars. *Figure 3-13*, for example, shows a huge cluster of stars as photographed through the telescope. Viewed without the telescope, this whole cluster appears simply as a single star. This cluster is located in the constellation Hercules.

In addition, careful observations made by astronomers using telescopes have revealed the information needed to calculate how far

Figure 3-13. This star cluster contains thousands of individual stars—more individual stars than you can see in the entire sky with your unaided eye.

Figure 3-14. To obtain this photograph of the Andromeda galaxy, the film had to be exposed for a relatively long time. Thus, the center of the galaxy —where the stars are closest together—appears very bright when compared with the wispy outer regions. The tiny points of light visible in the picture are stars in our own galaxy. The two bright spots are satellite galaxies of the Andromeda galaxy.

away some of the stars are. The first such calculations indicated the distances to be very great. In fact, the distances were so great that even those who made the calculations were surprised. The nearest star, *Proxima Centauri* (prok′sə mə sen tôr′ī), is so far away that it takes the light from this star more than four years to reach the earth. Since light travels at the rate of 186,000 miles per second, Proxima Centauri is about 25 trillion (25,000,-000,000,000, or 2.5×10^{13}) miles away.

It is almost impossible to imagine such a great distance. We might try to compare it with something we are more familiar with— the size of our solar system. Pluto, the outermost planet in the solar system, is 3,573,-000,000 (3.573×10^9) miles from the earth, a distance which is quite small compared with the distance to the nearest star.

The distance to the nearest star is how many times greater than the distance to the outermost planet?

You can see that the numerals needed to describe astronomical distances are difficult to write and difficult to use in calculations.

To avoid these difficulties, astronomers have devised a distance unit, called a *light-year,* which is often used when long distances are discussed. A light-year is the distance light travels in one year.

Measured in light-years, the distance to Pluto seems small. When measured in these units, the distance to Pluto is only 0.0006 light-years. In other words, it would take a flash of light only about five hours to travel from the earth to Pluto. In contrast, light would be four years on the way to the star Proxima Centauri. And this is the *nearest* star. Actually, individual stars which are thousands of light-years away can be seen quite easily, even when we observe them with our unaided eyes.

What calculations are necessary in order to determine the distance (the number of miles) which is equivalent to one light-year? How many kilometers are equivalent to one light-year?

Galaxies and nebulae. Some things that we see in the sky would have to remain forever mysterious without a telescope. One object, in the area of the constellation Andromeda, is of special significance. It appears to the unaided eye as a very faint blur of light. It was described by early astronomers as having the appearance of "a candle flame seen through the horn window of a lanthorn [lantern]." And indeed, it is something other than a star. A star appears as a point of light. The more clearly we see it, the sharper it becomes. But the object in Andromeda never becomes clear. It always appears blurred.

The object in Andromeda is easiest to see in the wintertime. However, seeing it requires a clear night, for this object appears only as a very faint blur. Because of its location in the sky and because of its appearance as a faint blur, this patch of light was originally called the Andromeda nebula. A *nebula* (neb′yə lə) is a hazy patch of light, like a small glowing cloud visible in the nighttime sky. In photographs taken through modern telescopes, the Andromeda nebula is revealed as a strangely beautiful object. (*Figure 3-14.*) Within the last fifty years, it has been determined that the Andromeda nebula is actually a *galaxy* (gal′ək si)—that is, a vast collection of stars, dust, and gas.

The Milky Way is another object of interest to astronomers. It is difficult to imagine how even a genius could have discovered—without the aid of the telescope—what the Milky Way really is. This glowing band of light across the sky seems to be a thin, luminous dust cloud. But if we observe the Milky Way through a telescope, we can see the band is composed of millions of separate stars. Of course, even when viewed through a telescope, some portions of the band still appear as hazy clouds of dust. The billions of stars in the more distant portions of the Milky Way are too numerous and too far away to be distinguished, even through a telescope.

Astronomers have determined that our sun and its system of planets are located within a huge galaxy. The galaxy of stars in which our sun is located is believed to be much like the Andromeda galaxy in its overall shape. The luminous band which we call the Milky Way is our edge-on view of the huge disk of stars which makes up the flat portion of our galaxy. (That is why our galaxy has been named the *Milky Way Galaxy*.) A portion of the Milky Way, as it looks through a telescope, is shown in *Figure 3-15.*

Figure 3-15. The Milky Way has a different appearance when seen or photographed through a telescope than it does when it is observed with the unaided eye. This picture of a portion of the Milky Way reveals that the Milky Way is not a faintly luminous cloud. Instead, the Milky Way is composed of millions of individual stars.

Figure 3-16. The Horsehead nebula is a dark cloud of gas which is seen against a background of light given off by glowing gases. Several stars can also be seen in this photograph. Why, do you suppose, are there more stars visible in the lighter regions of this picture than there are in the dark regions?

The, telescope makes dim objects appear brighter. Thus, some objects can be seen through the telescope although they are invisible without it. For example, clouds of gas and dust stretch between the stars. However, until telescopes were used for observation, the light we receive from these clouds was not detected. Now, however, we know that some of the clouds are glowing. In other cases, the clouds form black shadows as they cut off the light from more distant gas clouds or more distant stars. The *Horsehead nebula* shows both the light and shadow effects. (*Figure 3-16.*)

In the photograph of the Horsehead nebula, are there stars which appear to you to be beyond the clouds of dust and gas? If these stars actually are beyond the nebula, what does this indicate about the location of the Horsehead nebula?

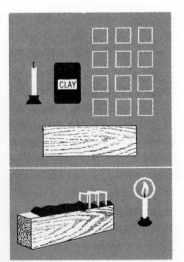

FIND OUT BY TRYING

Materials you will need: candle, candleholder, twelve 2″ × 2″ glass plates, modeling clay

Light the candle and place it in a holder on a table top. Observe the lighted candle. Then, using a piece of modeling clay as a support, stand one glass plate so that you look through it at the candle. Now look at the candle through two glass plates. Do you see a difference in the appearance of the candle flame? Continue placing glass plates so that you must look through them to see the candle. Does adding one plate make much difference in how well you can see the candle? Is there much difference between what you see through one plate and what you see through 12 plates? On the basis of what you have observed, explain the effects of nebulae on our observations of the stars beyond them.

56

One among many. Perhaps the most surprising discovery made through the use of the telescope is that billions of other galaxies exist in the distant reaches of space. Instead of just our own galaxy and the one in Andromeda, astronomers have found that the visible universe is full of galaxies. There are many which have the disk shape of ours, but some are more like balls. Some seem to be shaped like rods with wisps trailing from their ends. (*Figure 3-17.*) But astronomers are pretty certain that these fragile-seeming wisps are actually clusters of billions of stars.

Thus, our view through the telescope is a sky filled with millions of stars which were not visible before, but which are all in our galaxy. In addition, the telescope reveals other things we have never before seen—the shapes and sizes of the planets, the existence of gas clouds stretching between the stars, and a universe full of galaxies.

Figure 3-17. Galaxies differ in shape. Regardless of these differences, however, astronomers believe all galaxies contain billions of stars. Most galaxies also contain vast clouds of gas and dust.

FROM THE MOUNT WILSON AND PALOMAR OBSERVATORIES

3. How Telescopes Function

Basic types of telescopes. You have read how the use of the telescope has improved man's ability to see dim and distant objects in space. What happens to light when it passes through the telescope? Why do things, which are normally invisible, become visible when they are viewed through a telescope?

Essentially a telescope does two things. (1) The telescope collects the light that falls on a large area and concentrates this light in a small area. Concentrating the light coming from an object makes the object appear brighter. (2) The telescope produces a magnified image, and this magnification makes the object appear to be closer.

Some telescopes contain only lenses. A large lens collects the light and focuses it, forming an image. Other lenses magnify the image produced by the large lens. In other telescopes a large, curved mirror collects the light. In these telescopes, as in the others, lenses magnify the image. Because lenses work on the principle of *refraction,* or bending of light, those telescopes which contain only lenses are called *refractors.* Telescopes which have a large mirror as their main optical element are called *reflectors.*

Refractors. You know what a magnifying glass is. When you hold a magnifying glass close to an object and look through the glass, the object looks larger. But, if you hold the magnifying glass up in front of you, and try to look at some distant object, all you will see is a blur. How, then, can a lens be used to make a telescope?

Suppose you were to try this. By using modeling clay, or a lens holder, you could place a lens on a table so that you could look through the lens at some object outside the window. Then, using a sheet of white paper

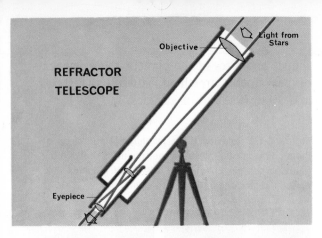

REFRACTOR
TELESCOPE

Light from Stars

Objective

Eyepiece

Figure 3-18. Light from a distant object passes through the objective lens. The light is focused, forming a small, bright image of the distant object. The eyepiece serves to magnify this image, and the observer sees the image very much enlarged.

as a screen, you could let the light from the window pass through the lens and strike the paper. If you were to move the paper, first toward and then away from the lens, you would see that when the paper is in a certain position, a picture would be clearly focused on the paper. Such a picture is called an image. In this particular case, the image would be a small, upside-down picture of the window and what is outside the window. Using a second magnifying glass you could examine the picture on the paper in detail. If the second magnifying glass were a good one, you could make the details of the picture appear quite large.

Of course, it would be rather awkward to look at the picture from the side toward the window, because you would be getting in the way of the light coming through the first lens. You could avoid this awkwardness by focusing the picture on a piece of thin, translucent material (for example, waxed paper) instead of regular paper. The waxed paper would let the picture show through, and you could examine it from the side away from the lens.

Because the picture would be seen through the paper, the picture would appear some-

what fuzzy. However, there is something you could do to make the picture clear. You could take the waxed paper away and still use the second lens to examine the image! This would be a more difficult experiment but if you were careful, you could do it.

You see, in a situation like this, the image formed by the first lens is the type of image known as a *real image,* and it would be in a certain place, whether the paper was there or not. But in order for you to see the image without the paper, everything would have to be lined up exactly right. That is, the second lens would have to be in precisely the right position behind the center of the first one, and you would have to be looking out right through the center of the first lens in order to see the image.

Some experimenting would show you that there is a limit to how much magnification you could get this way. You may guess that if you used a thicker, more curved lens out in front (one which would magnify more strongly if you used it as a magnifying glass), it would make a telescope having greater magnification. But some more experimentation would show you that telescopes just do not work that way. To make a telescope that magnifies a great deal, the lens in front should be quite thin. If you can find such a lens, you will discover that you must place a piece of paper quite far behind it in order to get a sharp image of the scene outside the window. This is another way of saying that a thin lens has a longer *focal length* than a thicker lens.

By experimenting with lenses, you would begin to understand why the long focal length lens gives bigger magnification. The image formed by the long focal length lens is a much larger image than the one made by the thicker lens. So, of course, the small details of the large image would be easier to see when the image is examined through a second lens. At the same time, you would find that the second lens should be the thick one, because it is the magnifier.

Experiments with lenses show that the best magnification is obtained if the first lens, called the *objective* (because it is nearest to the object being viewed), has a very long focal length, and the second lens, or *eyepiece*, has a short focal length. This rule can be written out as a mathematical equation. The equation is $M = f_o / f_e$, where f_o is the focal length of the objective lens, f_e is the focal length of the eyepiece, and M is the magnifying power of the combination of lenses.

If you were to do these experiments, you would undoubtedly notice how difficult it is to get the eyepiece lens and the objective lens properly lined up. Many years ago, telescope designers discovered that lining up the lenses was much easier if two lenses were

Figure 3-19. Big reflectors, such as this 120-inch one at Lick Observatory, have an open framework—not a tube—for the light to travel through.

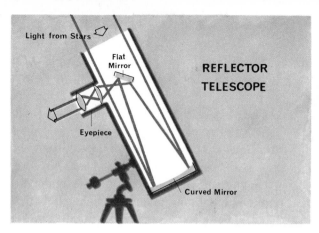

Figure 3-20. Light from a distant object is reflected by a curved mirror in a reflector. The reflected light forms a small, bright image of the distant object. As with the refractor, this image is magnified when viewed through the eyepiece.

used in the eyepiece instead of one. Therefore, the eyepieces used in modern telescopes usually have two lenses.

According to the formula given, magnification does not depend on the diameter of the lens or mirror used. Why, then, was so much money and effort spent in building a 200-inch telescope if the same magnification could be obtained with a 4-inch telescope?

Reflectors. A reflector follows the same rule for magnification as the refractor. In a reflector, however, a large, curved mirror forms the image which is examined through the eyepiece. This type of arrangement is shown in *Figure 3-20*. In both the reflector and the refractor, the image to be examined through the eyepiece is formed from light collected and concentrated by the objective lens (in a refractor) or the curved mirror (in a reflector). When the light from a distant object falls on a large lens or mirror and is concentrated into a small spot, the image formed will certainly be brighter than the image formed by only that light which would pass through the pupil of an eye.

So, a telescope gathers in light from a large area. The light is concentrated and formed into an image of the object being observed. The image is viewed through a small lens, the eyepiece. The eyepiece magnifies the image so that greater detail can be observed. Actually, scientists seldom look through telescopes. Instead they study the sky from photographs taken through telescopes. The film used is far more sensitive than the human eye.

Photography through the telescope. If you have ever used a telescope, you know that certain objects do not appear as bright when viewed through a telescope as they do in photographs. The reason for this difference in brightness is that photographs of these objects are usually produced by using time exposures.

For very dim objects, the exposure time may be several hours. The long exposure produces a bright image because the effects of the light striking the film can accumulate and build up a bright image. On the other hand, the image formed on the retina of your eye is produced only by the light entering your eye at that instant. So, although the telescope by itself is very useful for astronomers, even more information can be obtained when astronomers combine the use of the telescope with the techniques of photography.

It has been said that even the best telescopes were no better than the eyes of astronomers until the invention of photography. What reasons can you give to support this statement?

DO IT YOURSELF

Make a study of telescopes

Use astronomy books, encyclopedias, or other reference materials to make a study of the history of telescopes. Try to find answers to questions such as the following: Who first used a telescope for astronomical observing? Who made the first reflector? What advantage did reflectors have over the first refractors? Why must all telescopes with objectives of more than 40 inches be reflectors? Make a report of your findings to the class.

4. A Universe of Galaxies

Discovering galaxies. Now let us return to our examination of those strangely fascinating objects which the telescope has revealed —the galaxies. Galaxies are other families, or systems, of stars like the Milky Way Galaxy. However, they are located very far away from our own galaxy.

Although both galaxies and clouds of dust and gas were visible with the early telescopes,

it was impossible to see them clearly enough to get a good idea of their shape. The distant galaxies are so far away that the early telescopes could not detect the presence of individual stars within galaxies. Also, at that time there was no way for astronomers to determine the distance to these galaxies. Therefore, all the hazy patches of light were given the name nebulae. This name is still sometimes used, although the groups of stars are more usually called galaxies, leaving the name nebula for use with the clouds of dust and gas within our own galaxy.

It was not until the early part of the twentieth century that agreement was reached among astronomers that certain hazy patches of light were outside the Milky Way Galaxy. Not all astronomers believed that these patches of light were collections of billions of stars. Finally in 1923, the new 100-inch telescope at the Mt. Wilson Observatory was used to study three of these hazy patches of light which were believed to be outside our galaxy. In the photographs taken, astronomers observed individual stars of special types. Similar stars had already been found in our own galaxy. A careful examination of these special stars—*novae* (exploding stars) and *Cepheids* (stars which get brighter and dimmer at regular intervals)—revealed information by which astronomers were able to estimate the distance to the galaxies which contained these stars. The original estimate of the distance has been revised as new evidence has been gathered. Now, the Andromeda galaxy is believed to be more than two million light-years away—far beyond the limits of our own Milky Way Galaxy.

In some ways, astronomers know more about the Andromeda galaxy than they do about the Milky Way Galaxy. How would you explain this?

Shapes of galaxies. Both the Andromeda galaxy and the Milky Way Galaxy have a flat, disklike shape. *Figures 3-21* and *3-22* show other galaxies with similar shapes. However, because of the flat, disklike shape of this type of galaxy, the angle between our line of sight and the plane of the flat portion of the galaxy will determine the shape we see. For example, in *Figure 3-21* we are looking

at a galaxy in which the plane of the disk is perpendicular to our line of sight. In *Figure 3-22*, our view is edge-on. The angle of our view of the Andromeda galaxy (*Figure 3-14*) is somewhere between these extremes.

The flat, disklike galaxies we have been discussing have a central nucleus, or hub, which is a spherical region in which the stars are more closely packed. Galaxies of this general shape—flat and disklike and having

PHOTOGRAPH FROM THE MOUNT WILSON AND PALOMAR OBSERVATORIES

Figure 3-21. A spiral galaxy has this general appearance when viewed from directly above (or below) the plane of the galaxy.

Figure 3-22. A spiral galaxy has this general appearance when viewed edge-on. The Milky Way is our edge-on view of our own galaxy.

PHOTOGRAPH FROM THE MOUNT WILSON AND PALOMAR OBSERVATORIES

a spherical hub—are called *spirals*, or spiral galaxies. The name spiral was given because, in the flat portion of the galaxy, the regions containing the most stars seem to spiral out from the hub. These regions are called the *spiral arms*. Astronomers have been able to determine that some galaxies rotate about the central hub of the galaxy.

Some galaxies, although still spirals, seem to have only two arms in the flat portion. These galaxies are called *barred spirals*. *Figure 3-23* is a photograph which shows a barred spiral galaxy.

Many galaxies are spherical or elliptical in shape and have no spiral arms. *Figure 3-24* is a photograph of one such galaxy. Galaxies of this type are called *elliptical*.

There are some galaxies which have no central hub and no definite shape. Such galaxies are called *irregulars*. *Figure 3-25* is a photograph of two irregular galaxies, the *Magellanic* (maj′ə lan′ik) *Clouds*. These small, irregularly shaped galaxies are the nearest galaxies to the Milky Way Galaxy and are visible to the naked eye. Unfortunately for us, they are so nearly over the South Pole that they cannot be seen by observers north of the tropics.

PHOTOGRAPH FROM THE MOUNT WILSON AND PALOMAR OBSERVATORIES

Figure 3-23. You can see from this picture why this type of galaxy is called a barred spiral.

PHOTOGRAPH FROM THE MOUNT WILSON AND PALOMAR OBSERVATORIES

Figure 3-24. Some ellipticals are more spherical than this one. Others are more flattened.

HARVARD COLLEGE OBSERVATORY

Figure 3-25. The Magellanic Clouds appear to be luminous clouds, but they are really galaxies.

DO IT YOURSELF

Observe the Milky Way and the Andromeda galaxy

In the winter, the Milky Way can be seen stretching across the nighttime sky from the northern horizon to the southern horizon. Observe the Milky Way; first with the naked eye, then with binoculars or a telescope. Write a description of your observations.

Use star maps, such as those on pages 46 and 47, to help you locate the position of the Andromeda galaxy in the sky. The Andromeda galaxy is so distant that its overall shape can be seen. However, unless you are observing through a good telescope, the great distance causes the galaxy to appear only as a very faint blur. What similarities, if any, are there between what you can see of the Andromeda galaxy and what you see as you observe the Milky Way?

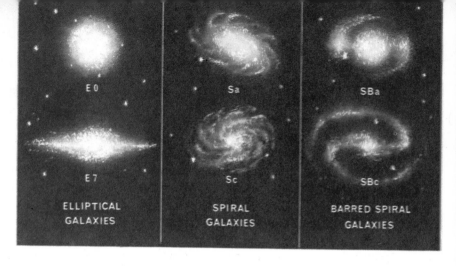

Figure 3-26. Almost every galaxy with an observable shape can be classified as either an elliptical, a spiral, a barred spiral, or an irregular. Except for the irregulars, a typical galaxy of each type is represented here. Irregulars are not shown, because they have no typical shape. However, like other galaxies, they do contain stars and gas clouds.

Classification of galaxies. A system for classifying galaxies has been devised. The basis for classification is the shape of the galaxy. The classification is shown in the diagram in *Figure 3-26.* The ellipticals are classed from *E0* (nearly spherical) to *E7* (very much flattened). Spirals are designated as *Sa, Sb,* and *Sc.* Naturally, the *S* is for spiral, while the *a, b,* or *c* designates the size of the hub, with *a* representing a large hub and *c* representing a small hub. The barred spirals are designated *SBa, SBb,* and *SBc* on the same basis.

Keep in mind that this system of classification does not represent any new understanding of the nature of galaxies. It is merely a way of organizing the observations that have been made. Often, through organizing observations, some new insights may be gained.

Galaxies contain matter. Is it possible that matter also exists between galaxies? If so, why can it not be seen?

Clusters of galaxies. As better telescopes and photographic techniques become available, more and more galaxies are observed in the sky. Using the 200-inch telescope at Mt. Palomar, astronomers can photograph more than half a billion galaxies. By carefully recording and plotting the positions of the

observed galaxies on a map, astronomers have found that galaxies tend to be grouped together into clusters. A portion of one such cluster is shown in *Figure 3-27.*

The Milky Way Galaxy is part of a cluster called the *Local Group.* The Local Group contains about seventeen galaxies, all within two and one-half million light-years of us.

Much remains to be learned about the motions and distribution of the galaxies of the universe. However, this much is well known. Our sun is only one of billions of stars in our galaxy. And our galaxy—huge and awesome as it is with billions of stars stretched over vast reaches of space—is only a tiny part of the complete structure of the universe.

Figure 3-27. Some astronomers believe that clusters of galaxies like this one are only parts of an even larger grouping. In other words, there may be clusters of clusters.

PHOTOGRAPH FROM THE MOUNT WILSON AND PALOMAR OBSERVATORIES

Checking Your Knowledge

1. Although the early stargazers had no telescopes, these men learned a great deal about the universe.

2. The discovery and development of telescopes greatly increased the range of man's observations of the sky.

3. Reflectors and refractors are the two basic types of optical, or light, telescopes.

4. Telescopes are used (1) to collect light in order to make objects appear brighter and (2) to magnify images in order to make objects appear nearer.

5. Our sun is part of a huge system of stars called a galaxy.

6. Billions of galaxies exist throughout the vast reaches of space.

USING NEW WORDS

Study the list of words below. On your paper write the numerals *1-5*. After each numeral, write words or statements to satisfy the instructions given for the corresponding numeral.

Polaris	retrograde motion	irregular
spiral	barred spiral	refractor
image	Milky Way Galaxy	Cassiopeia
galaxy	Local Group	elliptical
nova	constellation	reflector
nebula	Cepheid	objective

1. List those words which are names given to types of galaxies. After each word, use a sketch or a sentence to describe the shape of each type of galaxy listed.

2. Briefly describe how Polaris, Cassiopeia, and the Milky Way Galaxy differ.

3. List the words related to telescopes.

4. List the words related to stars.

5. List and define those words not applicable to *1, 2, 3,* or *4.*

TEST YOURSELF

Study the test below. On your paper write the numerals *1-10.* After each numeral write the correct response to that part of the test with the corresponding numeral.

1. The laws which describe the shape, size, and period of the orbits of planets were discovered by _____.

2. The man who first showed the sun, not the earth, to be the center of the solar system was _____.

3. Astronomers often use the term _____ to represent a distance equivalent to the distance light travels in one year.

4. The _____ is the name given to the small cluster of galaxies in which the Milky Way Galaxy is located.

5. The most important factor in determining the increase in apparent brightness gained by using a telescope is the _____ of the telescope's objective.

6. A vast collection of stars, located far from any other known object in space, is called (*a constellation, the solar system, a galaxy, a nova*).

7. A telescope which has a curved mirror to collect light and form an image, and which has a lens or lenses to magnify that image is called a (*reflector, refractor*).

8. There are many groups of stars arranged in such a way that their positions and brightnesses form patterns or designs. Such a group of stars is called a (*Local Group, constellation, pole star, Cepheid*).

9. Even when observing them with a telescope, we cannot distinguish the true shape of (*stars, nebulae, galaxies*).

10. In our observations of the planets, (*definite shape, retrograde motion, moons, novae*) can be detected.

Extending Your Knowledge

QUESTIONS TO EXPLORE

1. How would you describe the universe as you now imagine it to be?

2. Why can a photograph taken through a telescope reveal certain objects which are too dim to be seen when one is merely looking through the same telescope?

3. The Andromeda galaxy is 2.2 million light-years away. What would this distance be, expressed in miles? In kilometers?

4. Why are many astronomical observatories located on mountains? Would a large city be a good site for an observatory? What reasons can you give for your answers?

5. There are differences among the galaxies even though they may be of the same type. What differences are there between the subtypes known as Sa, Sb, and Sc?

6. Elliptical galaxies are represented with symbols ranging from E0 to E7. What do the numerals 0 and 7 indicate?

SOME THINGS TO DO

1. Estimate the number of stars shown in a photograph of a portion of the Milky Way. HINT: Use a transparent sheet marked off in squares and count the stars in several squares. Have other students make similar counts. How closely do the counts agree? How can you account for any lack of agreement? Is there a right answer? How would you estimate the total number of stars in the picture?

2. Find out what materials for the study of astronomy are available in your school library and in the public library in your community. Use these materials to aid you in writing a report on some aspect of space science which is of particular interest to you.

3. Observe the Andromeda galaxy. Use the star maps on pages 46 and 47 to help you locate the Andromeda galaxy. On a very clear, moonless night the Andromeda galaxy is barely visible. Binoculars or a small telescope will help somewhat, but even with these aids the galaxy will appear as a dim blur of light. The Andromeda galaxy, at 2,200,000 (2.2×10^6) light-years, is the most distant object which can be seen with the naked eye. Calculate how far away the Andromeda galaxy would be if the distance from the earth to the sun (93,000,000 or 9.3×10^7 miles) were scaled down to one inch.

4. If possible, visit an observatory or a planetarium. Find out what equipment, photographs, and reference materials are used by the astronomers. Ask if you may see demonstrations of how the equipment is used. If possible, talk to an astronomer about the education he has and the kind of work he does. Make a report to the class.

CHALLENGES IN SCIENCE

1. Find out what radio astronomy is. What can be accomplished with radio telescopes that cannot be done using light telescopes? Are there any disadvantages to radio astronomy? If so, what are they?

2. Using diagrams or models, show why the time for one complete rotation of the earth relative to the stars is less than the time of one complete rotation of the earth relative to the sun. What names do astronomers give these time intervals? How is our view of the nighttime sky affected by the difference in these times of rotation?

3. Recently a new type of object has been discovered in space. Objects of this type are called *quasars*. Learn as much as you can about these objects and try to form a theory as to what they are.

CHAPTER 4

Nebulae are major components of the Milky Way Galaxy.

Inside the Milky Way Galaxy

Since we are a part of it, the Milky Way Galaxy is certainly the easiest galaxy for us to study—at least in some ways. Being inside the galaxy, however, does have one disadvantage. We cannot see the complete galaxy. Thus, we will never have quite as detailed a picture of the general shape of our own galaxy as we have, for example, of the shape of the great galaxy in Andromeda. Yet, from our position we can study many of the individual stars which make up our galaxy. We can also determine the position and the nature of many of the clouds of gas and dust which float between the stars of our galaxy.

As you study this chapter, you will be finding out about the stars and nebulae within our galaxy. In gathering facts about these components of our galaxy, you will discover how astronomers have acquired some of the knowledge they have of the properties and characteristics of the stars and nebulae. Also, you will see in your mind's eye a model of our galaxy. In this model much of the information known about our galaxy is combined. Thus the model will enable you to have a composite view of the Milky Way Galaxy and our position within it.

1. Stellar Brightness

Differences in brightness. When observing the stars, one of the first things that we notice is that some stars appear brighter than others. When we look through a telescope or when we see photographs taken through a telescope, the differences in brightness persist. The telescope helps us to see dimmer stars because of its light-gathering power. At the same time, however, the telescope makes the bright stars appear even brighter.

Why do some stars appear brighter than others? Essentially, the reason is that more light reaches us from the bright stars than from the dim ones. But why does more light reach the earth from some stars than from others?

Two factors can affect the apparent brightness of a star—that is, the amount of light we receive from the star. One factor is the amount of light the star is emitting. A star may look very bright because it is very luminous—that is, because it is emitting a great amount of light. The second factor in determining the apparent brightness of a star is the distance from us to the star. Thus, two stars emitting the same amount of light but at different distances from us will not appear equally bright. Instead, the nearer one will appear to be the brighter.

The very early astronomers thought that all of the stars were attached to the celestial sphere and were, therefore, all at the same distance from earth. To these astronomers the observed differences in brightness were easily accounted for. Since they believed distance was not a factor, they said some stars appeared brighter than others because the brighter stars were emitting more light.

Of course, observers today know that all stars are not the same distance from earth. With this knowledge has come the realization that the brightness of a star—as it appears to an observer—depends not only upon how luminous the star is but also upon how distant the star is.

DO IT YOURSELF

Observe the brightness of different stars

Observe the sky on a clear, dark night. Select an area of the sky that is bounded by bright stars. You might select, for example, the bowl of the Big Dipper. Using your unaided eye, observe the area. Count the number of stars you can see inside this area. Then, using binoculars, observe the same area. Count the number of stars now visible within the area. Are more stars visible when you use the binoculars? If so, how many more? Do the bright stars you used as boundary markers seem brighter through the binoculars? What explanations can you give for the differences in the brightnesses of the stars you observed?

The magnitude scale. The early astronomers, in addition to observing differences in the brightnesses of stars, developed a system of classifying stars on the basis of brightness. The brightness of a star is recorded in terms of *magnitude*. The magnitude of a star is basically a comparison of the brightness of the star with the brightness of other stars. Dimmer

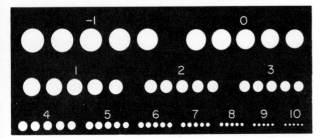

Figure 4-1. To estimate the magnitudes of the stars appearing on a photograph, astronomers use a scale like this. All stars appear to us as points of light. On photographs, however, the brighter stars appear as larger spots than do the dimmer stars. Comparing each spot with the scale indicates that star's magnitude.

stars are assigned greater numerical magnitudes. For example, *Betelgeuse* (bĕ′təl jüz), the brightest star in the constellation *Orion* (ô rī′en), is magnitude +0.9, and Polaris, which is somewhat dimmer, is magnitude +2.0. Usually a person with normal eyesight can see stars as dim as magnitude +6.0 on a clear, dark night.

> *Do you think the early astronomers classified any stars as magnitude +7.0 stars? Give reasons for your answer.*

The method of describing the brightness of a star by magnitude is more than two thousand years old. Of course, when the method was first used, magnitudes were assigned on the basis of visual observation.

Today, although the term magnitude is still used, a more precise method is used for determining the magnitude of a star. First, the amount of light being received from the star is measured by instruments. This measurement is then used as the basis for assigning a magnitude to the star.

One way of measuring the brightness of a star is to attach a photoelectric cell to the telescope in place of the eyepiece. As you might know, a photoelectric cell is a device—such as in a photographer's exposure meter—which is used to measure the brightness of light.

Thus, when the image of the star is focused on the photoelectric cell, the brightness of the star is determined. What other ways can you think of to measure the amount of light coming from a star?

After the amount of light being received from the star is measured, a numerical relationship is used to determine the star's magnitude. The numerical relationship is as follows. If 2.512 times more light is received from one star than from another—that is, if one star appears 2.512 times brighter than another—there is a difference of one magnitude in the brightness of these stars. Of course, a certain star must be picked as a standard, and the other stars are then compared with the standard. Polaris was selected as the standard, and a magnitude of +2.0 was assigned to Polaris.

The table in *Figure 4-2* shows the relationship between the difference in magnitude between two stars and the ratio of the brightness of the same two stars. Suppose you know that Star A is of magnitude +5.0 and Polaris is of magnitude +2.0. The difference in their magnitudes (5.0−2.0) is 3.0. The table indicates that a difference of 3 in magnitude means that

Figure 4-2. With this table, the ratio of brightness of two stars can be determined if the difference in their magnitudes is known. If their ratio of brightness is known, the difference in magnitudes can be found.

RELATING DIFFERENCE IN MAGNITUDE TO RATIO OF BRIGHTNESS	
Difference in Magnitude	Ratio of Brightness
1	$(2.512)^1$ or 2.5:1
2	$(2.512)^2$ or 6.3:1
3	$(2.512)^3$ or 16:1
4	$(2.512)^4$ or 40:1
5	$(2.512)^5$ or 100:1
6	$(2.512)^6$ or 250:1
7	$(2.512)^7$ or 630:1

one star is 16 times brighter than the other. Which star is brighter, Star A or Polaris? How do you know?

The table can also be used to find the magnitude of a star, if you know the brightness ratio of two stars and the magnitude of one of them. For example, Betelgeuse is approximately 2.5 times brighter than Polaris. The table shows that a brightness ratio of 2.5:1 means a difference in magnitude of 1. Polaris has a magnitude of +2.0. What is the approximate magnitude of Betelgeuse? (Remember that the magnitude of brighter stars is numerically less than the magnitude of dimmer stars.)

Limitations. In these examples, you may have discovered that the magnitude scale is not very convenient to use. First of all, you have to remember that brighter stars have lesser magnitude numbers. Furthermore, some stars are so bright that the magnitude scale must be extended to negative numbers to represent them in the scale. For example, *Sirius* (sir′i əs), the brightest star in the sky other than our sun, has a magnitude of −1.6. The magnitude of our sun is −26.7. At the other end of the scale, the faintest stars observable with the 200-inch telescope have a magnitude of +21.5. In spite of its limitations, the magnitude scale has been used for so many years and is used in so many reference books that developing a new system and changing over to it would not be worth the trouble.

2. Stellar Color and Temperature

Stars vary in color. Color is another property of stars. The color of a star can be determined by analyzing the light given off by the star. Although stars generally appear white, some have a slightly bluish cast, and others appear slightly orange. The differences in color are much more noticeable when a telescope or a pair of binoculars is used for observation. Can you imagine what accounts for this color difference? One reason you might suggest for the color difference is that not all stars are composed of the same elements. However, this is not the reason. Since most stars are made up of the same elements, differences in color among the various stars result from differences in their temperatures.

When something is hot enough to glow red, you know that it is, indeed, much too hot to touch. But even hotter than red hot is something which is white hot. Have you ever heard of something which is white hot? A star as hot as our sun is nearly white hot. (Actually, astronomers class our sun as a yellow star.) Blue hot (hot enough to emit blue light) is even hotter than white hot. Thus, a star which is hotter than our sun gives off a bluer light. A star cooler than our sun would give off a reddish light.

Can you imagine an object that is hot, but not hot enough to glow with a red light which we can see? Scientists know that such objects give off *infrared* (in′frə red′) *radiation* which we cannot see. Could we see stars which give off this type of radiation? If not, how might we detect such stars?

Now imagine a star so hot that the radiation it emits is not blue light which we can see. Instead, it emits *ultraviolet* (ul′trə vi′ə lit) *radiation*. As with infrared radiation, we cannot see ultraviolet radiation. Even if our eyes could detect it, the ultraviolet radiation from such a star would never reach the surface of the earth because our atmosphere absorbs ultraviolet radiation.

In the table in *Figure 4-3*, twelve stars are listed in order of decreasing temperature. The name and general color of each star is also listed. Notice that stars of different temperatures emit light of different colors. The hotter stars are blue and the cooler ones red. Unfortunately, to the naked eye, practically all stars appear white. It takes a very sharp eye to detect these colors. Determination of a star's color is made by measuring the amounts of the star's light that will pass through various colored filters.

Figure 4-3. The data in the table indicate a definite relationship between the temperature of a star and the general color of the star. What is the relationship?

TEMPERATURES AND COLORS OF SOME OF THE BRIGHTER-APPEARING STARS		
Spica (spī′kə)	24,000°K	blue-white
Rigel (rī′jəl)	12,000°K	blue-white
Vega (vē′gə)	11,300°K	blue-white
Sirius (sir′i əs)	10,600°K	blue-white
Canopus (kə nō′pəs)	8,200°K	white
Procyon (prō′si on)	6,600°K	yellow-white
Capella (kə pel′ə)	5,800°K	yellow
The Sun	5,750°K	yellow
Arcturus (ärk tŭr′əs)	4,500°K	orange
Aldebaran (al deb′ər ən)	3,600°K	orange
Antares (an tār′ēz)	3,200°K	red
Betelgeuse (bē′təl jüz)	3,100°K	red

FIND OUT BY TRYING

Materials you will need: two electric irons

Place two electric irons in an upright position on a table top, but have only one plugged in. Observe the irons. Is either iron giving off visible light? Without touching the irons, hold the back of your hand near one iron and then the other. Can you tell which one is hot? If so, how? Do you think that the hot iron is giving off any radiation? If so, what kind of radiation do you think it is? Do you think that any radiation like that given off by the hot iron is given off by the sun? Explain your answers.

Temperature scales. Note that in *Figure 4-3*, the temperatures of the stars are given in degrees K. The *K* is an abbreviation used to indicate the Kelvin temperature scale. The Kelvin scale uses *absolute zero,* the lowest possible temperature, for its zero point. Although ordinary thermometers are not marked with the Kelvin scale, the Kelvin scale is very often used in science.

How does the Kelvin scale compare with the temperature scales we are more accustomed to using? A careful study of *Figure 4-4* will give you many of the details you need to

know for understanding the various scales. The important thing to remember is that any temperature scale can be used in measuring the temperature of a certain object. The numerical reading on each scale will usually be different, even though the temperature is the same. (In just the same way, three different measurements of the length of a football field may give three different readings. Thus, 100 yards, 300 feet, or 91.44 meters are all measurements which represent the length of the same field.) In recording a temperature, it is important to indicate which of the scales has been used in measuring that temperature. For instance, to report a temperature as 85° is as incomplete as saying that a room is 10 wide.

Is the absolute temperature (Kelvin) of an object doubled when its temperature changes from 10°C to 20°C? If not, give an example of the absolute temperature being doubled.

How temperature affects the brightness of stars. You will recall that the determining factor in the color of a star is its temperature. The temperature of a star also affects the amount of light emitted by the star. If two stars are the same size, but have different temperatures, the hotter star will be the more luminous. This relationship of luminosity to

Figure 4-4. An understanding of temperature and a knowledge of temperature scales are important in many fields of science. Here, three temperature scales used in science are briefly explained and compared.

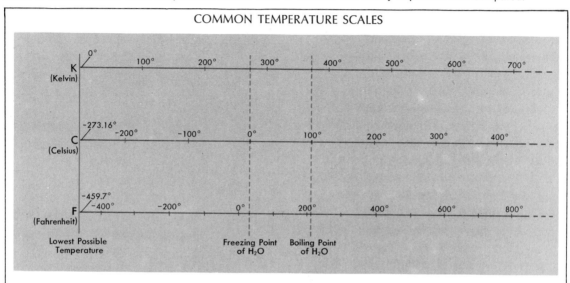

1. Temperature is an indication of the average kinetic energy of the molecules of a substance.
2. The lowest possible temperature (absolute zero) would occur when the molecules of a substance have the least amount of motion possible for them.
3. There is no maximum temperature, because molecules can be given any amount of energy.
4. Zero on the Kelvin scale is absolute zero, so there are no negative temperatures on this scale. It is an absolute scale.
5. Although the Fahrenheit scale is used by most people in the United States, scientists prefer the Celsius scale (formerly called the centigrade scale) and the Kelvin scale.
6. When the temperature of an object is measured, the numerical reading will differ, depending on which scale is used.
7. A Celsius degree is equivalent to a Kelvin degree, but a Celsius degree is greater than a Fahrenheit degree. That is, a change in temperature of 1 Celsius degree would be equivalent to a change in temperature of $\frac{9}{5}$ Fahrenheit degrees.
8. A reading on one scale can be converted to an equivalent reading on another scale. To convert from Celsius to Kelvin, use the following formula: $K = C + 273.16$. To convert from Celsius to Fahrenheit, use the following formula: $F = \frac{9}{5}C + 32$.

temperature is very important. The physical law which describes this relationship between temperature and luminosity is called *Stefan's law*. This law states that the energy emitted by a star depends to a very great extent on the temperature of the star. In fact, if all other conditions are the same, the energy given off by a star is proportional to the fourth power of the absolute temperature. For example, suppose a star has a surface temperature of 6,000°K, and another star of the same size has a surface temperature of 12,000°K—that is, 2 times as great as the first star. According to Stefan's law, the hotter star will be giving off more energy than the cooler one. But the ratio of the amounts of energy given off by these two stars will not be 2:1 (which is the ratio of their temperatures). Instead, it will be $(2:1)^4$, or 16:1. In other words, the star which is hotter by a ratio of 2:1 will be brighter by a ratio of 16:1.

How size affects the brightness of stars. If two stars are the same temperature, then the amount of light they radiate depends on how big they are. For example, suppose a certain star has a diameter twice as great as the diameter of our sun. This particular star has an area four times that of the sun. Therefore, this larger star would emit four times as much light as our sun.

Thus, by determining both the color and the brightness of a star, we can tell something about the star's temperature and size. We are able to do this even though the nearest star is so far away that it appears only as a point of light to us.

The luminosity of a star is dependent upon the temperature and size of the star. What other factors (if any) do you think might affect the amount of light emitted by a star?

3. Stellar Spectra

Analyzing starlight. So far in this chapter, you have read how astronomers have been able to learn about the stars by observing the brightness and color of the stars. The brightness of a star can be a clue to its distance and size, and the general color of a star's light indicates the temperature of the star. There is, however, much more that can be learned about a star by making a detailed analysis of the light we receive from the star.

But how can starlight be analyzed? The light from most stars is so dim that you can hardly detect it, much less analyze it. However, the light from one star—the sun—is very bright. In describing how light is analyzed, sunlight will be used as an example. You can easily imagine how astronomers, by using large tele-scopes to collect and to concentrate the light of the stars, are able to analyze starlight in much the same way as they do sunlight.

Producing spectra. The first step in this detailed analysis is to separate the light into various colors. The light we receive from the sun seems white. But, as you undoubtedly know, sunlight can be separated into the colors of the rainbow, or the colors of the visible spectrum. The array of colors produced when sunlight is separated is called the sun's spectrum, or the solar spectrum. It has the familiar pattern shown in *Figure 4-6*. The colors range from violet to red with indigo, blue, green, yellow, and orange in between.

Sir Isaac Newton, the great English scientist, made one of the first detailed studies of how sunlight can be separated into the various colors of the rainbow. By using a glass prism, which he had bought as a toy, he was able to produce a spectrum in his bedroom. As a result of his studies, Newton gave the first correct description of the dispersion—the separation into various colors—of sunlight.

The story of Newton's studies in optics makes fascinating reading. Newton was not satisfied with just describing dispersion. He worked out a theory which explained dispersion. However, the theory, which was based on some assumptions about the properties of light and about prisms, turned out to be wrong. The error in his theory about prisms led him to another mistake in describing the way telescopes work. This, in turn, led him to invent the reflecting telescope, which is shown in *Figure 3-8*. Thus, a vital discovery followed by a few crucial mistakes (and even the best scientists make them) led Newton to a fundamental invention in the field of astronomy—namely, the reflecting telescope.

Figure 4-5. Although the only apparatus available was very simple, Newton studied light and color very carefully. The picture above is one artist's conception of Newton examining the sun's spectrum in his study.

FIND OUT BY TRYING

Materials you will need: prism, sheet of white paper, newspaper or cardboard

Find a window that sunlight is coming through. Block out the sunlight by pulling the shade down part way and covering the remaining part of the window with some opaque material, such as newspaper or cardboard. Cut a slit about 1 millimeter wide in the opaque material. Sunlight should come in through this slit. Darken the room as much as possible by pulling down all the other shades in the room.

Place the prism in the beam of sunlight so that the light passes through the prism. By experimenting, find out how the prism should be positioned in the beam of sunlight so that a spectrum suitable for examination is produced. Place a sheet of white paper in a position such that the spectrum is spread out across the paper. Examine the spectrum closely. What colors are present in the spectrum? Is there a sharp distinction between the colors, or do the colors blend together? Can you observe any dark lines in the spectrum? If so, what explanation can you give for their presence?

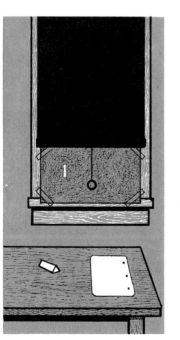

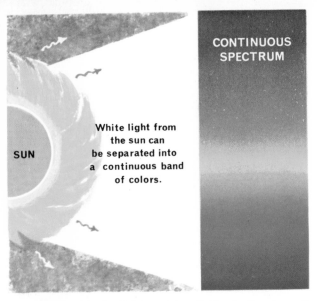

Figure 4-6. Sunlight contains light of all colors. If sunlight did not pass through any gases, a prism would disperse sunlight into a continuous spectrum.

Figure 4-7. Light from a glowing gas under low pressure is made up of only certain colors. A prism would disperse this light into a bright-line spectrum.

Types of spectra. The type of spectrum which is produced by the dispersion of sunlight is called a *continuous spectrum*. It appears to be a continuous array of colors ranging from red to violet. Continuous spectra are characteristic of glowing solids, liquids, and even of gases—when the gases are under great pressure or are present in great depth as is the case in stars.

Normally the spectrum of glowing gas contains only certain colors of light. The colors depend on the elements which make up the glowing gas. When this light is dispersed, the colors show up as a set of bright, isolated lines. The set of bright lines which is produced by the dispersion of the light emitted by a particular gas is called the *bright-line spectrum* of that gas. Each element, when vaporized and heated to incandescence, has a unique bright-line spectrum. Both continuous and bright-line spectra are called *emission spectra* because they are produced by emitted light.

About 150 years ago, a German scientist, *Joseph von Fraunhofer* (froun'hō'fər), con-

structed the first modern *spectroscope* (spek'trə skōp). The spectroscope combines the prism with the telescope. With this instrument Fraunhofer was able to examine the sun's spectrum in great detail. He noticed that the continuous spectrum of the sun was not actually continuous, but was crossed by many dark lines. Twelve years before, another scientist had observed four of these dark lines in a spectrum. He, however, did not understand their importance. Fraunhofer himself could not prove that the dark lines were properties of the light, and not simply the result of bad design in his spectroscope. Eventually, however, he did convince others that the lines were caused by the presence of certain elements in the sun's atmosphere.

The dark lines were finally explained by Gustav Kirchoff in 1859. Kirchoff was able to show, by experiment and with mathematical proof, that the black lines which Fraunhofer observed in the sun's spectrum were in precisely the same position as the lines observed in the bright-line spectra of certain elements.

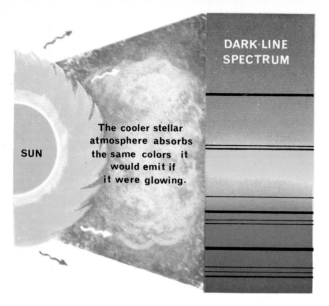

DARK·LINE SPECTRUM

SUN

The cooler stellar atmosphere absorbs the same colors it would emit if it were glowing.

Figure 4-8. Certain colors are absorbed when sunlight passes through a cool gas. Thus, a prism on earth disperses sunlight into a dark-line spectrum.

For example, when sodium vapor is heated it glows and gives off certain colors of light. The yellow light of sodium is particularly bright, and is seen when some salt (sodium chloride) is put in a fire. This bright, yellow light produces the bright-line spectrum that is unique to sodium. But suppose that light from an object like the sun, which forms a continuous spectrum, must pass through sodium vapor. Then the sodium vapor absorbs the same color

of light that it would emit if it were hotter. Since the light of this color is being absorbed by the sodium vapor, it will not show up in the continuous spectrum. Instead, a dark line will be present where light of that color had been. A spectrum formed in this manner is called a *dark-line spectrum*. Dark-line spectra are called *absorption spectra*, because absorption of light, not emission, causes the lines.

What differences would you observe between the spectra of a neon sign and an incandescent light? HINT: *Light is produced by a glowing gas in a neon sign and by a glowing wire in an incandescent light.*

Using spectra. The dark lines (named Fraunhofer lines) in the spectrum of the sun are the clues used by scientists to discover which elements are in the outer layers of the sun. The dark-line spectrum of the sun is compared with the bright-line spectra of various elements. If the bright lines of an element's spectrum coincide with dark lines on the sun's spectrum—as in *Figure 4-9*—it is convincing evidence that the element is present in the outer layer, or atmosphere, of the sun.

Spectra and color. At this point you may be somewhat confused about the spectrum of a

Figure 4-9. The sun's spectrum (center) is compared with the spectrum produced by an iron arc (top and bottom). Bright lines in the spectrum of iron coincide with dark lines in the sun's spectrum, indicating that the element iron is present in the sun's atmosphere.

PHOTOGRAPH FROM THE MOUNT WILSON AND PALOMAR OBSERVATORIES

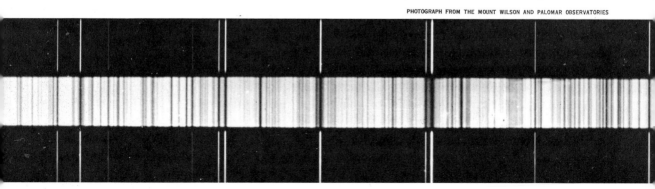

star and the color of a star. Previously, you had read that the color of the star is an indicator of the temperature of the star. Now you have read that the colors present in starlight (or any light, for that matter) depend upon the chemical elements which emitted the light. Which is right? Actually, both of these statements are correct.

Although the spectrum of each element does have its particular set of colors, each color does not have the same intensity. Most elements have a bright-line spectrum which consists of several different, characteristic color lines. As the temperature of the element changes, the same lines will always be present. However, at certain temperatures, the lines near the red end of the spectrum are brighter than those near the blue end. As the element is heated, the lines near the blue end of the spectrum become more intense than those at the red end.

By studying the position of the dark lines in a star's spectrum, scientists can tell which elements are present in the star. By comparing the brightness of the blue portion of the spectrum with that of the red portion, scientists can determine the temperature at the surface of the star. Thus, a careful examination of a star's spectrum reveals both the temperature and the chemical composition of the material near the surface of the star.

4. Double Stars and Variable Stars

Detecting double stars. You have read how precise measurements of the brightness of the stars can be made by attaching a photoelectric cell to a telescope and how the colors of stars can be used to determine their temperatures. You have also read how a spectroscope can be mounted on a telescope and used to determine the various elements that are found in the atmosphere of the stars. But some important discoveries have been made as a result of simply looking through a telescope.

An example of such a discovery is the detection of multiple stars in our galaxy. Soon after telescopes were invented, astronomers noticed that some stars appeared quite close to each other, as if they were a pair of stars rather than two single stars. In some instances, three, four, or even more stars appeared to be associated in a group. More than a hundred years later, about the time that the founders of our country were drafting our Constitution, an important observation was made concerning this type of star. The famous English astronomer,

William Herschel, discovered that in two-star systems, the stars were actually revolving about each other. Later on, when you study how the mass of a star is determined, you will better understand the importance of Herschel's discovery.

Each of these pairs of stars is called a *binary star* or a *double star*. The first double stars to be observed were of the type known as visual doubles; that is, each individual star could be detected visually. However, sometimes the individual stars within the double star cannot be distinguished, even when viewed through a telescope. By analyzing the light from stars, however, astronomers have found that many stars which appear as single stars are actually double stars.

Today, astronomers believe that more than one third of the number of stars which appear as single stars are either pairs of stars or multiple stars. Furthermore, within each system, the stars are revolving about each other or, to be more accurate, about a common point.

Observe a double star

On a clear, dark night, observe the middle star of the three stars in the handle of the Big Dipper. What do you observe that is unusual about this star? If you have a telescope, observe the same star through the telescope. Write a description of what you see.

Motions of double stars. The apparent orbit of one star of a double star about the other is shown in *Figure 4-10*. Each point on the orbit is labeled with the year in which the observation was made. Although the line connecting the points appears jagged, the actual orbit is smooth. The irregularity is the result of the difficulty of making precise measurements of the positions of stars.

There are two reasons why the orbit in this diagram is the apparent orbit and not the true orbit. First, the plane of the orbit is not at right angles to our line of sight. Thus, the true shape of the orbit is not seen. Second, the star inside the orbit would not remain in one place as it appears to do in this diagram. Whenever objects in space revolve about each other— whether they are two stars or the earth and the moon—they are actually revolving about a common point. *(Figure 4-11.)* This point is the *center of mass* of the system. The location of the center of mass within the system depends on the relative masses of the two objects. Two children use this principle when balancing each other on a teeter-totter. The balance point is the center of mass of the two children and the teeter-totter.

The discovery of double stars and the observation of their orbits has been of great importance to astronomy. Until these double stars were discovered and their motions observed, there was no way by which the mass of any star—except our sun—could be determined. Now, however, astronomers use the information obtained from observing a double

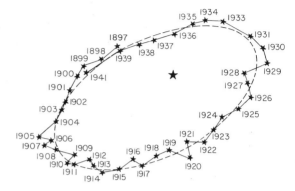

Figure 4-10. The apparent orbit of one star about the other in the double star η Coronae Borealis is shown. On the basis of these data, what is the period of revolution of this double star?

Figure 4-11. In the diagram below, two objects in space are represented as revolving about their center of mass (X). The mass of A is two times that of B. Thus, their center of mass is closer to A than it is to B. Later positions of A and B are also indicated. The dashed lines show that any line between A and B passes through this center of mass.

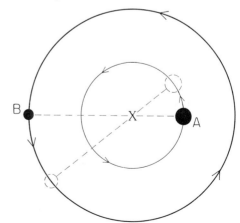

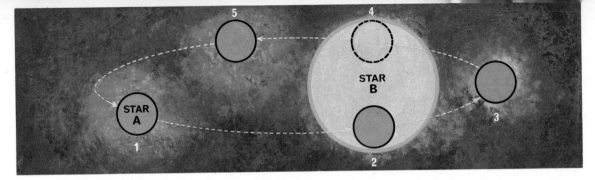

Figure 4-12. Shown in the diagram above is the apparent orbit of one star of an eclipsing double about the other. A double star such as this one appears brightest when we receive the maximum light from each star—for example, when Star A is in the positions marked 1, 3, and 5. When Star A is at 2, we receive light from Star A, but only part of the light from Star B. When Star A is at 4, we receive light from Star B, but no light from Star A.

star in order to calculate the total mass of the two stars in the double-star system. In fact, the mass of each of the individual stars within the double-star system can be determined in many cases.

Where would the center of mass of a double-star system be located if the two stars in the system were of equal mass? If one star were 50 times more massive than the other?

Eclipsing doubles. *Figure 4-12* is a sketch showing the positions of the two stars of an imaginary double star at various times. Suppose Star A—a dim star represented by the shaded circles—revolves about Star B in an apparent orbit as shown by the broken line.

The orbit of this double is like the orbit of many other doubles except that you are seeing this orbit nearly edge-on. Because of the nearly edge-on view, the two stars will alternately pass in front of, or eclipse, each other, causing the apparent brightness of the double-star system to vary. Hence a double star observed from this point of view is called an *eclipsing double.* If you could see a top view, the orbit of Star A would be more nearly circular, and one star would not pass behind the other. Also keep in mind that Star B is not stationary as Star A re-

volves about it. Both stars would be revolving about a common point, but in the diagram Star B is shown in only one place.

Do you think the sun is part of a double-star system? How would you justify your answer?

Variable stars. The variation in the brightness of an eclipsing double is not because of something happening inside an individual star. It is merely the result of one star blocking some of the light of another. However, there are some individual stars which do undergo changes in brightness because of an internal change.

The first variable stars were discovered before telescopes were invented. But, even if you use a telescope, it is difficult to discover a variable star. First you have to observe how bright the various stars are. Then, several days or weeks later, you have to remember the brightnesses of the stars and recognize any star which appears to be a little brighter or dimmer. You can imagine that it was usually a matter of chance when a variable star was discovered without the use of instruments.

The use of photography has made the task of finding variable stars much easier. Now, an exact record of the brightnesses of stars can be kept on a photograph. Photographs of a particular part of the sky taken several days apart can be compared with one another. This comparison quickly reveals any changes of brightness among the stars.

Cepheids. The most famous of all variable stars occurs in the constellation *Cepheus* (sē′fi əs). About 200 years ago, the star *Delta Cephei* (del′tə sē′fi ī) was discovered to be a variable star. The brightness of this star varies between the magnitudes of 3.5 and 4.4, and it takes 5.37 days to complete one cycle of brightness variation. Since the discovery of the variable star in Cepheus, many stars have been observed which behave in a similar manner. These stars are all called *Cepheid variables* or *Cepheids* (sef′i idz).

With the changes in the brightness of the light from a Cepheid, there is a change in the color of the light. The change in color indicates a temperature variation. Cepheids are hottest when they are brightest. The exact reason for this change in brightness and temperature is not known. The most widely accepted theory is that the brightness and temperature of this type of star vary because the star pulsates, or expands and contracts, at regular intervals. But neither this theory—nor any other so far suggested—can explain all of the detailed observations about Cepheid variables.

Novae. Some stars suddenly become much brighter because of the sudden release of huge amounts of energy. Ordinarily a star which undergoes such an explosive release of energy is called a nova. During the explosion the star usually becomes about 100,000 times brighter than normal. Ordinarily, the increase in brightness is rapid, sometimes requiring only a few hours or days. The brightness then diminishes over a period of months until the star again attains a brightness about the same as, or slightly less than, its original brightness.

Occasionally a star explodes so violently that it becomes 100,000,000 (1×10^8) times brighter and in the process destroys itself. A star which undergoes this extremely violent release of energy is called a *supernova*. The clouds of gas thrown out by exploding stars can take on quite unusual forms. *Figure 4-13* shows one of the more unusual forms.

The earliest recorded observation of a supernova was made in A.D. 1054. Chinese astronomers at that time reported a star that shone so brightly that it was visible even in the daytime. This brightness lasted two years, then faded away. When modern telescopes are pointed to the place in the sky where this supernova was observed, all that is seen is a vast, rapidly expanding cloud of gas called the *Crab nebula*. *(Figure 4-14.)*

Figure 4-13. Astronomers have given this nebula the unimaginative title NGC 2392. Undoubtedly, you can figure out a more descriptive name for it.

Figure 4-14. The Crab nebula is a huge, expanding cloud of dust and gas. It is believed to be the remnants of a supernova observed in A.D. 1054.

5. Clusters and Clouds

Star clusters. Within our galaxy there are about 100 billion stars. The distribution of the stars is such that our galaxy is a spiral galaxy. It has a central hub and spiral arms like other spirals. But, in addition to the usual hub and spiral arms, our galaxy has two features of special interest to astronomers. These features are two different types of star clusters.

Within the spiral arms of our galaxy, most of the stars are distributed in a random manner. But there are some stars that are bunched up in groups. Such a group of stars is called a *galactic* (gə lak′tik) *cluster*, or an *open cluster*. Each cluster of this type may contain several hundred stars. The stars which make up a cluster such as this are all moving in the same direction. Also, the stars within a particular cluster are all about the same distance from the sun. They are believed to have been formed at the same time. A photograph of a typical galactic cluster is shown in *Figure 4-15*.

A second type of cluster is called a *globular cluster*. Astronomers have been able to observe about 100 of these globular clusters in our galaxy. Unlike the galactic clusters, globular clusters are not located within the spiral arms. A photograph of a typical globular cluster is shown in *Figure 3-13*. What differences can you see between a galactic cluster and a globular cluster?

Each globular cluster contains tens of thousands of stars, and the stars are much closer together than are the stars in a galactic cluster. Astronomers have studied the stars in globular clusters in detail. They have determined that the stars of a globular cluster are all about the same age and that they travel together.

Globular clusters revolve about the hub of the galaxy, but not in the same plane as the spiral arms. If the orbit of each globular cluster were traced out, all the orbits taken together would form a spherical halo about the galaxy.

What reason or reasons can you give that might explain why the stars of a globular cluster are not pulled together by the gravitational forces within the cluster?

Figure 4-15. This photograph of a galactic cluster was made with the 200-inch telescope. Each of the bright stars seen in the photograph appears to have four points about a bright disk. Actually, the shape of these stars is no different from that of the other stars in the picture. The points are illusions brought about by the presence of braces in the structure of the telescope. The pointed appearance of the stars results when the braces within the telescope distort the incoming light.

Observe two types of star clusters

Use star maps to locate in the night sky the cluster of the Pleiades in the constellation Taurus. This cluster is a galactic, or open, cluster. What characteristics of an open cluster can you observe?

To observers in the middle-northern latitudes, the brightest and best-known globular cluster is seen in the constellation Hercules. Use the star maps to locate the constellation Hercules and then the cluster in Hercules. Although this globular cluster is the brightest one visible from the northern latitudes, it is relatively faint. A telescope must be used in order to recognize this source of light as a star cluster. This cluster is best seen early in August when it is highest in the sky at about 8:00 P.M. Why are space objects best seen when they are high in the sky?

Interstellar material. Astronomers estimate that there are 100 billion stars in our galaxy. However, the mass of the whole galaxy—as estimated from the observed speed of rotation of the galaxy—is much greater than the mass of 100 billion average stars. In fact, some astronomers have estimated that the mass of the stars represents only about one half of the total mass of the galaxy. What accounts for the rest of the mass? Is it in the form of planets like those in our solar system? Even if every star had a group of planets like our solar system, the planets would still represent only a fraction of one per cent of the total mass of each system. So planets cannot be used to account for the missing mass. Where, then, is the other half of the mass of the galaxy? If stellar material represents only part of the total mass, the other mass must be between the stars (interstellar material). But what materials exist between the stars?

To find out, suppose we turn our attention to the clouds of dust and gas which have been observed in space. The Horsehead nebula *(Figure 3-16)* is one of the most spectacular of these. Looking at the Horsehead nebula, it is easy to see that it is composed of vast clouds of some sort of material. Some portions of the cloud are glowing, but other portions are dark and block the light from behind them. There are two questions astronomers would like to answer about such clouds. What are they made of? Why do some of them glow?

Composition of nebulae. The first of these questions can be answered to some extent with the help of the spectroscope. Scientists compare the spectrum of the light from one of these clouds with the light given off by various gases in a laboratory experiment. These comparisons have shown that the nebulae contain many gases—including oxygen, nitrogen, hydrogen, and helium—with which we are quite familiar here on earth. Nebulae also contain other elements—including sulfur and carbon —which are usually in solid form on earth.

In general, astronomers are agreed that the nebulae consist of a very tenuous mixture of gases and dust particles. The gaseous portion is mostly hydrogen. Other gases are present in lesser amounts. The gases account for about 98 per cent of the matter in nebulae. The chemical composition of the dust particles—which represent the remaining 2 per cent of the matter present—is not known.

The total mass of all the interstellar matter in our galaxy is approximately equivalent to the mass of all the stars in our galaxy. The nebulae are more nearly like a vacuum than many so-called vacuums produced in laboratories. From these two assumptions, what can you infer about the size of the nebulae?

Light from nebulae. The spectroscope also can be used to tell us something about the source of the light which shines from these nebulae. Some of the nebulae, such as the Great Nebula in Orion shown in *Figure 4-16*, shine by *fluorescence* (flü′ə res′əns). In the center of this nebula is a group of six stars. It is impossible to see these stars in the photograph because the picture has been greatly overexposed in order to photograph the faint details around the edges of the cloud. The six stars, located in the bright spot near the center, appear simply as a white blur.

The six stars at the center of this cloud emit visible light along with invisible, ultraviolet radiation. The ultraviolet radiation interacts with the atoms of the gases in the cloud, causing the electrons in the atoms to gain energy. When the electrons give up the energy they gained, this energy is emitted in the form of light which can be seen. This phenomenon is called fluorescence. It is the same process by which the tube in a fluorescent light fixture gives off light.

Nebulae which shine by fluorescence have a different color than the stars which illuminate them. Some nebulae, such as those surrounding the Pleiades which are shown in *Figure 4-17*, have almost the same color light as the stars nearby. In these clouds something other than fluorescence is causing the glow. These clouds can be seen because of *light scattering*.

Light scattering is probably more familiar to you than fluorescence. Light scattering is what makes a ray of sunlight visible as it

Figure 4-16. When viewed with the unaided eye, the Great Nebula in Orion appears to be a star—the middle star in Orion's sword. Telescopes, however, reveal this "star" to be a huge, glowing cloud.

PHOTOGRAPH FROM THE MOUNT WILSON AND PALOMAR OBSERVATORIES

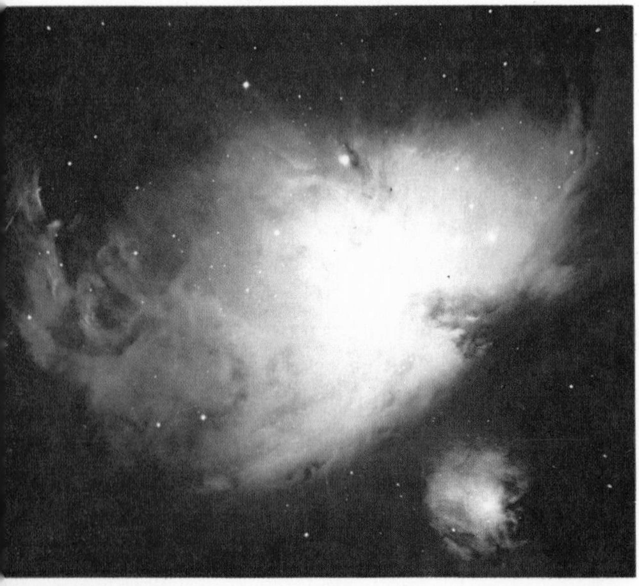

Figure 4-17. Clouds of gas and dust surround some of the stars within this galactic cluster. These clouds glow because light from stars within the cluster is scattered by the particles in the clouds.

PHOTOGRAPH FROM THE MOUNT WILSON AND PALOMAR OBSERVATORIES

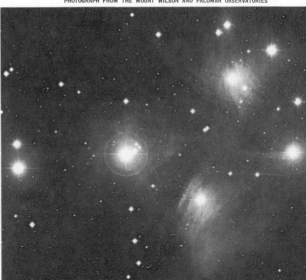

Figure 4-18. The Veil nebula, like the Crab nebula, is thought to be the result of a supernova. The Veil nebula cannot be seen with the unaided eye.

Figure 4-19. The Lagoon nebula is visible with the un-aided eye. However, a telescope and sensitive color film make the appearance of the nebula more striking.

shines through the window and across the room. In the atmosphere of the room, just as in a nebula in space, there are many tiny dust particles. Each particle reflects a little bit of the light which shines on it. The whole effect is that a slight glow is produced wherever the light passes.

Some nebulae are so faint that they cannot be seen, even by an astronomer using the best telescope. Although the astronomer may be able to make out a slightly hazy form, the de-tails are invisible to his eye. The only way that the true form of the nebula can be determined is to use the telescope as a camera and take a long time exposure with sensitive film. In re-cent years, sensitive color film has been avail-able. Pictures taken with this type of film are shown in *Figures 4-18, 4-19*, and *4-20*.

Figure 4-20. Through a small telescope, the Dumbbell nebula looks like two hazy patches of light. This picture was taken with a 100-inch telescope.

FIND OUT BY TRYING

Materials you will need: microscope, watch with luminous dial

Place the watch upon the stage of the microscope. Then, using the low power objective, focus the microscope on one numeral of a lumi-nous watch dial. Then darken the room completely. After several min-utes, your eyes will have become accustomed to the darkness. Then, look through the eyepiece of the microscope. Is light being emitted by the material of the numeral? If so, describe what you see. Use references to help explain what you observe.

83

6. The Milky Way Galaxy

Its structure. Our Milky Way contains stars of many different sizes and colors. It contains variable stars and multiple stars. There are star clusters containing thousands of stars, and there are huge clouds of gas and dust between the stars.

The overall shape of our galaxy is like a flat disk with a bulge in the center. The size of the galaxy has been determined. A diagram showing a cross section of our galaxy is shown in *Figure 4-21*. The dimensions in this diagram are in light-years. If we could get outside of our galaxy and look at it from the proper angle, it would look very much like the galaxy in Andromeda. *(Figure 3-14.)* But, of course, we are stuck inside it, and so we are denied this view of our own galaxy.

However, from our position on the inside, we can look along the plane of the disk and see the band where the stars seem to be concentrated. (We call this band of light in the night sky the Milky Way.) Or, we can look at right angles to that plane and see regions where the stars are much less concentrated.

A model. Suppose you could obtain a scale model of our galaxy. Imagine this model was constructed so that a distance of one inch on the model represented one light-year in the real galaxy. Then imagine getting inside this model so your right eye would be in the position of our own sun. Of course, you would have to push quite a few stars out of the way in order to fit your body into such a model. But suppose you have done that and are now ready to look around you.

If you were to look in the right direction, you would find the nearest star about three inches off the end of your nose. Actually, two

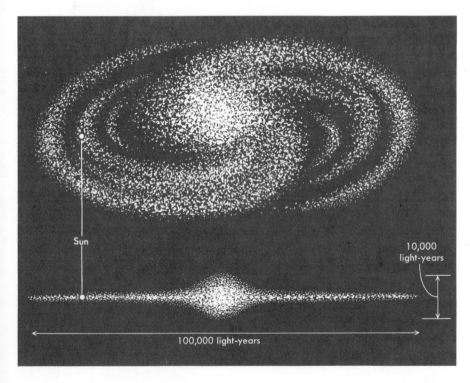

Sun

10,000 light-years

100,000 light-years

Figure 4-21. The Milky Way Galaxy is a huge, rotating system which contains billions of stars and vast clouds of gas and dust. These two diagrammatic views of our galaxy, along with the dimensions shown, give you an idea of the overall size and shape of our galaxy. In these diagrams, you can also see the position our sun occupies within the galaxy. If you could travel as fast as an orbiting astronaut (about 18,000 miles per hour), how long would it take you to get to the center of the galaxy?

stars would appear there, about one-half inch apart. One would be much dimmer than the other. These are the stars *Alpha Centauri* and *Proxima Centauri*. Alpha is much brighter than Proxima, in spite of the fact that Proxima is a little closer to you.

As you look around, you will find yourself inside a disklike pattern of stars. Where you are, the disk is about forty feet thick. One edge of the disk is about fifteen feet above your head. A little more than half a mile away is the center of the disklike array of stars. The center would be hard to see because of all the stars between you and the center.

The pattern of stars dwindles away into empty space about a quarter of a mile behind you. Right near your head, you would notice that the average distance between the stars is about two to three inches. The space near you is relatively crowded with stars. And yet, you could tell that near the center of the model the stars are even more closely packed.

If you looked in the proper direction, you could see the neighboring galaxy in Andromeda. It is about the same size as your own galaxy—that is, about a mile and a half in diameter. Since it would be more than twenty miles away from you, you could make it out only as a small blur, unless, of course, you had remembered to bring a telescope into the model with you.

With the help of the telescope, you might discover that your galaxy is surrounded by some rather strange-looking objects. Closer examination would reveal that these objects are composed of many stars grouped together. These clusters of stars are the globular clusters which were described before.

Finding out about our galaxy. It is impossible to count all of the stars in our galaxy. By measuring the light coming from various parts of it, however, it is possible to get an estimate of how many stars there must be. This esti-mate indicates there are about 100 billion stars in our galaxy. Three quarters of these stars are concentrated in the hub of the galaxy.

While inside the model, you would find that making estimates of size and distance would often be very difficult. Wherever you looked, your view would be blocked by many stars and also by clouds of gas and dust. The same situation exists for astronomers as they pursue their studies of our galaxy. Thus, some of what we "know" about our galaxy is really only an educated guess. Of course, it probably is a rather accurate guess, because it is based on data obtained by careful observation and measurement. However, you have the feeling that if you could get away from your position and float around at will through your galaxy, you might be able to make a considerable number of surprising discoveries.

In spite of the fact that man has not yet been able to float around at will through his galaxy, he has made some important discoveries about the stars. Studies of the stars have revealed many ways in which one star may differ from another. They may differ in size, brightness, composition, and distance from us. Often, the things we see in the sky are not what they appear to be. Sometimes what appears to be a single point of light turns out to be a double star or a multiple star. Sometimes what appears to be a single star is revealed to be a huge cluster of tens of thousands of stars. But probably the most significant discovery about stars is that they occur in huge aggregations called galaxies. Furthermore, every star which is close enough to appear to the naked eye as an individual point of light is in our own Milky Way Galaxy.

How long would it take to count the 100,-000,000,000 (1×10^{11}) stars in our galaxy, assuming you could count one star each second?

Checking Your Knowledge

IMPORTANT IDEAS

1. A star's brightness, or magnitude, is determined by comparing it with the brightnesses of other stars selected as standards.

2. How much light a star emits depends upon the temperature and size of the star.

3. The color of the light from a star depends upon the star's surface temperature.

4. Observing double stars makes it possible for astronomers to determine stellar masses.

5. Much of our information about the matter in space has been obtained by studying spectra of the light coming from space.

6. Although most stars are distributed in the galaxy in a random manner, some are bunched into clusters.

7. Interstellar material—vast clouds of gas and dust—accounts for an estimated one half of the total mass of our galaxy.

8. The brightness of some stars varies. The variation may be due to an external cause (an eclipsing variable) or it may be due to changes inside the star (a Cepheid variable).

USING NEW WORDS

Study the six groups of words below. Words within a group may be alike in some ways and different in other ways. On your paper, write the letters *a* through *f*. Beside each letter write two brief statements about each group of words. In one statement tell how the words in the group are alike in their meaning. In the other statement tell how the words in the group differ in their meaning.

    a. Fahrenheit—Kelvin—Celsius
    b. eclipsing binary—Cepheid
    c. light scattering—fluorescence
    d. infrared—spectrum—ultraviolet
    e. absorption spectra—emission spectra
    f. bright-line spectra—dark-line spectra

TEST YOURSELF

Study the test below. Write the numerals *1-10* on your paper. Beside each numeral write the correct response to that part of the test having the corresponding numeral.

1. If certain events within a star cause changes in the brightness of the star, that star is (*a nearby star, an eclipsing double, a Cepheid variable*).

2. The ratio of the mass of the stellar material in our galaxy to the mass of interstellar material in our galaxy is estimated to be (*1:2, 2:1, 1:1*).

3. An object which is not quite hot enough to give off visible light does emit (*infrared, ultraviolet, solar*) radiation.

4. The (*Kelvin, Celsius, Fahrenheit*) scale is an absolute scale—that is, its zero point is the lowest possible temperature, called absolute zero.

5. Smoke and dust particles that are normally invisible in the air are visible while a projector is in use because of (*fluorescence, light scattering, incandescence*).

6. Sirius with a magnitude of −1.6 appears to be (*brighter than, dimmer than, of the same brightness as*) Polaris, of magnitude +2.0.

7. The star Betelgeuse is of magnitude +0.9. Polaris is of magnitude +2.0. Therefore, the star _____ appears to us as the brighter of the two.

8. A star cluster which is located outside the plane of the spiral arms of the galaxy and which contains tens of thousands of stars is called a _____ cluster.

9. If the light emitted by a star is bluish in color, the star must have a very _____ temperature.

10. The dark lines observed on an absorption spectra are called _____ lines.

Extending Your Knowledge

1. If Star A has a magnitude of 3 and Star B has a magnitude of 1, which star appears brighter? How many times brighter?

2. Why is the Kelvin temperature scale called an absolute temperature scale? Do you suppose you would ever observe an object with a temperature of $-5°K$? Why?

3. When two stars appear very ·close together in the sky, are they necessarily components of a double star? If not, how would you explain their apparent proximity to each other?

4. What are some ways in which a Cepheid variable is different from a nova? In what ways are Cepheids and novae alike?

5. What are two reasons for believing that our galaxy is rotating around its hub? If the galaxy is rotating, do the stars near the hub travel as fast as those near the edge?

SOME THINGS TO DO

1. Make a graph which you can use to change any Fahrenheit reading to Celsius (or vice versa). On a piece of graph paper, mark Celsius temperature along one axis and Fahrenheit temperature along the other. Place a dot where the line representing $0°C$ crosses the line for $32°F$. Do the same for $100°C$ and $212°F$. When you draw a line through these points, you can use the line to find any temperature on one scale if you know the temperature on the other. Is there any place where both scales have the same reading? Could you make a graph like this for the Celsius and Kelvin scales? For the Kelvin and Fahrenheit scales?

2. Find out why stars have various types of names. If you have read enough literature about stars, you have noticed that stars are named in many different ways. Some have proper names—for example, Sirius and Polaris. But most stars have names such as Beta Andromeda, 61 Cygni, HD 32416, or Krueger 60. How are these names chosen? Is it possible for a star to be known by more than one name?

3. Observe the sky on a clear, dark night. Pick out the ten stars which you think are the brightest. Use star maps to find the names of the stars you have selected. Make a list of the stars you selected in order of their brightnesses. Is the order of brightnesses easy to determine? How do astronomers determine brightness? Compare your list with a list in an astronomy book. If the lists do not agree, explain why.

CHALLENGES IN SCIENCE

1. Calculate the speed of the sun as it revolves about the hub of our galaxy. What information will you need to obtain in order to make this calculation?

2. Suppose you observed the brightness of a star to vary in a regular, periodic way. What procedure could you follow to determine whether the star you are observing is an eclipsing binary or a Cepheid variable?

3. The early astronomers could not see the differences in structure among the hazy patches of light they called nebulae. As a result, many objects called nebulae are quite different from one another. Try to find out the meanings of the terms in the list below. Do some of these terms refer to objects which you may call by a different name? Find instances in which more than one name may be applied to the same object.

extragalactic nebula	dark nebula
diffuse nebula	nebular theory
reflection nebula	planetary nebula
Crab nebula	emission nebula

Complex instruments are used to make precise measurements.

CHAPTER 5

Measurements and Determinations

Scientists and engineers have designed and built many devices for making measurements. Some measuring instruments are very elaborate and are used to make very precise measurements. But scientists know that a measurement does not always need to be extremely precise to be useful. For example, the first estimates of the distances between our galaxy and the neighboring galaxies were only about one third as great as we now think these distances to be. But the first determinations, crude as they were, had great value. They helped to establish that other galaxies do exist and that the universe does, indeed, consist of much more than just the Milky Way Galaxy.

No measurement is exact. As techniques and instruments are improved, measurements are being carried out with more accuracy and precision. However, whether we achieve a precise determination or only a rough estimate, scientific progress is made when the theories and ideas of scientists are checked by measurement.

Astronomers, as do all scientists, seek ways of using every bit of information they have. They want to learn about the objects in space, but they can only observe them from a distance. In this chapter you will discover how astronomers use observations of objects in space in determining sizes, distances, masses, and velocities.

1. Size

Brightness and size. By studying the color and brightness of stars, we begin to get information necessary to determine their sizes and distances. Suppose you observe two stars in the sky which are the same color, but one of them appears much brighter than the other. What do you know about them? Before you had studied the effect of temperature, you might have believed that the brighter star was hotter. But now you know this is not true. Temperature differences would make color differences, and these two stars are the same color. If the temperatures of two stars are the same, the difference in their apparent brightnesses must depend on certain other factors. These factors are size and distance.

Now suppose that these two stars are the same color and are the same distance away. Then the difference in their brightnesses is related to the difference in their sizes. But how is size related to brightness when the temperature and distance are the same?

To find out, we can use the sun as an example. The amount of sunlight which comes to a particular place on the earth depends on the area of the sun that can be seen from that place on the earth. When the moon blocks off part of this area of the sun—say half of it—during an eclipse, then the brightness of the sun is reduced by one half.

The area that we ordinarily see of the sun (when there are no clouds or eclipses) is just the area of the sun's disk, πr^2, where r is the radius of the sun. The stars are so far away that they appear as points rather than as disks. Nevertheless, the relationship of brightness to area can also be applied to the stars. Thus, if two stars are the same color and are the same distance away, the ratio of their brightnesses is equal to the ratio of their areas. This relationship is expressed in the following equation.

$$\frac{B_1}{B_2} = \frac{\pi (r_1)^2}{\pi (r_2)^2}$$

In this equation, B_1 is the apparent brightness and r_1 is the radius of the first star. The apparent brightness of the second star is B_2, and r_2 is the radius of the second star.

MINNEAPOLIS STAR

Figure 5-1. Certain aspects of the sun's light cannot be studied under normal conditions. During an eclipse, however, some of these aspects can be studied. For example, scientists can measure the amount of light received at the earth's surface through observations made during the various stages of an eclipse. Such measurements have revealed that the amount of light received at a particular time is proportional to the area of the sun's surface which can be seen at that time.

Brightness and distance. Now imagine two stars in the sky that are the same color and the same size, but they differ in brightness. Then it must be that these stars are at different distances from us. You know that any luminous object—whether it is a star or a light bulb—appears dimmer the farther away it is.

As a matter of fact, there is a definite relationship between distance and brightness. The relationship can be expressed in the following way. The amount of light we receive—the apparent brightness—varies inversely as the square of the distance from the light source. For example, suppose you were 5 feet from a light bulb and then moved back to a distance of 10 feet from the bulb. Now you would be 2 times as far away from the bulb. Would the light seem half as bright as before? Actually, the light would seem $\frac{1}{4}$ as bright—that is, $(\frac{1}{2})^2$. See *Figure 5-2*. It will help you to understand this relationship better.

The relationship between the apparent brightnesses and distances of two stars having the same temperature and size is expressed in the following equation.

$$\frac{B_1}{B_2} = \frac{(d_2)^2}{(d_1)^2}$$

In this equation B_1 and B_2 are the apparent brightnesses of the stars. The respective distances to these stars are d_1 and d_2.

In relating the brightness of stars to their size and distance, why do we always include the statement that the stars must be the same color?

FIND OUT BY TRYING

Materials you will need: 100-watt light bulb, socket, light meter, meter stick, graph paper

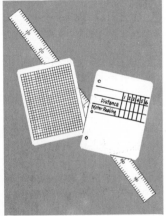

In this activity, the light meter represents the earth, and the 100-watt bulb represents a star. The meter reading will be a measure of the light received from the "star"—that is, how bright the star appears to be from the "earth." Darken the room except for the 100-watt bulb. Record the meter reading—the "brightness" of the star—and the distance between the star and the earth. Repeat the procedure several times, each time placing the bulb a different distance from the light meter. For each trial, the bulb represents a star which is just like the first star, except it is a different distance away. Record the distances and the brightnesses (meter readings) in a table such as the one shown below. Then draw a graph of the relationship of the meter reading to distance. Mark meter readings on the vertical scale and distances on the horizontal scale. Use your graph to determine how the brightnesses of identical stars are related to the distances of the stars. Is the formula above true for your data?

	1	2	3	4	5	6
Distance						
Meter reading						

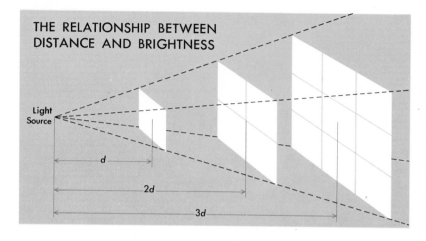

Figure 5-2. Suppose the light from a source is radiated equally in all directions. The light will be spread over an area 4 times as great at a distance of 2*d* than it is at *d*. Thus, from a distance of 2*d*, the light will appear to be ¼ as bright as it does from a distance of *d*. How bright will the light appear to be from a distance of 3*d*?

THE RELATIONSHIP BETWEEN DISTANCE AND BRIGHTNESS

Size, distance, and brightness. In most cases neither the sizes nor the distances of the stars are known. All that is known is that certain stars are the same color and have some particular ratio of apparent brightness which can be determined. From the equations on pages 89 and 90, a single equation has been derived which expresses the combined effect of size and distance on brightness.

$$\frac{B_1}{B_2} = \frac{\pi(r_1)^2\,(d_2)^2}{\pi(r_2)^2\,(d_1)^2} \quad \text{or} \quad \frac{B_1}{B_2} = \frac{(r_1)^2(d_2)^2}{(r_2)^2(d_1)^2}$$

In this equation, as in the previous ones, the temperatures of the stars must be the same. Using this equation you can calculate the relative sizes of stars. To do so, however, you have to know their relative distances and their apparent brightnesses. Or, you can calculate the relative distances of the stars if you know their relative sizes and their apparent brightnesses.

Explain why the combination equation has the form it has and not some other form, such as $B_1/B_2 = (r_1/r_2)^2 + (d_2/d_1)^2$.

Suppose that the apparent brightness of a certain star (Star 1) is 4 times that of another star (Star 2). Both stars are the same color, and distance measurements indicate that Star 1 is 3 times as far away as Star 2. What is the ratio of their radii?

When you substitute the values for brightness and distance in the equation, you obtain the following equation.

$$\frac{4}{1} = \frac{r_1^2(1)^2}{r_2^2(3)^2}$$

Notice that the numerals 1 and 3 are used for the distances. No mention is made as to whether these are miles or light-years or any other units. Likewise, only the ratio of brightness is used. Because we are only interested in the ratios, we do not have to include the units of measurement. It is only necessary that the units of measurement must be the same for both stars. By solving the equation, we find the ratio of the radii.

$$\text{If } \frac{(r_1)^2(1)^2}{(r_2)^2(3)^2} = \frac{4}{1}, \text{ then } \frac{(r_1)^2}{(r_2)^2} = 36.$$

$$\text{Thus, } \frac{r_1}{r_2} = \frac{6}{1}.$$

Apparent magnitude and absolute magnitude. You probably noticed that in this chapter, the term apparent brightness has been used quite often. Why is the word "apparent" being used? As you might guess, the brightness that has been talked about is how bright the star appears to us here on earth. This brightness is determined by both the size of the star and its distance from us. The same sized star appears dimmer if it is farther away.

Surely it would be worthwhile if there were a way of comparing all stars in some standard manner—for example, as if they were all the same distance away from us. Then, differences in brightness would be properties of the stars themselves and not just the result of the stars being a greater or lesser distance from us. Of course, a comparison can be made—at least mathematically. Once the size and temperature of a star have been determined, we can calculate how bright the star would be at a specific distance. Astronomers have chosen one particular distance as a standard for this calculation. The distance which has been chosen is 32.6 light-years, and later on you will find out why this distance was chosen.

The brightness that a star would appear to have if it were 32.6 light-years from the earth is called its *absolute brightness*. If two stars are compared, imagining them both to be this standard distance away, then the ratio of their brightnesses can be given in terms of a difference in *absolute magnitude*.

Thus, the absolute brightness, or absolute magnitude, of a star depends only on the size and temperature of the star itself. In contrast, the apparent magnitude of a star (how bright it appears here on earth) depends not only on the characteristics of the star but also on how far away the star is from us.

If a star is nearer to us than the standard distance, the absolute magnitude of the star is numerically greater than its apparent magnitude. Our sun, for example, would appear much dimmer if it were viewed from a distance of 32.6 light-years instead of the mere 93 million miles it is from us. In fact, the magnitude of the sun, if viewed from 32.6 light-years would be +4.7. Thus, the absolute magnitude of the sun is +4.7. This magnitude is much greater than the apparent magnitude of −26.7 which our sun has.

By using the same type of reasoning, you can understand why the absolute magnitude of stars more distant than 32.6 light-years is less than their apparent magnitude.

DO IT YOURSELF

Determine the radius, the distance, or the apparent magnitude of a star by computation

On your paper draw a table similar to the one below. Assume that all four stars are the same temperature. Only Star A has its radius, its distance, and its apparent magnitude listed. For each of the other stars, only two of the three properties are given. Complete the table by filling in the blank spaces. Use the equation in column 1, page 91 for your computations. You may find *Figure 4-2* helpful in determining the relationship between brightness ratio and difference in magnitude.

STAR	RADIUS (Compared with the Sun)	DISTANCE (In Light-Years)	APPARENT MAGNITUDE
A	1	100	2
B	4	1600	
C	5		5
D		100	7

2. Distance Measurements

Parallax. For many centuries, an unsolved problem in astronomy was how to determine the distances to the stars. The early scientists and philosophers believed that the stars were located on a giant sphere which surrounded the earth. They believed, therefore, that the stars were all the same distance away. By just looking at the stars, it is impossible to prove that this old idea is wrong. In fact, even with a telescope, it is still a tough problem.

How could the distance to a star ever be measured? One method, which was thought of by early astronomers, is the use of *parallax* (par'ə laks). Parallax is an apparent change in the position of an object. It occurs when the object is viewed from two different places.

You can see an example of parallax quite easily. Select an object which is a short distance away but closer than the wall of the room. Now close one eye and line up the object with some particular detail on the wall beyond. Move your head a little bit from side to side. Notice how the position of the nearby object appears to change with respect to the wall behind it. The apparent shift in position is an example of parallax.

DO IT YOURSELF

Observe parallax

Stand facing the chalkboard but about 6 or 8 steps away from it. Place one end of a 12-inch ruler on the bridge of your nose. With your index finger, hold the other end of the ruler out in front of your face. Using one eye, sight across the tip of the finger holding the ruler to a point on the chalkboard. Have someone mark the point. Without moving your head or the ruler, sight again, this time using the other eye. Is the tip of your finger still in line with the same point? If not, what do you think caused the apparent change in the position of your fingertip? Try this experiment again, but using a 6-inch ruler and then a 2-foot ruler. Is there any apparent change in the position of your fingertip when you use these rulers? If so, how does the apparent change compare with the change (if any) you noticed with the 12-inch ruler? On the basis of these observations would you say that a nearby object shows a greater or a lesser change in position than a distant object? What is the name given to this apparent change in the position of the object?

Stellar parallax. An apparent shift in the position of the stars—called *stellar parallax*—can be observed for some of the nearer stars. As the earth goes from one side of its orbit to the other, the nearer stars seem to move relative to the more distant ones. Such motion is illustrated in *Figure 5-3*.

Although the measurement of stellar parallax is theoretically possible, it is actually quite difficult. To use an imaginary model, suppose that the orbit of the earth were scaled down so that it would fit into the period printed at the end of this sentence. On this scale, the nearest star could be represented by a tiny speck

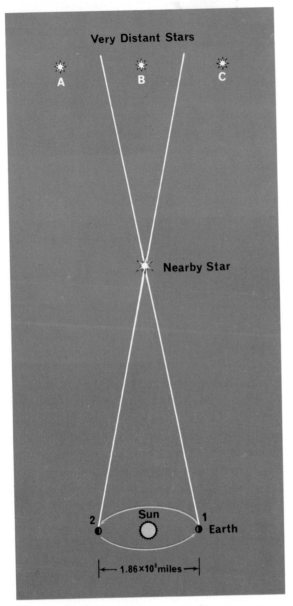

Very Distant Stars

A   B   C

Nearby Star

2   Sun   1

Earth

$\leftarrow 1.86 \times 10^8 \text{ miles} \rightarrow$

Figure 5-3. Viewed from the position marked 1, the nearby star appears to be between the distant stars A and B. From 2, the same star appears to be between the stars B and C. The apparent change in position of the nearby star is called parallax.

Early astronomers did not have instruments precise enough to detect stellar parallax. When Copernicus announced his theory that the earth traveled about the sun, some astronomers believed they had disproved his idea by pointing out that parallax had never been observed among the stars. Of course, the reason parallax had not been observed was because of the immense distances to the stars, not because of an error in the theory of Copernicus. It was not until 1838 that this effect was finally observed. Today, through the use of very accurate measuring instruments and good photographic equipment, the parallax of many thousands of stars has been measured.

Early astronomers knew that measuring the parallax of a star was more likely to be accomplished if a nearby star was chosen. What properties tend to indicate that a star is nearby?

Using parallax to determine distance. When a star has a measurable amount of parallax, the distance to the star can be determined. *Figure 5-4* shows how astronomers measure parallax so that it can be used to determine the distance to a star. When an astronomer measures the parallax of a star, he measures the angular change in the star's position between one observation and a second observation six months later.

In *Figure 5-4*, Star A appears behind the nearby star when the earth is in Position 1. Six months later, the earth is at 2, and Star B is behind the nearby star. The astronomers can measure the angle *b* between the lines of sight to Stars A and B. According to the theorems of geometry, this angle is the same size as angle *a*—the angle between two lines drawn from opposite sides of the earth's orbit to the nearby star.

You must realize, however, that *Figure 5-4* is not drawn to scale. Thus, angle *a* in the fig-

of dust about two hundred feet away. The trick is to measure the apparent change in the position of the dust speck as you view it, first from one side of the period, and then from the other.

ure is much larger than the angle which would be observed for any star. In fact, ever since 1852, when it became possible to photograph the stars, astronomers have determined angle *a* on the basis of measurements made on photographs of the stars rather than by measuring the angle directly.

As you know, angles are usually measured in degrees. However, the angles involved in stellar parallax are very small. Such small angles are usually given in terms of seconds instead of degrees. One second (1″) is $\frac{1}{3600}$ of a degree.

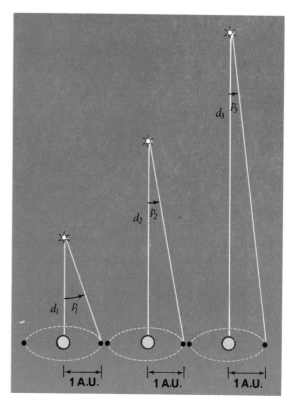

Figure 5-5. If a star's parallax is measurable, the star's distance can be determined. The inverse relationship of distance and parallax is illustrated above. The greater the distance is, the less the parallax is.

Figure 5-4. A star's parallax is determined by measuring the angle through which the star appears to move. The diagram below indicates the angles involved in parallax determinations.

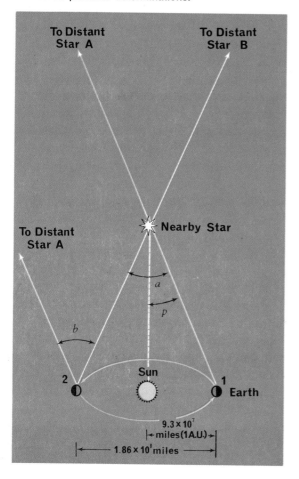

Astronomers, when determining parallax, use the radius of the earth's orbit instead of the diameter. A distance equal to the radius of the earth's orbit is called an *astronomical unit*, or A.U. Stellar parallax is, therefore, the angle marked *p*. Angle *p* is half as large as angle *a*. Because of the great distance to even the closest star (other than the sun), no star has a parallax greater than one second. The largest stellar parallax is 0″.76 for the multiple star Alpha Centauri.

The relationship between the amount of parallax and the distance to the star is shown in *Figure 5-5*. As the distance *d* becomes greater, the angle *p* becomes smaller. The relationship between distance and amount of parallax is another example of an inverse proportion or inverse variation. Shown below is the formula which gives the distance in light-years. In this formula, p is the stellar parallax in seconds.

$$d \text{ (in light-years)} = \frac{3.26}{p}$$

However, the unit most used by astronomers to express stellar distances is not the light-year. When the parallax method became useful for measuring stellar distances, a new unit called a *parsec* (pär′sek) was introduced. A parsec is the distance to a star which has a parallax of one second. Perhaps remembering the word parsec and its meaning will be easier if you notice that parsec is derived from the first syllables of parallax and second. The formula for finding distance in parsecs is much like the one for finding the distance in light-years, except the 3.26 is replaced by 1.

$$d \text{ (in parsecs)} = \frac{1}{p}$$

Using this formula, you can see that if the parallax is only $\frac{1}{2}$ second, the distance is 2 parsecs. If the parallax is $\frac{1}{4}$ second, the distance is 4 parsecs. How far away is a star which has a parallax of 0.1 second?

By comparing the two formulas, you can see that one parsec is equivalent to 3.26 light-years. You will recall that the standard distance for determining absolute magnitude is 32.6 light-years. Since this distance is equivalent to ten parsecs, a star at the standard distance has a parallax of 0.1 second.

As a matter of fact, the standard distance of ten parsecs was chosen because of the amount of parallax a star has at that distance. No star is so close that it has a parallax as great as 1 second. On the other hand, parallax measurements of less than 0.01 second are so difficult to make that they are not very accurate. However, a stellar parallax of about 0.1 or 0.2 second can be measured quite accurately. In ad-

dition, there are numerous stars which have this amount of parallax, and astronomers soon found their notebooks filled with fairly accurate parallax measurements of about 0.1 second. Therefore, they chose this value (and the distance of ten parsecs or 32.6 light-years that goes with it) as a convenient standard for comparing the brightnesses of different stars.

How could the range of parallax measurements be extended? Will interplanetary space travel aid in extending this range?

Using Cepheid variables. Measurement of distance by the parallax method is limited to fairly small astronomical distances. Parallax measurements of distances beyond 350 light-years are considered to be unreliable. Our galaxy has dimensions that far exceed the 350 light-year limit of parallax measurements. What about the millions and millions of stars in our galaxy that do not have a measurable amount of parallax? And what about other galaxies? Can their distances be determined?

About fifty years ago, a discovery was made which greatly increased the range of distance measurements. This discovery concerned the Cepheid variables. As you probably remember, Cepheid variables are stars which undergo periodic changes in brightness. That is, they get brighter and dimmer in a regular cycle. The significant discovery about Cepheids was that the period of their brightness cycle is directly proportional to their size. That is, the longer the period, the larger the star.

When two Cepheids have the same period of brightness variation, they are the same size. Therefore, they have the same absolute magnitude and their apparent magnitude will depend on how far away they are. So if two Cepheid variables are the same distance away and are the same size, they will have the same period of brightness variation. Furthermore, they will appear equally bright at corresponding times in their brightness cycles.

But what if two Cepheids with the same absolute magnitude are not the same distance from us? Suppose instead that one of them is twice as far away. The nearer star would then appear four times as bright as the farther one. Why not twice as bright?

Measuring relative distances. In the imaginary situation described in the last paragraph, we knew ahead of time that one star was twice as far away as the other. In most instances, this would not be known, because most stars are so far away that it is very difficult to measure the distances to them.

However, you can learn the relative distances of two Cepheids by simply watching them and measuring their periods and their apparent brightnesses. Suppose you observe two stars and notice these properties.

1. They are both Cepheid variables.
2. They both have the same period of variation.
3. One appears four times as bright as the other.

You can, by using this information, figure out that one star is twice as far away from us as the other.

Now, suppose two Cepheid variables have the same average apparent brightness, but one has a much longer period of brightness variation. Because of the direct relation between absolute brightness and period of brightness variation, the Cepheid with the longer period must be a much brighter star. However, since they have the same apparent brightness, we infer that the one with the longer period is farther away than the one with the shorter period.

Finding distances. Unfortunately, there are no Cepheid variables close enough for us to get a determination of their distance by using the parallax method. Therefore, a more indirect method had to be found for determining the distances to these stars. This method is a fascinating example of scientific deduction, and you may be interested in reading about it in a book on astronomy. The results are not very precise, and many astronomers are still working to improve it.

The results so far obtained are given as a relationship between the period of a Cepheid and its absolute magnitude. The graph in *Figure 5-6* indicates this relationship. The graph is in two distinct pieces. Astronomers believe there are two types of Cepheid variables, short period and long period. However, the reason for the difference is still a mystery.

The period of most Cepheids is easy to observe. After the period is known, the absolute magnitude is found from the graph in *Figure 5-6*. Then, by comparing the absolute magnitude with the apparent magnitude, it is possible to determine the distance to the Cepheid.

Figure 5-6. The relationship of a Cepheid's absolute magnitude to its period of brightness variation is shown below. Using this relationship, astronomers determine the distances to these stars.

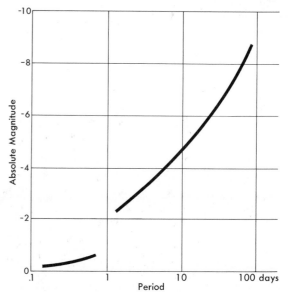

When Cepheids occur in clusters of stars, such as the cluster in Hercules (*Figure 4-13*), the variable stars are used to determine the distance to the cluster. When Cepheids can be observed in another galaxy, such as the Andromeda galaxy (*Figure 4-14*), then astronomers can use the Cepheids in determining how far that galaxy is from us. Thus, by using the Cepheids as a yardstick, astronomers have been able to measure very great distances, such as the distance to other galaxies.

Are there very many stars in our galaxy with distances which cannot be determined either by the parallax method or the Cepheid method? Explain your answer.

DO IT YOURSELF

Compare units of distance

Make your own table in which you compare the various distance units used by astronomers. Set up the table as shown below. Then use reference materials and calculations in filling in the spaces.

	KILOMETER	MILE	ASTRONOMICAL UNIT	LIGHT-YEAR	PARSEC
1 Kilometer =	1				
1 Mile =		1			
1 Astronom-ical unit =			1		
1 Light-year =				1	
1 Parsec =					1

3. Velocity

The fixed stars. As we observe the nighttime sky, the stars always seem to be in the same place relative to one another. The positions seem so unchanging that many times the stars are referred to as fixed stars. But are the stars really fixed in their positions relative to one another in the sky? Just because we cannot easily see any motion does not mean the stars are not moving. (Remember, parallax was not observed until more than two centuries after the telescope was invented because very accurate instruments are required to observe parallax.)

There is reason to believe that the stars are moving. Every star we can see without a telescope is in the Milky Way Galaxy. As components of the galaxy, it is necessary that they be revolving about the center of the galaxy. Otherwise, gravity—which we assume works in galaxies and everywhere else in the universe —would cause all the stars of the galaxy to be attracted toward and move to the center of the

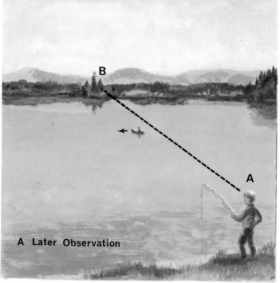

Figure 5-7. In some ways, the proper motion of a star can be compared with the motion of a boat at some distance from you. That is, sometimes the motion of the distant boat can only be detected by noticing the changes in the boat's position relative to the background.

galaxy. In the same way, an astronaut will remain in orbit if he maintains a certain speed, but gravity pulls him to the surface of the earth when he slows for reëntry.

Observing and measuring the rotation of the galaxy is too difficult to be done by "naked-eye" astronomy. Some special methods and tools are needed. Photography is one of these special tools. Two pictures of the same region in the sky can be taken some time apart and then compared. When this is done, astronomers can see that the positions of some of the stars change with respect to the surrounding stars. The change is very small, but it can be detected and measured.

To make a comparison, on a very much smaller scale, imagine that you are on the bank of a wide lake (point A on the diagram in *Figure 5-7*). Two miles away on the opposite shore, at B, are some very large trees. In the middle of the lake is a rowboat moving in the direction of the arrow. The movement of the rowboat may be too slow for you to see. How-

ever, you can tell it is moving because its position with respect to the distant trees will change with time.

Proper motion. When a star moves across our line of sight so that its position is changed with respect to the more distant stars, it is called *proper motion*. Proper motion is measured in seconds of arc per year.

The observations made to measure proper motion are similar to those made for measuring parallax. In both cases, astronomers measure the change of position of a nearby star compared to more distant stars in the background. But there is an important difference. In measuring parallax, the motion of the star is only apparent, caused by the actual motion of our earth traveling in its orbit. Proper motion, however, is the motion of the star itself. How do you suppose astronomers can tell the difference?

For a star moving across our line of sight, the amount of proper motion depends on two factors. One factor is the velocity of the

Figure 5-8. Barnard's Star—indicated by the arrow on each photograph—has the greatest proper motion of any known star. These photographs were taken 22 years apart. Notice the change in the position of Barnard's Star relative to the other stars shown in the photographs.

star. The other factor is how far the star is from us. If two stars are moving with the same speed but are different distances away, the closer one will have the greater proper motion. If two stars are the same distance away but moving at different speeds, the faster one will have the greater proper motion.

For a star that is visible to the unaided eye, an average proper motion is only about .03 second per year. This is only 3 seconds per century. However, some proper motions are much greater. The greatest proper motion observed for a star is a little over 10 seconds per year. Ten seconds per year is much larger than the average proper motion. It is, however, still a very small angle, and precise methods are needed to measure it.

The angle through which the star moves will become greater if we wait for a longer period of time. Therefore, the usual practice is to use time intervals ranging from ten to fifty years. Once the proper motion has been measured, the actual speed across our line of sight can be calculated if the distance to the star is known.

What problems might be encountered in conducting an experiment which spans a fifty-year period? For each problem you can think of, try to find a possible solution.

Radial velocity. Can the motion of a star moving parallel to our line of sight be detected? Think back to the example of the rowboat on the lake, but now imagine the boat is moving directly toward you or directly away from you. You know that this motion is hard to detect because the boat's position, as we see it relative to the background, does not change. If a star were moving directly toward or away from the earth, its position relative to the other stars would not change. How, then, could the rate of this motion, called *radial* (rā′di əl) *velocity*, be measured for a star? Surprisingly, the measurement of radial velocity is easier than the measurement of proper motion. It can be accomplished by analyzing the spectrum of the star.

Doppler effect. In studying the spectra of distant stars, astronomers have discovered a curious detail. The pattern of dark lines in these stellar spectra is quite similar to the pattern of the sun's spectrum. However, the Fraunhofer lines of the stellar spectra do not line up exactly with the lines of a spectrum created in the laboratory. It is as if the spectrum of each star had been shifted slightly to one side. *Figure 5-9* shows how such a shifted spectrum looks. As you can see, the shift is very small, yet it is very important. This shift —called the *Doppler* (dop′lər) *effect*—actually allows us to measure the speed with which these stars are moving toward us or away from us.

The Doppler effect is a result of the fact that light has a wavelike nature as it travels from one place to another. In this way, light can be compared with sound. Have you ever noticed that the pitch of a train whistle seems higher when the train is approaching than it does when the train is moving away? The same effect can be noticed with any fast-moving source of sound, such as a low-flying airplane or a racing car.

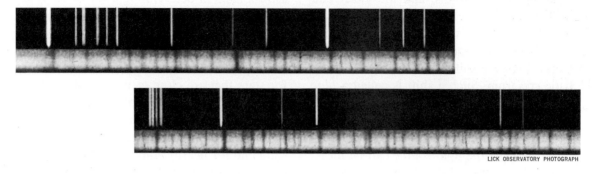

Figure 5-9. Portions of a stellar spectrum (the lower, dark-line spectrum in each of the segments shown) are compared with portions of a bright-line spectrum produced in the laboratory. Spectral lines in the laboratory-produced spectrum are also present in the stellar spectrum. However, their positions are shifted to the right in the stellar spectrum.

In *Figure 5-10* the circles represent the wave fronts and the dots represent the position of the source when it produced the corresponding wave front. If you were on the right, the source would be approaching you. When the source of the waves is moving toward you, the source tends to keep catching up with the waves. The second wave is sent out before the first has had time to travel very far. As a result, from the point of view of the person standing still, the distance between the waves—the wave length—is shortened. The opposite happens when the source is moving away. The source tends to leave the waves behind. The waves are emitted at the same frequency in the backward direction, but between one wave and the next the source has moved a little farther away. In this case, from the point of view of a stationary observer, the wave length is lengthened.

The wave length of sound waves determines the pitch of the sound. Long waves produce sounds of lower pitch than short waves do. With light, the colors we see are determined by the wave length of the light entering our eyes. In a spectrum which ranges from red through violet, the red end of the spectrum has

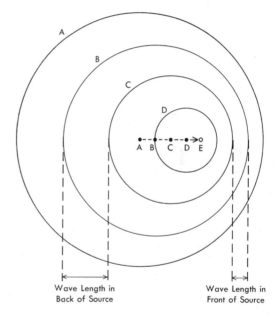

THE DOPPLER EFFECT

Figure 5-10. A source of waves moves from Point A to Point E in the time it takes to emit five waves. The first wave (labeled A) was emitted when the source was at Point A. The wave labeled B was emitted at Point B, and so forth. At Point E, the source is just emitting a fifth wave. The wave length—the distance between successive waves—in front of the moving source is shorter than the wave length behind the source. This phenomenon is called the Doppler effect.

the longer wave lengths, and the violet end has the shorter wave lengths.

Therefore, if the wave length is shortened (as with an approaching light source) the spectral lines are shifted toward the blue end of the spectrum. Such a shift is called a *blue shift*. When the source is moving away from the observer, the shift is toward the red, so it is called a *red shift*.

The speed of the light source can be measured by the amount of the shift of the spectral lines. The greater the shift, the greater is the speed. The relation between speed and amount of shift makes the Doppler effect very useful to astronomers in determining a star's radial velocity. In observations made by astronomers, some stars have been found to be traveling toward us and some are moving away.

Proper motion can be measured most easily for stars that are close to us. It is difficult or, in most cases, impossible to measure the proper motion of distant stars. However, radial velocity can be measured equally well for distant stars and for nearby stars. The Doppler effect does not depend on distance. All that is necessary is that enough light is received from the star to make possible an observation of its spectrum.

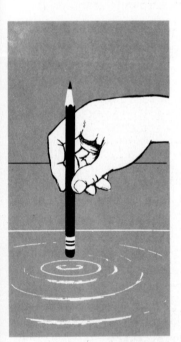

FIND OUT BY TRYING

Materials you will need: sink filled with water, a pencil

Make a series of waves by repeatedly dipping your pencil into the same place in the water. Dip the pencil into the water about 3 or 4 times per second. What is the shape of each wave made as the pencil touches the water? What pattern do the waves make as they move away from the place where the pencil touched the water? Are the waves moving to the left the same distance apart as those moving to the right? Repeat the experiment. This time, dip the pencil into the water at a different place each time, so that with each dip, the pencil touches the water about $\frac{1}{2}$ inch directly to the right of where it had touched the previous time. Is the shape of each individual wave the same as in the first part of the experiment? Is the pattern of waves the same as when you dipped the pencil in the same spot each time? Are the waves to the left the same distance apart as the waves to the right? If sound waves and light waves behave in the same way as these water waves, what will be the effect when a source of sound or light waves is moving toward you? Away from you?

Space velocity. Every star is not moving either parallel to or perpendicular to our line of sight. In fact, most stars are moving so that the direction of their motion is at some other angle to our line of sight. To determine the actual speed and direction of a star's motion, we need to find both the radial velocity and the proper motion and add them.

Suppose an analysis of the star's light reveals the speed of a star to be 100 kilometers per second away from us. From the proper motion we can calculate that the star is moving at 150 kilometers per second to the right. What is the actual speed and direction of the star's motion? To find out, we add these velocities. Because velocity involves both speed and di-

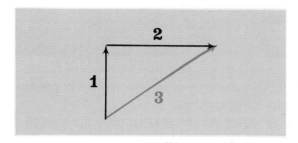

Figure 5-11. Vector addition is a special way of adding those quantities, such as velocity, which have both direction and magnitude to be considered.

rection, velocity is a *vector quantity*. Therefore, to add velocities, or any other vector quantities, we use a special type of addition called vector addition.

The easiest way is to draw a diagram such as that shown in *Figure 5-11*. In this figure, Arrow 1 represents the radial velocity and Arrow 2 represents proper motion—that is, the speed at which the star is moving across the line of sight. The arrows are drawn so that they point in the direction of the motion. The arrows are also drawn to scale, so that 1 centimeter of length represents 50 kilometers per second of speed. These arrows are placed so that the tail of 2 is at the head of 1. Arrow 3 is drawn from the tail of 1 to the head of 2. Arrow 3 shows the true direction of the star's motion. When 3 is measured, you will see that its length is about 3.6 centimeters. Since a length of 1 centimeter represents 50 kilometers per second in the diagram, the star is moving about 180 kilometers per second in the direction of Arrow 3. The motion which is represented by Arrow 3 is called the *space velocity* of the star.

What are some quantities (other than velocities) which have to be added by the vector method? What properties do these quantities have that makes it necessary to use the vector method for adding them?

An effect of stellar motion. The stars are moving with various amounts of proper motion and radial velocity. Does this mean that the familiar arrangements of the constellations were not always as they appear now? Will they eventually change? Although the change is very slow and probably has not been noticeable during recorded history, the patterns are changing. In a few hundred thousand years many of the familiar groups such as the Big Dipper will be unrecognizable. In *Figure 5-12*, part *A* shows the Big Dipper as it looked 100,000 years ago. How it looks today is shown in part *B*. The arrows represent the directions of the stars' proper motions. Part *C* shows what it will be like in another 100,000 years.

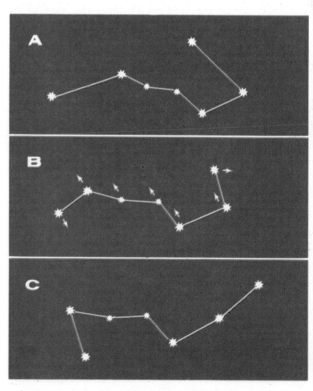

Figure 5-12. The shape of the Big Dipper slowly changes as a result of the motions of the stars which make up this familiar constellation. The change is too slow, however, to be noticed during your lifetime.

4. Mass

The mass of a double star. Two separate events were necessary before the mass of any star could be calculated. Astronomers had to observe that the two stars of a double-star system revolve about each other. Then, the relationship between period of revolution, distance between the stars, and total mass of the double star had to be discovered.

Isaac Newton, the man who explained the dispersion of light, also formulated the law of gravity and the laws of motion. From these laws, an equation has been derived which relates the total mass of a double-star system (M), the major axis—that is, the longest axis —of the apparent, elliptical orbit of one member about the other (a), and the period of revolution (T). The formula is written below.

$$M = a^3/8T^2$$

In using this formula, the mass of the sun is used as the unit of mass instead of kilograms. The year is used as the unit of time instead of seconds or days, and the astronomical unit is the unit of distance instead of miles or kilometers.

Figure 5-13. This table indicates the values of a and T for several double stars. The total mass of one such star is given. Find the total mass of the others.

STAR	PERIOD (Years)	MAJOR AXIS (A.U.)	SUM OF MASSES
Capella	0.285	1.51	5.3
Sirius	50.0	41.0	
Castor	341	153	
Procyon	40.2	29.2	
∝ Ursa Major	44.0	57.6	

The data to be obtained by observation are the value of T and the value of a for the double star being investigated. The period of revolu-

tion, T, is easy to obtain. By simply watching the double star over a period of years, the time it takes the stars to revolve about one another can be discovered.

Finding the distance between the stars of a double star can be compared with the method of finding parallax. (*Figure 5-14.*) In finding parallax, we know the distance a, the radius of the earth's orbit, and we measure the angle p. From this, we determine the large distance d. In finding the distance between the members of a double-star system, we measure the angle p, but we also have to know the large distance, d, before we can figure out the small distance, a. For those stars that are close enough, the parallax method is used to determine d. If one of the stars is a Cepheid variable, then it can be used to determine d.

The components of a visual double are very far apart. Would such a double have a long or short period of revolution?

Masses of individual stars. In order to calculate how the mass of a double-star system is divided between the two stars, additional measurements are needed. We see the stars

Figure 5-14. Finding the distance between the two stars in a double star is, in some ways, similar to determining the distance to a star by parallax.

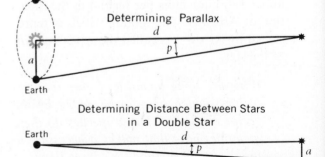

Determining Parallax

Earth

Determining Distance Between Stars in a Double Star

Earth

move compared with the distant stars behind them. If both of them wobble back and forth about the same amount as they revolve about each other, then they both have the same mass. If one stands still, while the other does all the moving, then the one standing still is much more massive than the other.

The moon, for example, is only 1/83 as massive as the earth. Therefore, the earth moves very little as the moon revolves about it. Nevertheless, the earth does move. It is like a teeter-totter with a very big person on one end and a little person on the other. The teeter-totter has to be moved far off center in order to balance these masses. The balance point is called the center of mass for the combination of the two people (plus the teeter-totter). For a system consisting of two objects moving about each other in space, the point about which they both revolve is the center of mass of the system. The center of mass is closer to the more massive of the two objects which are revolving about each other. By comparing the sizes of the separate orbits of the two stars, we can determine the ratio of their masses. (*Figure 5-15.*)

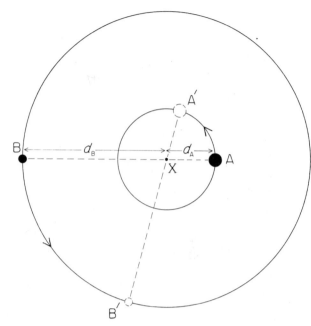

Figure 5-15. In this diagram, Star A and Star B are the two stars of a double-star system at a certain time. Later, as they revolve about each other, Star A will have moved to A' and Star B to B'. Any line between the stars will pass through X, the center of mass of the system. The ratio of the masses of the two stars is the reciprocal of the ratio of their distances from X. Thus, the mass of Star A is to the mass of Star B as the distance d_B is to the distance d_A.

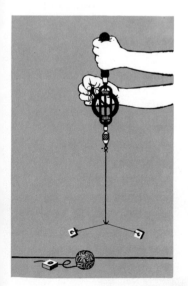

FIND OUT BY TRYING

Materials you will need: hand drill, string, screw eye, 3 small balls or other objects (2 of equal weight, one heavier than the others)

Tie the two objects of equal weight at the ends of a piece of string about 6 inches long. Tie one end of another piece of string about 10 inches long to the midpoint of the string connecting the objects. The other end of the longer string is to be attached to the screw eye which is held in the chuck of the hand drill. Hold the drill vertically as shown and cause the chuck to rotate by turning the handle. Describe the motion of the system as a whole. Then describe the motion of the individual objects. Where is the point about which revolution is taking place?

Repeat the experiment. This time use two objects of unequal mass. Observe the motion of these objects. Compare their motion with that of the two objects of equal mass.

5. Combining Measurements

Related information. When various measurements and determinations are combined, a picture of the universe gradually emerges. In astronomy, as in other sciences, there are few measurements which have much meaning by themselves. Most measurements have to be combined with other measurements before they have much significance. For example, we can easily observe and determine the apparent brightness of a star. However, this determination does not reveal much about the star itself. If we combine our observation with some other measurement, such as the distance to the star, we begin to learn something about the characteristics of the star.

On page 91 the following equation was given.

$$\frac{B_1}{B_2} = \frac{(r_1)^2(d_2)^2}{(r_2)^2(d_1)^2}$$

This equation is a good example of how measurements must be combined to learn about the stars. The equation describes the relationship between brightness, radius, and distance for two stars of the same temperature. It also points out that before we can calculate the distance, we must know the brightness and the radius. Or, before we can calculate the radius, we must know the distance and the brightness.

Combining reasoning and determinations. To determine the distance to a star, we can use the parallax method or the method involving Cepheid variables. But the parallax method can be used only for stars which are comparatively close-by, and the Cepheids are all very far away. For the rest of the billions of stars in our galaxy, there is no certain way to measure their distances.

Sometimes astronomers can learn about a star by comparing its properties with the properties of other stars. For example, suppose a star is not a Cepheid variable and it is too far away to measure its distance by the parallax method. The distance to such a star can be determined, but only by a combination of measurements and some reasoning.

Here is one way the distance to the star could be determined. The color of the star

Figure 5-16. The task of obtaining precise and useful information about the stars is much more complex than many people realize. Even the determination of an object's position in the sky requires painstaking effort and complex equipment if the results are to be accurate. This man is using a coordinate measuring apparatus to determine the positions in the sky of the objects he is studying.

Figure 5-17. One of the most important methods of acquiring information about the stars and other objects in space is to examine the spectra produced by the light received from these objects. The astronomer shown at the right, is adjusting some of the equipment used in obtaining stellar spectra for study.

could be observed. Thus its temperature could be determined. In most cases, stars of the same temperature are approximately the same size. By studying nearby stars, astronomers have determined what the radius is for stars of a given temperature. If it is assumed that the distant star has this radius, then the approximate distance to the star can be calculated. (You made similar calculations in the examples at the beginning of the chapter.)

There are times when a process involving reasoning and assumptions will lead to an incorrect conclusion. For example, the rule just described for relating temperature and size does not work for all stars. In studying a particular star, we may discover that it is one of those for which the rule is wrong. In that case, the conclusion about its distance would also be wrong.

What happens when new evidence indicates that a wrong assumption has been made or a wrong answer obtained? We simply admit that an error has been made and tackle the problem again. This has happened many times in science, as in any human activity, and it will certainly happen many times more.

Our knowledge of the stars. By using modern equipment and techniques, the temperature and chemical composition of practically all visible stars can be measured. We are able to measure the distances to the closest few thousand stars and to a number of the more distant ones. We can measure the masses of the stars in several double-star systems. We can measure the radial velocities of most stars, and the proper motion of those near us. All in all, a surprisingly great number of facts about the stars have been discovered. By combining these measurements, even more information can be obtained. All the information is obtained in spite of two great limitations. First, the closest star is so far away that it takes light more than four years to travel from it to the earth. Second, all stars (except our sun) are so far away that even when we use the best telescopes we see them only as slightly fuzzy points of light.

If you had access to any or all of the instruments and techniques available to astronomers today, what research would you attempt? Explain your choice.

107

Checking Your Knowledge

IMPORTANT IDEAS

1. The apparent brightness of a star is directly proportional to the square of its radius and inversely proportional to the square of its distance from us.

2. The parallax method can be used to measure the distance to a star which is within 350 light-years of the earth.

3. The distance to a Cepheid variable or to any group of stars containing Cepheids can be measured, because the relationship between absolute magnitude and period of brightness variation has been discovered.

4. Stars are not really motionless in the sky, but they are so far away that their motion is difficult to detect.

5. The Doppler effect indicates that some stars in our galaxy are moving toward us and some are moving away.

6. Observing double stars has enabled scientists to determine some stellar masses.

USING NEW WORDS

Study the list of words below. Write the numerals 1-4 on your paper. Beside each numeral write words or statements to satisfy the instructions given for that numeral.

parallax	Doppler effect
parsec	astronomical unit
blue shift	proper motion
vector	radial velocity
red shift	space velocity

1. List those words which are related to the measurement of stellar distances.

2. Write those words which name distance units. Which unit is the larger? The smaller?

3. List those words related to stellar motion. Tell the relationship of each.

4. Describe the differences between radial velocity, proper motion, and space velocity.

TEST YOURSELF

Study the test below. Write the numerals 1-10 on your paper. Beside each numeral write the correct response to that part of the test having the corresponding numeral.

Beside each of the numerals 1-6 on your paper, write a word from the list below. Be certain the word is related to the statement having the corresponding numeral.

parallax	Doppler effect
proper motion	parsec
radial velocity	Cepheid variable
double star	apparent magnitude

1. Method first used for measuring stellar distances

2. Used in measuring radial velocity of stars and galaxies

3. Used to find stellar masses

4. Type of star used to find distances to galaxies

5. Depends on several factors, including temperature, size, and distance

6. Motion of a star across our line of sight

Use the following information in answering questions 7-10. An astronomer has obtained this information about the two stars, X and Y. Star X is twice as far away as Star Y. The apparent brightness of X is 4 times that of Y. Both X and Y are the same color.

7. The temperature of Star X is (*the same as, greater than, less than*) that of Star Y.

8. The ratio of the size of Star X to that of Star Y is (*1:1, 2:1, 4:1, 1:2*).

9. The ratio of the absolute brightness of Star X to Star Y is (*8:1, 1:4, 16:1, cannot be known from information given*).

10. The ratio of the mass of Star X to that of Star Y is (*1:1, 2:1, 1:2, cannot be known from information given*).

Extending Your Knowledge

QUESTIONS TO EXPLORE

1. In what way was the discovery of the motion of the stars within a binary important?

2. How many light-years away is a star which shows a parallax of 0.5 second? How many parsecs is this?

3. Why do the stars appear fixed in their positions relative to one another, even though some have speeds of many miles per second?

4. How are astronomers able to determine that some stars are hotter than the sun and others are cooler than the sun?

5. What reason did the very early astronomers have for believing the earth was stationary rather than moving about the sun?

SOME THINGS TO DO

1. Show how the distance between viewing positions (called the baseline) affects parallax. As shown below, punch holes labeled *a*, *b*, *c*, and *d* in a $28'' \times 4''$ piece of cardboard. Then place the cardboard on a tabletop as shown. The cardboard should be 15 or 20 feet from a chalkboard and parallel to it. Between the cardboard and the chalkboard, place a meter stick held vertically—perhaps by taping the meter stick to a chair.

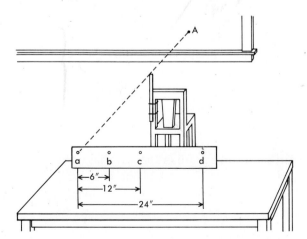

Now, while you look through hole *a*, direct someone to mark with an *A*, the point on the chalkboard in line with *a* and the tip of the meter stick. Repeat the procedure for holes *b*, *c*, and *d*, marking the chalkboard with *B*, *C*, and *D*. The distance between *A* and *B* is the parallax when the baseline is *ab*. Does the amount of parallax increase or decrease when you use a longer baseline?

2. Make a list of the practical applications of the principles of parallax.

CHALLENGES IN SCIENCE

1. Find out why the first determinations of distance made by using Cepheids were in error. Is there more than one type of Cepheid? If so, how was it discovered that more than one type of Cepheid exists?

2. Find the center of the mass of the earth-moon system. Make a model to represent the system by using a meter stick and two objects having a mass ratio of 1 to 83 (the same ratio as the masses of the moon and the earth). First, balance the meter stick. Then, without moving the pivot point, place one object on each side of the pivot point as shown. Make sure the stick is again balanced.

If the distance from the center of the earth to the center of the moon is 240,000 miles, where is the center of mass of the system? Is the center of mass closer to the center of the earth or the center of the moon? Where is the center of mass in relation to the surface of the earth?

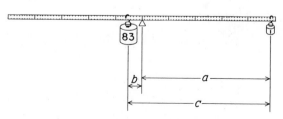

A blink comparator is used in finding clues to the mysteries of the universe.

CHAPTER 6

The Origin and Development of Stars

Several important clues are available to a scientist trying to figure out the pattern of evolution of the stars. Naturally, these clues—such as temperature, size, and mass —are provided by the stars themselves. These clues are revealed when astronomers make careful observations and measurements in order to get accurate descriptions of the stars.

In Chapter 5, you studied some ways by which descriptions of stars are obtained. However, obtaining and tabulating accurate information about stars is only the first step toward an understanding of the processes of star formation and evolution. The information must then be arranged and organized into a sensible theory of stellar development. Developing such a theory is the task of the astrophysicist.

As you study this chapter, you will find out how the clues gathered by astronomers have been used in discovering relationships among stars. You will realize that only a framework of a scheme for describing the birth, life, and death of the stars has been completed. You will see that there are many factors still to be worked out. However, the basic ideas of the framework agree well enough with observations to convince astronomers and astrophysicists that they are making progress in their attempts to understand the stars.

1. The Hertzsprung-Russell Diagram

Tabulating brightness and temperature. The distances to some of the stars in our galaxy can be measured. You may recall that a knowledge of the distance to a star, together with the star's apparent brightness, can be used to find the absolute magnitude of the star. Thus, astronomers can calculate how bright the star would appear if it were placed some standard distance away. In other words, for any star at a measurable distance, the absolute magnitude can be determined.

You may also remember that by observing the color of a star, it is possible to determine the surface temperature of the star. Thus, there are many stars about which astronomers know both the absolute magnitude and the surface temperature. It is only natural, then, that astronomers should try to compare stars according to these two properties. For example, tabulations of the absolute magnitudes and surface temperatures of many stars can be made. Such a tabulation is shown in *Figure 6-1*. Although this is only a very short list, you can get an idea of the information being tabulated.

When such tabulations are made, the other stars in the galaxy are usually compared with our own sun. The term *luminosity* (lü′mə nos′ə ti) is used to describe the brightness of the star. Luminosity and absolute magnitude have the same general meaning. Both terms refer to the actual amount of light being emitted by the star. In using the term luminosity, our sun is the standard, and it has a luminosity of 1. A star with a luminosity of 100 is 100 times as luminous as the sun. A star with a luminosity of .01 is only $\frac{1}{100}$ as bright as the sun.

On the basis of such a tabulation, it has been found that most of the observed stars are more

Figure 6-1. This table of stellar information is only a small sample of the information which astronomers have gathered about the stars.

STAR	SURFACE TEMPERATURE (°K)	ABSOLUTE MAGNITUDE	LUMINOSITY
Betelgeuse	3,100	−5.8	16,000
Polaris	5,400	−4.6	5,500
β Centauri	25,000	−3.3	1,700
Achernar	17,400	−2.7	1,000
Antares	3,200	−2.6	910
Spica	24,000	−2.4	760
Aldebaran	3,600	−0.7	160
Regulus	13,600	−0.7	160
Arcturus	4,500	−0.2	100
Vega	11,300	+0.5	50
Sirius	10,600	+1.5	20
Fomalhaut	9,600	+2.0	12
Altair	8,400	+2.3	10
Procyon	6,600	+2.7	6
α Centauri	6,000	+4.1	2
Sun	5,750	+4.7	1
τ Ceti	5,600	+5.8	0.4
ε Indi	4,400	+7.0	0.1
Lacaille 8760	3,500	+8.6	0.03
40 Eridani B	9,000	+10.0	0.01

luminous than the sun. This result is to be expected. As a matter of fact, it is related to an important rule about scientific experiment and observation.

Observational bias. A very luminous star can be seen at a much greater distance than a dim one can. Therefore, when we look at the sky, we see very luminous stars whether they are nearby or far away. However, the only dim stars visible are those which are relatively close-by. In other words, bright stars can be seen even when they are far away. Therefore, we see a greater number of them.

111

There are many situations in which the results of an observation are not completely reliable. For example, the instrument used for the observation may be faulty. Perhaps the person doing the observing is prejudiced, so that he records only those things which do not disagree with his own ideas. Or it could be—as it is in the case of observing the stars—that our senses are not able to detect all of the objects or events we are trying to observe. Whenever factors such as these influence an observation, the effect is called *observational bias.*

Thus, observational bias helps to explain why we observe more stars which are brighter than our sun than we do stars dimmer than our sun. Actually, there may be many more dim stars than bright ones, but the dim stars are not as easy to see.

What examples of observational bias can you think of in fields of study other than astronomy?

Constructing an H-R diagram. When you look at *Figure 6-1,* you can see that most of the stars in the list are hotter than the sun.

This observation, all by itself, is not necessarily one we would have expected. But now we are challenged to combine the information about luminosity and temperature to find out if there is a relationship between the luminosity of a star and its temperature.

One of the best ways to find such a relationship is with a graph. The first such graphs were drawn by two scientists who were working independently. These men were E. Hertzsprung of Leyden, Germany, and H. N. Russell of Cambridge University in England. Because they were first to tabulate such data, any graph of the relationship between luminosities and temperatures of stars has been called a *Hertzsprung-Russell diagram,* or an H-R diagram. One of the most complete H-R diagrams ever to be constructed is shown in *Figure 6-2.* This diagram includes all stars for which the absolute magnitude and surface temperature are known.

In this H-R diagram, luminosity is shown along the side. The brightest, or most luminous, stars are near the top. Temperatures are shown along the bottom, with the coolest stars at the right and the hottest stars at the left.

Figure 6-2. The points on this H-R diagram represent more than 6,000 stars. Notice that the temperature scale on an H-R diagram does not have a fixed unit. That is, the distance on the diagram between 5,000°K and 6,000°K is not the same as that between 6,000°K and 7,000°K. Also, notice that luminosity can be expressed in terms of absolute magnitude.

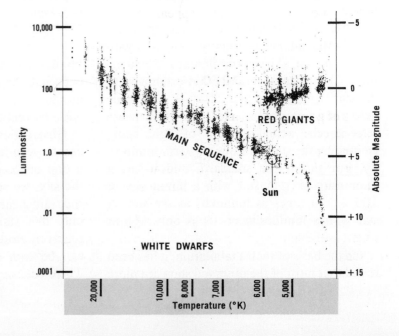

Construct an H-R diagram

Draw temperature and luminosity scales on a piece of graph paper. Use the H-R diagram in *Figure 6-2* as a guide in setting up these scales. After the scales are drawn, use the data from the table in *Figure 6-1* to construct an H-R diagram. Compare your H-R diagram with the one in *Figure 6-2*. Is the graph you drew similar to the one in the textbook? If so, describe the similarities. Are there any ways in which your graph is different from the one in the text? If so, explain the differences and tell why you think they occurred.

Features of an H-R diagram. The H-R diagram in *Figure 6-2* indicates that there is a relationship between temperature and brightness. Bright stars are generally hot, and dim stars are generally cool. Most of the stars are represented by points which lie along a diagonal from the upper left corner to the lower right corner of the diagram. The region near this diagonal on the diagram is called the *main sequence*. The sun, shown by a small circle on the diagram, is in the main sequence. Thus, the sun is a main-sequence star.

Another noticeable feature of this H-R diagram is the large group of points just above the main sequence and to the right. These points represent stars which appear quite bright but which are, at the same time, relatively cool. The relatively low temperature of these stars causes them to emit a reddish light. The stars of this group are called *red giants*.

A third group of points is also evident. These points are below the main sequence. They represent only a few stars. These stars—although they are hot enough to be white, or even slightly bluish—are very dim. Stars which are in this group are called *white dwarfs*.

Why, do you suppose, are there only a few white dwarfs in the H-R diagram shown in Figure 6-2? *Is there only a relatively small number of these stars in our galaxy?*

2. Temperature, Brightness, Size, and Mass

Sizes of giants and dwarfs. If two stars have the same color and, therefore, the same surface temperature, the brighter one must be the bigger. This relationship can be used in comparing the sizes of red giants with the sizes of stars of the main sequence directly below them on the H-R diagram. (If two stars are on the same vertical line on an H-R diagram, the stars have the same temperature.) Many red giants are a thousand times brighter than the main-sequence stars directly below them. In a few cases, the red giants are brighter by a factor of a million.

Do you remember how brightness and size are related? If all other factors are the same, brightness is proportional to the square of the radius. Another way to say this would be to say that the radius is proportional to the square root of the brightness. We can use this relationship to compare the sizes of a red giant and

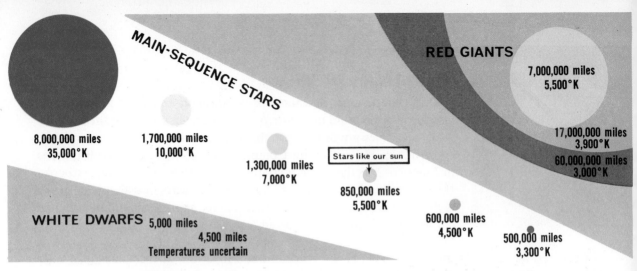

MAIN-SEQUENCE STARS

RED GIANTS

7,000,000 miles
5,500°K

8,000,000 miles
35,000°K

1,700,000 miles
10,000°K

17,000,000 miles
3,900°K

60,000,000 miles
3,000°K

1,300,000 miles
7,000°K

Stars like our sun

850,000 miles
5,500°K

600,000 miles
4,500°K

500,000 miles
3,300°K

WHITE DWARFS 5,000 miles

4,500 miles
Temperatures uncertain

Figure 6-3. Except for the white dwarfs, the stars on this diagram are drawn to a scale of 1 mm = 250,000 miles. Why were the white dwarfs not drawn to this scale? The actual colors of the stars are not as vivid as shown here. Note that not all red giants are red. Some are hot enough to be yellow. Note, also, that the main-sequence stars vary in size. How does the variation in their sizes compare with the variation in their brightnesses?

a main-sequence star. Suppose the two stars are the same temperature, but the red giant is 1,000 times brighter than the main-sequence star. Then, the radius of the red giant must be $\sqrt{1,000}$ or about 30 times greater than that of the main-sequence star. Certain red giants are a million times brighter than main-sequence stars of the same temperature. Such a red giant has a radius about 1,000 times as great as the radius of a main-sequence star of that temperature. Now you can understand why these stars are called red giants.

You can make a similar comparison for the white stars shown below the main sequence. These stars are only 1/1,000 to 1/1,000,000 as bright as stars of the same temperature in the main sequence. Thus, the radii of these stars range from thirty to perhaps a thousand times smaller than the radii of main-sequence stars of the same temperature. No wonder they are called white dwarfs!

Sizes of main-sequence stars. Along the main sequence, the stars which are the hotter stars are also the brighter stars. Are these stars brighter because they are hotter or is it because they are larger? How can the sizes of stars with different temperatures be compared?

By using the rules of physics which can be checked in a laboratory, scientists have figured out the relationships between brightness, temperature, and size. These relationships reveal that brightness depends on both temperature and size. However, temperature is the much more important factor of the two. Taking this into consideration, it turns out that the increase in brightness, from the bottom of the main sequence to the top, is almost completely accounted for by an increase in temperature. Therefore, all the stars along the main sequence have roughly the same diameter.

Despite what the laws of physics indicate, you may still think that a hot, bright star ought to be much bigger than a cool, dim one. Certainly if a star is brighter, it is producing more energy. It seems logical that the extra energy would cause the star to expand. However, observations indicate that hot, bright stars on the main sequence are not much

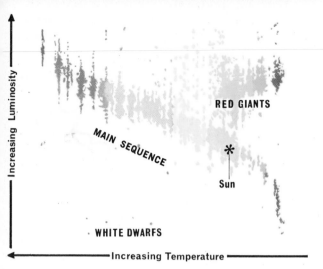

Figure 6-4. The colors of various types of stars and their positions on an H-R diagram are shown here. Notice that the range of colors is similar to the range of colors in a continuous spectrum, except that no stars appear green. How would you explain this?

larger than other main-sequence stars. Since the extra heat and light do not cause the star to expand, there must be some counteracting force holding the star together. This counteracting force can only be gravitational force. But to have greater gravitational forces, hot, bright stars must be more massive than the cool, dim ones. If so, the star's own mass compresses it and holds it together.

You remember that the masses of stars can be measured if the stars are members of a double-star system. Using the masses determined for these particular stars, we could make a graph showing the relationship between luminosity and mass. Such a graph is called a *mass-luminosity diagram. (Figure 6-5.)* Luminosity is again listed along the side. Mass, compared to the sun, is listed across the bottom. These stars are main-sequence stars. On the mass-luminosity graph, the points which represent these stars are along a diagonal across the graph. This time the diagonal is from the lower left to the upper right. The dim stars which have little mass are

at the lower left. The bright, more massive stars are at the upper right. The mass-luminosity diagram verifies the prediction that hot, bright stars are more massive than cool, dim stars.

Types of stars. Scientists, by using measurements of brightness, temperature, and—whenever possible—mass, have discovered some intriguing relationships among stars.

1. Most stars are main-sequence stars. Within this group the brighter stars are more massive and hotter. The dimmer stars are less massive and cooler.

2. In addition to the main-sequence stars there is a group of generally cooler, reddish stars. These stars are much larger than those of the main sequence. These stars are the red giants.

3. A third group contains relatively few stars. These stars appear to be quite hot. At the same time, they are very small. These are the white dwarfs.

When a mass-luminosity diagram is drawn for main-sequence stars, all the stars are represented in a line from the lower left to the upper right. On such a diagram, where would the points be which represent white dwarfs? Red giants?

Figure 6-5. Each symbol on the diagram below represents a star of known mass and luminosity. Each star represented (except our sun) is part of a double-star system. The symbol's shape denotes the type of double-star system of which the individual star is a part.

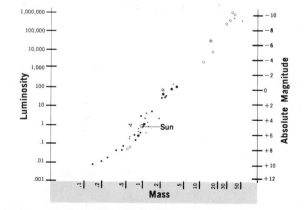

Observe a red giant and a main-sequence star

Unfortunately, white dwarf stars are not visible unless you use a very good telescope. However, red giants and main-sequence stars are quite easy to observe. Use star maps to help you locate in the sky Betelgeuse (a red giant) and Procyon (a main-sequence star). Observe them with the naked eye, binoculars, or a telescope. On the basis of your observation, can you tell what kind of star each one is? How do astronomers decide whether a star is a red giant, a white dwarf, or a main-sequence star?

3. Inside a Star

Conditions and materials. What kind of matter can exist inside a star? Of course, we know that the inside of a star is very hot. In fact, it is so hot that all chemical elements are at temperatures above their boiling points. None are in solid or liquid form. They are all gases. Even such substances as iron, tungsten, and graphite, which we know as solids on earth, exist as gases within a star.

The temperature within a star is so high, in fact, that no molecules can exist. Each individual atom has too much energy to remain joined to other atoms in a molecule. Thus, none of the elements which are present are combined. Each element occurs as separate atoms of that element. For example, although hydrogen atoms and oxygen atoms are present in most stars, there is no water—not even water vapor —in a star.

Within a star, gravitational force acts to pull the hot, gaseous matter of the star together. At the same time, internal pressures caused by heat and light tend to cause the star to expand. When the gravitational force pulling inward balances the heat and light pressure pushing outward, the size and the shape of the star do not change.

Perhaps you were surprised to read that light pressure is one of the forces which tend to cause a star to expand. Here on the earth, the pressure exerted by any light source, including the sun, is very slight compared to other pressures we experience. In fact, it is so slight that you may not have even been aware that light exerts pressure. However, inside the sun—or any other star—the light is so intense that its pressure plays an important part in maintaining the size of the star.

What experiments or observations have been made which indicate that light does exert pressure?

Stellar energy. How are heat and light energy produced in a star? This question baffled scientists for many years. They could think of ways by which huge amounts of energy could be produced; however, a star which produced energy in these ways could not last more than a few million years. For example, one of the early ideas was that stars converted gravitational energy into heat. As the gravitational force caused the star to contract, atoms in the star would bump against one another more and more often during the process. Thus, compression would raise the temperature inside the star enough to cause heat and light to be emitted. However, calculations based on this theory indicate that a star in which this process produced heat and light would not last more than a few million years. Of course, if the star were only a few million years old, any planets revolving about the star could have received heat and light from the star for only a few million years. However, evidence from studies of rocks on the earth indicates that the earth and life on earth are much older than a few million years. The earth must have been receiving light from the sun for hundreds of millions of years. Thus scientists know that the conversion of gravitational energy into heat and light is not a satisfactory explanation for the source of a star's energy.

Nuclear reactions. In 1921 a French physicist, Jean Perrin, suggested an answer to the question about the source of stellar energy. His idea was that the energy comes from nuclear reactions taking place in the stars.

What is a nuclear reaction? How is it different from a chemical reaction such as burning? To answer these questions you will have to review your knowledge of atoms. As you probably know, atoms are not indivisible as they were once thought to be. They, too, have parts. In general, an atom can be thought of as having two distinct regions—a central core and an outer region. The core is called the *nucleus*. It contains two types of particles—*protons,* each of which has a positive electric charge, and *neutrons,* each of which is electrically neutral. (The hydrogen atom is the only exception to this statement. The nucleus of a hydrogen atom is simply one proton.) In an atom the region about the nucleus contains *electrons,* each of which has a negative charge.

Scientists have also discovered other particles within atoms. But these three—protons, neutrons, and electrons—are the ones you need to know about in order to understand the difference between a nuclear reaction and a chemical reaction.

In a chemical reaction only electrons of the atoms are involved. The nuclei are not changed in any way. Therefore, the kind of element is not changed. However, a nuclear reaction involves changes in the nucleus of an atom. Either the number of protons changes, or the number of neutrons changes, or both. If the number of neutrons changes, the mass of the element changes, but the kind of element is not changed. However, with a change in the number of neutrons, the nucleus might become unstable. That is, it might have a tendency to break apart and form new elements.

Perrin's suggestion. The nuclear reaction which Perrin suggested as the source of stellar energy seems simple enough. He suggested that four hydrogen nuclei (simply four protons) combined to form the nucleus of a helium atom (two protons and two neutrons). In this reaction two of the protons must somehow become neutrons.

The important point is this. When four hydrogen nuclei are converted into a helium nucleus, the mass of the helium nucleus is slightly less than the total mass of the four separate protons. To account for the slight loss of mass, Perrin proposed that some matter had been converted into energy.

Perrin's hypothesis was based on Einstein's theory that energy and mass are equivalent and could be interchanged one for the other. Einstein had already derived the equation for the equivalence of matter and energy.

$$E = mc^2$$

In this equation E stands for energy, m for mass, and c for the speed of light. When mass is converted into energy, the exact amount of energy released could be calculated by using the equation.

As the equation indicates, the amount of energy which is equivalent to even a very small amount of mass is enormous. If only one gram of mass—about one-third the mass of an ordinary penny—is converted, the amount of energy released is 25,000,000 (2.5×10^7) kilowatt-hours.

How much energy is this? If you were to switch on ten 100-watt light bulbs, they would use 1,000 watts, or one kilowatt, of power. There are about 9,000 hours in a year. If you kept the ten 100-watt bulbs lighted for one year, they would use about 9,000 kilowatt-hours of energy. In order to use 2.5×10^7 kilowatt-hours—the energy equivalent of one gram of mass—the ten bulbs would have to stay lighted for almost 3,000 years!

Perrin's theory suggested a source for the enormous amounts of energy stars are known to produce. Nuclear reactions can produce such large amounts of energy that stars are able to last for a long time. In fact, our sun could last for 40,000,000,000 (4×10^{10}) years before it used up all of its hydrogen.

Proton-proton and carbon-nitrogen cycles. During the last few years, scientists have learned a great deal about nuclear reactions. Scientists now believe they understand the processes by which the conversion of hydrogen into helium takes place.

There are two different processes by which the conversion from hydrogen to helium can occur. One is the *proton-proton cycle*. The other is the *carbon-nitrogen cycle*. In either process, the conversion of hydrogen to helium does not happen directly. That is, four hydrogen nuclei do not get together all at once to make a helium nucleus. Examine the diagrams

Figure 6-6. The proton-proton cycle described below is one nuclear reaction which is important in the release of the enormous amounts of energy radiated by the stars.

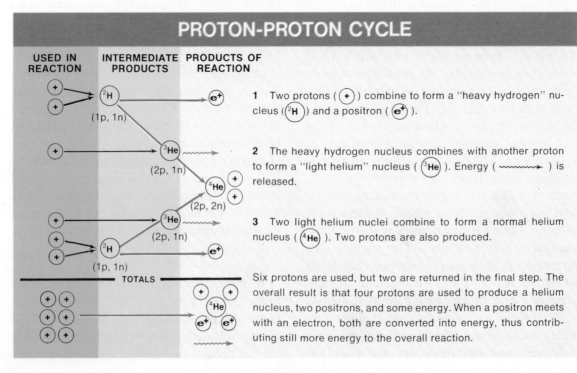

118

CARBON-NITROGEN CYCLE

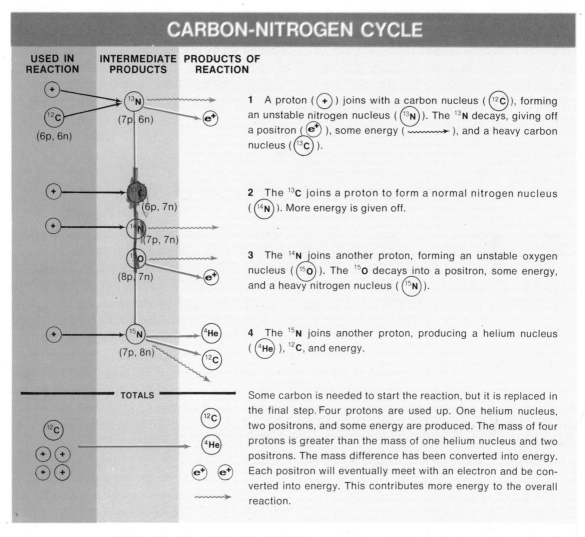

USED IN REACTION | **INTERMEDIATE PRODUCTS** | **PRODUCTS OF REACTION**

1 A proton ((+)) joins with a carbon nucleus ((^{12}C)), forming an unstable nitrogen nucleus ((^{13}N)). The ^{13}N decays, giving off a positron ((e$^+$)), some energy (~~~~>), and a heavy carbon nucleus ((^{13}C)).

2 The ^{13}C joins a proton to form a normal nitrogen nucleus ((^{14}N)). More energy is given off.

3 The ^{14}N joins another proton, forming an unstable oxygen nucleus ((^{15}O)). The ^{15}O decays into a positron, some energy, and a heavy nitrogen nucleus ((^{15}N)).

4 The ^{15}N joins another proton, producing a helium nucleus ((^{4}He)), ^{12}C, and energy.

TOTALS

Some carbon is needed to start the reaction, but it is replaced in the final step. Four protons are used up. One helium nucleus, two positrons, and some energy are produced. The mass of four protons is greater than the mass of one helium nucleus and two positrons. The mass difference has been converted into energy. Each positron will eventually meet with an electron and be converted into energy. This contributes more energy to the overall reaction.

Figure 6-7. The carbon-nitrogen cycle is another nuclear reaction occurring within stars. Carbon is required to start this reaction, but the carbon is not used up in the reaction.

in *Figures 6-6* and *6-7* which illustrate the two processes. In each process there is more than one step. Although the steps are different in the processes, the final result is the same. Four hydrogen nuclei have fused into one helium nucleus and some energy has been released.

Several factors determine which of these two processes occur. The temperature is one factor. Another factor is the kind of elements that are present in the star. The two processes may go on simultaneously if the proper conditions exist within the star.

Each of the cycles would take a very long time if only a small number of atoms were present. For example, consider the first step in the carbon-nitrogen cycle. A proton (a hydrogen nucleus) joins with a carbon nucleus. Considering the number of hydrogen and carbon nuclei present, this does not happen very often. Inside a star, the average carbon nucleus exists for hundreds of thousands of years before taking part in a reaction. A hydrogen nucleus must be moving at just the right speed and in just the right direction to join with a carbon nucleus to begin the cycle. However, there are so many nuclei in the sun that the steps in the cycle go on continuously. Although many nuclear reactions are occurring, only a very small fraction of the matter in the star is reacting at any one time. Thus a star can produce energy for a very long period of time.

4. Structure of Various Types of Stars

Main sequence. Having an idea of what is happening inside a star helps to explain the relationships indicated by the H-R diagram. In the main sequence, the hotter stars are brighter. Our concept of the interior of a star can be used to explain this. The hotter a star is, the more vigorous is the nuclear reaction (conversion of hydrogen to helium). The more vigorous the reaction is, the greater is the energy production. If more energy is produced, more energy must be radiated away as light. Thus, the hotter stars are brighter than the cooler ones.

From the mass-luminosity relationship, we know that the hotter, brighter stars are also more massive. This, too, can be explained on the basis of our concept of a star's interior.

If a star has more matter in it, then the gravitational force pulling it together is much greater. But you have already learned that the gravitational force tending to compress a star must be balanced by the heat and light pressure tending to expand it. Therefore, if the gravitational force is greater, the heat and light pressure must also be greater. The more massive stars, then, must be hotter and brighter. The inward gravitational force balances the outward force of heat and light pressure. That is, an *equilibrium* (ē′kwə lib′ri əm) exists within the star.

Give examples from your everyday experiences of situations in which you think an equilibrium exists.

FIND OUT BY TRYING

Materials you will need: a balloon

Partially inflate the balloon. Then, using the pressure of your breath, hold the balloon so that no air escapes. Does it maintain its size and shape? Force more air into the balloon. What happens to the size? Allow some air to escape. What happens to the size? What forces cause the change in size?

When the size stays the same, we say an equilibrium exists. Does this mean no forces are acting? What happens to the balloon when the equilibrium is upset? Describe how the equilibrium in an inflated balloon is like the equilibrium in a star. In what ways is it different?

Red giants. Can the nuclear reaction theory explain the nature of other stars as well as it does the nature of main-sequence stars? The formation of red giants can be explained in the following way. Most of the conversion of hydrogen to helium takes place near the center of a star, where the temperature is highest. Gradually the hydrogen in this region is converted into helium. If gases were mixing inside the star, then hydrogen from the outer regions of the star would be stirred down into the center to replace the converted hydrogen. Apparently this doesn't happen, so gradually a core of helium—in which no energy is produced—grows inside the star. The energy is produced at the interface of the helium core and the hydrogen which surrounds it. For a while the star grows brighter.

Why does the brightness of a star increase as the core of helium grows within the star?

Eventually, as the helium core grows, its own gravitational force begins to pull it together. The helium core starts to contract. This compression causes the temperature to rise. However, since there is no more hydrogen in this region to be converted, there is no increase in the reaction rate. But the contraction of the helium core does cause some stirring of the hydrogen near the outer edge of the core. Hydrogen is brought down a little way into the core where the temperature is now very high. This hydrogen begins to react very vigorously, and a very hot shell develops around the collapsing core. The high temperature of this hot shell upsets the equilibrium between the inward and outward forces. The outward pressure is now greater, and the portion of the star outside the core expands.

The result is a red giant—a star with a greatly expanded outer region and a greatly condensed central core. It is the expanded

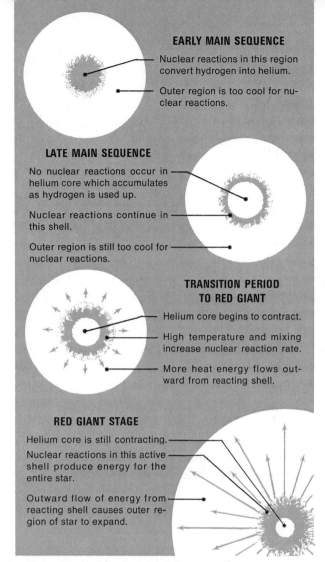

EARLY MAIN SEQUENCE

Nuclear reactions in this region convert hydrogen into helium.

Outer region is too cool for nuclear reactions.

LATE MAIN SEQUENCE

No nuclear reactions occur in helium core which accumulates as hydrogen is used up.

Nuclear reactions continue in this shell.

Outer region is still too cool for nuclear reactions.

TRANSITION PERIOD TO RED GIANT

Helium core begins to contract.

High temperature and mixing increase nuclear reaction rate.

More heat energy flows outward from reacting shell.

RED GIANT STAGE

Helium core is still contracting.

Nuclear reactions in this active shell produce energy for the entire star.

Outward flow of energy from reacting shell causes outer region of star to expand.

Figure 6-8. Theoretically, the evolution of a main-sequence star into a red giant should take a few million years for a large star. For stars like the sun, the process would require several billion years.

outer shell that we see. The expansion has caused the outer part to become cooler, so now it is only red hot instead of white hot. The energy for the whole star is supplied by the conversion process going on right at the outer edge of the central core. See *Figure 6-8.*

White dwarfs. How does a knowledge of what is happening inside a star help explain the existence of white dwarfs? For these stars, there is no satisfactory explanation. Apparently, a white dwarf is the leftover core of helium, with almost no hydrogen left to convert and with no outer shell of expanded hydrogen around it. What has happened to the outer shell is still an unanswered question.

As you can see on the H-R diagram, white dwarfs are rather rare compared with other kinds of stars. We have only a very few of them to examine. This makes it difficult to obtain enough information to develop theories about white dwarfs. Observational bias may be responsible for the fact that only a few white dwarfs are observed. However, there is a way to make some correction for observational bias in order to estimate how many more dim stars there might be. We can assume that the rest of the galaxy is pretty much like the region around us. In the nearby regions of our galaxy, the number of stars dimmer than our sun is greater than the number of brighter stars. Therefore, if we assume that all of the galaxy is like the nearby regions, then most stars in the galaxy are dimmer than the sun.

But the assumption that there are many white dwarfs does not explain how a star becomes a white dwarf. If a white dwarf is the helium core left from a red giant, there must be some explanation to account for the disappearance of the outer shell of hydrogen. Could it have been blown away by some explosion, or perhaps a series of explosions?

Novae. Astronomers have seen stars that actually explode. When this happens, the star becomes very much brighter within a few days. Typically, it becomes as much as 100,000 times brighter than it was before the explosion. In some cases, the star is so far away that it is invisible before the explosion. The star is discovered only when it suddenly gets very bright. (*Figure 6-9.*) To observers in earlier times, such a star seemed like a new star. For

this reason, astronomers about 350 years ago would give to such a star the name "nova," which is Latin for "new." Today we still use the term nova for such an exploding star.

Even though such a star gets bright in a period of a few days, it usually takes several months for it to gradually fade to its original brightness. Sometimes the gases which are blown out from the star in this explosion are visible afterwards as a ring around the central star.

There is a theory that a nova will explode regularly at fairly long intervals—say every few hundred or every few thousand years. But as you can imagine, there are very few observations to check this theory. However, one nova has been observed twice—once in 1866 and again in 1946. So, it is possible that a nova will explode repeatedly over a long period of time. If this happens, its hydrogen would gradually be blasted away until nothing is left but the core of helium. Possibly, white dwarfs are stars that have lost all of their hydrogen through a series of explosions.

Figure 6-9. The same portion of the sky is shown before and during the occurrence of a nova. This particular star increased in brightness by a factor of about 150,000.

YERKES OBSERVATORY

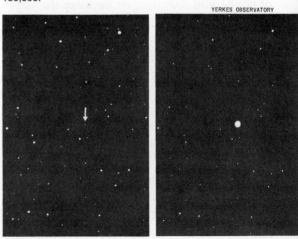

5. The Evolution of a Star

Questions to be answered. Stellar evolution is one of the most challenging mysteries of astronomy. Astronomers and astrophysicists all over the world are trying to solve this mystery. The solution involves finding the answers to these questions.

1. How is a star formed?
2. How does a star change with time?
3. How rapidly do these changes take place?
4. What happens when a star finally has radiated away all of its energy?

It must be kept in mind that in seeking answers to these questions, scientists are dealing with theories. Since the whole process of stellar evolution takes many millions of years, it is impossible to actually follow the course of change in any single star. Man's knowledge of the stars is like an array of snapshots of the millions of stars as they appear now. These snapshots have been taken during a period of about 100 years, but 100 years is only an instant in the life of a star. Scientists assume that there are examples of all stages of stellar development represented in our array of snapshots. By mentally arranging these stages in a sequential order which is consistent with previous observations, a theory of stellar evolution has been formulated. Besides giving a sensible explanation to our array of snapshots, the theory must also agree with what is known about physics. If it does these two things, it is accepted—not as a law, but as a theory which will be checked and rechecked as new information becomes available.

The formation of a star. Of course, no one knows exactly how a star is formed. The most widely accepted theory is that a star forms when a vast cloud of dust and gas slowly condenses. Gravitational force causes the cloud to condense. As the cloud—composed mainly of hydrogen—becomes more and more tightly packed, compression causes it to heat up. Some of this heat will be radiated off into space. However, the center of the cloud is insulated by the surrounding layers. Therefore, the center will get hotter and hotter. Finally, the temperature will be high enough so that the hydrogen begins to fuse into helium. The cloud of gas has become a star. Of course, if this theory is correct, the new star will not be a red giant. It will probably be a main-sequence star.

It would be helpful if we could check this theory by observing a few stars in the process of being formed. This, however, is very difficult. During the process of formation, the star is still surrounded by the dust cloud. This cloud obscures our view. The light from the new star is not seen, therefore, until the light is intense enough for the light pressure to push away the cloud.

Nevertheless, there are a few things that can be checked. If new stars really do form from dust and gas clouds, then new stars should appear near large clouds of dust. Older stars, such as red giants, should be located where there is little or no dust. This conclusion can be checked. Many galaxies are surrounded by dust clouds. Some of these galaxies are quite spectacular, such as the galaxy shown in *Figure 6-10*. Here our view is edge-on, and the cloud of dust around the edge of the galaxy is so dense that it blocks out the light of the stars behind it. In fact, most spiral galaxies that have been observed have dust clouds around their outer edges but not near their centers.

Astronomers have examined photographs of the Andromeda galaxy in detail. They have found the location of reddish stars in Andromeda and, indeed, they are near the center.

The hot, blue stars are near the edge where there is still some dust remaining. These observations, although they do not prove the theory of stellar formation, certainly help to support it.

How stars change. Astronomers are pretty certain they have discovered some answers to the questions about how stars change. A theory to account for the formation of red giants has already been described. The process of becoming a red giant undoubtedly takes hundreds of millions of years. However, it is important to realize that the process will happen faster for some stars than for others. Think back over what you have learned about the H-R diagram. The stars in it near the top left corner have greater mass and are brighter than those farther down and to the right. The fact that they are brighter indicates they are producing more energy. Because they are producing more energy, they might go through the growth process more quickly.

By looking at the H-R diagram, we can see that this prediction seems to be correct. We can infer that the hot, bright stars evolve into red giants sooner than the cooler, less luminous stars, on the basis of the following observations.

1. The observed red giants are big and massive. (In fact, that's why they are called giants.) They must have developed from stars that were big and massive from the beginning. Thus, the red giants must have evolved from stars represented by points near the top of the main sequence.

2. The stars represented by points near the bottom of the main sequence have not begun the process of turning into red giants.

What do you think will happen to the earth when the sun evolves into a red giant? How will the other planets be affected?

How long does it take? Scientists know how much energy the sun is giving off and how much hydrogen it has to be converted into helium. Using this information, it has been calculated that the sun has about 40 billion years of life ahead of it. Calculations have also been made for hotter stars. The results indicate that some of them have evolved from main-sequence stars into red giants in 5 to 10 billion years.

Geologists have determined that the earth is about 4½ billion years old. It is reasonable to believe that the sun is at least this old—maybe even a little bit older. Therefore, during the life of our solar system, some of the larger stars have evolved from main-sequence stars and become red giants.

Some large stars use up their hydrogen 300 times faster than the sun. If the sun has a 40 billion-year lifetime, then these stars could last only about 100 million years. It is very likely that some of them have passed

Figure 6-10. The dark band around this galaxy is caused by clouds of gas and dust which obscure the stars behind them. Most spirals contain such clouds, but the dark bands are not always so obvious.

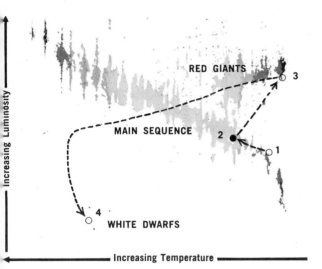

Increasing Luminosity

RED GIANTS

MAIN SEQUENCE

WHITE DWARFS

Increasing Temperature

Figure 6-11. The sun's evolution can be traced by plotting where the sun would be represented on an H-R diagram at various stages. From a condensing cloud of dust and gas (1), the sun became a main-sequence star (2). Billions of years from now, it will become a red giant (3). After the red giant stage, the sun will become smaller and hotter. Finally, it will become a white dwarf (4). Astronomers believe that all stars follow similar evolutionary patterns. However, stars formed from larger gas clouds become hotter, brighter, main-sequence stars. The hotter, brighter stars go through the evolutionary process more rapidly.

converting helium into a heavier element. When all of the helium is used up, then it might contract still more and get hot enough to start still another nuclear reaction. If so, the star has reached a level of nuclear reaction about which scientists know very little. Experiments here on earth simply have not provided enough answers to help scientists construct a theory for such stars.

There have been many ideas suggested concerning the last stage of a star. One of the most interesting comes back again to the idea of the white dwarfs. Careful measurements have been made of the amount of light from such dwarf stars and of their mass. (Some of them are members of double-star systems.) These white dwarfs have been discovered to be extremely compact. In fact, some of them are so dense that a cubic inch of their material would weigh fifteen tons here on the earth. The way scientists account for this great density is to say that the atoms in these stars have either lost or absorbed their electrons. Thus, the nuclei are packed together into a very dense form of matter. This kind of matter can only be described theoretically. So far there is no way for scientists to produce it in any laboratory on earth.

Of course, even white dwarfs must have some energy left in order to give off the light that we see. But we can guess that eventually even this last bit will be radiated away, and the star will become dark and cold. It will be a small, extremely compact ball of material—a material unlike anything we have ever seen on earth.

beyond the red giant stage. They may have converted all their hydrogen to helium. Or, they might have exploded and blasted the hydrogen in their large outer shell away. At the end of that process, they might have become white dwarfs.

The last stage. The last question—What happens when a star finally has radiated away all of its energy?—is a most difficult question to answer. Scientists simply do not know enough about nuclear physics to describe this process. Suppose our theories are correct. What happens to a star after it converts all of its hydrogen to helium? Perhaps gravity continues to compress the star. If so, it might get hot enough to start another nuclear reaction—

As the temperature of a white dwarf becomes lower, the light it radiates away must change color. The change would be from white to yellow to orange to red. Why, do you suppose, is there no visible evidence of orange or red dwarfs?

Checking Your Knowledge

IMPORTANT IDEAS

1. An H-R diagram shows a relationship between a star's luminosity and temperature.

2. A mass-luminosity diagram reveals dim stars to be less massive than bright ones.

3. Observational bias probably accounts for the fact that most of the stars we observe are brighter than our sun.

4. The interior of a star is very hot.

5. Stellar energy is from nuclear reactions.

6. Stars form as gravitational force causes huge clouds in space to compress, producing temperatures high enough for nuclear reactions.

7. In stars there is an equilibrium between the inward gravitational force and the outward force of the pressure of heat and light.

8. The probable pattern of stellar evolution is from main-sequence star, to red giant, to white dwarf, to an unknown fate.

USING NEW WORDS

Study the list of words below. Write the numerals *1-4* on your paper. Beside each numeral, write words or statements to satisfy the instructions given for that numeral.

proton	mass-luminosity diagram
luminosity	main sequence
nucleus	white dwarf
equilibrium	helium
H-R diagram	proton-proton cycle
red giant	carbon-nitrogen cycle

1. Which terms are the names of graphs used to compare the properties of stars? Describe how these graphs differ from each other.

2. List those words which are related to conditions or materials inside a star.

3. Which words are names of types of stars? Describe the differences between these types.

4. Which word refers to the amount of light emitted by a star?

TEST YOURSELF

Study the test below. On your paper write the numerals *1-10*. Beside each numeral write the correct response to that part of the test having the corresponding numeral.

1. Our sun is a (*red giant, main-sequence star, white dwarf*).

2. If two stars are on the same horizontal line on an H-R diagram, the radius of the hotter one is (*greater than, less than, the same as*) the radius of the cooler one.

3. If two stars are on the same vertical line on an H-R diagram, the radius of the brighter one is (*greater than, less than, the same as*) the radius of the dimmer one.

4. The interior of a star does not contain (*extremely hot gases, molten metals, protons*).

The following list contains statements related to the sentences numbered *5-10*. Beside each of the numerals *5-10* on your paper, write the letter of that statement most closely related to the sentence having the corresponding numeral.

a. The conversion of hydrogen into helium

b. More vigorous fusion reactions result from closely packed hydrogen nuclei.

c. A violently exploding star, or nova

d. Red giants are old stars.

e. New stars form from dust and gas clouds.

f. Observational bias

g. No molecules exist inside stars.

5. The interior of a star is very hot.

6. Few white dwarfs are observed.

7. Hot, bright stars are more massive than cool, dim stars.

8. We cannot see a star being formed.

9. This is the energy source for most stars.

10. This might be a step in the evolution of a red giant into a white dwarf.

Extending Your Knowledge

QUESTIONS TO EXPLORE

1. Why were the early theories about the source of energy in our sun considered to be unacceptable? What reasons (if any) are there which indicate that nuclear reactions may not be the only source of stellar energy?

2. What information about the stars do scientists need in order to construct an H-R digram? How do they obtain this information?

3. Suppose you could use a table of data which contained all the information known about the stars within 100 light-years of the earth. Suppose, too, that you use this information to construct an H-R diagram and a mass-luminosity diagram. Which diagram will include the greater number of stars? Explain your answer.

4. What problems would a scientist have if he wished to study a star at close range?

5. Stars are objects far out in space. They do not seem to have any great influence on our everyday lives. How would you justify spending class time to study them?

6. Does the nuclear reaction in the sun more nearly resemble that in an atomic bomb or in a hydrogen bomb? Has a reaction like that in the sun ever been produced and controlled in a laboratory? If so, how? If not, why not?

SOME THINGS TO DO

1. Draw a graph representing your idea of how the amount of energy released from a star changes with time. Use the vertical axis for the amount of energy released and the horizontal axis for the time.

2. Set up a classroom demonstration of an equilibrium. If the jet of air from a vacuum cleaner is directed upward, it will support a ping-pong ball or a very lightweight beach ball.

Tell what forces are in equilibrium in this demonstration. Explain how this equilibrium is like the equilibrium in a star. (There is another important scientific principle that is demonstrated by this activity. What principle is it?)

3. Make a list of the characteristics of a star which has a temperature of 3,500° K and a luminosity of 10,000.

4. If the theory of stellar evolution proposed in this chapter is correct, the sun will become a red giant at some future time. Of course, the effect on the earth will be disastrous. Make a list of some of the things man could do to survive.

CHALLENGES IN SCIENCE

1. Find out what is studied in the science of plasma physics. How is plasma physics related to astrophysics? What type of research is being carried out at the present time?

2. What variables can be found in stars that are along a vertical line on the H-R diagram? A horizontal line on the diagram?

3. Use your knowledge of the stars to explain each of the following statements.

   a. A hot star is smaller than a cool star of the same luminosity.

   b. A bright star has a greater mass than a dim star of the same color.

4. Find out what is meant by the conservation of matter and energy. Are the principles of conservation disproved in a nuclear reaction? Explain your answer.

5. Obtain the necessary information and construct an H-R diagram for those stars within 5 parsecs of our sun. How many stars are on the diagram? Which type of star does not appear on your diagram? HINT: *Elementary Astonomy* by Struve, Linds, and Pillans is one source of the necessary information.

CHAPTER 7

A variety of seemingly unrelated objects fill man's environment.

The History of the Universe

Man is constantly trying to solve the mysteries of the universe. He finds himself living on the solid portion of the earth, enveloped by the atmosphere, and surrounded by the waters of the oceans. The sun moves across the sky each day. At night, the moon and stars appear. They, too, move in a regular, predictable way. This regularity is interrupted by such happenings as storms, eclipses, and the appearance of comets. Can these seemingly unrelated phenomena be fitted into one composite theory of the universe?

Man has explained some of the things that used to baffle him. For example, he can predict and explain eclipses. He can predict the reappearance of many comets. He even knows about the reactions which produce the light of the stars. However, in finding out these things, many other phenomena have been observed. These new observations must then be explained. Thus, as advances in science improve our picture of the universe, new details are always being found. These details must be fitted into the framework of existing knowledge.

In this chapter, some theories of the origin of the universe are presented. You may be surprised to learn that such far-ranging theories are not just wild guesses. Certain aspects of these theories can be checked. You will also discover that none of the present theories is completely satisfactory, and that much remains to be explained.

1. Cosmology

Frustration and challenge. How did the universe begin? Is it growing and changing? What might happen to it in the distant future? These are the same questions that were asked about stars in the last chapter. Now they are being asked about the whole universe.

The study of these questions is one of the most frustrating and, at the same time, one of the most challenging fields of science. It is called *cosmology* (koz mol′ə ji). It is frustrating because it deals with phenomena that are completely outside of our ordinary experience. Furthermore, data which might be used to check cosmological theories are very difficult to obtain. Cosmology is challenging because it seeks to answer the deepest questions which man has been asking about nature ever since he has had a recorded history.

The process which cosmologists are setting out to discover spans many billions of years. There are rocks on earth and in meteorites that seem to be about 4.5 billion years old. Theories about the growth of stars like our sun give similar ages for the stars, though some may be a few billion years older. The universe which contains these objects must be at least this old. Very likely the universe is even older than these objects.

Checking with data. Gathering data for cosmology is extremely difficult. Astronomers are in much the same position that was described in the last chapter—that is, they have what amounts to a snapshot of the universe as it appears to us today. There is no way of knowing how it might have appeared billions of years ago when the early formative processes were going on. Yet, even with only a snapshot, there are some things which can be done. For example, scientists learn about the composition of distant galaxies by using the spectroscope. Furthermore, the spectroscope reveals another rather surprising piece of information. Most galaxies are moving away from the earth—some of them at very high speeds.

There is another important factor to remember when examining evidence about the universe. Some galaxies are so far away that the light which we see now, left these galaxies more than a billion years ago. Thus, the light received from very distant galaxies gives information about conditions which existed a long time ago. By comparing this information with information from nearby galaxies, scientists may be able to detect some differences. They may learn how galaxies change. Of course, this procedure has a built-in difficulty. Light from the most distant galaxies would tell them the most about conditions in the past. But, because they are distant, these galaxies appear only as small, very faint blurs—even on pictures taken through the biggest telescopes. About all that can be done is to obtain the spectra of these galaxies and measure the amount of light received from them.

A possible origin. In Chapter 3, the universe was described as consisting of billions of galaxies, scattered out across space as far as we can observe. Each galaxy consists of many billions of stars. According to the theory in Chapter 6, these stars were formed from clouds of gas and dust.

If this is true, each galaxy was, at first, simply a huge, swirling mass of gas and dust. Having no stars within it, this mass would be diffuse and dark. After many billions of years, the material in the cloud would begin to condense to form the stars. The first stars would form near the center where the cloud was thickest. This seems logical, but is it possible to check such an idea?

The present theory of star formation seems to confirm this hypothesis. That is, red stars

Figure 7-1. Color photographs reveal that many galaxies, such as this spiral galaxy in the constellation Sculptor, have reddish stars near the hub of the galaxy and bluish stars near the outer edges.

(which are believed to be older) are usually located in the center of a galaxy. White or blue stars (which are believed to be younger) are located near the edge of the galaxy—often quite close to the remaining clouds of gas and dust. (*Figure 7-1.*) Of course, although this evidence supports this idea of a possible origin of a galaxy, such evidence is not definite proof. Moreover, we are still left with the question of where the huge clouds of matter came from.

Cosmological theories attempt to tell what has happened to matter in the past, but they do not explain how the materials of the universe came into existence initially. What field of study, would you say, is concerned with the initial creation of the matter in the universe?

2. The Expanding Universe

Distance estimates. The parallax method of determining distance, which works for nearby stars, is useless for galaxies because they are so far away. In fact, most galaxies are so far away that individual stars within each galaxy cannot be distinguished. Thus, even Cepheid variables cannot be used to determine the distances to these faraway galaxies.

However, Cepheid variables have been used to determine the distances to some nearby galaxies. By combining these known distances with apparent brightnesses, scientists have decided that each of the nearby galaxies is emitting about the same total amount of light. In other words, each galaxy has about the same absolute brightness as the other galaxies. They are not exactly the same in brightness. In fact, the brightest ones seem to emit about ten times as much light as do the dimmest ones. Nevertheless, astronomers have decided to use the average brightness of the nearby galaxies to represent the average brightness of all galaxies. If each galaxy is assumed to have the same absolute brightness, its apparent brightness depends upon its distance from us. Thus, the amount of light we receive from a galaxy—its apparent brightness—is used to estimate the distance from us to that particular galaxy.

The calculation of relative distances is made in the same way for galaxies as it is for stars. That is, the same equation is used.

$$\frac{B_1}{B_2} = \frac{(d_2)^2}{(d_1)^2}$$

Therefore, if one galaxy appears four times brighter than another, we conclude that the brighter one is only about half as far away. Since average values are used for the absolute brightnesses of the galaxies, the calculations for a number of galaxies will be correct on the average, but not in each specific case.

Does knowing the distance to the galaxies aid in formulating a theory of the universe? If so, how? If not, of what value is the knowledge of the distance to other galaxies?

Doppler effect. With brightness measurements to indicate how far away galaxies are, and with the spectroscope to indicate something about their composition, we have begun to gather the information needed for formulating cosmological theories. But, as was mentioned before, the spectroscope reveals a rather surprising piece of additional information.

The spectra from distant galaxies all have spectral lines that are shifted toward the red end of the spectrum. (*Figure 7-2.*) The only way to explain this strange phenomenon is to assume that the galaxies are moving in relation to us. The motion of a star or a galaxy toward or away from us causes a change in its spectrum because of the Doppler effect. The Doppler effect causes the red shift in the spectrum of nearly every galaxy. From this, we infer that the galaxies are moving away from us. The speed at which they are moving is shown by the amount of the red shift in their spectra. The greater the shift, the greater is the speed. Astronomers have discovered that the dimmer galaxies (which are believed to be further away) are moving away from us at a greater speed than are the brighter ones (which are believed to be closer).

Scientists say that the universe is expanding. Do you think that the rate of expansion has always been the same? How would you account for an increase in the rate of expansion? A decrease?

Going back in time. What can be inferred from the relationship between the distances to galaxies and their speeds of recession? Observations show that the more distant gal-

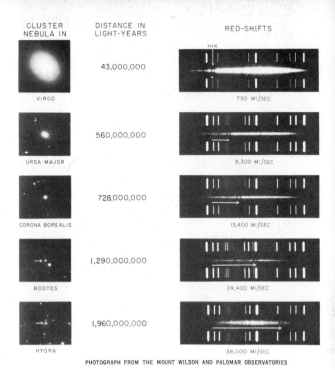

CLUSTER NEBULA IN — DISTANCE IN LIGHT-YEARS — RED-SHIFTS

VIRGO — 43,000,000 — H+K — 750 MI/SEC

URSA MAJOR — 560,000,000 — 9,300 MI/SEC

CORONA BOREALIS — 728,000,000 — 13,400 MI/SEC

BOOTES — 1,290,000,000 — 24,400 MI/SEC

HYDRA — 1,960,000,000 — 38,000 MI/SEC

PHOTOGRAPH FROM THE MOUNT WILSON AND PALOMAR OBSERVATORIES

Figure 7-2. Pictures of galaxies (left column) are paired with their spectra (right column). In each spectrum, an arrow points to the same spectral lines. The more distant the galaxy, the farther the lines are shifted toward the red end of the spectrum.

axies are moving faster than the nearby ones. Suppose there is a definite proportion between a galaxy's speed of recession and its distance from us. Then, we could express this relationship as an equation.

$$\frac{d_1}{d_2} = \frac{r_1}{r_2}$$

In this equation, d_1 is the distance to Galaxy 1 and d_2 is the distance to Galaxy 2. The rates of recession for Galaxy 1 and Galaxy 2 are r_1 and r_2. By using the techniques of algebra, we can express the same relationship with this equation.

$$\frac{d_1}{r_1} = \frac{d_2}{r_2}$$

Now suppose we go one step farther. You undoubtedly know that, no matter what kind of problem you are working on, the relationship between distance, rate, and time is expressed in the following equations.

(1) $d = rt$　　(2) $\dfrac{d}{r} = t$　　(3) $r = \dfrac{d}{t}$

Using (2) in our previous equation, we obtain the following results.

$$\frac{d_1}{r_1} = t_1 \qquad\qquad \frac{d_2}{r_2} = t_2$$

But, $\dfrac{d_1}{r_1} = \dfrac{d_2}{r_2}$. Therefore, $t_1 = t_2$.

Here, t_1 is a time characteristic of Galaxy 1, and t_2 is a time characteristic of Galaxy 2. The equation $t_1 = t_2$ states that the time characteristics are equal for any two galaxies in the universe.

This is a statement which can be checked very simply. Astronomers have measured both the distances to and the speeds of recession for many galaxies. When they divide the measure of the distance to a galaxy by the measure of its speed, the quotient is nearly the same for each galaxy. The average value of the quotient is about 10 billion.

The meaning of this result is still a mystery. However, one way to look at it is as follows. Suppose the galaxies have all been traveling in straight lines for 10 billion years. Suppose, too, that each galaxy's speed has been constant for 10 billion years. Then, 10 billion years ago the galaxies were all squeezed together in one point.

Regardless of what the universe was like 10 billion years ago, the picture we now have is a picture of the galaxies moving away from each other and away from us. However, not all the galaxies are moving away from us at the same rate. The further away a galaxy is from us, the more rapidly that galaxy seems to be moving away from us.

Does this mean that we are in the center of the universe with everything flying away from us? Not necessarily. No matter where you are in the universe, if there is a general, uniform expansion in all directions, it will always appear to you that you are in the center.

FIND OUT BY TRYING

Materials you will need: round balloon, felt-tip pen

Blow up the balloon so that it is about as big as your fist. Now put about thirty spots on the balloon with the felt-top pen. Each spot represents a galaxy. The spots should be applied to the balloon in a random manner.

Select one spot to represent our home, the Milky Way Galaxy. While standing in front of a mirror, blow up the balloon some more. Notice how the spots move relative to the one you selected as home. Also observe how the spots move relative to each other. Do any of the spots get closer together? Do any of the spots get farther apart? Do all the spots move the same distance from the home galaxy? Do all the spots move with the same speed relative to the home galaxy?

Pick a different spot to represent home. As you blow up the balloon some more, notice how the spot you selected as home moves relative to the second spot you chose. Can you pick one spot which is the center of your universe of spots?

3. Theories of Origin

The big-bang theory. The observation that the galaxies are all moving away from each other is one of the most important observations ever made about the universe on a large scale. This observation must be taken into account in any theory which attempts to explain the development of the universe.

There are three current theories of how the universe began. One is called the *big-bang theory*. This theory assumes that initially all of the matter and energy in the universe was concentrated into one region. This region exploded. Some of the energy was transformed into matter. The material from this gigantic explosion shot out across empty space. Atoms, mostly hydrogen, were pushed steadily outward by the heat and light behind them. Gradually, the atoms were slowed in their flight because the gravitational force of the whole expanding mass tended to pull everything together.

As the material (mostly gas) continued its flight through space, slight concentrations of material developed here and there. These concentrations developed simply because the original explosion did not have exactly the same effect in all directions. These concentrations of material were the beginning of galaxies. Within them, billions of stars would eventually form.

You will notice that this theory does not quite get to the real origin of the universe. That is, it does not state where the initial concentration of material and energy came from.

The oscillating-universe theory. A second theory—the *oscillating-universe theory*—offers a slightly different explanation. This theory also states that a big bang occurred. However, the oscillating-universe theory goes on to say that there is a periodic repetition of the explosion. The gas cloud will expand outward for many billions of years, condensing into galaxies and stars in the process. According to this theory, however, the gravitational attraction between all of the far-flung galaxies will cause the outward expansion to slow down and eventually stop.

Then, the motion will slowly reverse and the galaxies will begin to fall back together again. As time passes, they will fall more and more rapidly. They will be moving approximately toward that point where they started billions of years ago in the big bang. According to this theory, when the galaxies come smashing together again, there will be another huge explosion and the whole process will repeat.

The oscillating-universe theory holds that there was no actual beginning, but that this process has been endlessly repeating itself and will continue to repeat itself endlessly.

The steady-state theory. A third theory avoids both oscillations and explosions. It is called the *steady-state theory*. In this theory, it is suggested that the universe has always looked as it looks now. That is, the galaxies are a few hundred thousand light-years apart and are all moving away from each other. Of course, if the galaxies are all moving away from each other, and if the universe still continues to look generally the same way it does now, then something must be steadily filling up the empty space between them.

The basic assumption of the steady-state theory is that atoms of hydrogen are being formed throughout the universe at a slow but steady rate. As the atoms are formed, they are affected by gravitational forces, either from a nearby galaxy or from each other. If they are attracted to each other, a cloud of newborn hydrogen might eventually form a new galaxy, filling up the empty space formed as the surrounding galaxies move away from each other.

THE BIG-BANG THEORY	THE OSCILLATING-UNIVERSE THEORY	THE STEADY-STATE THEORY

The expansion of the universe began with the explosion of a great concentration of matter and energy, and it will continue indefinitely.	The universe has always existed. However, it expands and contracts periodically. It is now in a period of expansion.	The overall condition of the universe does not change. As the galaxies move apart, new matter is created in the empty space.

Figure 7-3. The three current theories by which scientists have attempted to explain the origin of the universe are briefly described above.

Where do all the atoms of hydrogen come from? Here again, the origin of the universe is not completely explained, for we are still left without an explanation of this continual creation of hydrogen atoms.

Do you think it is probable that the correct theory of the origin of the universe has yet to be proposed? If so, explain how you think it will differ from the theories proposed so far.

DO IT YOURSELF

Describe the universe as it might have appeared in the distant past

Based on the implications of the big-bang theory, describe how the universe might have appeared one billion years ago. Then, describe the universe during this same period based on the oscillating-universe and steady-state theories. How would the descriptions be different if you described the universe as it might have appeared ten billion years ago? Fifteen billion years ago?

4. Testing the Theories

Implications and observations. Of course, there is no way of going back several billion years in time to find out which (if any) of the three theories is correct. Nevertheless, there are some ways to check them. Each theory implies something about conditions in the universe of today. The implications are difficult to determine, and even if they are determined, they cannot be used to prove a theory. A theory cannot be proven correct. However, the implications might indicate that a theory is incorrect. In that case, the incorrect theory must be modified or discarded.

Suppose our observations check with the implications of one of the theories. Although that supports the theory, it is not conclusive proof. There might be other theories—not yet proposed—which would lead to the same implications and which would check just as well with our observations. On the other hand, suppose our observations disagree with the implications of a theory. Then it is probably safe to throw out the theory and not worry about it any more.

Many scientists feel that this philosophy is true for all of science. That is, they feel that the real basis of science is the possibility of using experiments and observations to *disprove* theories. Proof of any particular scientific theory can never be absolute, because there is always the chance that a still better theory will come along later. However, we can say with certainty that one or another theory is definitely wrong if it does not agree with our observations.

Is there any way by which an astronomer can detect an event that is happening in the Andromeda galaxy at this very instant?

Quasars and the steady-state theory. According to the steady-state theory, all portions of the universe should appear the same when the universe is viewed as a whole. This should be true no matter when we view the universe. Distant galaxies should have the same characteristics as nearby galaxies. If any differences between the distant galaxies and the nearby ones can be detected, this will be a strong point against the steady-state theory.

For many years, astronomers have tried to find some differences by searching among the faint objects in the sky. They hoped that perhaps the distant galaxies would be packed more closely together than those nearby. Or, perhaps the temperature or spectra of distant galaxies would indicate a difference between distant and nearby galaxies.

In general, this search has been unsuccessful. During the last few years, however, some strange, previously unknown objects have been discovered in space. These are called *Quasi-Stellar Radio Sources*, or *quasars* for short. Quasars are very unusual masses of matter. If the brightness rule is used to estimate their distances, they seem to be only a few million light-years away. But quasars have very large red shifts in their spectra. In fact, quasars have larger red shifts than any other of the galaxies observed so far. Thus, if the amount of red shift is used to estimate their distances, quasars seem to be more than a billion light-years away.

A number of quasars have been discovered, and astronomers have studied them in as much detail as is possible. Their conclusion is that quasars are indeed very distant objects. Their extra brightness is due to some peculiar physical process which is not understood. They must have some source of energy which is unfamiliar to scientists here on earth.

Quasars seem to be the kind of evidence that astronomers are looking for. Quasars are objects at very great distances from us, and they are definitely different from objects near us. As far as astronomical observations are concerned, seeing an object at a very great distance is the same thing as seeing an object a very long time ago. Something was going on a long time ago that is not happening now. This implies that the steady-state theory is wrong.

Both the big-bang theory and the oscillating-universe theory can explain (at least to some extent) the observation of the quasars. According to these theories, we would expect to find something peculiar as we look back a few billion years. This would have been nearer to the time of the big explosion, and things which we are not at all familiar with in our everyday world might have been going on then.

Velocity and the oscillating-universe theory. If the oscillating-universe theory is true, the universe will eventually stop expanding. Then gravitational force will begin to pull it back together. But, if the galaxies are moving fast enough, they will overcome the gravitational attraction which they all exert on each other. They will continue to move away from each other indefinitely, because each one of them started with a velocity greater than the *escape velocity* of the universe.

You have probably heard the term escape velocity as it applies to rockets which are sent to the moon or to the planets. If a rocket gets going fast enough as it leaves the earth, the earth's gravity cannot pull it back to the earth. Of course, after the rocket's fuel is used and it continues out away from the earth, it will be going slower and slower. But, at the same time, the force of gravity on the rocket will get weaker and weaker as the rocket gets farther away. It is like a race being run by two runners, each getting more and more tired. The rocket is one runner. The farther it goes, the slower it goes because it is still being pulled back by gravity. The second runner is the force of gravity itself. The farther out the rocket gets, the weaker gravity becomes. Thus, gravity is less able to pull the rocket back. If the rocket has a fast enough start, it can win the race and escape forever from the force of the earth's gravity. In the same way, a more powerful rocket might reach a speed great enough to escape the gravity of the sun. That is, it would leave the solar system and continue on out into interstellar space.

Now, what about the galaxies? According to the big-bang and oscillating-universe theories, the material in the galaxies certainly got a fast start in the big bang. Even though this material has been clumping into galaxies and stars ever since, it is still flying outward from that start. But, is it moving with a velocity greater than escape velocity? In order to answer this question, scientists have to be able to compute the gravitational force tending to pull the galaxies back together. For a particular galaxy, this is the force exerted on it by the rest of the universe.

To compute this gravitational force, scientists need to know the masses of all the galaxies, their distances apart, and the total number of galaxies. Naturally, these things can only be estimated. Using these estimates, scientists calculate that the galaxies are, indeed, traveling outward with a velocity greater than escape velocity. Thus, the galaxies will never return. If the reasoning that led to this conclusion is right, then the oscillating-universe theory has to be discarded.

Suppose great amounts of matter, which are not known at the present time, are discovered to exist between the galaxies. What effect would this have on the calculations of the escape velocity of the receding galaxies?

Uncertainty still exists. Only the big-bang theory remains without some questionable aspect. But we cannot be too hasty about accepting it. Remember, we are trying to figure out the condition of the universe far beyond the range of even the best telescopes. We are applying the physical laws that work in our tiny solar system to the vast reaches of space where different laws may operate.

At present, the edge of the universe is far beyond the edge of our knowledge, and it is likely to be many years before we will be able to check our educated guesses with actual measurements and observations.

Checking Your Knowledge

IMPORTANT IDEAS

1. Cosmology is the study of the general nature of the universe in space and time.

2. The galaxies probably formed from huge clouds of gas and dust.

3. Distances to far-off galaxies are estimated by comparing their apparent brightness with that of galaxies at known distances.

4. One very important observation about the universe on a large scale is that the universe is expanding.

5. Experiments and observations can be used to support a theory, but not to prove it. The results of experiments and observations, however, may be used to disprove theories.

6. The three current theories about the beginning of the universe are: the big-bang theory, the oscillating-universe theory, and the steady-state theory.

7. Because each theory has shortcomings, it is impossible to say which one (if any) is an accurate explanation.

USING NEW WORDS

Study the words listed below. On your paper write the numerals *1-4*. After each numeral write words or statements to satisfy the instructions given for the corresponding numeral.

big bang	escape velocity
cosmology	oscillating universe
steady state	quasar

1. List words which are names for the current theories of the universe.

2. Write the word which names a type of object recently discovered in space. Then, write a brief description of such an object.

3. Write the word which describes a requirement for interplanetary space travel.

4. Which word is the name given to a study of the universe in space and time?

TEST YOURSELF

Study the test below. Write the numerals *1-10* on your paper. After each of the numerals *1-3* write the word that best completes the sentence having the corresponding numeral.

1. The study of questions about the origin, history, and future of the universe as a whole is known as _____.

2. The _____ effect is responsible for the red shift in the spectrum of practically every galaxy which has been observed.

3. The discovery of quasars tends to disprove the _____ theory of the universe.

Beside each of the numerals *4-10* write a term from the following list. Make certain the term you select is closely related to the sentence having the corresponding numeral.

red shift	escape velocity
blue shift	Cepheid variable
gravitation	apparent brightness
quasars	expanding universe

4. This force causes clouds of gas and dust to condense and form galaxies.

5. This characteristic of the spectrum of a galaxy indicates that the galaxy is moving away from us.

6. This phenomenon is probably the most important observation ever made about the universe as a whole.

7. This name is given to very distant, very luminous, recently discovered objects in space.

8. This type of star is useful in determining the distances of nearby galaxies.

9. This property of the light from a galaxy can be used as a basis for estimating the distance to the galaxy.

10. The theory of an oscillating universe seems doubtful because galaxies appear to be moving faster than this.

Extending Your Knowledge

QUESTIONS TO EXPLORE

1. As stated in this chapter, what are the limitations of each of the three current cosmological theories?

2. What is meant by the statement, "A look into space is a look backward in time"?

3. How is it possible to photograph an event that happened two million years ago?

4. Why is it impossible for astronomers to measure the distances to galaxies by using the parallax method?

5. Which of the current cosmological theories is often called the "continuous-creation" theory? How rapidly would matter have to be created to make this theory acceptable?

SOME THINGS TO DO

1. Look up some of the earliest theories proposed as possible origins of the universe. Have these theories been rejected? If so, for what reasons? Then compare the cosmological theories of a few decades ago with those of the present day. Use Sir James Jean's *The Mysterious Universe,* (1930), George Gamow's *The Birth and Death of the Sun,* (1940), and William Bonner's *The Mystery of the Expanding Universe,* (1964) as references.

2. Conduct a "three-sided debate." Work with two other students. Each of you learn as much about a particular cosmological theory as you can. Then have a discussion in which you present evidence which will uphold the theory you have chosen and discredit the other theories. (Remember, just because you feel you win the debate does not mean your theory is right. How correct the theory is does not depend on how good a debater you are.)

3. So far in your study of *The Earth-Space Sciences,* you have learned many things about the universe. Using this information, formulate a cosmological theory that differs from the three described in this chapter. Be prepared to defend your theory against challenges from your teacher and fellow students.

CHALLENGES IN SCIENCE

1. Give reasons why the most distant galaxies are moving the most rapidly.

2. Formulate a theory to explain the amount of radio energy given off by a quasar.

3. In the table below, the radial velocities and the distances of some galaxies outside the Local Group are given. On a piece of graph paper, mark a velocity scale on the horizontal axis and a distance scale on the vertical axis. Using ordered pairs of the form (*velocity, distance*), draw a graph showing the relation between radial velocity and distance. What does the velocity of -50 for M81 indicate? Do most of the points lie along a straight line? If so, find the slope of the line. What significance, if any, can be attached to the slope of the line? If any points are very far off the line, try to explain why.

GALAXY	RADIAL VELOCITY (Km/Sec)	DISTANCE (10^6 Light-Years)
M49	850	29
M51	250	15
M60	1100	38
M63	450	18
M64	150	7
M65	800	25
M66	650	22
M81	-50	12
M82	300	13
M83	500	15
M84	1050	30
M85	500	19
M94	300	15
M96	950	29

BREAKTHROUGHS IN SCIENCE

Sometimes a discovery of great significance has a very insignificant beginning. The discovery of radio waves coming from sources outside the earth is an example of such a discovery. The knowledge gained from these waves has had a great influence on the field of space science.

In the late 1920's Karl Jansky was assigned the task of determining the source of static in certain radio equipment. Jansky went to great lengths to determine the source of this static. He built a radio antenna that was sixty feet long and mounted on wheels so that it could be rotated. He found that, even when no earthly cause of static—such as a thunderstorm—was present, his equipment constantly hissed with static. Furthermore, the hissing reached a maximum every 23 hours and 56 minutes. This is the length of the *sidereal* (sī dir'i əl) day—the time it takes the stars to apparently go around the earth. It was reasonable to assume that the static was coming from somewhere among the stars.

After Jansky published his results in 1932, another non-astronomer, Grote Reber, became interested in these extraterrestrial radio waves. He confirmed Jansky's findings and extended the work further. Reber's work, published in 1940, attracted the attention of astronomers. World War II prevented any experimental work from being done at that time, but astronomers did much theoretical work. They began to realize that radio waves, like light waves, were bringing information to the earth from outer space. Thus Karl Jansky, while trying to improve radio communication here on earth, had tuned in on radio signals from outer space.

A scientist must be able to notice little things, even when he is not really looking for them. Karl Jansky noticed the slight hissing in his earphones and did not ignore it. His investigations laid the foundation for radio astronomy—that is, using radio waves to study the universe.

Through radio astronomy, scientists have discovered many regions in our galaxy where there is matter which had not previously been detected. These regions are called radio sources because they emit radio waves, but very little visible light. Locating these regions is resulting in a more complete knowledge of the structure of our Milky Way Galaxy. In addition, radio telescopes have been used to detect radio sources which are far beyond the Milky Way Galaxy. In fact, one type of radio source, the quasar, emits such powerful radio waves that scientists are unable to explain how these strange objects produce such large amounts of energy. Moreover, quasars are believed to be over 6 billion light-years away and traveling away from us at a speed of more than 124,000 (1.24×10^5) miles per second.

The discovery of extraterrestrial radio waves was definitely an important breakthrough in science. In the 25 years since its beginning, radio astronomy has played an important role in man's attempts to understand the universe. Scientists now have a new way to observe the universe. They have some new clues to aid them in their attempts to solve the mysteries of the universe.

REVIEWING UNIT TWO

SUMMARY

1. The discovery and use of telescopes and photography has greatly increased the scope of man's observations of the universe.

2. Stars occur in huge groups or aggregations called galaxies. Billions of such galaxies exist throughout the observable universe.

3. The Milky Way Galaxy contains our solar system, huge clouds of dust and gas, and about 1×10^{11} stars, including double stars, variable stars, novae, and clusters of stars.

4. Although the various distances to the stars are all very great, scientists have devised ways to determine the brightness, size, temperature, composition, distance, motion, and mass of many of the stars.

5. After discovering the source of a star's energy and the relationships among stars, scientists have determined a probable pattern of evolution in the life of a star.

6. The origin of the universe is still a mystery, but there are three current theories which attempt to explain the observed phenomenon of an expanding universe.

QUESTIONS TO DISCUSS

1. How can scientists learn about the chemical composition of the materials in a galaxy which is millions of light-years away?

2. What evidence is there that the universe is expanding? What, if anything, could affect our observations in the same way as the effect caused by outward motion?

3. Why, do you suppose, are questions concerning the origin of matter usually avoided by astronomers?

4. Why are scientists unwilling to assume that scientific laws in space are different from the laws which describe the behavior of matter on the earth?

UNIT TEST

Study the test below. On your paper write the numerals *1-10*. After each numeral write the correct response to that part of the test with the corresponding numeral.

1. A time interval of (*exactly, a little less than, a little more than*) 24 hours occurs between two successive appearances of the same star directly overhead.

2. Of the stars represented in an H-R diagram, the hottest ones would be (*red giants, white dwarfs, stars like our sun*).

3. A situation in which a star the size of our sun is located in a galaxy like the Milky Way Galaxy (*very likely occurs, may possibly occur, could never occur*) somewhere else in the universe.

4. Parallax cannot be used to measure the distance to a galaxy because (*there are too many galaxies, galaxies are too far away, galaxies are too dim*).

5. The most dense stars—that is, stars with the most mass for their size—are (*main-sequence stars, red giants, white dwarfs*).

Beside each of the numerals *6-10* write a term from the list below. Make certain the term you select is closely related to the statement having the corresponding numeral.

Doppler effect   quasars
nuclear reaction   nova
Fraunhofer lines   cosmology

6. The explanation given for the red shift

7. A study of questions concerning the origin, history, and future of the universe

8. Very distant sources of radio waves

9. Characteristics of spectra which identify the elements in stellar atmospheres

10. May be a step in the formation of white dwarfs

ENRICHING YOUR SCIENCE EXPERIENCES

INVESTIGATIONS TO CARRY OUT

1. Make a spectroscope from a cigar box (or any rigid box of similar dimensions). Paint the inside of the box black. Cut a slot about ¼ inch wide and about 1 inch long in one end of the box. Tape two razor blades over this slot so that the edges of the blade form a narrow slit about 1mm or less wide. At the other end of the box, drill a hole ¾ inch in diameter. Tape a piece of plastic replica grating over the hole. Replica grating is inexpensive and can be obtained from a science supply house. The lines in the grating must be parallel to the slit formed by the razor blades. Tape the lid of the box shut with black tape to keep out stray light. Let the light from the source to be studied shine in through the slit while you observe through the grating. Use light sources of known wave lengths to calibrate your spectroscope. Devise and conduct experiments in which you use your spectroscope to observe various sources of light. Note and record the properties of each spectrum you observe.

2. Keep a record of the apparent motion of one of the bright planets as it moves relative to the background of fixed stars. Draw a diagram which represents the pattern of the background of stars. On this diagram mark the position of the planet you have selected. Also record the date. Each evening, when the weather permits, observe and record the position of the planet. Do this for several months if possible. Try to observe both the direct motion and retrograde motion of the planet.

ADDITIONAL READING IN SCIENCE

Abell, George, *Exploration of the Universe*. New York, Holt, Rinehart and Winston, Inc., 1964. 646 pp.

Arp, Halton C., "The Evolution of Galaxies." *Scientific American* (January, 1963), pp. 71-84.

Bergamini, David, *The Universe*. New York, Time Incorporated, 1962. 192 pp.

Bondi, Hermann, *The Universe at Large*. Garden City, New York, Doubleday & Co., Inc., 1960. 154 pp.

Greenstein, Jesse L., "Quasi-Stellar Radio Sources." *Scientific American* (December, 1963), pp. 54-62.

Hynek, J. Allen, and Anderson, Norman D., *Challenge of the Universe*. Englewood Cliffs, New Jersey, Scholastic Book Services, 1965, 144 pp.

Kahn, Fritz, *Design of the Universe, The Heavens and the Earth*. New York, Crown Publishers, Inc., 1954. 373 pp.

Moore, Patrick, *Naked-Eye Astronomy*. New York, W. W. Norton and Co., Inc., 1965. 253 pp.

Page, Thornton, ed., *Stars and Galaxies; Birth, Ageing, and Death in the Universe*. Englewood Cliffs, New Jersey, Prentice-Hall, Inc., 1962. 163 pp.

Zim, Herbert, *Stars*. New York, Simon & Schuster, Inc., 1956. 160 pp.

UNIT **3**

THE SOLAR SYSTEM

Chapters

Now that you have some idea of the immensity of the universe, we can again ask, "Where *do* we live?" and "How *does* our home fit into the galactic picture?" You already know that we live in the solar system and that the solar system contains the sun and a group of planets. You probably know, too, that there are other objects in the solar system, including comets, asteroids, and meteoroids. You may not have a detailed knowledge of these objects, but you do know something about them. You know, for example, that some planets are bigger than others and that the planets revolve about the sun. When you stop to think about it, you find that you know many things about the solar system that were not known—even to learned astronomers—500 years ago.

But there are still many unanswered questions about the solar system. Some day man will visit one or more of the other planets which circle the sun. What will he find there? Will he find life? Or are the other planets dead, lifeless spheres? In addition to finding out about the planets, man wants to know more about the gravitational forces within the solar system. How do gravitational forces affect motion? How are gravitational forces related to the other cosmic forces—electric, magnetic, and nuclear? This leads to one of the most interesting questions of all. How was the solar system formed?

You will explore these and other questions in UNIT 3. The laws of nature are presented in order that you may have an understanding of the origin of the solar system and how it is changing and developing today. As you study UNIT 3, you will add to your knowledge of the universe. Furthermore, you will improve your understanding of how man and his planet fit into the pattern of nature—the same pattern that includes the most remote galaxies in space.

◀ To man, the most important object in the universe is the sun—his source of energy.

KITT PEAK NATIONAL OBSERVATORY PHOTOGRAPH

CHAPTER **8**

The McMath Solar Telescope, the world's largest, is at Kitt Peak, Arizona.

The Sun

The sun is an average star. However, do not let the word "average" fool you. The sun is average only when compared with other stars. It is immense—both in mass and in volume—when compared with any other object in the solar system. Because of its obvious influence on man's life, the sun has been considered the most important heavenly body throughout man's history. In fact, the sun was the object of worship in the earliest religions. The sun has had a prominent place, not only in religion, but also in art, poetry, and magic for thousands of years. But only recently has man begun to understand the nature of the sun and the source of its almost endless supply of energy. As in many fields of science, much of our knowledge and understanding of the sun has been gained in the last two decades.

Of course, much remains to be learned about the sun and the other stars. Astronomers are happy to have an average star nearby for purposes of study. No other star can be seen well enough to observe details on its surface. Furthermore, average stars last a long time. It is unlikely that the sun will become a nova or supernova in the near future.

In this chapter, you can read about the sun. As you do, you will undoubtedly discover some things that you did not know before. For example, you will find out how conditions on the sun affect conditions here on earth. In fact, one of the main reasons for studying the sun is to learn how the sun affects us and how it fits into the overall concept of the universe.

1. Size and Temperature

A representative star. The sun is a typical star in the main sequence of the H-R diagram, as was described in Chapter 6. Actually, the sun is smaller than most of the stars that we can see in our galaxy. Nevertheless, it is a respectable member of the family. As a matter of fact, detailed observations of the sun are used in developing theories about the stars. The sun is used because the other stars are so far away that they appear only as points of light. However, when we look at the sun, we can see its surface and its atmosphere, and so study its characteristics.

As well as being a representative star, the sun is the central body of our solar system. Our own earth and all the other planets revolve about it. It is the source of heat and light and all of our energy, except for that fraction that scientists and engineers have managed to get from atomic reactions. So, as we turn from our study of the starry universe to the study of our own relatively close planetary neighbors, it is reasonable that the sun should be the turning point in our study.

If our sun were a red giant or a white dwarf, how could astronomers use it as a basis for forming theories about the stars in general?

Size, mass, and density. The sun is a ball of gas with a radius of 696,000 (6.96×10^5) kilometers (km). This is about 109 times the radius of the earth. The mass of the sun is more than 332,000 times that of the earth. Expressed more precisely, the mass of the sun is 1.99×10^{30} kilograms (kg). The sun's mass is determined from measurements of the earth's orbit.

Another property of the sun—its density—is determined by dividing the measure of the mass of the sun by the measure of its volume. (The volume of a sphere is $\frac{4}{3}\pi r^3$.) Using the information given above, the density of the sun can be calculated. The accepted value for the density of the sun is 1.41 grams per cubic centimeter (g/cm^3). A density of 1.41 g/cm^3 means that, on the average, the matter in the sun is 41 per cent more dense than water.

FIND OUT BY TRYING

Materials you will need: 3 × 5 index card, pin, ruler, sheet of paper

On the sheet of paper, draw 2 parallel lines, 2 millimeters apart. Then, with a pin, punch a hole near the center of the index card. Now hold the card in the sunlight so that the shadow of the card falls on the paper. The card and the paper should be parallel to each other and perpendicular to the rays of sunlight. If you observe carefully, you can see an image of the sun on the paper. The image is produced by the light coming through the pinhole. Move the card so that the sun's image just fills the space between the two lines. Measure the distance from the pinhole to the paper when the diameter of the image is 2 millimeters. How can you use the size of the sun's image, the distance from the pinhole to the paper, and the distance from the earth to the sun to determine the radius of the sun? How closely does the value you obtain correspond with the value given in the text?

Surface temperature. The temperature of the sun is difficult to determine. First of all, we have to decide what part of the sun we are referring to. Because the sun is a ball of gas, it has no distinct surface boundary. However, the surface we can see—the *photosphere* (fō'tə sfir)—is usually picked as the surface to talk about.

There are two ways to determine the temperature of the photosphere. One way is to use the sun's color, just as is done for other stars. The intensity of various colors (wave lengths) of the light from the sun is measured by passing the light through colored filters. Then, a graph is drawn from the data collected. Such a graph is shown in *A* of *Figure 8-1*. In *B* of *Figure 8-1* there are two curves. One is labeled 5,750°K and the other is labeled 6,000°K. These curves were developed by using the laws of theoretical physics. They indicate the intensity of the various wave lengths in the light being emitted by objects at the indicated temperatures. These curves represent the radiations of imaginary objects which are perfect radiators—that is, objects which have no color themselves, but radiate as easily in one wave length as another. The apparent color of such imaginary bodies depends only on their temperature. In *C* of *Figure 8-1*, you can see that the curve of the sun's radiation is nearly like that of a perfect radiator at 6,000°K. Thus, according to the color of the sun, its temperature is about 6,000°K.

A second method of determining the sun's temperature depends on a knowledge of the size of the sun and of the total amount of energy it emits. Using this information, scientists can compute the temperature the sun must have. But, measuring the total amount of energy from the sun is difficult here at the surface of the earth. Some of the energy is absorbed by the earth's atmosphere before it reaches us. However, by using balloons and rockets

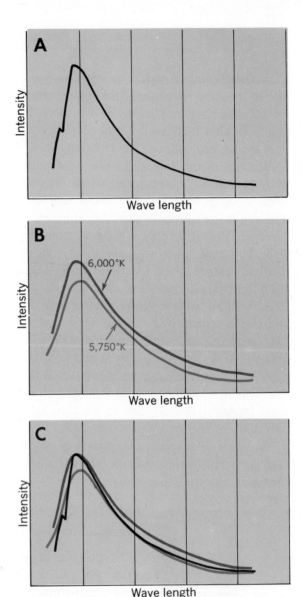

Figure 8-1. These curves represent an analysis of the color (wave length) of the light emitted by certain glowing objects. The curve in A is of the sun's light. The curves of the light from two imaginary, perfect radiators are shown in B. Such perfect radiators are called "black bodies" by scientists. Data for curves of black-body radiation are obtained mathematically, not by experiment. In C the curve of the sun's light is superimposed on the curves of the light from the two perfect radiators.

to carry instruments high above the earth, scientists can make accurate measurements of the sun's energy output.

Unfortunately, the second method does not give the same temperature as the first, but 5,750°K instead. This temperature is usually given as the temperature of the sun's photosphere. Remember, however, that the photosphere is not a true surface. It is simply a layer of hot gases that radiates the light we see. Careful measurements indicate that this layer is about 300 km thick. Using color as an indicator, scientists have found that the temperature at the outer portion of this layer appears to be about 4,300°K, rising to above 6,000°K near the inner portion.

How would you explain why the temperature of the sun, as derived by one method, is slightly different from the temperature derived by a different method?

Interior temperature. The temperatures inside the sun are, of course, much higher than the temperatures at the sun's surface. In a star, there is an equilibrium between the gravitational force which tends to pull the star together and the outward pressure caused by heat and light which tends to increase the size of the star. Energy is being generated inside the sun and emitted by radiation at its surface. Therefore, the inside must be hotter than the surface.

In order to calculate the temperature at the center of the sun, the composition of the sun must be known. Scientists would have to know what elements are there in order to figure out the weight of the material pressing down from above on any interior point. From their analysis of the sun's spectrum, scientists estimate that the mass of the sun is 75 per cent hydrogen and 23 per cent helium, with all the other elements making up the remaining 2 per cent. Using this estimate, together with measurements of the energy the sun is radiating away, the temperature at the center of the sun is calculated to be 25 million degrees Fahrenheit or about 13 million degrees Kelvin. The pressure is 200 billion times that of the atmospheric pressure at the surface of the earth, and the density of the material at the sun's center must be 110 times as great as the density of water. Such extreme conditions are very difficult to imagine.

2. The Solar Spectrum

Elements in the sun. In the spectrum of the sun, we can identify most, but not all of the elements that are found on earth. There are a number of reasons why evidence of the presence of some elements should be missing, even if the elements are actually in the sun's atmosphere. Only certain wave lengths of radiation reach the surface of the earth. Other wave lengths are absorbed by our atmosphere. For example, ultraviolet radiation and some infrared radiation are absorbed by our atmosphere. Thus, radiation of these wave lengths never reaches the surface of the earth. Suppose the spectral lines of certain elements are in these absorbed wave lengths. Then, evidence of the presence of these elements in the sun's atmosphere cannot be observed from the earth's surface. However, rockets have been used to carry spectroscopes above the earth's atmosphere. Thus, a spectrum obtained above the atmosphere does contain light which is ordinarily absorbed by the earth's atmosphere.

What portions of the spectrum, which were not used 50 years ago, are now being used by astronomers in their studies?

Another problem in analysis of the solar spectrum is that some of the elements are present in such small proportions that their spectral lines are too weak for us to see. (A weak spectral line is one that is very faint and not easy to see. A strong spectral line is one that shows up very plainly.) To overcome this problem, scientists and engineers are constantly designing and building better spectroscopes and more sensitive light-measuring instruments.

Suppose some spectral lines are missing because the elements which produce these lines are present in a very small proportion. Does this mean that a very strong spectral line indicates that the corresponding element makes up a large proportion of the sun's atmosphere? For example, look at the lines marked Sodium in the picture of the solar spectrum in *Figure 8-2*. These lines are very strong. Is there a large proportion of sodium in the sun's atmosphere?

As a matter of fact, sodium is a common element in the sun and on the earth. But, in general, we cannot assume the strength of a spectral line to be proportional to the relative abundance of that particular element. In dark-line spectra, the lines of one element may be stronger than the lines of another element, even if the elements are present in the same amounts. For example, suppose light were passed through a gas composed of equal amounts of sodium vapor and calcium vapor. If the light were then dispersed into a spectrum, the characteristic dark lines for both these elements would be present. However, the lines would be of different strengths, even though the mixture was precisely fifty-fifty.

Relative abundance. Suppose a scientist wishes to use the sun's spectrum to figure out relative abundances of the elements in the sun's atmosphere. First, the characteristic absorption strength of each element must be measured in a laboratory. Then, the strengths of the lines in the solar spectrum can be compared with the strengths of the lines in the laboratory measurements. Based on such comparisons, scientists can make fairly accurate

Figure 8-2. Shown below is a small segment of the sun's spectrum. In this segment of the solar spectrum, there are two very strong lines. By comparing the solar spectrum with various spectra produced in the laboratory, scientists have determined that the presence of the element sodium in the sun's atmosphere causes these two strong lines. Although the other lines in this spectrum are not labeled, scientists have also determined which elements cause these other spectral lines in the sun's spectrum. Thus, the chemical composition of the sun's atmosphere has been determined.

PHOTOGRAPH FROM THE MOUNT WILSON AND PALOMAR OBSERVATORIES

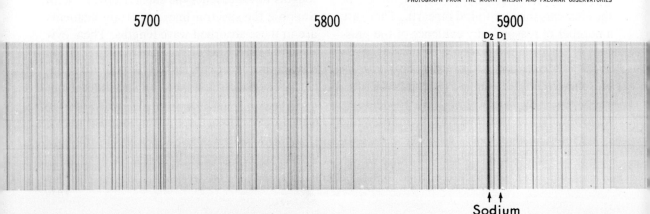

5700   5800   5900

D_2 D_1

↑ ↑
Sodium

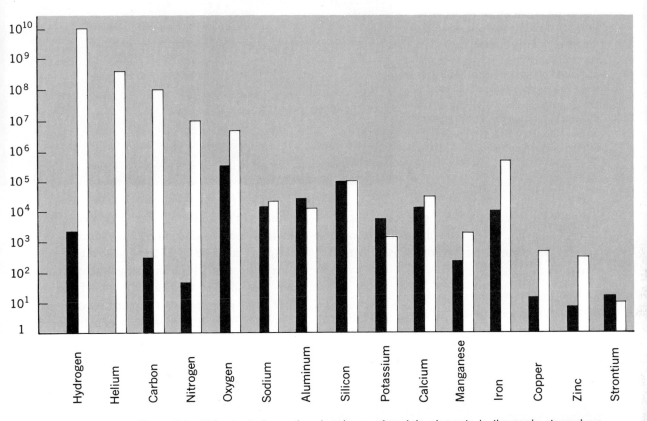

Figure 8-3. This chart shows the abundance of certain elements in the sun's atmosphere (white) and their abundance in the earth's crust (black). The abundance is given in terms of the number of atoms of each element per 100,000 (1 x 10^5) atoms of silicon. For some elements, the white column is about the same height as the black column. In other words, the abundance of these elements is about the same in the earth's crust as it is in the sun's atmosphere. However, there are some striking differences. These differences are important, and they show up particularly well in the relative abundances of hydrogen and helium. In fact, helium is so scarce in the earth's crust that there is less than 1 atom of helium in the earth's crust per 100,000 atoms of silicon there.

estimates of the relative abundances of the various elements in the atmosphere of the sun. *(Figure 8-3.)*

The spectroscope also reveals information about how the different elements are distributed over the surface of the sun. From a spectrum which has been spread out by using a spectroscope, one particular wave length can be selected. Then, a picture of the sun can be taken using light of that wave length alone.

Such a picture—called a *spectroheliogram* (spek'trō hē'li ə gram)—is shown in *Figure 8-4*. One photograph of the sun was taken in ordinary sunlight, but the other photograph was taken by using the light from only one spectral line of hydrogen. As is indicated by the various intensities of the light, there are regions on the sun where the hydrogen gas is either hotter or denser than in other regions. The hydrogen is certainly not spread uniformly

Figure 8-4. Each of the photographs at the right is of the sun. However, the one farthest to the right is a spectroheliogram. That is, only one particular wave length of light was used to expose the film. Such photographs are useful in studying the distribution in the sun's photosphere of the element which produces light of the wave length used.

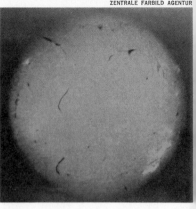

over the surface. A detailed picture of a portion of the sun, taken with light of this same special wave length of hydrogen, is shown in *Figure 8-5*.

Figure 8-5. The sun's surface, as shown in the spectroheliogram below, resembles a picture of clouds over the surface of the earth. The swirling pattern in the gases is very similar to the pattern of a hurricane in our own atmosphere.

PHOTOGRAPH FROM THE MOUNT WILSON AND PALOMAR OBSERVATORIES

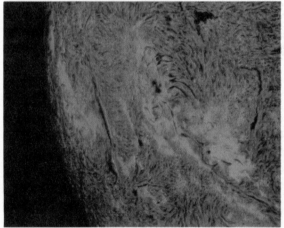

The sun's rotation. The Doppler effect, which is used to determine the speed of galaxies, can also be used to measure the rotation of the sun. By comparing the spectrum from one edge of the sun with that from the other edge, scientists can detect that one edge is moving toward the earth, while the other is moving away.

A picture of a portion of such a spectral comparison is shown in *Figure 8-6*. The upper and lower spectra are of the west edge of the sun. The middle spectra is of the east edge. Lines in the sun's spectrum are marked by arrows. You can see the slight shift. Using the Doppler effect and this method of observing the solar spectrum, it was discovered that the sun rotates in 24.7 days at its equator and in 34 days near its north and south poles.

What is one way by which astronomers can determine which absorption lines are caused by elements in the sun's atmosphere and which are caused by elements in the earth's atmosphere?

Figure 8-6. On this small portion of the solar spectrum, the lines marked with arrows are shifted slightly. The shift is caused by the rotation of the sun. Some lines, however, are not shifted. How would you explain this?

PHOTOGRAPH FROM THE MOUNT WILSON AND PALOMAR OBSERVATORIES

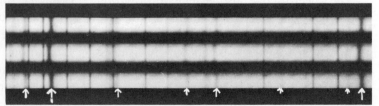

3. Sunspots and Solar Prominences

Sunspots and magnetism. When astronomers began using telescopes to examine the sun, one of their first discoveries was the occurrence of *sunspots*. Sunspots are spots on the sun's surface which appear black compared with the rest of the surface. *(Figure 8-7.)* CAUTION: Do not look at the sun without using the proper protection. Looking at the sun directly can cause very serious damage to the eyes. Using binoculars to observe the sun increases the danger of eye damage. With a medium-sized telescope, the result could be permanent blindness. A good book on amateur astronomy will contain some techniques for examining the sun safely.

The nature of sunspots, although they were discovered some three hundred years ago, remains as something of a mystery today. No one knows how sunspots are formed. During the last few years, however, scientists have gathered quite a bit of information on which to base new theories about sunspots.

One of the most important measurements is that of the magnetic field around a sunspot. In addition to all the other information that is revealed through spectrum analysis, the solar spectrum can also yield information about the sun's magnetic field. For some elements, the amount of space between certain spectral lines depends on the magnetic field in the gas that is producing the spectrum. By analyzing the light from only a small portion of the sun's surface at a time, and by measuring the spacing between the special spectral lines, a map of the magnetic field of the sun can be made. *(Figure 8-8.)*

As *Figure 8-8* reveals, the magnetic field on the surface of the sun is not at all regular. Instead, very strong north and south magnetic poles show up from time to time in various regions, and then disappear. Such strong fields always appear around sunspots.

Why do sunspots appear to be dark areas on the sun's photosphere? If the whole photosphere were the same temperature as a sunspot, would the sun be black?

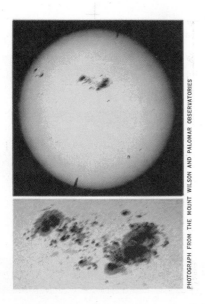

PHOTOGRAPH FROM THE MOUNT WILSON AND PALOMAR OBSERVATORIES

Figure 8-7. The photograph of the sun's disk (top) shows an exceptionally large sunspot. An enlarged view of the same large sunspot is shown in the bottom picture.

Figure 8-8. A small area near a sunspot group on the surface of the sun is represented below. The polarity and the strength of the magnetic field on two separate days are indicated. How does the sun's magnetic field differ from that of the earth?

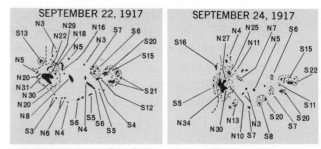

Observe sunspots

Use a telescope (or one side of a pair of binoculars) to project an image of the sun on a piece of paper. CAUTION: Do not look through the eyepiece while the telescope (or the pair of binoculars) is pointed at the sun. Instead, while the telescope is pointed at the sun, hold a sheet of white paper about 20 or 30 centimeters from the eyepiece. Focus the telescope so that a clear image of the sun appears on the paper. Sunspots will be observed as dark spots on the image. Observe the sun on several consecutive days. Do the sunspots stay in the same position? If not, do they all move in the same direction?

Solar prominences. Another phenomenon that often occurs near a sunspot is a *solar prominence. (Figure 8-9.)* Solar prominences are gigantic streamers of hot gas. These streamers are often seen more than 200,000 (2×10^5) miles—or 320,000 (3.2×10^5) km —above the surface of the sun. These prominences can be seen most easily near the edge of the sun, but they can also be seen against its face. In fact, the thin, long, dark lines stretching across the spectroheliogram in *Figure 8-5* are such prominences.

Scientists are certain that these streams of hot gas, the sunspots near them, and the strong, local magnetic fields in the same vicinity are all related in some way. It would seem that, by now, scientists would have enough knowledge of atoms, hot gases, and magnetism to figure out what is happening at the sun's surface. After all, it was almost a hundred years ago that the famous British scientist, James Clerk Maxwell, figured out the mathematical equations that describe how matter, electricity, and magnetism are related.

Unfortunately, although Maxwell's equations seem quite simple, their solution for some problems is very difficult. Even the best computers cannot handle them. Problems about the atmosphere of the sun are among these very difficult problems.

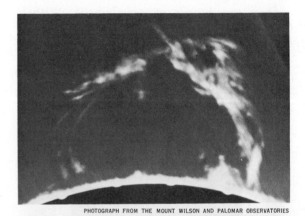

PHOTOGRAPH FROM THE MOUNT WILSON AND PALOMAR OBSERVATORIES

PHOTOGRAPH FROM THE MOUNT WILSON AND PALOMAR OBSERVATORIES

Figure 8-9. The top picture is of a large solar prominence that occurred July 2, 1957. The bottom picture shows the entire disk of the sun, with several prominences visible.

Ionized gases. In the sun's hot atmosphere, many of the atoms of gas are *ionized* (ī′ə nīzd). An atom is ionized when one (or more) of its electrons has broken loose from the atom and is moving about with its negative electrical charge. What remains of the atom, called an *ion* (ī′ən), is left with a positive electrical charge, and it is also moving about. The result is a gas which conducts electricity very well.

Scientists and electrical engineers know a great deal about electricity and its effects in the electrical equipment which they design and build. They can figure out the relationship between the electric currents and the magnetic fields in electrical circuits. But in most circuits, the wires are tied down, and they are of a known size. In addition, the amount of current flowing through the wires can be regulated or at least measured.

On the surface of the sun, however, things are not so simple. The electric currents are conducted by streams of gas. As these electrified gases move, they create magnetic fields. The magnetic fields cause forces between various gas streams. These forces change the motion of the streams. The change in motion of the streams causes a change in the magnetic fields which, in turn, produces another change in the forces affecting the gas, and so on.

Solar prominences, for example, seem to be great streams of dense, ionized gas moving through a portion of the sun's atmosphere where the pressure is normally very low. Careful observation of prominences indicates that these streams of gas bring gas down out of the atmosphere to the surface of the sun. Rather than flames shooting up from the sun, they seem to be slightly cooled masses of gas descending to the sun's surface. They carry an electric current as they move—creating magnetic fields and, in turn, being shaped by these same magnetic fields.

4. The Solar Wind and the Corona

Solar flares. Near sunspots there are often sudden increases in the brightness of the sun's surface. These increases in brightness are called *solar flares. (Figure 8-10.)* Usually when such a flare occurs on the surface of the sun, there is a reaction here on earth. About one and a half or two days after the flare is detected on the sun, there are small but important changes in the earth's magnetic field. Quite often, radio signals are affected, and it becomes impossible to transmit radio messages long distances over the earth.

Rockets and satellites are now used to investigate solar flares. These spacecraft carry instruments high above the earth's atmosphere. Data collected by these instruments have revealed that whenever a solar flare occurs,

Figure 8-10. A large solar flare, such as the one shown here, can temporarily affect the magnetic field of the earth. On the earth, interference in radio communications and a glow in the upper layers of the atmosphere are two noticeable effects of solar flares.

PHOTOGRAPH FROM THE MOUNT WILSON AND PALOMAR OBSERVATORIES

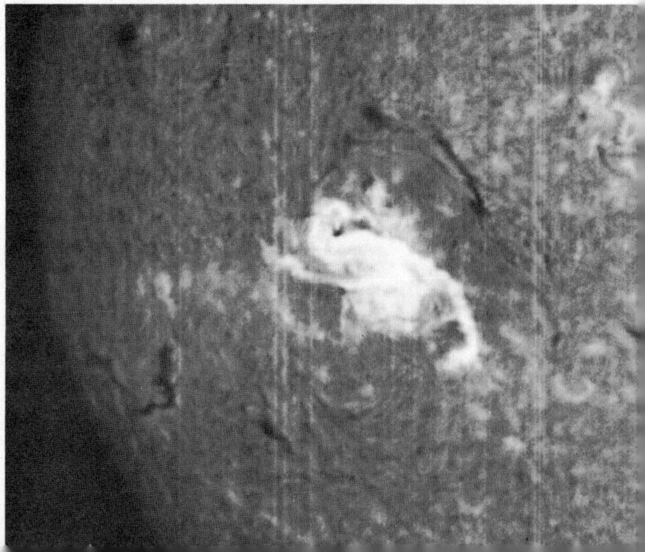

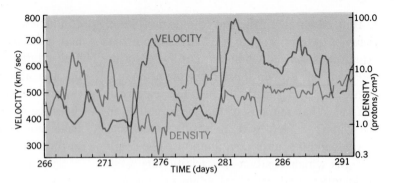

Figure 8-11. *Mariner II* collected these data about the number of particles per cubic centimeter in the solar wind and about the velocities of these particles. The data were collected from the 266th day until the 292nd day in 1962—that is, from late September to late October.

streams of charged particles are detected moving away from the sun. These charged particles travel through space at about 2,500 kilometers per second (km/sec), and so reach the earth in about 18 hours.

Because they are electrically charged, the motion of these particles through space is actually an electric current. This electric current has a magnetic field associated with it. When the particles reach the region near the earth, the electric current and the magnetic field interact with the magnetic field of the earth. This interaction causes disturbances which we detect here on the surface of the earth. Some of the effects of these disturbances are radio static, erratic motion of a compass needle, and a glow in the upper atmosphere of the earth.

Many people need to know when a solar flare has occurred so that preparations can be made for the effects. For this reason, one radio station in France sends out a daily bulletin on the condition of the sun.

Whenever solar flares cause a glow in the earth's upper atmosphere, that glow is more noticeable near the poles of the earth. How would you explain this?

The nature of the solar wind. The streams of charged particles that are associated with solar flares are only part of a steady wind of charged particles—the *solar wind*—which

is always moving away from the surface of the sun. Even when there are no sunspots, flares, or other disturbances on the sun's surface, there is a steady stream of charged particles moving away from the sun in all directions. Most of these particles are protons—the nuclei of hydrogen atoms. This is reasonable, since most of the gas in the solar atmosphere is hydrogen. The sun seems to be boiling away, but at a very slow rate.

Mariner II, the spacecraft which flew by Venus in the fall of 1962, carried instruments to observe the solar wind. These instruments could measure the speed and density of the particles which they encountered. A chart showing some of the data collected by these instruments is presented in *Figure 8-11.*

Study *Figure 8-11.* Then compare these data with the information we have about solar flares. The particles which shoot out whenever a solar flare occurs are traveling at 2,500 km/sec, or five times as fast as most of the particles measured by *Mariner II.* The density of particles in the streams associated with solar flares is also higher, between 100 and 1,000 particles per cubic centimeter.

In this instance, density has a different meaning than it has when the density of the sun is given as 1.41 g/cm³. Space is so nearly like a vacuum that its density in g/cm³ is insignificant. It is more meaningful to know how many particles there are in a certain volume than it is to know the mass of the particles in that volume.

How, do you suppose, does the density of the solar wind compare with the density of the earth's atmosphere at sea level? At an altitude of two miles?

The corona. Where do the particles in the solar wind come from? Do they come from the surface of the sun itself? Perhaps not. The sun has around it a tenuous but very far-reaching atmosphere called the *corona* (kə rō′nə). A picture of the corona taken during an eclipse is shown in *Figure 8-12*. Of course, special equipment enables astronomers to view the corona any day, and not just during an eclipse.

The corona may be the source of the solar wind. The particles of the solar wind may be speeded up by electric and magnetic forces in the corona and thus be fired off into space. On the other hand, it may be that the corona is actually part of the solar wind, which starts at the surface of the sun. If so, the corona is not a stable atmosphere surrounding the sun the way our atmosphere surrounds the earth. Instead, the corona would be a cloud of streaming gas, constantly moving away from the sun in all directions.

The corona glows for two reasons. Near the sun the particles are more dense—that is, there are more particles per cubic centimeter. Part of the glow is sunlight being scattered by these particles. The corona also glows because of its own high temperature. In fact, for reasons that are still not understood, the corona is much hotter than the photosphere. The temperature of the corona may be more than one million degrees Kelvin. As the gas which composes the corona streams out into space, however, it expands and cools until it is no longer visible.

Whatever the source of the solar wind and whatever the cause of the flares and sunspots, one thing is certain. The surface and the atmosphere of the sun are very stormy, turbulent regions. They are regions which are beset with electrical storms and rapidly changing magnetic fields. Scientists are still a long way from having a completely accurate picture of the region near the sun's surface. But perhaps this is not too surprising. After all, the sun is 93 million miles away. Scientists have yet to explain the lightning bolts in a summer thunderstorm here on earth. And these storms are often close enough to cause us considerable discomfort.

Figure 8-12. The corona may be seen during a total eclipse. At other times, the dim glow of the corona is lost in the bright light from the photosphere.

Figure 8-13. This astronomer is using a piece of equipment called a coronagraph, with which the sun's corona may be observed whenever the sun is visible.

155

Checking Your Knowledge

IMPORTANT IDEAS

1. Our sun is an average star, representative of the main sequence on the H-R diagram.

2. The temperature of the sun's photosphere is very high, but the temperature of its interior is even higher.

3. The sun's mass is about 75% hydrogen, 23% helium, and 2% other elements.

4. The sun and its atmosphere contain the same elements which are present on earth.

5. Atoms in the sun are ionized.

6. Sunspots, solar flares, and prominences reveal the sun's surface to be very stormy.

7. There seems to be a close connection between sunspots, flares, prominences, and the sun's changing magnetic field.

8. There is a constant stream of particles —the solar wind—moving away from the sun in all directions.

9. The corona is a very tenuous and far-reaching atmosphere which surrounds the sun.

USING NEW WORDS

Study the words listed below. On your paper write the numerals *1-4*. After each numeral write words or statements to satisfy the instructions given for the corresponding numeral.

solar prominence	ionize
spectroheliogram	solar wind
photosphere	sunspot
solar flare	corona

1. Write the words related to electrically charged particles. Tell how they are related.

2. Which word refers to a photograph of the sun? How is this special photograph different from an ordinary photograph of the sun?

3. Write the words which name portions of the sun or its atmosphere.

4. Which words are names of visible disturbances about the sun's surface?

TEST YOURSELF

Study the test below. Write the numerals *1-10* on your paper. After each numeral write the correct response to that part of the test having the corresponding numeral.

1. The most abundant element in the sun is the element _____.

2. The surface of the sun which is visible and can be observed under normal conditions is called the _____.

3. An atom is said to be _____ when one (or more) of its electrons has broken loose from the atom.

4. The _____, which is best seen during a total eclipse of the sun, is a very tenuous and a very far-reaching region of the sun's atmosphere.

5. A constant stream of charged particles, called the _____, has been detected moving away from the sun in all directions.

6. The average density of the sun is *(the same as, greater than, less than)* the density of water.

7. If you could somehow take a trip to the center of the sun, you would find that the temperature *(becomes higher, becomes lower, remains the same)* as you approach the center of the sun.

8. When photographed in white light, the sun's surface is often marked with dark regions called *(solar flares, sunspots, solar prominences)*.

9. Close to the dark regions on the sun's surface, astronomers often see very bright, but short-lived, bursts of light called *(solar flares, sunspots, solar prominences)*.

10. Gigantic streamers of hot gases—sometimes as high as 320,000 km above the surface of the sun—are called *(solar flares, sunspots, solar prominences)*.

Extending Your Knowledge

QUESTIONS TO EXPLORE

1. How can the sun have a density greater than the density of water if it is composed of hydrogen and helium, the two elements having the simplest atoms—that is, the two atoms with the least mass?

2. If space is nearly a perfect vacuum, how does it make sense to talk about a solar wind?

3. How might our environment on earth be different if the sun were like those stars which are higher or lower on the main sequence than it is? How would these differences affect life as we know it on earth?

4. Some authors state that the sun is the source of all our energy. Is this statement accurate? Explain your answer.

SOME THINGS TO DO

1. Compute the density of the earth. Then compare the earth's density with the density of the sun. HINT: The diameter of the earth is 1.27×10^4 km. Its mass is 5.98×10^{24} kg.

2. Find out what techniques can be used for observing the sun safely. Then, using one of these techniques, observe sunspots for a period of several weeks. See if you can determine the rate of the sun's rotation from your observations. If there are no sunspots, find out why. Report your research to the class.

3. Prepare a report to the class on one of the following topics.

   a. The effects of the solar wind that are observed on the earth

   b. How the occurrence of sunspots affects our earthly environment

   c. Hazards from space radiations that are encountered during space travel

4. Find out how the magnetic fields associated with the currents flowing in two parallel wires will affect each other. Use a D.C. source

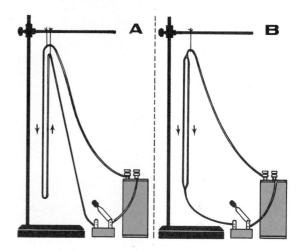

and small, insulated copper wire, (#22 or #28) arranged as shown in the diagram. Suppose the electrons in each wire are traveling in opposite directions, as in *A*. Suppose they are traveling in the same direction, as in *B*.

CHALLENGES IN SCIENCE

1. Explain what would happen if the radiation pressure (pressure of heat and light) inside the sun suddenly increased greatly. What if the radiation pressure decreased a great deal? What factors could cause a sudden increase or decrease? Is it likely that any such increases or decreases will occur within the sun in the near future?

2. Study a motion picture of solar flares. What evidence of magnetic fields can you detect? NOTE: There is a short film clip, "N 1-Solar Flares," which may be borrowed from NASA, Code FAV, Washington, D.C. 20546.

3. Suggest a model to explain why sunspots are cooler than the surrounding regions of the photosphere. Are there similar instances of temperature difference in the earth's atmosphere? If so, describe them.

The sizes and shapes of the planets were discovered through the use of telescopes.

CHAPTER 9

The Planets

To the astronomers of ancient times, the planets had the same appearance as the stars. They all appeared as points of light. Like other objects in space, planets were believed to be satellites of the earth. Because they seemed to move about among the stars, however, the planets were observed more carefully. With the invention of the telescope, the study of the planets became even more intensive. Using telescopes, man could see the sizes and shapes of the planets. They were no longer thought of as stars. Astronomers realized that the planets—including the earth—were satellites of the sun. Astronomers wanted to find out how the other planets were like the earth and how they were different.

As you study this chapter, you will discover some of what is already known about the planets. You will find out how information about the planets is obtained. Keep in mind, however, that one chapter is not going to make you an expert on the planets. Whole books have been written about just one planet. One purpose of this chapter is to introduce you to a subject which you may find fascinating and one which you may wish to continue to explore.

1. Size and Density

Observing the planets. The solar system contains bodies of many kinds and sizes. In addition to the sun, there are the planets with their moons. There are comets, asteroids, meteorites, and dust particles. There are charged particles coming from the sun, and cosmic rays coming from distant parts of space. The solar system also contains electric fields, magnetic fields, and, of course, light of all possible wave lengths. But of all of these members of the sun's family, the ones easiest to see are the planets. So far, nine planets (counting the earth) have been discovered.

The first astronomers, with no telescopes to help them, saw the planets as points of light, just as they saw the stars. But there was a difference between the two. The stars always appeared in the same patterns, night after night, year after year. The planets, on the other hand, moved around among these patterns. Furthermore, this motion was not regular. For example, they observed that Mars moved more or less steadily from west to east within the pattern of the stars for several months. Then, in a period of a few days, it reversed its direction of motion, and went from east to west for a few weeks. Then it reversed again, taking up once more its west-to-east motion. Such retrograde motion is illustrated in *Figure 3-7.*

Explaining retrograde motion was a great problem for the ancient astronomers. How they solved that problem will be discussed later. Now, the planets themselves will be described, particularly what has been learned about them in more recent times through the use of telescopes and spacecraft.

The telescope has enabled man to see the planets more clearly. In addition, the telescope made possible the discovery of three

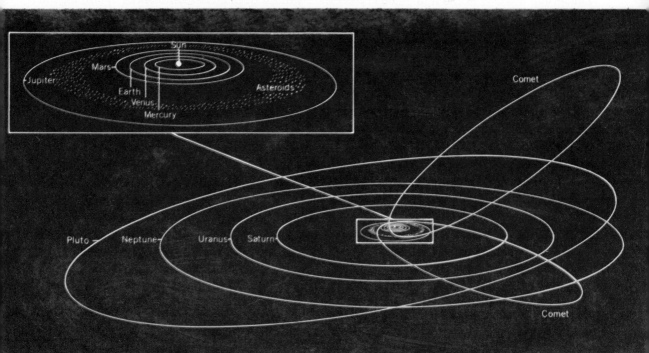

Figure 9-1. The planetary orbits within the solar system are diagramed below. Using Kepler's laws and the laws formulated by Newton and Einstein, modern scientists can explain all the observed aspects of the planets' orbital motions.

Figure 9-2. These photographs of Pluto were taken twenty-four hours apart. Pluto (indicated by the arrows) is so small and dim that it can hardly be distinguished from the faint stars on the photographs. However, its motion reveals that Pluto is a planet.

planets. The most distant one, Pluto, was discovered only thirty years ago. Since that time, there have been a few astronomers who have searched the sky for evidence of a still more distant planet. So far, their search has been without success.

Size and density. One of the first things that the telescope revealed about the planets was a great difference in size. On the basis of size, the planets seem to be divided into two distinct groups. One of these groups is called the *terrestrial* (tə res′tri əl) *planets.* This group consists of the four planets closest to the sun. The smallest of these is Mercury, having a diameter only 40 per cent as large as

that of the earth. The largest is the earth itself. The planets in the other group are called the *Jovian* (jō′vi ən) *planets,* meaning the "Jupiter-like" planets. This group includes all the planets from Jupiter out through Neptune. The sizes of the planets and some other information about them is given in the table in *Figure 9-3.* The largest one—Jupiter—has a diameter more than eleven times the diameter of the earth. The smallest is Neptune with a diameter about four times as great as the earth's diameter. Notice that the size of Pluto is not known. Thus, we cannot say with certainty which group it belongs in.

The table also shows the average density of each of the planets. Here again, you will notice a difference between the terrestrial planets and the Jovian planets. The terrestrial planets all have a high density—higher than the average density of the rocks here on the surface of the earth which is 2.8 g/cm³. But the Jovian planets have a low density—most of them being only a little more dense than water. Saturn, with an average density of 0.69 g/cm³, is even less dense than water.

This striking contrast between the two groups of planets—differences in size together with differences in density—is an important feature of the solar system. Scientists believe

Figure 9-3. Data about the planets are summarized in this table. Certain data about Pluto have not been determined. Thus, Pluto cannot be classified as a terrestrial or a Jovian planet.

| NAME | MASS (Compared to Earth) | RADIUS (Compared to Earth) | DISTANCE FROM THE SUN (In A.U.) | | | PERIOD (Time in Years) | AVERAGE DENSITY (g/cm³) |
			Closest Point	Farthest Point	Average Distance		
Mercury	0.055	0.40	0.31	0.47	0.39	0.24	5.61
Venus	0.81	0.99	0.72	0.72	0.72	0.62	5.16
Earth	1.00	1.00	0.98	1.02	1.00	1.00	5.52
Mars	0.107	0.53	1.38	1.66	1.52	1.88	3.95
Jupiter	317.4	11.19	4.97	5.47	5.22	11.9	1.34
Saturn	95.03	9.35	9.07	10.13	9.60	29.3	0.69
Uranus	14.50	3.72	18.32	20.14	19.23	84.1	1.36
Neptune	17.2	3.50	29.8	30.4	30.1	165	1.30
Pluto	Unknown	Unknown	29.6	49.2	39.4	248	Unknown

that the reasons for these differences must be directly related to the processes going on at the time the solar system formed. Somehow, matter composed of more massive atoms was concentrated into comparatively small bodies near the sun. At the same time, matter with the least massive atoms became part of the much larger bodies farther from the sun.

What ways do you know of or can you think of to classify the planets other than as terrestrial and Jovian?

DO IT YOURSELF

Make a scale drawing

Use the information in *Figure 9-3* to make a scale drawing of the distances within the solar system. Locate the sun near one corner of a large sheet of paper. Select a suitable scale and mark off distances which represent the distances from the sun to each of the planets. Using the same scale, what would be the sizes of the sun and the planets? Could commonplace objects (Ping-pong balls, peas, pinheads, and so on) be used to represent the sun and each planet? If so, place these objects in their proper places on your scale drawing. If not, explain why. Then select a different scale with which commonplace objects could be used to show the relative sizes of the sun and the planets.

Determining mass. The diameter of most planets in the solar system can be measured with the aid of telescopes. But how, you may ask, is the mass of a distant planet measured? The same methods must be used that are used to calculate the masses of double stars and to calculate the mass of the sun. To determine the mass of any body in space, we must first find a second body which goes about it in an orbit. In other words, we must find a satellite of the body. Then, the characteristics of the satellite's orbit will enable us to calculate the mass of the larger body.

Fortunately, most of the planets have moons revolving about them. The orbit of any one of these moons will give the information needed to calculate the mass of the planet it is circling, at least if the moon is small compared to the planet. The earth has one moon, of course, and Mars has two. Jupiter has twelve moons, making this planet and its satellites almost like another solar system.

Two of the twelve are larger than our own moon. Saturn has a set of ten moons and also its famous rings, which are shown in *Figure 3-12*. Uranus has five moons, and Neptune has two.

How can astronomers determine the masses of Mercury and Venus, neither of which has moons? In order to measure the mass of either of these planets, astronomers must wait until an asteroid happens to go close by on its elliptical orbit about the sun. If an asteroid should come close to Mercury, for example, astronomers can measure how much the gravitational force of Mercury changes the orbit of the asteroid. From this information, they can calculate the mass of Mercury.

But an asteroid does not pass near a planet very often. Even when one does, its distance from the planet is several million miles, and the deviation in the asteroid's orbit is slight. Thus, the mass of Mercury is not as accurately known as the masses of the other planets.

161

JPL PHOTO   JPL PHOTO

The mass of Venus, too, was not well established, until 1962. Then the spacecraft *Mariner II*—shown in *Figure 9-4*—went past Venus at a distance of only a few thousand miles. By tracking the spacecraft with radio telescopes at that time, scientists were able to get the data they needed for a much more accurate calculation of the mass of Venus.

2. Copernicus and Kepler

The Ptolemaic system. The early astronomers were convinced that the earth was the center of the universe and that all things revolved about it. It is easy to understand this belief, since that is the way events in the sky appear to happen. The sun, the moon, and all the stars do seem to be moving steadily in circles about the earth. Furthermore, these observations agreed with their philosophy. It was the belief of Greek philosophers that all things in the sky must be perfect, and a circle was the most perfect form. Thus, it seemed sensible to them that everything in the sky should move in circles with the earth at the center. Only one thing, the retrograde motion of the planets, did not fit into their idea.

Finally in A.D. 130, in Egypt, the brilliant astronomer *Ptolemy* (tol'ə mē) figured out a system which explained these strange motions of the planets. At the same time, his system preserved the idea of perfect circles in the sky with the earth at the center.

The concept which bears his name—the *Ptolemaic* (tol'ə mā'ik) *system*—is illustrated in *Figure 9-5*. Instead of saying that each planet—Mars, for example—revolved about the earth in a circle, as the astronomers before him had believed, Ptolemy pictured a circle—called the *deferent* (def'ər ənt)—along which an imaginary point moved in a regular manner. Centered on this imaginary point was still another circle called the *epicycle* (ep'ə sī kəl). Mars moved on this epicycle, as shown in the diagram. It was thought of as one wheel turning around another wheel. The resulting motion very nearly reproduced the observed pattern of the planets' motions through the stars. Ptolemy drew a separate deferent and a separate epicycle for each of the six planets which were known in his time.

In the Ptolemaic system, would the sun's apparent motion about the earth have an epicycle, or just a deferent? Why?

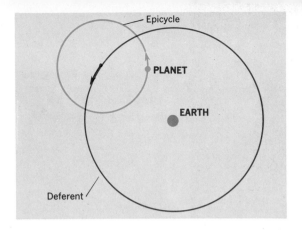

Figure 9-5. The Ptolemaic system is a geocentric (earth-centered) system. If just the right speeds are assigned to the center of the epicycle and to the planet, the resulting motion is very nearly the same as the observed retrograde motion of the planet.

The Copernican system. Although we realize now that the Ptolemaic system was wrong, it was a magnificent piece of theoretical work. It is still recognized as a triumph of scientific reasoning. Fourteen centuries passed before Nicholaus Copernicus, a Polish astronomer, destroyed this beautiful theory by showing that the sun, not the earth, is the center of the solar system. In the Copernican system, the earth—like the other planets—moves in an orbit about the sun. *(Figure 9-6.)*

Unfortunately, some of the scientists who followed Copernicus were accused of religious heresy. During the preceding fourteen centuries, the Ptolemaic system had somehow become a part of religious belief. Anyone who disagreed with it was looked upon as a criminal by the very powerful religious leaders of the day.

But, this was the beginning of one of the most exciting periods of history—the *Renaissance* (ren′ə säns). Men were getting new ideas about themselves and about the universe in which they lived. They were beginning to understand the value and power of scientific research compared to ancient superstition. Thus, although the Ptolemaic system was still taught in universities for another 100 years, the Copernican system not only lived, but slowly grew. Today, the Copernican system is recognized as a milestone in the history of human thought.

Figure 9-6. Copernicus proposed a heliocentric (sun-centered) model of the solar system in 1543. Some details of his model have been revised. However, the important concept—that of the central sun—is accepted today as the correct model of the solar system.

DO IT YOURSELF

Make a comparison

Find out what you can about the ideas of Copernicus and of Ptolemy. Use encyclopedias and other reference books. Imagine you are a scholar in the Renaissance and have no telescope. What arguments would you give to support the Copernican system? The Ptolemaic system?

163

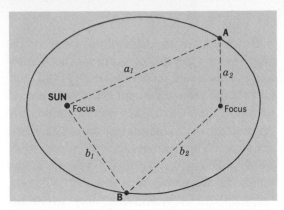

Figure 9-7. An ellipse is a closed curve. Inside an ellipse are two points, each called a focus (plural is foci) of the ellipse. The shape of an ellipse is such that the distance from one focus to a point on the ellipse and then to the other focus is the same, no matter which point you choose on the ellipse. For example, $a_1 + a_2 = b_1 + b_2$.

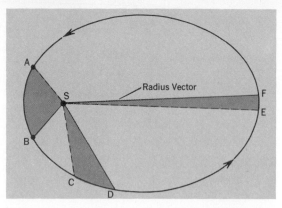

Figure 9-8. As the planet moves from A to B, the radius vector sweeps out the shaded area ABS. According to Kepler's second law, if the shaded areas CDS and EFS are equal to ABS, the time required to go from C to D or from E to F is the same as the time to go from A to B. Hence, the planet is moving faster at perihelion than at aphelion.

Kepler's laws. Less than 100 years after Copernicus' time, the German astronomer and mathematician Johannes Kepler worked out the laws which describe the orbital motion of the planets. These laws were another great step forward in unraveling the mystery of the strange motions of the planets. In formulating these laws, Kepler used the Copernican system and the data obtained from an extremely accurate set of observations of the planets and stars.

The first of Kepler's laws destroyed the old idea that all objects in the heavens must move in perfect circles. Kepler's first law may be stated in the following way.

| The orbit of each planet as it revolves about the sun is an *ellipse* (i lips′). The sun is at one focus of each planet's elliptical orbit. See *Figure 9-7*.

There is one point on the elliptical orbit where the planet is closer to the sun than at any other point. This point is called *perihelion* (per′ə hē′li ən). The point on the orbit where the planet is farthest from the sun is called *aphelion* (ə fē′li ən).

The information in the table in *Figure 9-3* reveals how elongated some planetary orbits are. Look at the data for Mercury, for example. The distance from Mercury to the sun is 50 per cent greater at aphelion than at perihelion.

Kepler's second law accounts for the changes observed in the speed of the planets in their orbits. These changes had not been successfully explained by either Copernicus or Ptolemy. Kepler's second law may be stated as follows.

| The radius vector drawn from the sun to any planet sweeps out equal areas in equal time intervals. See *Figure 9-8*.

Kepler's third law relates the time it takes for a planet to revolve about the sun once—the period of its orbit—to the size of the planet's orbit. Kepler's third law may be stated in the following manner.

| The squares of the periods of revolution of planets about the sun are in the same ratio to one another as the cubes of the major axes of their orbits. See *Figure 9-9*.

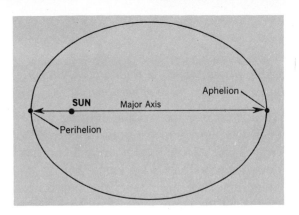

Figure 9-9. The major axis is the longest axis of an ellipse. In a planetary orbit, it is the distance from aphelion to perihelion. According to Kepler's third law, the greater the major axis of a planet's orbit is, the longer the period of revolution is. Kepler's laws refer to the planets. Would they also apply to objects in orbit about the earth?

Kepler's work had another important outcome. With the knowledge he had gained of the planets' orbits, he was able to explain retrograde motion in a simple, logical way. *(Figure 9-10.)* Of course, when Kepler formulated these laws, he was not attempting to explain why the planets moved as they did. His work was based entirely on the results of observation. Kepler had no understanding of the force which acted in the solar system and which lay at the root of the rules he had discovered. Later, Newton identified that force as gravitational force. Scientists could then explain why the planets moved as they did, and Kepler's laws were supported in theory as well as by observations.

You can use the data from *Figure 9-3* concerning our own planet and the planet Mars to check Kepler's third law. The major axis of a planet's orbit is the distance from its perihelion to its aphelion. For the earth, this is 2 A.U. For Mars, it is 3.04 A.U. In order to verify Kepler's third law, cube these two numbers and then find their ratio.

$$\frac{(3.04)^3}{2^3} = \frac{28.1}{8} = 3.51$$

Next, square the periods of the two planets, and find the ratio of those numbers. The period for earth is one year, and its square is one. The period for Mars is 1.88 years, and the square of that is 3.53. Thus, the ratio of the square of the period of Mars to that of the earth is as follows.

$$\frac{(1.88)^2}{1} = 3.53$$

Our data are not completely accurate. Within the limits of the accuracy of our data, however, the two ratios are the same, just as stated in Kepler's third law.

Figure 9-10. The earth's positions at intervals of one month are indicated by numerals on the inner circle. The positions of Mars during the corresponding months are shown on the outer circle. As viewed from the earth, Mars first appears to move from west to east. Then it reverses itself and appears to move from east to west before again resuming its west-to-east motion.

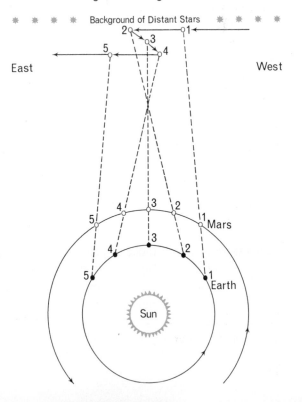

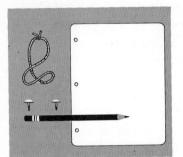

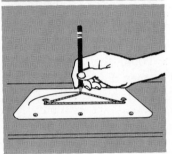

FIND OUT BY TRYING

Materials you will need: string, pencil, paper, 2 thumbtacks, drawing board or a large piece of cardboard

To draw an ellipse, place a sheet of paper on the drawing board. Stick two thumbtacks through the paper into the drawing board. Do not put the tacks in all the way. Place a loose loop of string around the tacks. Now place the point of your pencil inside the loop.

By moving your pencil point, make the string taut. The loop is now a triangle. With the pencil marking the paper, move the pencil about the tacks, keeping the string taut. The figure you draw will be an ellipse. The thumbtacks are at the foci of the ellipse. Use the same loop to draw several ellipses, but change the distance between the tacks for each loop. What is the effect of having the foci closer together? Of having the foci farther apart?

Once you know how to draw an ellipse, make a scale drawing of the orbit of each planet. Is it easy to see that the orbits are not circular? How far is it between the foci of the earth's orbit?

3. Atmospheres

The roles of gravity and temperature. The earth has an atmosphere about it. As far as we can tell, so do the other planets—that is, all but Mercury. Mercury, as we have observed, is the smallest planet and the closest one to the sun. As a result of these two conditions, Mercury has lost any atmosphere that it might once have had. Furthermore, these same conditions prevent it from accumulating another atmosphere. Planets retain their atmospheres because of their gravitational forces.

The molecules in the atmosphere are constantly moving. The warmer the atmosphere is, the faster the molecules in it move. In fact, this is really a definition of temperature—the temperature of a substance is proportional to the square of the average speed of its molecules. If the temperature of the atmosphere of a planet is high enough, then the molecules will have escape velocity. They will be moving fast enough to escape completely from the gravitational pull of the planet, like a tiny rocket ship headed out into space.

Since the planet Mercury is very small, its gravitational force is weak. Since it is also so close to the sun, the temperature of any gas which might come near Mercury, or which might come from volcanoes on its surface, is quite high. Consequently, the molecules have enough speed to leave Mercury and never return.

Near the earth's surface, many molecules in the earth's atmosphere are moving with speeds greater than escape velocity. Why do these molecules not escape the earth's gravity and leave our atmosphere?

A similar situation occurs on our moon. Of course, our moon is farther away from the sun than is Mercury. Thus, any gas near the moon is colder, and its molecules do not move so fast. However, the moon is smaller than Mercury so its gravitational force is weaker, and escape velocity from the moon is less than it is from Mercury. This means that the moon cannot retain the molecules of a gas which has the average temperature of the surface of the moon (about 0°C). Therefore, we could expect the moon to be without an atmosphere.

Astronomers have made careful observations of starlight as the moon passes between us and the stars. They have observed that whenever the moon passes in front of a star, the starlight suddenly blinks off without any gradual fading or change in color. In this way, they have demonstrated that the density of gas near the surface of the moon corresponds to a vacuum more nearly perfect than any we can make in a laboratory.

The other planets have more mass than Mercury, and they are also farther away from the sun. Thus, they have been able to keep at least part of their atmospheres. We say "part of their atmospheres" because for Venus, our own planet, and Mars it is very likely that a major portion of their original atmospheres has been lost. Scientists believe that this lost portion was mainly hydrogen and helium.

Why, do you suppose, were hydrogen and helium lost from our atmosphere while nitrogen was retained?

Atmospheres of terrestrial planets. On earth, we have an atmosphere that is about 78 per cent nitrogen, 21 per cent oxygen, and a little less than 1 per cent argon. Carbon dioxide, neon, and other gases—including some traces of helium—are also found in small percentages in our atmosphere.

These percentages are average values for dry air. But another gas—water vapor—is in the earth's atmosphere. The percentage of water vapor in the atmosphere varies greatly from one place to another. Water vapor is one of the most important parts of the atmosphere.

It accounts for many of our changing weather conditions when it changes into liquid or solid water and falls to earth as rain or snow.

It is very difficult to discover which gases are in the atmospheres of other planets. You may recall that the identity of the gases in the atmosphere of the sun and other stars was discovered through examining the spectra of these stars. The same method can be used to investigate the atmospheres of the planets. But, in the case of the planets, the job is much more difficult.

First of all, planets shine only with reflected sunlight, so the light we get from them is comparatively dim. Second, the spectra of elements are the same whether the elements are in our atmosphere or in that of another planet. As you know, we must look out through our own atmosphere to observe the atmospheres of other planets. Thus, it is difficult to tell whether the lines in the spectra we observe are due to the earth's atmosphere or to the atmosphere of the other planet we are observing. There is a large percentage of nitrogen in the earth's atmosphere. Therefore, measuring the

Figure 9-11. Experiments such as this one may reveal how life on earth originated. The gases in the apparatus simulate the gases of the earth's primitive atmosphere. An electric spark interacts with the gases, forming molecules basic to the existence of a living cell.

NASA, AMES RESEARCH CENTER

amount of nitrogen in the atmosphere of another planet is particularly difficult. As a matter of fact, scientists have never measured the amount of nitrogen in the atmosphere of another planet. But, if a planet has much more of a certain gas in its atmosphere than the earth does, then scientists can get a pretty accurate measurement of the abundance of that gas. For example, measurements can be made of the abundance of carbon dioxide in the atmosphere of Venus.

A thick cloud layer prevents scientists from seeing very far into Venus' atmosphere. However, two American and two Russian spacecraft have been sent to Venus. These spacecraft have given some indication of what the lower atmosphere is like. It seems to be mainly carbon dioxide, with a small amount of nitrogen, and a few other gases like carbon monoxide. As for the surface of Venus, the atmospheric pressure is about 100 times as great as that on the earth. The surface temperature of Venus is over 400°C.

Mariner spacecraft which flew past Mars carried instruments to investigate the atmosphere of that planet. See *Figure 9-18*. These instruments showed that the atmosphere of Mars is mainly carbon dioxide, with only a trace of oxygen. The instruments detected no nitrogen at all. The average pressure of Mars' atmosphere at the surface of the planet is only 0.6 per cent as great as the average atmospheric pressure on the earth's surface.

Atmospheres of the Jovian planets. The major portion of the atmospheres of the Jovian planets is hydrogen. Because each of these planets has a large mass, each has a strong gravitational field. Also, these planets are far enough away from the sun to have kept some of the hydrogen that was in their atmospheres when they formed. Their atmospheres also contain other gases. These other gases, such as methane and ammonia, have hydrogen atoms in their molecules. If a large amount of oxygen were present in these atmospheres, the methane and ammonia would disappear because of chemical reactions with the oxygen. However, these atmospheres contain little or no oxygen. Therefore, methane and ammonia—which are harmful to us—are plentiful in the atmospheres of Jovian planets.

What reasons can you give for thinking that some form of life could exist on a planet which has an atmosphere consisting chiefly of methane and ammonia?

4. Temperatures

Problems of measurement. One way to measure the temperature of the sun is to measure the amount of energy which the sun emits and then calculate how hot the surface must be in order to emit that much energy. This same method may be used in determining the temperatures of the planets.

Of course, the light observed coming from a planet is not produced within the planet. Instead, it is reflected sunlight. Observing this light might tell us something about the planet's temperature. Or, at least it might tell us something about the temperature of the atmosphere through which the sunlight passed before it was reflected to us. But better temperature measurements can be made by detecting the invisible radiation which the planet itself emits.

You may wonder what sort of radiation this could be since planets, including the earth, are certainly not stars. The planets are certainly not glowing brightly because of any nuclear reaction within them. However, every object in the universe is constantly radiating energy, and the nature of that radiation depends on the temperature of the object. You already know that the hotter stars are blue and the cooler stars are red. You also know that the wave length of red light is longer than the wave length of blue light. This means that cooler stars radiate light with longer wave lengths. Since the planets are even cooler than the coolest stars, the planets emit infrared radiation which has an even longer wave length than red light. Although infrared radiation is invisible to the eye, it can be detected by specially designed instruments. Such instruments are now being used by astronomers.

Measuring the radiation which a planet gives off because of its own heat is very difficult. A sensitive instrument designed to detect infrared radiation is needed. This instrument is then attached to a telescope in such a way that the telescope focuses the radiation from the planet onto the infrared detector. When the telescope is pointed at the planet, a determination of the amount of radiation given off by the planet because of its own heat is possible. Of course, these amounts are very small. Therefore, the measurements are not very accurate. The average values of several different measurements made by different astronomers are given in *Figure 9-12*.

PLANET	TEMPERATURE	
Mercury	616°K	649°F
Venus	241°K	−26°F
Mars (equator)	286°K	55°F
Mars (south pole)	211°K	−80°F
Jupiter	149°K	−191°F
Saturn	111°K	−260°F

Figure 9-12. These temperatures were determined by measuring the infrared radiation coming from the planets. From Mercury and Mars, the radiation was emitted by the solid surface. The infrared radiation came from the atmospheres of the other planets. Why, do you suppose, are there no data from the more distant planets—Uranus, Neptune, and Pluto?

Radio waves. There is another way scientists can measure the temperature of planets— that is, by using a radio telescope. The only difference between radio waves and light waves is in the wave lengths. The total known range of radiation is called the *electromagnetic spectrum*. The electromagnetic spectrum includes visible light, infrared and ultraviolet radiations, and several other kinds of radiation, as shown in *Figure 9-13*.

The general rules which apply to one portion of the electromagnetic spectrum also apply to the other portions. If each object in the universe is emitting infrared radiation, each

Figure 9-13. The electromagnetic spectrum contains radiation of many wave lengths. Each object in the universe emits radiation in all these wave lengths, but most of the radiation coming toward us is absorbed by the earth's atmosphere. However, waves in certain portions of the spectrum do penetrate the atmosphere. These portions of the spectrum are the "windows" through which scientists can observe the universe.

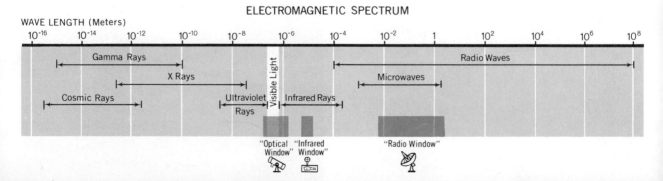

ELECTROMAGNETIC SPECTRUM

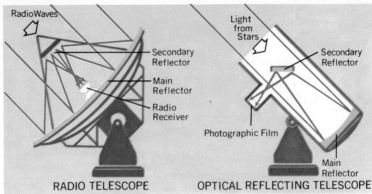

RadioWaves

Secondary
Reflector

Main
Reflector

Radio
Receiver

Light
from
Stars

Secondary
Reflector

Photographic Film

Main
Reflector

RADIO TELESCOPE   OPTICAL REFLECTING TELESCOPE

Figure 9-14. Radio telescopes, such as the one on the left, are used to study objects in space and to track spacecraft. The diagrams illustrate how a radio telescope is similar to a reflecting telescope. In each, incoming energy is focused by a large reflector. Another reflector directs the energy to a sensing device. In a radio telescope, the sensing device is a radio receiver. Photographic film or the observer's eye is used with an optical telescope.

object in the universe is also emitting radio waves. The warmer the object is, the more energy it radiates. It is possible, then, to measure the temperature of an object by carefully measuring the amount of energy which it emits in the form of radio waves.

There are a number of problems involved in trying to use radio waves for this type of measurement. First of all, the amount of energy emitted in the form of radio waves by the planets is extremely small. Thus, it takes a very large radio telescope, such as the one in *Figure 9-14* or the ones on page 42, to collect enough of this energy to make a measurement. That is one reason why radio telescopes are so very big. The big dish of a radio telescope is a reflector, just like a mirror. The radio waves which strike it are reflected to a radio receiver. The receiver records the intensity in a way very much like a piece of photographic film or any other sort of light-sensing device does in an ordinary telescope. *(Figure 9-14.)*

Another problem in radio astronomy is that man's everyday activities create a great amount of radio energy. This energy is not only produced through radio and television

stations, but also through the use of electrically operated machinery. Man-made radio energy tends to mask the signals coming from space. Therefore, radio telescopes are usually located away from populated areas. Furthermore, they are often located in a valley where the surrounding hills will help to shield the reflectors from stray radio waves.

Although they have some disadvantages, radio telescopes also have some very great advantages. They can "see" things that light

Figure 9-15. The world's largest radio telescope is in a natural valley in the hills near Arecibo, Puerto Rico. The primary reflector is 1,000 feet across and consists of nearly 20 acres of wire mesh suspended several feet above the floor of the valley.

telescopes cannot. For example, radio telescopes can measure the radiation coming directly from the surface of Venus. In contrast, infrared detectors can only measure the radiation coming from the surface of the clouds which surround that planet.

The mystery of Venus. When radio telescopes were used to observe Venus, the data gave a very surprising result. The temperature of the surface of Venus was indicated to be about 800°K—that is, about 425 degrees above the boiling point of water.

When this information was first announced by the scientists who made the measurements, some other scientists were not convinced of the accuracy of the information. It seemed unreasonable that the planet could be that hot. One suggested explanation was that a number of extremely hot spots, such as volcanoes,

might be accounting for all of this radio energy. The rest of the surface, then, might be quite a bit cooler.

In order to help settle this controversy, the spacecraft *Mariner II* carried a small radio telescope. *(Figure 9-4.)* As *Mariner II* passed Venus, this telescope slowly scanned the surface of the planet. The data obtained showed the temperature to be very nearly the same over the whole surface. The temperature determined was 800°K. Since then, most scientists have concluded that the surface of Venus really is that hot. Thus, there is little chance that any form of life would be found there.

If you could live on the surface of Venus, do you think that you would know much about the rest of the solar system? How would you obtain your information?

5. Satellites of the Sun

Planets. All the planets are satellites of the sun. Their orbital motion is principally controlled by the sun's gravitational field, just as the motion of our moon is controlled by the earth's gravity. But the planets are not the only such satellites. In the solar system there are many other bodies with orbits controlled by the sun.

Asteroids. The asteroids are a group of objects with orbits controlled by the sun. These objects appear to be solid bodies, but they are much smaller than the planets. The largest asteroid so far discovered, named *Ceres* (sir′ ēz), appears to be about 480 miles in diameter. Three others with diameters between 200 and 300 miles, and about a thousand more with diameters between ten and sixty miles, have been discovered. About 1,500 even smaller objects have also been found. One

astronomer has predicted that tens of thousands more asteroids could be discovered with the telescopes now in use. Asteroids are discovered by looking for streaks of light in a time-exposure photograph of the sky. *(Figure 9-16.)*

Figure 9-16. The arrow indicates the trail of the asteroid Icarus. In this time-exposure photograph, the camera followed the motion of the stars. Therefore, the stars appear as points of light. Objects with motions different from that of the stars—asteroids, for example—show up as streaks on such photographs.

PHOTOGRAPH FROM THE MOUNT WILSON AND PALOMAR OBSERVATORIES

Many asteroids have orbits between Mars and Jupiter. Two other large groups are trapped in two special locations by the combined gravitational forces of Jupiter and the sun. These two groups of asteroids move around the sun in the same orbit as Jupiter itself—one group ahead of the planet and one behind it.

There are many theories about the nature of asteroids. However, the theory which has been discussed most often concerns the space between the orbits of Mars and Jupiter. If you examine the data in *Figure 9-3,* you will find that there is quite a bit of space between the orbit of Mars and the orbit of Jupiter. For many years, astronomers have believed that at one time there may have been a planet in an orbit between Mars and Jupiter. Somehow, this planet was broken up, forming the asteroids. The fact that many asteroids have orbits in this general region gives some support to this hypothesis. However, this one fact does not prove it.

Meteorites. Meteorites which fall to the surface of the earth may actually be small asteroids. That is, they may have had the same origin. Most meteorites are rather small, weighing only a few kilograms. There are a few which are much larger, and occasionally something large enough to cause a sizeable crater will hit the earth. One such crater is the Great Meteor Crater located in Arizona. It is shown in *Figure 9-17.*

Many scientists believe that the craters which cover the surface of the moon were caused by the impact of meteorites and asteroids. If many of these bodies have orbits near and beyond Mars, then that planet also must show the markings of meteorite impacts.

Photographs of Mars taken through telescopes on earth are not clear enough to see whether or not the surface of Mars has craters. *(Figure 3-10.)* In fact, such photographs are not clear enough to tell very much of anything about the Martian surface. However, with the help of the Mariner spacecraft, we now have

Figure 9-17. The Great Meteor Crater in Arizona is sometimes called Barringer Meteorite Crater or the Canyon Diablo Meteorite Crater. It is the largest crater on the earth that has been positively identified as a meteorite impact crater. The crater is 4,200 feet across and 570 feet deep. The meteorite which caused the crater was more than 200 feet in diameter and weighed more than 1,000,000 tons.

NASA

Figure 9-18. The photograph on the left shows the *Mariner VI* spacecraft as it looked in flight. *Mariner VII* was identical. Below is a close-up of some of the instruments aboard the spacecraft.

NASA

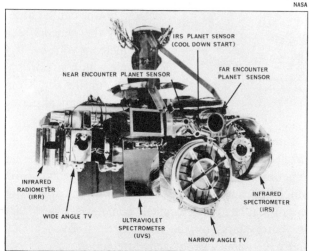

IRS PLANET SENSOR (COOL DOWN START)

NEAR ENCOUNTER PLANET SENSOR

FAR ENCOUNTER PLANET SENSOR

INFRARED RADIOMETER (IRR)

INFRARED SPECTROMETER (IRS)

WIDE ANGLE TV

ULTRAVIOLET SPECTROMETER (UVS)

NARROW ANGLE TV

some comparatively sharp pictures of the surface of Mars.

The *Mariner VI* spacecraft shown in *Figure 9-18* passed within 2,000 miles of the surface of Mars in 1969 and transmitted to earth a series of seventy-four television pictures. The television camera is also shown in *Figure 9-18*. Two of the pictures taken of Mars' surface are shown in *Figure 9-19*. As you can see, there are many craterlike formations which are very similar to those on the moon.

Although these pictures give us a closer look at the surface of Mars than we have ever had before, the detail is limited. The smallest features that can be seen are more than a mile across. We still have much to learn about Mars, even though we have had a closer look at it than at any of the other planets.

Figure 9-19. These are two of the pictures taken of the Martian surface by the television equipment aboard *Mariner VI* and *Mariner VII*, when they passed about 2,000 miles from Mars. In the picture on the left, the largest crater is 250 km across. The white area in the picture on the right is the south pole of Mars. Scientists believe it is covered with frozen carbon dioxide.

JPL PHOTO

JPL PHOTO

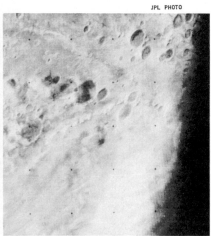

Observe a meteor shower

Consult an almanac or other reference source to find out when a meteor shower can be observed. See if you can determine which section of the sky the meteors seem to be coming from. Try to make a count of the meteors you see. If you can get several friends to help you, you can each watch a portion of the sky. By working together you can watch the entire sky. Compare your results with those reported in a current astronomical periodical, such as *Sky and Telescope.*

Comets. For centuries sky-watchers were puzzled by another type of object which could sometimes be seen in the sky. These objects, which appeared suddenly and without any apparent regularity, were called "cometes asters" or "hairy stars" by the early Greeks. Eventually the name was shortened to *comet.*

A comet does have an appearance somewhat like a fuzzy star. Some comets are easily distinguished from stars and nebulae because they are accompanied by long, glowing stream-ers of gas, called tails. However, all comets do not have tails. They do have a small nucleus of material which is surrounded by an envelope of gases. This envelope of gases gives the fuzzy appearance. In fact, comets (without tails) and nebulae look somewhat alike. They were often mistaken for each other by early astronomers. *(Figure 9-20.)*

Throughout most of his history, man considered comets to be omens of misfortune and impending doom. In the seventeenth century,

Figure 9-20. As these two photographs illustrate, comets vary greatly in appearance. Comet Cunningham (top) has only a small tail, while Halley's comet (bottom) has a long, glowing tail. In these photographs, stars appear as streaks of light. Why, do you suppose, are the streaks made by the stars longer in the top photograph than in the bottom photograph?

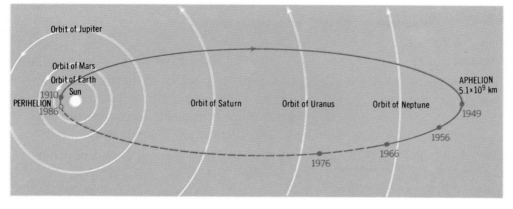
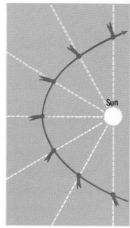

Figure 9-21. The orbit of Halley's comet is a very elongated ellipse, as shown above. The portion of the orbit near perihelion is shown in an enlarged view (at the right) in order to illustrate the effect of the sun on the position of the comet's tail.

however, the English scientist and mathematician Edmund Halley studied the path of one comet very thoroughly. By using Kepler's laws, Halley was able to predict the reappearance of that comet. That comet—now called Halley's comet—becomes visible about every 75 years. It will be visible again in 1986.

Halley's comet is in a very elongated, elliptical orbit about the sun. Thus, the motion of Halley's comet is controlled by the sun and Halley's comet is a member of the solar system. But, are all comets which are seen members of our solar system? So far, there is no way to be sure.

Some scientists think a comet is a cluster of frozen pieces of matter, such as methane, ammonia, and water vapor. Although we know these substances as gases or liquids, they exist as frozen solids in the coldness of space. According to this theory, these pieces of frozen matter are held in a loose cluster by their own gravitational forces.

As the comet nears perihelion, the sun's energy causes some of the frozen matter to become gas. This gas surrounding the mass of frozen particles produces the comet's fuzzy appearance by scattering the sun's light.

As the comet gets closer to the sun, the sun has a greater effect on the comet. Some of the gases are pushed out from the surrounding envelope of gases to form the long, streaming tail. Two factors cause scientists to think that light pressure is a major force in producing a comet's tail. First, the tail of the comet is directed away from the sun. Second, the tail is always longest when the comet is nearest the sun where the light pressure is greatest. *(Figure 9-21.)*

There is still much to be learned about comets. Indeed, there is much to be learned about each object in the solar system. But comets are a particularly good example of how increases in man's knowledge of nature can change his attitude concerning his surroundings. Man once viewed the appearance of a comet with dread, for he was convinced that some catastrophe was about to happen. Today, many people search for comets, not to forecast death and destruction, but to study them or simply to appreciate their beauty.

What are some other satellites of the sun? HINT: *These satellites are of very recent origin.*

Checking Your Knowledge

IMPORTANT IDEAS

1. The solar system consists of the sun, planets, comets, asteroids, meteorites, and other objects.

2. The Ptolemaic system, which was accepted for more than 1,000 years, is a geocentric (earth-centered) model of the universe.

3. The Copernican system, a heliocentric (sun-centered) system, is the basis of our present concept of the solar system.

4. Kepler derived the following laws which describe the orbital motions of the planets.

   a. Planetary orbits are ellipses.
   b. Radius vectors sweep out equal areas in equal time intervals.
   c. The squares of the periods of revolution of the planets are in the same ratio as the cubes of the major axes of their orbits.

5. The differences between the atmospheres of different planets are related to differences in planetary sizes and temperatures.

6. Space probes have revealed much information about the surfaces of Venus and Mars.

7. Infrared radiation and radio waves are used to determine the temperatures of the surfaces and atmospheres of the planets.

USING NEW WORDS

Study the five groups of words below. On your paper, write the letters a through e. Following each letter, explain the similarities and differences in the meanings of the words in the group designated by that letter.

   a. terrestrial — Jovian
   b. asteroids — comets — meteorites
   c. epicycle — deferent
   d. perihelion — aphelion
   e. Ptolemaic system — Copernican system

TEST YOURSELF

Study the test below. Write the numerals *1-10* on your paper. Beside each numeral write the correct response to that part of the test having the corresponding numeral.

1. Which of the following *is not* a probable cause of the lack of an atmosphere on Mercury? (a) nearness to the sun, (b) small size, (c) high temperature, (d) speed about the sun.

2. Which of these men first suggested the sun as the center of the solar system? (a) Copernicus, (b) Kepler, (c) Ptolemy.

3. Which of the following planets has the most nearly circular orbit? (a) Mercury, (b) Venus, (c) earth, (d) Mars.

4. Which of these planets has its surface hidden from our view by a dense atmosphere? (a) Mercury, (b) Venus, (c) Mars.

5. Which of the following *is not* an object that is part of the solar system? (a) Halley's comet, (b) Jupiter, (c) Orion, (d) Ceres.

Beside each of the numerals *6-10,* write a word from the list below. The word written beside each numeral must be related to the sentence having the corresponding numeral.

satellite	comet
Mars	epicycle
asteroid	deferent

6. This object has the most elongated orbit of any satellite of the sun.

7. This name is given to any object which orbits about another object.

8. One theory states that this object could be part of an exploded planet.

9. In the Ptolemaic system, a circle having this name is centered on the earth.

10. In the Ptolemaic system, this name was given to the circular path in which the planets were thought to move.

Extending Your Knowledge

QUESTIONS TO EXPLORE

1. What reasons can you give to explain why some religious leaders in the Middle Ages were opposed to Copernicus' idea of a heliocentric solar system?

2. What information has been obtained about the planets Venus and Mars from the Mariner space probes?

3. Kepler suggested that angels kept the planets in their orbits. Why do you think he suggested this rather than proposing a reason based on scientific principles?

4. What information can you obtain firsthand by studying photographs of the planets?

5. Why was Ptolemy's idea of a geocentric universe discarded and replaced by a heliocentric model of the solar system?

6. The planet Venus is sometimes called the twin of the earth. What reasons can you give to explain this statement? Do you think any other planet is more like earth than Venus is? If so, which one do you think is most like earth?

SOME THINGS TO DO

1. If possible, use a telescope to observe the planets. Observe and sketch the positions of the moons of Jupiter on successive nights. Also, draw sketches of as many of the other planets as you can observe. How can you distinguish a planet from a star without a telescope? With a telescope?

2. Some of the early Greeks suggested that the earth was round. Others suggested that it revolved about the sun. Find out why these ideas were forgotten for such a long time.

3. The words in our language that we use to describe the apparent motions seen in the heavens reflect the "common sense" idea of a geocentric system. There is no simple way of expressing the motions of a heliocentric system. For example, we say that the sun rises and sets. Express this idea so that it implies a heliocentric system. Think of other similar examples.

4. Use the data in *Figure 9-3* to find the ratio of the major axis cubed to the period squared for each of the planets. Do your answers correspond with the results predicted by Kepler's third law?

CHALLENGES IN SCIENCE

1. Conduct an experiment to determine if any type of plant life you are familiar with could exist on another planet. Place several different kinds of plants in airtight containers. Then, introduce into these containers the gases that are believed to exist in the atmospheres of the other planets. Try to duplicate the environmental conditions found on the other planets, such as temperature, atmospheric pressure, and amount of light. Be sure to include simple forms of life such as algae, lichens, and mosses.

2. Make a study of the rings of Saturn. Find out what modern astronomers think is the nature of these rings. What is their composition? How were they formed? Why doesn't every planet have a similar set of rings?

3. Make a list of some of the aspects of the solar system which must be explained in any attempt to describe the origin of the solar system. For example, the occurrence of two separate types of planets (terrestrial and Jovian), differences in atmospheres, differences in rates of rotation, and so on. Are there any aspects that are especially difficult to explain? HINT: Find out about the axis of rotation of Uranus and about Uranus' satellites.

4. Explain why Mercury and Venus show phases, while none of the other planets do.

The effects of gravitation are well known, but its true nature is not understood.

CHAPTER 10

Gravitational Forces and Their Effects

No one knows who first made the statement, "What goes up must come down." Undoubtedly, it was made long ago. Although the statement has not changed, man's ideas of "up" and "down" have changed. When man believed the world was flat, "up" could mean only one direction. In fact, a spherical earth was incredible to some people because of their ideas of "up" and "down." They thought that if the earth were a sphere, people on the "lower" side of the earth would fall off.

Later, the idea that the earth is spherical became firmly established in man's mind. The idea that "up" could be only one direction in space had to be discarded. Also, man began to realize that just thinking about and talking about natural phenomena was not satisfying his desire to know. He began using experiments to check theories and ideas. Along with many other natural phenomena that had previously been taken for granted, the mysterious force of gravitation was studied.

In Chapter 10, you will investigate man's knowledge of gravitation. You will find out how gravitation affects objects on and about the earth. You will read about Galileo's studies and how Newton extended the concept of gravitation beyond the earth and formulated the law of gravitation. Then, you will find out about Einstein's idea that gravitation is the curvature of space near any mass. In spite of all that these men have done, however, the nature of gravitation is still not completely understood. In fact, modern scientists do not all agree on the approach to be used in further attempts to solve the mysteries of gravitation.

1. Newton's Idea

The falling apple. According to a famous legend, Isaac Newton was inspired to discover the law of gravitation by observing a falling apple. Whether or not the story is true, it is certainly widespread. It was repeated by Lord Byron, one of England's famous poets, in *Don Juan,* Canto the Tenth, I and II.

When Newton saw an apple fall, he found
  In that slight startle from his contemplation—
'Tis said (for I'll not answer above ground
  For any sage's creed or calculation)—
A mode of proving that the earth turn'd round
  In a most natural whirl, called "gravitation";
And this is the sole mortal who could grapple,
Since Adam, with a fall or with an apple.

Men fell with apples, and with apples rose,
  If this be true; for we must deem the mode
In which Sir Isaac Newton could disclose
  Through the then unpaved stars the turn-pike road,
A thing to counterbalance human woes;
  For ever since immortal man hath glow'd
With all kinds of mechanics, and full soon
Steam-engines will conduct him to the moon.

But what exactly did Newton discover, with or without the help of the apple? Certainly, he did not discover gravity itself. The force that made an apple fall from a tree or a stone drop from the hand was already well known. Many years before Newton's time, the Italian scientist Galileo had made careful measurements of the effect of gravity to show that gravity causes a steady acceleration.

Galileo's measurements showed that a falling body steadily speeds up, or accelerates, during its fall. For every second it falls, the body gains an additional 9.8 meters per second (32 feet per second) of speed. *(Figure 10-1.)* Galileo had also proven that the acceleration of a falling body due to gravity is independent of the weight of the object that is dropped. According to some accounts, he did

this with an experiment at the Leaning Tower of Pisa. But this may be another story like Newton and the apple. According to the accounts, Galileo dropped two objects having different weights from the tower. Philosophers and students standing on the ground observed

Figure 10-1. A falling object is accelerated by the force of gravity. During each 1-second interval of fall, the object's speed is increased 9.8 meters per second. Scientists say the object is accelerating at the rate of 9.8 meters per second per second (9.8 m/sec^2). Compare the object's speed at the end of each second to the distance traveled in that interval. In this diagram, the object shown took 3 seconds to fall to the water. Can you figure out how high the bridge is?

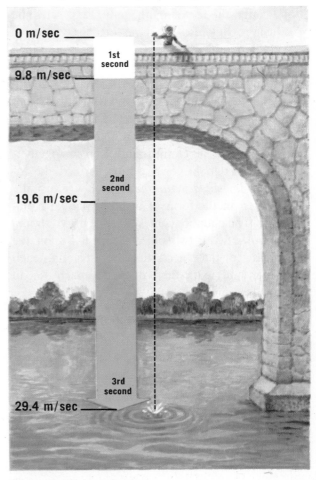

that both of the objects hit the ground at the same time. To some of these observers, this came as a distinct surprise.

A sky diver does not gain speed at the rate of 9.8 m/sec each second during the entire time before his parachute opens. How would you explain this?

Newton did not discover the force of gravity. What he did do was make two very important discoveries about that force. He discovered that the same force of gravity which makes an apple fall from a tree keeps the moon in orbit about the earth. Gravitational forces also keep all of the planets in orbit around the sun. Furthermore, he discovered the relationships that permit the force of gravity to be calculated. He discovered these things not only through the use of mathematics and scientific insight, but also by using the discoveries of Galileo and Kepler. Galileo had described and measured the effects of gravity on objects near the surface of the earth. Kepler, as you will recall, had worked out the exact rules for the motions of the planets about the sun.

The law of gravitation. Newton brought these ideas of Galileo and Kepler together, and through his own genius derived the famous *law of gravitation*. This law is usually written in the form of a mathematical equation. The equation states that the gravitational force between two objects depends upon the masses of the objects that are attracting each other and upon their distance apart. It can be written as follows.

$$F = G \frac{m_1 m_2}{r^2}$$

In this equation, F is the force of attraction between the two objects. The masses of the two objects are m_1 and m_2, and r is the distance between their centers. The G represents the *gravitational constant*.

The equation indicates how to calculate the force between two objects. First, we must determine the mass of each object. Then, we need to find the product of these two measures. Next, we must determine the distance between the centers of the objects and then calculate the square of that measure. Having done these things, we divide the product of the masses by the square of the distance. Finally, we multiply this quotient by the gravitational constant. The product is the gravitational force between the two objects.

The gravitational constant. The gravitational constant is the same for all bodies, whether we are figuring out the force between the sun and one of the planets, between the earth and the moon, or between the earth and an apple.

If the masses are expressed in grams and the distance in centimeters, then the gravitational constant (G) is $6.673 \pm 0.003 \times 10^{-8}$ cm³/g $\times$ sec². The figure ± 0.003 in this expression represents the present uncertainty scientists have about the exact value of the constant. The determination of the value of G is difficult. Different determinations give slightly different values. In the value given for G, the number 6.673×10^{-8} represents the average of many determinations. The figure ± 0.003 indicates that, on the basis of all of these determinations, scientists are certain that the true value of the gravitational constant lies between 6.670×10^{-8} and 6.676×10^{-8}.

In making calculations, the average value is always used. We keep the uncertainty in mind so that we will know how accurate the resulting calculations will be. Uncertainty of exact value comes into each physical quantity which is determined by experimental measurements. By its very nature, measurement is only an approximation. No measurement ever gives a perfectly exact answer.

If the masses were expressed in kilograms and the separation in kilometers, a different value for the gravitational constant would have to be used. For whatever set of units is used in the measurement, we must use the correct gravitational constant to go with that particular set of units. Once we have decided on the set of units, then the constant will be the same for all gravitational problems.

Whenever grams are used to measure mass, centimeters to measure distance, and seconds to measure time, the force will be in *dynes* (dīnz). One dyne is, very roughly, about the force which would be exerted on your hand by a postage stamp held in your palm. It is the unit of force which is always used when working with centimeters, grams, and seconds—that is, in the cgs system.

DO IT YOURSELF

Find out how the gravitational constant was determined

When Newton derived the law of gravitation, he did not know the numerical value of the gravitational constant. What type of experiment is needed to determine the constant? Who was the first scientist to make the determination? Do you think you could devise an experiment to determine *G*? Make a sketch of an apparatus which could be used to determine *G*. Think of Newton's equation for gravitational force. In your investigation you would have to be able to measure everything except *G*. That is, you would have to be able to measure the masses, the distance between the masses, and the force between the masses. Page 97 of the March, 1961, issue of "Scientific American" shows one such apparatus.

2. An Explanation of Orbits

Shapes in nature. You know that the orbits of planets are ellipses, rather than perfect circles. Some orbits—like that of Venus—are almost circular. But none are perfect circles. In fact, we would not expect to find a perfectly circular orbit, because that is such a special case. We seldom find perfect circles in nature, any more than we would find a perfectly straight tree, or a perfectly straight crack in the sidewalk.

It is rather interesting to realize that the early philosophers believed that all things in the heavens had to be circles. They considered the circle to be the perfect shape, and of course (so they thought) nature would always do

things perfectly, at least in the heavens. Since the time of the early philosophers, however, man has discovered that nature seldom produces anything so simple as a straight line or circle. Instead, nature does things in a more complex and fascinating manner.

In order to understand the complex ways of nature, we often study simple models of natural phenomena first. Thus, we will talk about circular orbits first. Once we understand these, the step to the realistic elliptical orbits will not be too difficult.

Centripetal force. You are probably familiar with something that has been called *centrifugal* (sen trif′ə gəl) *force.* When you swing

Figure 10-2. The faster the thrower whirls the hammer, the greater is the inward force he must exert to keep the hammer moving in a circle.

a weight around your head on the end of a string, the weight does not fall to the ground. Instead, it tugs outward. You can even swing a bucket of water over your head without spilling a drop. When you swing something like this, you can feel the tug on your hand. It feels as if the object you are holding is trying to fly away. That is where the word centrifugal comes from. It means "fleeing from the center."

But, if you stop to think about it, you will realize that your sensations have misled you somewhat. The motion of the object is controlled by the force which you exert in pulling it toward you, but not by any centrifugal force. We would describe the force you are exerting as a *centripetal* (sen trip′ə təl) *force*. Centripetal means "seeking the center." You are pulling at the object and by your pulling are forcing it to travel in a circle. If you let go of the string—that is, if you stop exerting the centripetal force—the object goes in a straight line, as indicated in *Figure 10-3*.

When you swing something around on a string, it feels exactly as if somebody were on the other end of the string pulling outward. For our present understanding, however, we must realize that the important force is that which your hand exerts pulling inward on the object. The sensation of the outward tug comes from the motion of the object that is swinging around. You are changing its motion away from a straight line, and it resists this change. It is the same kind of resistance that you feel when you push a wagon to speed it up or pedal a bicycle to go faster. You are changing the motion of an object, and the object resists this change—seemingly by exerting another force in the opposite direction.

The earth's gravity is constantly changing the motion of the moon away from the straight line in which the moon would tend to travel. If the earth's gravity were suddenly cut off, the moon would move in a straight line out into space. Only the pull of the earth's gravity keeps it moving in a curved path. *(Figure 10-4.)* In other words, gravity is the centripetal force which holds the moon in its orbit.

Figure 10-3. If you were to release the string as you whirled an object about your head, a centripetal force would no longer be acting on the object. The object would move in a straight line in the direction it was moving when you released the string, as shown by the dashed arrow in the diagram below.

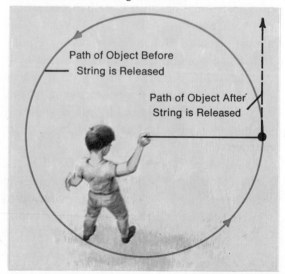

Path of Object Before String is Released

Path of Object After String is Released

Why is it wrong to say that an orbiting satellite escapes the earth's gravity? If the satellite does not escape from the effects of gravity, why does it not come back to the earth's surface?

Gravity and the moon's orbit. Newton's law of gravitation explains why the moon is held in orbit, but it does more than that. The equation he derived enables us to relate the speed of the moon in its orbit, the distance of the moon from the earth, and the masses of the moon and the earth.

However, there is another relationship we need to know first. We must know how circular motion and centripetal force are related. This relationship—another of Newton's discoveries—can be expressed as follows.

$$F = m \frac{v^2}{r}$$

In this equation, F is the centripetal force, m is the mass of the object, v is the speed of the object in its circular path, and r is the

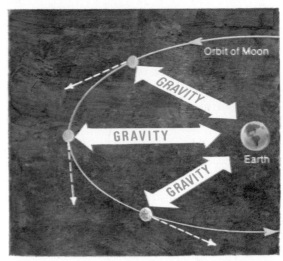

Figure 10-4. The gravitational attraction between the earth and the moon keeps the moon in its orbit. The dashed arrows show the direction in which the moon would have moved if gravity had ceased when the moon was at each of the indicated positions.

radius of the circular path. This relationship is true whether the force is the gravitational pull of the earth on the moon or the pull of your hand on a string as you swing a weight around your head.

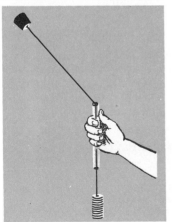

FIND OUT BY TRYING

Materials you will need: glass tube (15 cm long), fishing line, #4 rubber stopper with one hole, 20 iron washers

Assemble the materials as shown in the diagram. Use ten washers the first time you try the apparatus. Hold the glass tube in your hand and whirl the rubber stopper above your head. Control the speed of the rubber stopper so that the weight of the ten washers is just enough to keep the radius of the circular motion from changing. Repeat the procedure several times. Each time, change one factor—the radius of the circular motion, the number of washers, or the rate of rotation. How can you determine the centripetal force in each case? What factors affect the centripetal force?

Use the device to measure the centripetal force acting on the whirling rubber stopper. Then, use the equation given on this page to calculate the centripetal force acting on the stopper under the same conditions. How closely does your measured value agree with the calculated value? How do you account for any difference?

Determining the moon's speed and period.
The equations which Newton derived can be used to study the orbits of many types of heavenly objects. For example, we can study the orbit of our moon. We have two equations in which force is a term.

$$F = G \frac{m_1 \, m_2}{r^2} \qquad F = m_1 \frac{v^2}{r}$$

Notice that m_1 instead of m is used in the equation on the right. This is done because we are investigating the specific case of the earth and the moon. Since m_1 refers to the mass of the moon in the equation on the left, we will use the same symbol to represent the moon's mass on the right.

In the equation on the left, F is the force of gravity between the earth and moon. In the equation on the right, F is the centripetal force which holds the moon in its orbit. But, the force of gravity is the centripetal force which holds the moon in its orbit. Therefore, in each equation, F refers to the same force. Since the right-hand members of the equations are equal to the same force, they must be equal to each other. We can express this in the following way.

$$G \frac{m_1 \, m_2}{r^2} = m_1 \frac{v^2}{r}$$

This equation can be solved for v^2, as indicated below.

$$v^2 = G \frac{m_2}{r}$$

This is a very interesting equation, because m_1 does not appear in the final equation. Thus, the equation tells us that the speed of the moon in its orbit has nothing to do with the mass of the moon. In fact, according to the equation, only three factors affect the velocity of an object orbiting the earth. These factors

are the gravitational constant, the mass of the earth, and the radius of the orbit. The gravitational constant and the mass of the earth do not vary. Therefore, the speed of an object orbiting the earth depends solely on the radius of the object's orbit. For example, any object circling the earth in the moon's orbit—whether it is the moon or a small spacecraft—will have the same speed.

Suppose we use this equation to calculate how fast the moon is traveling. The mass of the earth is 5.98×10^{27} g. The distance from the center of the moon to the center of the earth is 3.8×10^{10} cm. You will remember that the gravitational constant is 6.673×10^{-8} cm^3/g $\times$ sec^2. Substituting these values gives the following equation.

$$v^2 = \frac{6.673 \times 10^{-8} \, \dfrac{\text{cm}^3}{\text{g} \times \text{sec}^2} \times 5.98 \times 10^{27} \, \text{g}}{3.8 \times 10^{10} \text{cm}}$$

Solving the equation gives the following value for v^2.

$$v^2 = 1.05 \times 10^{10} \, \frac{\text{cm}^2}{\text{sec}^2}$$

Then, taking the square root of each side of the equation gives the rate at which the moon moves in its orbit about the earth.

$$v = 1.02 \times 10^5 \, \frac{\text{cm}}{\text{sec}}$$

Actually, we cheated a little bit in working out the equations we used to find the speed of the moon. But it makes only a very small difference in our answer. We used the distance from the earth's center to the moon's center for r. But the center of the moon's orbit is not the center of the earth. Instead, the center of the moon's orbit is the center of mass of the earth-moon system, and this center of mass is about 3,000 miles from the earth's center. Therefore, the distance we used as the radius of the moon's orbit was in error by about 3,000 miles. However, this small inaccuracy will not bother us too much. The distance to the moon is almost 239,000 miles, and if we are in error by about 3,000 miles, the error will not make a great deal of difference in our solution. Moreover, disregarding such minor errors has the advantage of saving us a lot of complicated arithmetic.

Perhaps we should go a little further and figure out how long it takes the moon to go around once in its orbit. The distance it has to go is the circumference of a circle with a radius the same as we have used before. To calculate the time the moon takes to go around once, we must divide this circumference ($2\pi r$) by the moon's speed. If we call the time T, the equation we should use in making the calculation is as follows.

$$T = \frac{2\pi r \text{ cm}}{v \dfrac{\text{cm}}{\text{sec}}}$$

By substituting the values of r and v and then carrying out the indicated operations, we can find the period of the moon in its orbit.

$$T = \frac{2\pi \times 3.8 \times 10^{10} \text{ cm}}{1.02 \times 10^5 \dfrac{\text{cm}}{\text{sec}}}$$

$$= 2.3 \times 10^6 \text{ sec}$$

Our answer of 2.3×10^6 seconds is equivalent to about 27 days, since one day is equivalent to 8.64×10^4 seconds. Thus, our answer indicates that the moon takes 27 days to travel once about the earth. If we check with a book of astronomy, we will find that our value corresponds with observations. The small error introduced by using the wrong center for the orbit did not have a great enough effect to show up. However, if we made a more accurate determination, using hours and minutes, then our small error would be apparent.

Elliptical orbits. The motion of a planet in an elliptical orbit about the sun is controlled by gravitational forces. When the planet is at aphelion, the gravitational pull of the sun is the weakest. When the planet is at perihelion, the gravitational pull is the strongest. Furthermore, as Kepler pointed out in his second law, the planet is moving more slowly at aphelion than when it is at perihelion.

Imagine a circular orbit and an elliptical orbit as shown in *Figure 10-5*. The center of the circular orbit is in the same position as one focus of the elliptical orbit—the point labeled S. Also, the two orbits coincide at the aphelion of the elliptical orbit. Now, suppose we compare the speed of Planet E in the elliptical orbit with the speed of Planet C in the circular orbit. Planet E would be moving more slowly at its aphelion than Planet C would be at this same point in its circular orbit. Therefore, the gravitational force of the sun will begin to pull Planet E in closer to the sun, starting the planet toward its perihelion.

Figure 10-5. Point S is at the center of Planet C's circular orbit and at one focus of Planet E's elliptical orbit. At aphelion, Planet E moves more slowly than Planet C does when Planet C is at the same point.

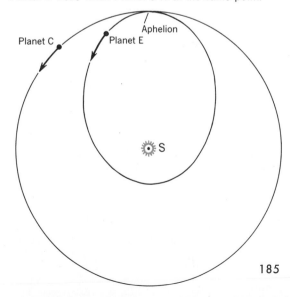

Figure 10-6. Suppose Planet E and Planet C are in elliptical and circular orbits, respectively. Suppose, too, that the orbits are situated as shown below. Planet E would move faster at the perihelion of its elliptical orbit than Planet C would when Planet C was at the same point in its circular orbit.

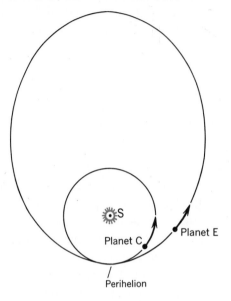

Figure 10-7. In the diagram shown below, the major axis of the elliptical orbit is equal in length to the diameter of the circular orbit. Although the speed of Planet E in its orbit varies and the speed of Planet C in its orbit is constant, the time for one revolution of Planet E would be equal to that of Planet C.

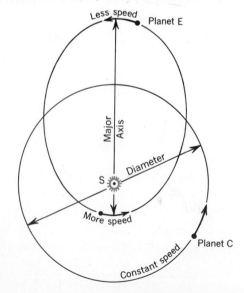

Now imagine a circular orbit and an elliptical orbit as shown in *Figure 10-6*. Again, the center of the circular orbit and one focus of the elliptical orbit are at the same point —Point S. In this situation, however, the circular orbit and the elliptical orbit coincide at the perihelion of the elliptical orbit. As Planet E in the elliptical orbit goes through its perihelion, it is moving more swiftly than Planet C in the circular orbit would be moving at the same point. Therefore, the gravitational force of the sun is not strong enough to hold Planet E in as tight a curve as the circle. Planet E moves out into a wider orbit. As it moves out—going in a curve, but still getting farther and farther from the sun—the sun's gravitational force slows Planet E until the planet reaches the far end of its orbit. Then the planet turns back and starts moving closer to the sun. The planet is actually falling toward the sun. It is being accelerated in the process, until, going much more rapidly than it was at aphelion, it comes to its perihelion. Then the cycle is repeated.

You will recall that, according to Kepler's third law, the time it takes a planet to go around in its orbit depends upon the major axis of its orbit—that is, the distance from perihelion to aphelion. Of course, in a circular orbit this is simply the diameter of the circle. Now, imagine two orbits like those shown in *Figure 10-7*. One is a circle, and the other an ellipse. The diameter of the circle is exactly the same length as the major axis of the ellipse. Kepler's third law tells us that planets in these two orbits would take exactly the same amount of time to make one complete revolution.

Why do few (if any) satellites—whether they are natural or artificial—have circular orbits? Do you know of any that actually have circular orbits?

3. Man's Understanding of Gravity

The first step. Using the law of gravitation, it is possible to calculate the gravitational force between any two objects. But being able to calculate its force does not mean that we understand the nature of gravitation. What is implied by the phrase "understanding the nature of gravitation"? Galileo first worked toward gaining such an understanding by conducting experiments which showed that gravity causes falling objects to steadily speed up. Thus, he showed a relationship between gravity and motion.

Before Galileo's time, philosophers and scientists generally believed that heavy objects fell faster than lighter ones. It is easy to see how they could make this mistake. Everything they watched fall, fell through the air. And, air resistance brings a great complication into the problem. In air, a feather falls more slowly than a lead weight. But, in a tube from which the air is removed, they both fall at the same speed.

Galileo had no equipment to produce a vacuum for his experiments. However, he realized that he could avoid any great effect of air resistance by always working with dense materials. Using dense materials did not eliminate air resistance, but at least the air resistance did not have an important effect. He did most of his experiments with iron and wooden weights of different sizes.

Another concept that the philosophers before Galileo did not understand was the concept of steady acceleration. They knew that things speeded up when they fell. But these early observers had never bothered to make careful measurements to find out exactly how this speeding-up process worked. Galileo was the first to make such measurements. He proved that the effect of gravity on motion was not accidental. This effect did not vary from place to place or from object to object. This effect was a steady rule of nature which worked in a predictable manner time after time. By careful calculation and observation, he began the development of man's understanding of the nature of gravity.

Ordinarily, a sheet of paper would fall to the floor more slowly than a pencil dropped from the same height. What is the reason for this difference? What techniques could be used to get these objects to fall at the same rate?

The second step. Isaac Newton's work was basically similar to Galileo's, but it was the next step. He, too, showed a relationship between two aspects of nature—namely, the motions of the moon and planets and the motions of things which we drop near the surface of the earth. Newton's calculations and careful observations enabled him to demonstrate that the relationship between gravitational forces in space and gravity in the world around us is not accidental. In space or on earth, the relationship follows a single, understandable rule. Thus, Newton extended our understanding of gravity to the planets.

Another significant step. It was more than two hundred years after Newton's discoveries that another significant step was taken in our understanding of gravitational forces. This step was the development of Einstein's *general theory of relativity*. It is a very complex theory, and more will be said about it in the next section. Even with the help of this additional step, however, there are still more steps that must be taken to increase our understanding of gravitational forces.

For example, scientists would like to know the relationship (if there is any) between gravitational, electrical, and magnetic forces.

The relationship between two of these great forces of nature—electrical and magnetic—is fairly well understood. But, somehow, gravitational force always stands apart.

Scientists also would like to know why it is that the gravitational force between two bodies depends upon the square of the distance between the two bodies. Why not just the distance? The fact that gravitational force depends upon the square of the distance makes this force seem very much like light. In Chapter 5 it was pointed out that the amount of light we receive depends on the square of its distance away. Thus, if you move twice as far away from a light source, the light appears only one fourth as bright.

This same relationship holds for gravitational force. For example, right now you are about 4,000 miles from the center of the earth. Suppose you could stand on a long pole sticking 4,000 miles out into space. Then, you would be a total distance of 8,000 miles from the center of the earth. If you brought a set of scales with you, you would discover that you weigh only one fourth as much as you did on the surface. You would observe that *increasing* the distance by a factor of 2, *decreased* the force of gravity by a factor of 4.

The unified field theory. Does the similarity between gravity and light mean that gravity, too, is transmitted by waves? You probably know that scientists talk about light in terms of either waves or particles. However, scientists cannot see how to put these two ideas together in a very understandable manner. Can gravity, also, be explained either by waves or particles? Some scientists think so. They have even given a name to the particles of gravitational energy. Such a particle has been given the name *graviton* (grav′ə ton). So far, however, no one has been able to observe a graviton or to prove in any way that such a thing as the graviton exists.

Figure 10-8. Albert Einstein, a man unique in his various abilities, contributed much to man's understanding of gravitational forces. His theories of relativity and his efforts to formulate a unified field theory opened new avenues of scientific inquiry.

The possibility that gravitational forces could be explained in terms of particles and waves brings us to an attempt to understand the relationship between gravitation, electricity, and magnetism. Einstein employed the last thirty years of his life trying to formulate a theory which would show this relationship. Scientists refer to such a theory as a *unified field theory*. Einstein was not successful in working out a satisfactory solution, although his work did advance our understanding of gravity quite a bit. Thus, a complete understanding of gravity—in spite of developments by Galileo, Newton, Einstein, and many others—remains as one of the deepest and most challenging mysteries of physics today.

What leads some scientists to suspect that there is a relationship between gravitation and light?

4. Modern Ideas about Gravitational Force

Inertial and gravitational mass. There is another curious characteristic of gravitational force which mystified Isaac Newton and scientists since Newton's time. This curious characteristic is the relation between inertial mass and gravitational mass.

You know that all objects have *inertia,* the tendency to resist any change in their motion. If you try to speed them up, they resist your effort. If you try to slow them down, they tend to keep going. This property of inertia is proportional to the mass of the object. Suppose

Figure 10-9. In order to move the load of logs, the man must overcome the inertia of the logs. He overcomes the inertia by exerting a force on the logs—that is, by pushing or pulling them. The greater the force he exerts, the faster the logs will move when he pushes or pulls them.

AUTHENTICATED NEWS INTERNATIONAL

253

you push with a certain force on an object and measure the object's acceleration. If you double the mass of the object but push with the same force as before, the object will accelerate only half as fast. Or, if you double the mass of the object and also double the force, then you would again produce the original acceleration.

The relationship between force, mass, and acceleration was described by Newton in the most famous of all physical laws. The relationship is stated as follows. Force equals mass times acceleration, or $F = ma$. The mass in this relationship is called *inertial mass* because it is measured by observing its inertia—that is, its response to a force.

There is also a mass which appears in the law of gravitation. This mass, called the *gravitational mass,* determines the amount of gravitational force which one body exerts on another. If you were to double the mass of the earth, for example, it would pull on the moon with twice as much gravitational force.

The surprising and mystifying fact is that gravitational mass and inertial mass are identical. Scientists have reasoned that this cannot be accidental. There must be some very natural reason behind it.

For two hundred years, scientists conducted experiments of greater and greater precision to make sure that gravitational mass and inertial mass were identical. Finally, scientists have concluded that inertial mass and gravitational mass are identical. But still, they cannot explain why.

The special theory of relativity. Albert Einstein suggested a reason for the relationship between gravitational mass and inertial mass when he worked out his theories of relativity. His first step was called the *special theory of relativity.*

189

The special theory of relativity has to do with steady motion in a straight line. For example, if you were on a train moving at a steady speed on a straight track and if you pulled the curtains down on the windows, there would be no way for you to tell that you were moving. That is, there is absolutely no experiment you could do completely within the body of the train (or any other system that is moving steadily in a straight line) which would enable you to detect your motion. Only by looking at the outside world could you tell. And then, you could just as well say that the outside world is moving backwards. There is no physical basis to establish which one is moving, since all physical laws would be operating the same in either case.

The general theory of relativity. Accelerated motion is a subject of the general theory of relativity. Again, suppose you are standing in a closed compartment. This time, however, the closed compartment is in a rocket ship instead of on a train. Next, suppose you are far out in space—so far from any star that there is almost no gravitational force pulling you in any direction. As long as the rockets are turned off, you are in free fall—just as an astronaut is in free fall while in orbit.

Now, suppose the rockets are turned on. You are pushed down against the floor by the sudden acceleration. The rockets continue to operate, the spaceship continues to speed up, and you are steadily pushed against the floor.

If you were holding a book, you would find that it seems to have weight, because it, too, is sharing this steady acceleration. If you let the book go, it would fall to the floor.

But remember, you are not being affected by a gravitational force. All of these sensations you are having are just because the rockets are accelerating the compartment in which you stand. When you dropped the book from your hand, it was already going at a particular speed, because it had already been accelerated somewhat by the rockets. But the rockets continued to accelerate the compartment, and the floor speeded up to overtake the book.

Remember, you have supposed that your compartment is closed. In this circumstance, how could you tell the difference between simply sitting on a launching pad with gravity pulling you down against the floor and accelerating through space with the rockets' acceleration seeming to force you down against the floor? Actually, there is no way to tell the difference. A steady acceleration produces effects exactly like those caused by gravity. A steady acceleration is exactly like gravity as far as all physical experiments go. In other words, gravity and a steady acceleration are equivalent. This fact was called the *principle of equivalence* by Einstein.

Figure 10-10. A student is weightless. Suddenly, his feet press against the floor. The book he releases apparently falls to the floor. Did a gravitational force pull the book to the floor? Or, was the floor accelerated so that it moved up to the book? We can see that, in this case, acceleration caused the effects. But, from within the ship the student cannot answer these questions, since the effects produced by gravity and those produced by acceleration are the same.

Many books have been written which attempt to explain relativity without getting involved in complicated mathematical computations. Use such books to find answers to questions such as the following. Does traveling at a very high rate of speed affect the size of an object? What is the "twin paradox"? Is the mass of an object affected when the object moves at a very high rate of speed? What is meant by relativistic speed? Is there a limit to the speed which an object can attain? If so, what is it?

Curved space. To follow Einstein on his next step, you must be ready to stretch your imagination. When you began your imaginary trip in the spaceship, you supposed that you were very far from any star, so that gravitational forces were so small they could be neglected. Now, suppose you are with two astronauts circling the earth in a capsule. As you know, you would feel no gravitational force. You would be in free fall. If you were prevented from looking outside the windows of the capsule, you could not tell the difference between this situation and the other situation where you were far from any star. You would experience no acceleration.

But according to Einstein, gravity and acceleration are equivalent. If you can feel no acceleration, does this mean there is no gravity? In the earlier part of this chapter, we showed how the force of gravity keeps you in your orbit, but now we seem to be saying that the force of gravity is not there at all.

This is exactly the conclusion Einstein wants us to reach. The motion of a freely falling object far out in space is exactly like your circular motion in orbit about the earth. It is not that the earth is pulling on you with a gravitational force, but rather that the earth has changed the shape of space in its vicinity. The presence of the earth has made the space around it curved. In this curved space, the curved path taken by a freely falling object is the shortest distance between two points.

Understanding curved space. The idea of curved space is almost impossible to comprehend. Perhaps the best we can do is to think of an analogy. Ancient people thought the earth was flat. The idea of a spherical earth was inconceivable to them. They were certain that if you walked west far enough, you would fall off the edge of the flat earth. But we know that if you travel west far enough, you will go around the earth and return to your starting point.

We know even more about the characteristics of our spherical earth. Suppose we wanted to go from Richmond, Virginia, near the east coast to San Francisco, California, on the west coast. We know that the shortest route is not due west, but along a curve called the great circle, which bends slightly north as shown in *Figure 10-11*. The fact that the earth has a curved surface instead of a flat one makes a difference in how we should think about directions and distances.

How would you explain the fact that, although a straight line is the shortest distance between two points, a great circle is the shortest route you can follow in traveling between two points on the surface of the earth?

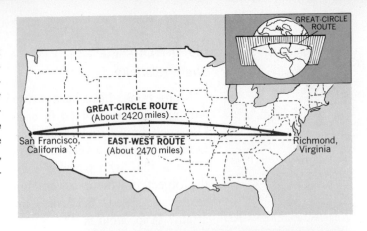

Figure 10-11. At first glance, the east-west route appears to be the shorter route between Richmond and San Francisco. However, the great-circle route is shorter by 50 miles, as revealed by the distance measurements. The great circle shown is the intersection of the earth's surface and the plane which passes through San Francisco, Richmond, and the center of the earth. (See inset.)

Great-circle routes are all very well and good when we are talking about the difference between a curved surface and a flat one. But what about a curved space and a flat space? Unfortunately, there is no very good picture to help us understand these ideas. But still, we can go back to our ideas of straight lines. We always think of a straight line as the shortest distance between two points. How are we to measure that? One way is to send a beam of light, because we ordinarily think of light traveling in straight lines. But, if we do this out in space, we will discover that the light beam curves as it goes by a massive object like the sun.

Einstein predicted that this would happen, and a few years later, scientists made careful measurements during an eclipse and discovered that it was true. *(Figures 10-12, 10-13, 10-14.)*

Einstein's theory and the measurements made by astronomers both indicate that light does not travel in a straight line. Einstein's explanation of this idea took into account the fact that we must talk about both space and time when we discuss the motion of anything. From his point of view, the "shortest distance" between two points must be calculated not just by measuring the space between the points, but also by measuring the time the object takes to get from one place to another. Furthermore, corrections have to be made for

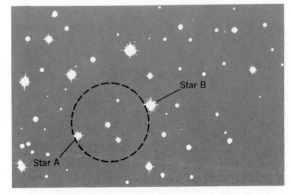

Figure 10-12. A group of stars might have this appearance in the sky at a time of the year when the sun is not near them. That is, they are visible at night. The dashed outline shows the position of the sun against this background of stars several months later.

Figure 10-13. Now the sun is in front of these stars. If the moon were to eclipse the sun, then these stars would become visible. Star A and Star B, at positions very near the sun's edge, would appear to have moved out and away from the edge of the sun.

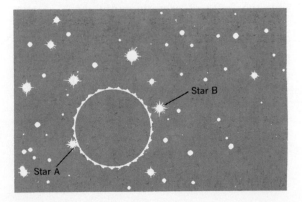

this "distance," depending upon various large massive bodies that are nearby.

From Einstein's point of view, then, a beam of light is actually traveling the shortest distance as it goes around the sun, even though it appears to us to follow a curved path. In exactly the same manner, the moon is following the "shortest path" in its journey around the earth, even though this path is an ellipse. The gravitational field of the earth has changed the shape of space around it. Thus, for the moon traveling about the earth at the speed that it has, the shortest path in space-time is its elliptical orbit.

It may be that our view of space around us, based on our everyday experiences, is wrong. Our view of the earth—based on our experiences with a flat map—is misleading. We now know that the shortest distance between two points on the earth's surface appears as a curve (not a straight line) on a flat map of the earth. It is possible that the "map" which we carry in our minds to describe the universe is also wrong.

Einstein's view of gravity is a curvature of space resulting from the presence of a large massive body. Using this point of view, Einstein was able to prove that the inertial mass and the gravitational mass had to be one and the same. He solved the riddle that had baffled scientists for the previous two hundred years. Nevertheless, his theories left many unanswered questions.

How could the bending of light as it passes near an object of great mass be explained by Newton's law of gravitation?

Fundamental particles. In more recent years, scientists have tended to turn away from the geometrical ideas of Einstein. Instead, scientists are attempting to understand the nature of gravitational forces through a study of the fundamental particles of nature. Some scientists hope to be able to observe the graviton. If the graviton could be observed, scientists could see specifically how this particle interacts with the other particles about which they already know. It may be that this study of particles is the route which will lead to a greater understanding of the nature of gravitational forces. Or, it may be that those who are still following the course set down by Einstein will discover the nature of gravitational forces by means of complicated geometrical pictures of space. There is a very good possibility, however, that still another route—as yet unthought of—will have to be laid out before we can take the next major step in the development of our understanding of gravitational forces.

Figure 10-14. As light from the stars passes close to the sun, the path of the light is bent by the sun's gravitational field. Thus, it appears that the stars have changed their positions. Of course, the distances and sizes of the objects are not shown to scale, and the change in the path of the light is greatly exaggerated. When the light passes the moon, the moon's gravitational field also changes the path of the light. But we cannot observe this change. How would you explain this?

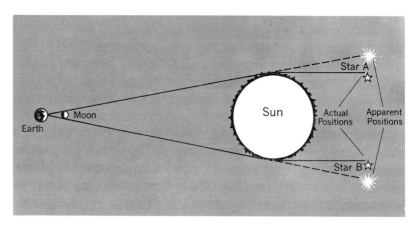

Checking Your Knowledge

IMPORTANT IDEAS

1. Newton did not discover gravity. He did extend the idea of gravitation to all objects, and he derived the following equation for determining the gravitational attraction between two objects.

$$F = G \frac{m_1 m_2}{r^2}$$

2. The gravitational constant—G in the above equation—is the same for all objects everywhere in the universe.

3. If there were no air resistance, all objects would fall to earth at the same rate.

4. An object moving in a circular or an elliptical path is held in its path by a centripetal force acting on the object.

5. Satellites usually travel in elliptical orbits. An orbit the shape of a circle—a special kind of ellipse—is practically impossible to achieve.

6. Within a closed system, it is impossible to distinguish between gravitational force and the force produced by acceleration.

7. Einstein proposed that gravitation is a curvature of the space about any mass.

USING NEW WORDS

Study the six pairs of words below. On your paper write the letters *a* through *f*. Following each letter, write a brief explanation of the similarities and differences in the meanings of the words within the pair having the corresponding letter.

   a. gravitation — graviton
   b. gravitational mass — inertial mass
   c. dyne — gram
   d. centripetal force — centrifugal force
   e. general relativity — special relativity
   f. great circle — curvature of space

TEST YOURSELF

Study the test below. On your paper write the numerals *1-10*. Beside each numeral write the correct response to that part of the test having the corresponding numeral.

1. Which of the following did Newton discover? (a) the force of gravity, (b) why apples fall, (c) why the moon stays in orbit.

2. The shape of the orbit of a satellite is *(circular, elliptical, dependent on the satellite's mass)*.

3. The period of a satellite in an elliptical orbit will be *(greater than, less than, the same as)* the period of a satellite in a circular orbit with a diameter equal to the major axis of the ellipse.

4. The *(gravitational, inertial)* mass of an object is measured by observing its acceleration in response to an applied force.

5. The shortest travel distance between two points on the earth is along a _____.

6. The unit of force which is about as great as the gravitational force on a postage stamp is called a _____.

7. The particle which some scientists think may be associated with the effects of gravitational forces is called the _____.

8. According to legend, the scientist _____ experimented with gravity by dropping two objects having different weights from the Leaning Tower of Pisa.

9. While whirling an object about your head, the inward force you exert on the string to keep the weight moving in a circle is called _____ force.

10. While whirling an object about your head, suppose you increase the speed of the weight, but do not change the length of the string. The amount of force you must exert on the string is *(increased, decreased, unchanged)*.

Extending Your Knowledge

QUESTIONS TO EXPLORE

1. Is the moon in the earth's gravitational field? If not, what keeps it in orbit? If so, why do objects—such as the Ranger and Surveyor spacecraft—fall onto the moon instead of coming back to the earth?

2. What ways can you think of for producing "artificial gravity" on space platforms or on spaceships making journeys through space?

3. Is the velocity of an object orbiting far above the earth greater than or less than the velocity of an object orbiting at a lesser altitude? Is the period longer or shorter for the satellite at the higher altitude? How can you justify your answers?

4. One definition of weight is "the pull of gravity on an object." Why, then, do astronauts float about in space while they are in orbit within the earth's gravitational field? Are they really weightless? How would you explain your answers?

5. Why should Einstein's theories of relativity be checked? What are some effects predicted by the theories of relativity? What aspects of relativity have been verified by experimental evidence?

SOME THINGS TO DO

1. Find out the masses of the earth and the sun and the average distance between their centers. Use this information to find the gravitational force between the sun and the earth. Then, calculate the period of the earth's orbit and check your answer by comparing it with the length of a year.

2. Repeat some of Galileo's experiments related to the question of how things fall. In the first chapter of his book *Gravity*, George Gamow describes some of Galileo's experiments. Try doing experiments with pendulums, with freely falling objects, and with objects rolling down inclined planes. Are these experiments difficult to do? Do your observations agree with Galileo's? If your observations do not agree with Galileo's, try to explain why.

3. On a globe, locate the cities of Athens, Greece, and San Francisco, California. Use a string to measure how much farther it is to fly due east from San Francisco to Athens than it is to fly from San Francisco to Athens along a great circle. Over what cities or places would you pass as you flew along the great-circle route?

CHALLENGES IN SCIENCE

1. Draw a diagram of the motion of the earth-moon system as it travels through space. Include the moon's motion about the earth, the motion of the earth-moon system about the sun, and the motion of the sun due to galactic rotation. Is it likely that the earth ever returns to the same place in space? If so, how could we tell that the earth had returned to the place in space where it is now?

2. How fast will a freely falling object near the earth's surface be moving at the end of 1 second? At the end of 5 seconds? At the end of 20 seconds? How far would it fall during each of these intervals? How would air resistance affect these speeds and distances? What is meant by terminal velocity?

3. Use algebra to show that Kepler's third law is true for circular orbits. Start by writing Kepler's third law as an equation. Then, use algebra to combine the equations about circular motion from this chapter to obtain an equation that resembles Kepler's third law. Compare the two equations, and show why the equation you have derived indicates that Kepler's third law is true.

11

Learning about the solar system fascinates people of all ages.

The Origin of the
Solar System

In your study of *The Earth-Space Sciences,* you probably have noticed the emphasis placed on the way in which scientists seek understanding. The desire to know is characteristic of man and motivates him in his study of the world about him. Through his studies, man has learned that a scientific approach to a problem is an effective way to solve the problem. Scientists believe that there is a reason for each event. Therefore, they are constantly trying to determine the causes of the various effects they observe.

For example, the formation of the solar system must have been the result of a certain chain of events. Scientists would like to know what caused the solar system to evolve into its present condition. But trying to determine the causes of events which happened in the very distant past, when the solar system formed, is a difficult task.

In Chapter 11, you will find out about certain theories of the origin of the solar system. The theories presented are not the only ones that have been proposed. Neither are these theories completely acceptable. The purpose of this chapter is not only to present these theories. It is also to show their strengths and weaknesses. In this way, you will discover the thorough manner in which such theories are investigated before they are completely accepted, partly accepted, or rejected. Each theory must be examined carefully because it may contain an important contribution to man's understanding of the universe.

1. Early Theories

Lack of information. The earliest writings of ancient man, dating back more than five thousand years to the ancient Egyptians, describe ideas about the origin of the earth and the universe. This ancient record and all the writings in subsequent years indicate that this problem has been important to man throughout the centuries of his existence. On the basis of modern scientific standards, we cannot accept these early descriptions. Nevertheless, many of them are quite picturesque and imaginative.

It is understandable why the early theories about the origin of the solar system should have been wrong. At that time, man did not have the basic information needed to develop accurate theories. Many people believed the earth was flat, and almost everybody believed that the earth was the center of the universe. There were no telescopes to reveal the differences between the appearance of the planets and that of the stars.

Checking ideas with observations. It was not until the Renaissance—about four hundred years ago—that man's ideas about the earth and the rest of the universe began to change. Observations made by early scientists, including Copernicus and Galileo, resulted in the theories which put the earth in its proper place in man's understanding of the universe—namely, that the earth is one of several planets which orbit the sun. From that time on, theories about the origin of the earth became more scientifically oriented. When it was understood that the earth was only one of several planets, scientists realized that any theory which accounted for the origin of the earth would also have to account for the origin of the other planets.

There were other observations that also had to be explained. For example, all the planets were observed to move in the same direction about the sun in almost circular orbits. Furthermore, these orbits were observed to be in very nearly the same plane.

As telescopes and other instruments of astronomy improved, many other observations were made. For example, many planets were observed to have satellite systems very much like small models of the solar system. Also, quite a difference in size was discovered between the planets nearer the sun—the terrestrial planets—and the giant planets farther out—the Jovian planets.

What are some other planetary properties which must be accounted for by any theory which attempts to explain the origin of the solar system?

Bode's law. About two hundred years ago, an astronomer named *Titius* (tish'əs) discovered another interesting fact about the planets. A definite relationship exists between the sizes of the planets' orbits and a series of numbers obtained in the manner described in the following paragraphs.

Consider the series of numbers indicated below. Notice that after the first one, each indicated number is twice the preceding number.

$$3, 6, 12, 24, 48, 96, \cdots$$

Now suppose zero is included in the series as the first term. Then, four is added to each number in the above series. The following series of numbers results.

$$4, 7, 10, 16, 28, 52, 100, \cdots$$

Next, think of a scale of distances in which the earth is ten units away from the sun. Using this scale, the average distance from the sun to Mercury is 3.9 units, to Venus is 7.2 units, and so on. The average distances (from the

NAME OF PLANET	AVERAGE DISTANCE FROM SUN	TITIUS' SERIES
Mercury	3.9	4
Venus	7.2	7
Earth	10	10
Mars	15	16
Asteroids	27	28
Jupiter	52	52
Saturn	96	100
Uranus	192	196
Neptune	301	388
Pluto	394	772

Figure 11-1. The interesting relationship which exists between the sizes of the planets' orbits and the series of numbers discovered by Titius is apparent in the table above. This relationship is known as Bode's Law.

sun) for all the planets are shown in the middle column of the table in *Figure 11-1*. The column on the right shows the series of numbers which Titius had worked out. Of course, at the time Titius developed his idea, Saturn was the farthest planet discovered. As you can see, there is surprisingly good agreement between the sizes of the orbits and Titius' series of numbers, at least for the planets out through Saturn.

When Uranus was discovered, its distance, too, agreed very closely with the next number shown in the series. The average distances of Neptune and Pluto do not agree very closely with the series. It is interesting, however, that the distance of Pluto (394) corresponds very closely to the ninth number (388) in the series derived by Titius.

Although it was Titius who first noticed the correlation between the distances to planets and this series of numbers, an astronomer named *Bode* (bō′dē) publicized the relationship. Hence, the relationship became known as "Bode's law."

You may notice another unusual item in the table in *Figure 11-1*. Listed between Mars and Jupiter is the term Asteroids instead of the name of a planet. You may wonder why the asteroids are included here. Many of the rocklike objects in the solar system have orbits which are between the orbits of Mars and Jupiter. In fact, there are so many asteroids there that this region is sometimes referred to as the belt of asteroids. Many astronomers believe that the asteroids are pieces of a destroyed planet that once orbited in this region. If the asteroids are not included at this point, the agreement between the sizes of orbits and Titius' series of numbers is ruined for the planets beyond Mars.

Explaining our observations. No simple picture of the solar system is exactly correct. For example, none of the planetary orbits is exactly a circle, although some orbits are nearly circular. The orbits do not all lie exactly in one plane, but only near it. The sizes of the orbits do not follow exactly the numerical series of Titius, but come close to it. Scientists have felt that these regularities, although they do not describe the solar system exactly, cannot be accidental. Whatever theory correctly explains the origin of the solar system must explain these regularities.

In the remainder of this chapter, some theories concerning the origin of the solar system will be described. Not only will a description of each theory be given, but some of the weak points of each theory will also be given. For, the fact is, no theory yet devised has been able to explain all of the phenomena observed in the solar system. Furthermore, no matter which theory is considered, some observations seemingly contradict it. Thus, even though man has come a long way from the ancient myths and stories about the earth and sun, it appears that he still has a long way to go. With all of his knowledge about physics and chemistry and with all of his astronomical observations, man still has not been able to develop a satisfactory theory for the origin of the solar system.

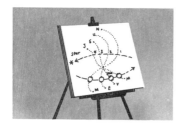

DO IT YOURSELF

Make a report

Investigate some of the early theories about the formation of the solar system. Make a report to the class about some of the more interesting and unusual theories. HINT: A good reference to use is the book *And There Was Light* by Rudolf Thiel.

2. Two-Star Theories

The tidal theory. In one group of theories about the origin of the solar system, each theory begins with the sun already formed and existing in space without any planets about it. Then, according to one of these theories, another star passed close by the sun. It came so close, in fact, that it almost hit the sun. Of course, gravitational attraction between the two stars would cause huge tides to be raised on each of them. The closer the two stars passed, the larger would be these tides.

This theory is called the *tidal theory,* for obvious reasons. According to this theory, the tides were so great that material was actually ripped away from the two stars, as shown in *A* of *Figure 11-2*. As the two stars continued to move farther apart, this material would be stretched out into a filament reaching across space between the two stars, as shown in *B*.

Finally, after the passing star had moved far away, some of the material that had been pulled away from the two stars would stay in the gravitational field of the sun. This material would have been pulled sideways during the encounter, and so the lumps of material would all be traveling in orbit, as shown in

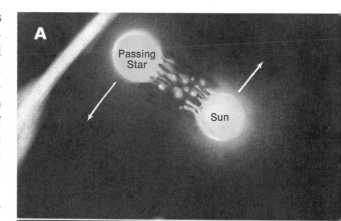

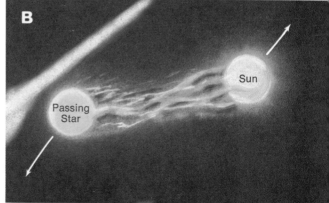

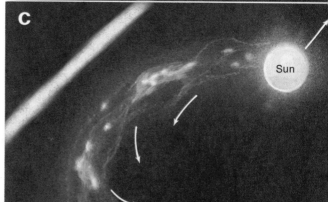

Figure 11-2. According to the tidal theory, the planets were formed out of stellar material—material that came from the sun and another star. This material, which eventually became the planets, was torn from these two stars as they passed very close to each other.

C of *Figure 11-2*. According to the tidal theory, this material would then condense into larger lumps forming the planets, the planets' moons, and the many other objects which make up the solar system.

Assume the passing of a star near our sun caused the solar system to be formed about our sun. What might you expect to happen in the region surrounding the other star?

Faults of the tidal theory. The tidal theory has two major faults. First of all, careful calculations about the behavior of hot, gaseous material in space indicate that the material would tend to expand and become less dense rather than to condense and form planets. Suppose a star had passed close to the sun, as the tidal theory suggests. Suppose, too, that the gravitational interaction had pulled hot, gaseous material from the stars out into space. The result would very likely be a ring of gas and dust around the sun, but not the formation of planets.

The theory's second major fault was not discovered until many years after the theory was first proposed. Modern computing machines were used to make careful calculations of the effects of gravitational force on the material pulled loose from the passing stars. These calculations indicated that the material, although expanded rather than condensed, would fall back into the sun after the stars had moved far away from each other. According to these calculations, the material would not remain in orbit around the sun. Thus, there would be little or no material about the sun from which planets could form.

The double-star theory. A different theory, but one which still involved two stars, was suggested in order to avoid the second fault of the tidal theory. This second theory also starts with the sun already formed. In this theory, however, the sun is a member of a double-star system. Then, this theory suggests, the second star—the companion to the sun—became a supernova, completely destroying itself with a terrific explosion. Most of the material from this explosion was thrown far out into space. But some, a small fraction of the material from the explosion, remained. From this fraction, the planets and their moons supposedly condensed.

Faults of the two-star theories. Here again the problem of condensation comes up. Once more, careful calculations indicate that the material from this explosion would remain spread out. The material that did not escape far out into the galaxy would remain as a thin cloud of gas and dust around the sun, but not as a family of planets.

There is another fault of both the tidal and the double-star theories. Each theory is based on an event or happening that is not at all common. A close miss between two stars is a very rare event, as is a supernova explosion. Of course, such rare events are not completely impossible, but most scientists would like to find a theory which did not rely on occurrences so improbable. In fact, most scientists have concentrated on explanations based on occurrences which would be typical rather than unusual—that is, occurrences which might happen to almost any star. Such theories would make the formation of a solar system a rule rather than an exception. There are such theories, and most of them involve the formation of both the sun and the planets in a single process.

Some calculations indicate that gaseous material in space would spread out instead of condensing. Yet, stars are believed to form as gaseous nebulae in space contract. How would you explain this apparent contradiction?

3. Nebular Theories

How nebulae contract. Another group of theories does not involve already formed stars. Each of these theories has as its starting point a gigantic cloud of dust and gas, much like the gaseous nebulae which we can now see within our galaxy. Gradually, because of its own mass and gravitational force, such a nebula would start to pull itself together. There would probably be some place in the nebula where the concentration of material was a little more dense than at other places. The exact location of this place would be a matter of chance. But such a place would naturally become the place about which the materials in the nebula would become concentrated. As more and more material was drawn toward this place, the concentration of material there would increase, causing a steadily increasing gravitational effect.

Not all the particles in the cloud would move directly toward this center of concentration. Depending upon their random motions in the cloud, the particles would be following different paths. As the particles were attracted by the gravitational force of the concentration, they would move toward the concentration in a wide variety of orbits, as indicated in *Figure 11-3* below.

As the cloud became more and more compact, the particles would bump into each other more and more often. Some of their energy of motion would be changed into heat, and the particles would be slowed down. Whenever two particles struck, each would change direction a little bit. As long as the particles continued to cross each other's orbits, they would keep on bumping. Eventually, this bumping would tend to make all the particles go in the same direction. The direction of their final motion would depend upon the direction in which most of the particles were originally moving. But eventually, some orbital plane would be

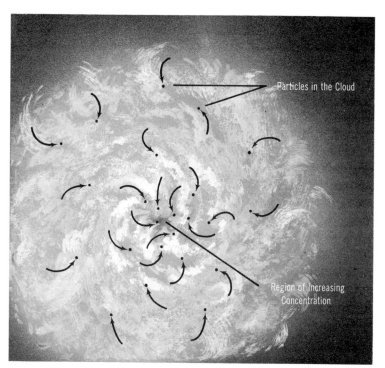

Particles in the Cloud

Region of Increasing Concentration

Figure 11-3. In a huge cloud of gas and dust in space, the dust and gas would not be uniformly distributed. There would probably be some region in which the gas and dust would be more concentrated than in the other regions. The gravitational force would be greater in the region of concentration and would attract material from other portions of the cloud. Thus, the region of the cloud that was already concentrated would become even more concentrated. Since particles in the outer regions were originally moving at random, each particle would follow a unique course on its way to the region of increasing concentration.

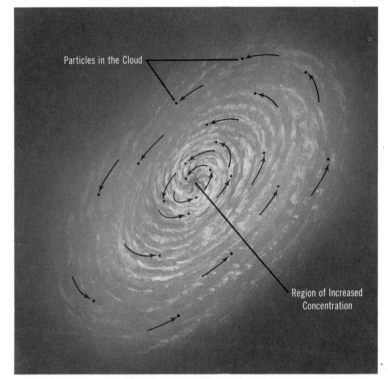

Figure 11-4. Materials in all regions of the condensing cloud are affected by gravitational force. As the region of increased concentration becomes smaller because of gravitational force, it spins faster and faster. Eventually, the condensing cloud becomes a large, rotating, disk-shaped cloud with the region of greatest concentration at its center.

Particles in the Cloud

Region of Increased Concentration

favored. Therefore, all of the particles would eventually be moving about the central condensation in orbits in approximately the same plane.

Even when the particles were all in the same plane, some bumping would still take place, since the orbits would not all be perfect circles. With each bump, the particles would lose some energy of motion. Thus, the particles would be drawn closer and closer to the center by the gravitational force. However, as they moved in, their orbital speed would steadily increase. Eventually, a rapidly spinning mass would accumulate in the center with a large rotating disk of material spreading out around it, as shown in *Figure 11-4.*

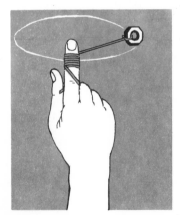

FIND OUT BY TRYING

Materials you will need: string, weight (¼" hex nut will do)

Tie the weight to the string. Then, hold one end of the string and whirl the weight around in a circle about 15 inches in radius. As the weight revolves, allow the string to wrap around your finger. Does the speed of the weight change as the string winds up on your finger? If so, does it increase or decrease? Does the rate of revolution change as the string winds around your finger? If so, does it increase or decrease? If a rotating mass of gas were to contract because of gravitational force, what would be the effect on the speed at which the molecules of gas revolve about the center of the mass?

Forming a star. Because of all the impacts between molecules and because of the pressure created by gravitational forces, the particles at the center of the cloud of gas and dust would be quite hot. The center of the cloud would finally get hot enough to start converting hydrogen to helium. The mass of gas would now become a star. The material around this newborn star would be rotating too rapidly to get into the center. It would be left in the spinning disk outside.

A similar situation can be observed every time you watch the water go down the bathtub drain. A whirlpool forms around the drain, and most of the water spins around a long time before managing to get to the drain itself. In fact, when the water is almost all gone, you will notice that practically none of the water moving in the whirlpool goes down the center of the drain.

Forming planets. What happens to the swirling disk of gas around the newborn star? According to the theory, small concentrations would have already developed here and there within the rotating disk. Gradually, these concentrations pull more and more of the gas toward them. These concentrations are similar to the original condensation, but on a smaller scale. These condensations, still traveling in orbit about the central sun, eventually grow into planets. But here we begin to run into some difficulties.

Loopholes in this nebular theory. In this theory, we are considering a mass of gas condensing because of its own gravitational force. How do we imagine this will happen? Consider the room in which you are sitting. It is filled with air which is a gas. Yet this gas does not condense into a single lump. The reason is that the pressure of the air keeps the particles in the air fairly evenly distributed. If the air should accidentally become a little more condensed in one place than in the others, then the pressure there would be higher. The particles of gas would immediately push away from each other. Actually, it takes quite a bit of work to compress air, as you know if you have ever pumped up a bicycle tire.

According to the nebular theory, gravitational attraction supplies the force necessary to compress the gas. It should be possible to check this. Using Newton's law of gravitation to determine the strength of that force, scientists can calculate how much mass it takes in a concentration to produce the gravitational force needed to compress the gas. From such calculations it appears that a mass of gas weighing the same as the sun would, indeed, contract and compress itself by its own gravitational forces. On the other hand, a mass of gas weighing only as much as the earth would not contract. The gravitational forces within it would be too weak to cause contraction.

Of course, the earth has an atmosphere around it now. Therefore, the earth's gravity must now be strong enough to hold this gas and prevent its expanding out into space. But this is the earth after it has already condensed. As the earth is now, the gas is much nearer the center of gravitational force than it would be if the earth were still a very large and gaseous mass.

You will recall that gravitational force is inversely proportional to the square of the distance between the centers of the objects. If all the earth's material were diffused out into a huge cloud, the total mass would be the same, but the concentrating force would not be nearly as strong as it is now.

If the earth had the same mass, but ten times its present diameter, how would the force of gravity at the earth's surface be different from what it is now?

The moon is another example of an object that could not have condensed from a cloud of gas. The moon has no atmosphere because its gravitational force is not even great enough to hold gas molecules near its surface. Instead, they fly off into space. And the moon is solid. If the solid moon cannot hold gas molecules, it is difficult to imagine how a body the size of the moon could have ever condensed out of a cloud of gas.

4. The Protoplanet Theory

A revised nebular theory. According to the original nebular theory, the amount of material in the condensing cloud of gas and dust was about the same as the amount of material in the present solar system. Most of this material condensed to form the sun. The amount left over was just enough to form the planets and their moons, with a little remaining to account for the comets and meteorites.

A newer version of the nebular theory, called the *protoplanet* (pro′tə plan′it) *theory,* has quite a different starting point. This newer theory suggests that the original mass of dust and gas was considerably larger than the present amount of material in the solar system.

After the sun had condensed at the center of this mass, the amount of material left over in the rotating disk might have been 10 to 100 times more than that which is now present in the planets and their satellites. With this extra mass of material, there would be enough gravitational force at various points of condensation to compress the gas and to cause the development of the planets.

The protoplanet theory assumes that the mass of material rotating about the sun was originally 10 to 100 times greater than it is now. What fault in the nebular theory is eliminated by this assumption?

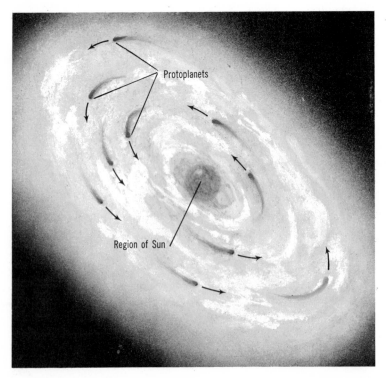

Protoplanets

Region of Sun

Figure 11-5. According to the protoplanet theory, the solar system was formed from a huge, condensing cloud of gas and dust. Material condensed (or became concentrated) at several places within the rotating cloud. The largest concentration of material within the condensing cloud eventually became the sun. Smaller concentrations, called protoplanets, eventually became the planets.

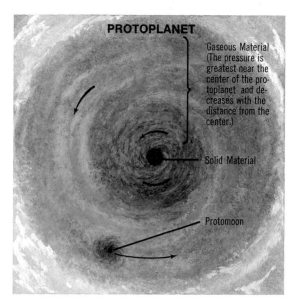

PROTOPLANET

Gaseous Material (The pressure is greatest near the center of the protoplanet and decreases with the distance from the center.)

Solid Material

Protomoon

Figure 11-6. A protoplanet, seen at one stage of its formation, might have a structure similar to that shown in the diagram above.

Protoplanets and protomoons. Suppose that the process of condensation in the huge cloud of dust and gas has progressed rather far. The material in the region where the sun will form is pretty well condensed at the center of the disk. Smaller concentrations are beginning to form within the disk, as shown in *Figure 11-5*. These smaller condensations, along with all of the particles of gas and dust in the surrounding ring, are moving in orbits about the region where the sun will be. These smaller condensations are called *protoplanets,* and it is from these condensations that the planets will form.

At the center of such a protoplanet, solid material begins to condense and to be compacted together by the gravitational forces within the protoplanet and by the pressure of the gas cloud surrounding it. Almost all of the other material in the protoplanet is, however, still in a gaseous form. Although it is gaseous, this other material is a great deal more condensed and compressed than the material in the rest of the disk around the

sun. *Figure 11-6* is a diagram of a cross section of such a protoplanet.

The condensation in the center of the protoplanet continues to draw in more and more of the particles about it. These particles start moving in orbits about the center of the protoplanet, just as the particles in the original cloud began moving in orbits about the central condensation where the sun formed. At the same time, the swirling mass which contains the protoplanet is moving about the sun as part of the flat, rotating cloud.

Perhaps, as indicated in *Figure 11-6,* somewhere in the compacted cloud around this protoplanet, another condensation center might begin. This condensation would represent a *protomoon* (prō′tə mün).

Accounting for the extra mass. According to the protoplanet theory, the mass of the materials remaining in the rotating disk around the newly formed sun could have been 10 to 100 times greater than the mass of the present planets and their satellites. You will recall that this extra mass was required so that the gravitational forces within the disk would be great enough to produce the protoplanets and protomoons. Of course, a theory which assumes that the solar system had more mass originally than it now has, must also explain how that extra mass was lost. The protoplanet theory explains the loss of mass in the following way.

While the smaller concentrations—protoplanets and protomoons—are building up a core of solid material, nuclear reactions are beginning in the sun. As sunlight begins to penetrate the cloud, light pressure pushes away molecules of gas and small particles of dust.

The presence of light means that another force has entered the picture. Up to now, only two forces were important—gravitational force pulling the cloud together and pressure within the gas tending to avoid this compression. Light pressure from the sun acts in the opposite direction of the sun's gravitational force, and so acts with the gas pressure to push the gas out into space again. Gradually, the light pressure from the sun clears away much of the gas and dust surrounding the protoplanets, leaving only the central core which had time to condense before the sun was "turned on."

Of course, light pressure from the sun would be strong near the sun and would be weaker farther away from the sun. Thus, sunlight would do a pretty good job of clearing away the extra gas and dust from about the near planets. However, quite a bit of dust and gas might be left about the distant planets. Thus, the theory accounts for the fact that the distant planets are much larger than those nearer the sun.

Relative abundance of elements. There is another important question which this theory answers. As you remember from Chapter 8, the atmosphere of a star like the sun contains about 75 per cent hydrogen, 23 per cent helium and only 2 per cent of all the other elements put together. It is reasonable to believe that the relative abundance of elements throughout the universe is generally like this. Yet, the earth contains very little hydrogen and helium—certainly much less than the average for the universe. A long-standing question is this. If the earth condensed out of average universe material, what happened to all the hydrogen and helium?

The protoplanet theory gives an answer, for hydrogen and helium are the gases which are the most difficult to condense. They form liquids only at exceedingly low temperatures —hydrogen at –252°C and helium at –272.2°C. The latter is less than one degree above absolute zero. Thus, as the center of the protoplanets condensed into a solid form with perhaps some liquids on the surface, hydrogen and helium would still be left outside. These gases would be most easily pushed out into space by the pressure of light from the sun.

DO IT YOURSELF
Study the atmosphere

Look up a recent description of the composition of the atmosphere. Only a very recent account will be accurate. Diagram the various layers, including the layers of hydrogen and helium that have been found. How were these layers found? By whom? When? How does the amount of these gases compare with the rest of the atmosphere?

Faults in the protoplanet theory. The protoplanet theory explains many features of the solar system. However, there are some things which do not appear to fit into place. For example, according to this theory, we would expect that the planets closer to the sun would be smaller than the planets farther away from the sun. We would expect this because the planets closer to the sun would have more of their material blown away because of the stronger light pressure. Furthermore, there is more material to be collected in the larger orbits traveled by the planets farther from the sun. At the same time, however, the very distant planets would probably be relatively small. They would have been formed near the edge of the original condensing cloud, where there was simply not much material available. By putting these ideas together, we can get a rough estimate of how planetary sizes should change with distance from the sun, at least according to this theory. See *Figure 11-7*. However, the sizes of the planets are quite different from this theoretical picture. Very roughly, their relative sizes are shown by the graph in *Figure 11-8*.

There is another aspect of the solar system that is not explained by the protoplanet theory. This aspect is the regularity of the sizes of orbits which was discovered by Titius two centuries ago. According to the protoplanet theory, there is no particular reason why a protoplanet should form in one spot and not another.

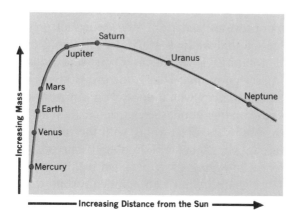

Figure 11-7. According to the protoplanet theory, the masses of the planets would be related to their distances from the sun as indicated above.

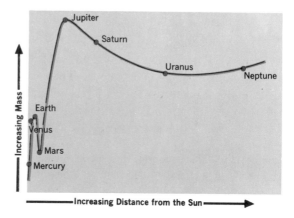

Figure 11-8. According to data obtained by observation, the masses of the planets are related to their distance from the sun as indicated above.

5. The Vortex Theory

The condensing cloud of gas and dust. In discussing the vortex theory, suppose we start again with a picture of a condensing cloud of gas and dust. All the particles and molecules are moving in their separate orbits about some point where the concentration of material is a little greater than average. Gradually, as a result of collisions, the motions of the particles come to be in approximately the same plane.

But what kind of an orbit does a particular molecule or dust particle follow within this plane? As you recall, at the center of the condensing cloud is a large concentration of material. Even though it is not yet compact

enough and hot enough to become a star, this concentration exerts a powerful gravitational force. Thus, the particles that move about this concentration must move in orbits, just as tiny planets would.

Circular orbits. Most theories state that the particles would move in circular orbits, yet we know that the orbits of planets are generally ellipses and not perfect circles. Why should the original particles be moving in perfect circles?

The following explanation is usually given to explain why the orbits of the particles are circular. First, suppose the particles are not moving in circular orbits. Let us trace the

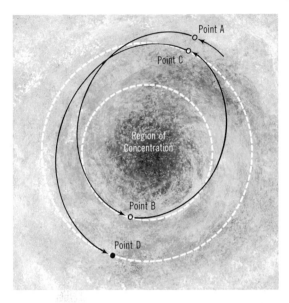

Point A

Point C

Region of
Concentration

Point B

Point D

Figure 11-9. Particles moving in elliptical orbits within a cloud could be forced into circular orbits through collisions with other particles.

path of some particular particle, as shown in *Figure 11-9*.

We know from our study of orbits in Chapter 10 that as the particle moves from Point A to Point B, its speed increases. As it reaches Point B, the particle will be moving faster than particles that are following a circular orbit through this point (shown by the smaller of the dashed circles). When the faster moving particle collides with particles in the circular orbit, the faster moving particle will be slowed down. It will not go out again to Point A where it started. Instead the particle will only get out as far as Point C on its next trip. But at Point C, the particle will be moving slower than the particles going in circular orbits (shown by the larger of the dashed circles) through this point. Now, collisions will tend to increase the speed of the slower moving particle. Instead of returning again to Point B, the particle will be going fast enough to come around to Point D. Using this reasoning,

we reach the conclusion that all the particles will finally be traveling in circular orbits. But is this picture correct?

The formation of vortexes. A little more than twenty years ago, the German scientist C. F. von Weizsäcker presented a different picture of the orbits of the particles which would eventually form the planets. His picture was quite different from the pictures proposed in previous theories. Von Weizsäcker suggested that we look at the particle orbits from a rotating viewpoint, as if we were riding a merry-go-round. That is, he drew the particle orbits as they would appear on a picture that was rotating about the central mass. Since we, as observers, are turning with the picture, we are in what is called a rotating frame of reference. In *Figure 11-10* you can see the appearance that circular and elliptical orbits would have in such a rotating frame of reference.

If a particle were moving in a circle about the center, O, and through Point C, the particle would appear on this picture as a single point. Remember, we are imagining that the picture is rotating at the same rate that the particle is revolving in its orbit. Thus, the particle never changes its position on our picture.

If the orbit is an ellipse, however, the particle will be farther away from the center of rotation at certain times than at other times. Moreover, a particle in an elliptical orbit does not always travel at the same speed. When the particle is at the farthest point in its orbit (Point A), the particle will be moving more slowly than if it were in a circular orbit of that radius. Thus, in the rotating frame of reference, the particle would appear to be moving backwards relative to the direction of rotation. When the particle is at its nearest point (Point B), it would be moving faster than if it were in a circular orbit of that radius. Hence, the particle would appear to

Figure 11-10. According to the vortex theory, the orbits of revolving particles must be viewed from a rotating frame of reference. That is, the orbits are pictured as they would appear to an observer on a plane which is rotating with the condensing cloud.

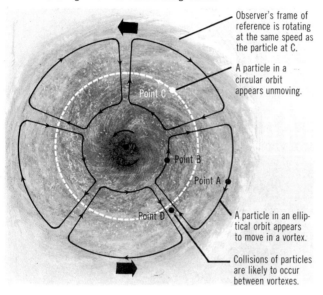

Observer's frame of reference is rotating at the same speed as the particle at C.

A particle in a circular orbit appears unmoving.

Point C

Point B

Point A

A particle in an elliptical orbit appears to move in a vortex.

Point D

Collisions of particles are likely to occur between vortexes.

Figure 11-11. By considering additional rings of vortexes, the vortex theory can be expanded to account for the formation of the solar system.

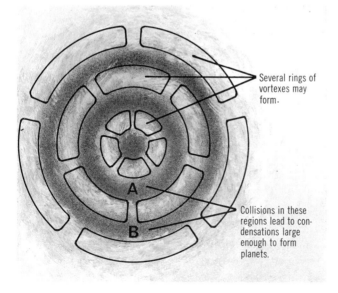

Several rings of vortexes may form.

A

B

Collisions in these regions lead to condensations large enough to form planets.

be moving forward. So, in this rotating frame of reference, the particle would move from A to B and then continue on to A in a continuous pattern.

After carefully calculating the sizes of possible orbits, von Weizsäcker reasoned that five such patterns, or *vortexes* (vôr′tex iz), would fit in a single ring around the center of the whole system. At the boundaries of the vortexes, such as at Point D of *Figure 11-10,* particles moving in opposite directions would very likely collide with each other. The colliding particles would be pulled into one or the other of the two neighboring vortexes, until gradually, no more collisions took place.

The formation of planets. The next step in the vortex theory is illustrated in *Figure 11-11.* Outside the ring of vortexes nearest the center, a second ring can form. It also would contain five vortexes. Outside of that ring, a third ring would form, and so on. Where the rings of vortexes meet, such as the regions A and B of *Figure 11-11,* impacts between particles occur. The particles from the inner set of vortexes will be speeded up slightly by such collisions, and the particles from the outer set will be slowed down. It is in these regions that concentrations large enough to start the formation of planets will finally develop. These concentrations will follow circular orbits.

The most fascinating part of this theory is that the boundaries between vortex rings, worked out in this way, correspond almost exactly to the distances predicted by Bode's law for the orbits of the planets. Apparently, von Weizsäcker's different point of view on the geometry of orbits suggested a possible solution to this particular mystery.

Faults in the vortex theory. The main objection to the vortex theory is in the last step of the theory—that is, the development of planets along the boundaries between the rings of vortexes. Of course, this is the place where many collisions would occur. But what would be the result of such collisions? Some scientists argue that the collisions would continually scatter the material and prevent it from condensing. How can two particles, moving together with speeds of thousands of miles an hour possibly stick together and begin the condensation of a planet? Even if some condensation could begin, and if small lumps of solid material were formed, what would happen when they struck one another at this speed?

Actually, these are unanswered questions since very little is known about the condensation of solid material under these conditions. We imagine the process required hundreds of millions of years, since the space in which the condensation began was very nearly a vacuum. Unfortunately, there is no laboratory experiment which can possibly duplicate these conditions, and we must reason from very sketchy experimental evidence.

It is possible that von Weizsäcker's theory is right. Someday, perhaps with the help of experiments carried out in space, scientists will understand how particles of dust and gas can stick together and begin the formation of a planet. But at present, the crucial process by which nebulae contract in space remains a mystery.

Why, do you suppose, is it not possible for scientists to duplicate the conditions which existed in space when the solar system formed?

6. A Modern Theory

Acceptance of theories. Scientists generally favor those theories of the origin of the solar system which contain the idea that one vast cloud of gas and dust condensed to form the sun and the planets. There is not much more evidence to support this type of theory than there is for the theories that begin with stars already formed. However, there are some reasons to believe that the condensing-cloud type of theory is probably closer to the truth than the theories which start with already formed stars.

The condensing-cloud idea agrees with the present theory of stellar formation which was described in Chapter 6. In addition, the condensing-cloud idea does not depend upon unlikely events such as a near collision between stars or the occurrence of a supernova. On the basis of arguments such as these, most modern astronomers accept the idea that the solar system formed when a vast cloud of gas and dust condensed.

The rotation of the sun. There are some observations which are not explained by any of the theories so far proposed. One of the most important observations which has not yet been explained is rate of rotation of the sun on its axis.

The sun rotates on its axis once in about twenty-five days. This rotation can be observed by watching a family of sunspots as they move day by day. Now, suppose the sun condensed from a mass of gas. What happened to the gas particles that were quite near the edge of the growing sun?

Theoretically, particles that were revolving slowly enough to become part of the central concentration would help to form the sun. Those that were revolving a little bit too fast would not be able to get into the center. In a similar manner, the water whirling around the bathtub drain has difficulty in getting to the center of the drain and going down the pipe.

Of course, there is no friction in space, except between the particles themselves. Thus, not all the particles can be slowed down the way the water particles are slowed in their spin around a bathtub drain. Some of the particles in space would be left spinning around the rim of the sun. What would separate the particles that just barely get into the sun from those that just barely do not get into the sun?

The separation is the result of a very slight difference in speed. The particles that were going just a bit too fast would be left in orbit about the sun. These particles would form a close-in ring. Each particle in the ring would be traveling at the proper speed of a particle orbiting the sun at that distance from the sun's center. The particles that had

been drawn into the outermost surface of the sun would be traveling only slightly slower. Therefore, according to this explanation, the edge of the sun should be traveling at very nearly the orbital speed of a particle in an orbit at that distance from the sun's center.

A major problem. The speed of an object orbiting just above the surface of the sun has been calculated. The rotation of the sun has been observed and measured. The observed rotation of the sun is 200 times slower than the calculations indicated it should be.

If the sun were formed in the way the theory suggests, how could the sun's rotation possibly get slowed down? If it was formed of particles which were traveling more slowly, why weren't more particles drawn into the sun? That is, why don't we have a bigger sun? The difference between the observed rate of rotation of the sun and the rate of rotation that is to be expected from calculations creates a very big and unexplained problem.

FIND OUT BY TRYING
Materials you will need: rotating stool, 2 bricks

Sit on the stool. With a brick in each hand, extend your arms out from your sides. Now have someone push your arms so that you spin slowly. As you spin, pull the bricks in toward your body. What happens to your rate of rotation? Then extend your arms again, pushing the bricks away from you. How does this affect your rotation? If you can do this experiment in a place where no damage will result from dropping the bricks, try dropping the bricks while you are rotating. What effect does dropping the bricks have on your rate of rotation? Try to explain how the effects you observe in this experiment are related to problems in explaining the origin of the solar system.

More problems. Another set of problems is presented by our observations of the only pieces of interplanetary material which can be observed in the laboratory—the meteorites. A careful analysis of the minerals in meteorites indicates that they must have gone through

a complicated process of heating and cooling. If scientists are interpreting their observations correctly, the meteorites could not have reached their present stage of development by a simple process of accumulation, heating up, and then cooling down again.

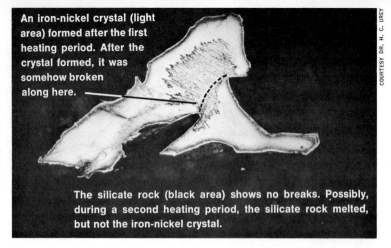

An iron-nickel crystal (light area) formed after the first heating period. After the crystal formed, it was somehow broken along here.

The silicate rock (black area) shows no breaks. Possibly, during a second heating period, the silicate rock melted, but not the iron-nickel crystal.

Figure 11-12. This photograph shows a cross section of a tiny crystal of iron-nickel inside a silicate rock meteorite. By carefully studying the crystal and the meteorite, scientists have reasoned that the meteorite went through two distinct periods of heating and cooling. Between these periods of heating, the crystal was somehow broken. The dashed line shows where the break occurred in the crystal.

The kinds of crystals found in meteorites and the way in which these crystals have been broken and reformed give clear evidence of at least two periods of heating. Between the periods of heating, the particles must have somehow been broken up and then pressed back together again. *(Figure 11-12.)*

Any theory which describes the formation of the planets must also describe the formation of the meteorites. Perhaps meteorites are remnants of a broken-up planet. This might explain the two periods of heating. One occurred when the planet was formed and the other occurred when it was destroyed. But what could possibly destroy a planet?

Perhaps the meteorites are leftovers from the early days of the solar system. That is, meteorites might be pieces of material that never quite condensed into large planets. In that case, how can we account for the complicated history their structure implies?

Professor Harold Urey has suggested that the first of these two ideas is more nearly correct. According to his theory, the condensation of the original cloud of dust and gas resulted first in the formation of thousands of moon-sized bodies. Even as they were being formed, and for millions of years thereafter, these bodies were colliding with one another. Finally, these bodies were almost completely destroyed.

Thus, Professor Urey visualizes many centers of condensation in which small bodies of solid material were formed. In fact, there were so many of these bodies that they could not avoid colliding with one another. The result of these collisions was not a return to the original dust and gas, but rather, many broken up pieces of rock—the meteorites and the asteroids.

The next step in this theory is a recombination of most of these lumps of material into the planets as we know them now. This somewhat complicated theory would account for the observations scientists make of the chemical and mineralogical nature of meteorites. This theory might also help to account for some other observations, such as the relatively small size of Mars and the belt of asteroids between Mars and Jupiter.

If we combine Professor Urey's theory of the multiple creation and destruction process with von Weizsäcker's theory of vortexes in order to explain the original condensations, we get a very convincing picture of how the solar system was formed. But still, this combination of theories gives no solution to the major problem of the rate of the sun's rotation. Why does it turn so slowly?

This is where the theories of the origin of the solar system stand today. As you can see, we still have a way to go.

Checking Your Knowledge

1. Each proposed theory of the solar system's origin must be investigated to determine if it explains observations made concerning the solar system. At the same time, the theory must not violate known scientific principles.

2. In general, there are two classes of theories which attempt to explain the origin of the solar system.

3. Two-star theories assume that the sun was formed without planets and that the planets were formed later by a separate event.

4. Condensing-cloud theories assume that the formation of the sun and planets occurred as part of a single process in which a vast cloud of gas and dust condensed.

5. A completely acceptable theory—that is, one which can explain all observations about the solar system—has not been formulated.

6. The slow rate of the sun's rotation is an observation that is not satisfactorily explained by any theory.

USING NEW WORDS

Study the words listed below. On your paper write the numerals *1-4*. Beside each numeral write words to satisfy the instructions given for the corresponding numeral.

vortex	protoplanet theory
tidal theory	double-star theory
Bode's law	protoplanet
nebular theory	vortex theory

1. List those theories which are based on the condensing-cloud idea.

2. List those theories which assume the sun to be already formed, but without planets.

3. Which term refers to an observation about the size of the planets' orbits?

4. Which words refer to steps in the formation of the solar system?

TEST YOURSELF

In addition to conforming to all the laws of physics, a satisfactory theory of the origin of the solar system must explain all the observations made by scientists. Each observation fits into one of these categories.

a. Favors the two-star theories
b. Favors the condensing-cloud theories
c. Can be explained by either theory
d. Cannot be explained by either theory

Listed below are ten observations that have been made by scientists. Each observation fits into one of the categories listed above. On your paper write the numerals *1-10*. Beside each numeral tell the category to which the observation having the corresponding numeral belongs. (Use the letter to designate the category instead of writing the complete statement.)

1. The planets are spaced at predictable intervals.

2. The asteroid belt consists of large chunks of rock orbiting the sun.

3. Astronomers have never observed two stars colliding.

4. The sun rotates on its axis once every 24.7 days.

5. The planets have nearly circular orbits.

6. There is little helium or free hydrogen about the earth.

7. Meteorites appear to have been reheated after they were first formed.

8. The sun, the earth, and meteorites seem to be about the same age.

9. A large mass of very hot material would tend to expand if it were suddenly thrust into space.

10. All the planets orbit in approximately the same plane.

Extending Your Knowledge

QUESTIONS TO EXPLORE

1. Why were ancient man's explanations for the origin of the solar system impractical?

2. What problems did early scientists encounter with public opinion when they first proposed theories of the nature and origin of the solar system?

3. How does a collision between two molecules differ from a collision between two small particles, such as marbles or beads?

4. What are some reasons why it is so difficult to formulate an acceptable theory for the origin of the solar system?

5. What are some reasons for believing that the asteroids are the remains of a planet that was somehow broken up?

SOME THINGS TO DO

1. Make a list of as many observations as you can find which cannot be explained by the present theories for the origin of the solar system.

2. Divide the class into four groups. Have one group study about tidal theories of the formation of the solar system, one group about the binary-star theory, another group about the protoplanet theory, and the fourth group about the vortex theory. Plan an informal discussion in which individuals from each of the groups attempt to justify the validity of the various theories.

3. Make a graph on which you plot the sizes of the planets on the vertical axis and their distances from the sun on the horizontal axis. Compare your diagram with the ones in *Figures 11-7* and *11-8*. Try to explain any similarities or differences.

4. Find out how the presence of a magnetic field affects the motion of certain objects. Cut a disk about 4 inches in diameter from some nonmagnetic metal, such as copper. Punch a small hole near one edge, so the disk can be suspended as a pendulum. Let the disk swing between the poles of a strong horseshoe magnet. What do you observe? Would the effect be the same if the disk were made from cardboard or some other nonconductor of electricity? Can you suggest any way in which the effects noted in this experiment might be related to the sun's motion?

CHALLENGES IN SCIENCE

1. What is the difference between the solar wind and light pressure? What can you suggest as possible effects of the solar wind on the formation of the protoplanets?

2. Find a recent reference which states the rate at which the earth is losing its atmosphere into space and the amount of meteoric material that is being added to the earth from space. Is the mass of the earth increasing or decreasing? At what rate?

3. Some scientists believe that the elements heavier than carbon—that is, elements with an atomic number greater than that of carbon—must be formed in the center of a star. If so, what are the implications for the formation of the solar system?

4. Some theories about the formation of the solar system are based on a very unusual event that has never been observed by astronomers. According to these theories, the formation of a solar system is quite an unusual event. According to other theories, which are based on events that are occurring all the time, the formation of solar systems is quite common. What are the implications of these two ideas as far as our concept of life on other planetary systems is concerned? Are there other implications?

BREAKTHROUGHS IN SCIENCE

Man thought about and wrote about exploring space for many years. During these years he made remarkable progress in improving his ability to study the many different objects in space. His main tools were telescopes and related instruments, such as the camera and the spectroscope. But man's greatest adventure in astronomy, and perhaps his greatest scientific achievement, is his exploration of space.

In satisfying his curiosity about space, man has not been content to just look at the objects in space from his earthbound laboratories. He has searched for ways to find out firsthand what the planets and the moon are like. And, space exploration provides a way. Some people, of course, think man should explore space simply because it is there and because he has the ability to do so. Many scientists believe that through space exploration, some of the mysteries of the universe, such as how the planets and stars were formed, can be solved. But, the main reason for man's explorations of space is his inborn curiosity. Man has a long history of wanting to explore the unknown.

There are many aspects to space exploration. For one thing, success in space ventures has become a yardstick to measure a nation's leadership in science and engineering. Some people claim that space exploration has a role in national defense. Whatever else is involved, however, one of the goals has been to explore firsthand the surface of the moon and possibly that of Mars. Much preliminary work was done before man could go to the moon. Even greater amounts of planning and even more sophisticated spacecraft will be needed before man goes to another planet.

A major achievement in space exploration was the placing of the first artificial satellite—Russia's *Sputnik I*—into orbit about the earth. This was accomplished on October 4, 1957. The next great achievement, also by the Russians, was when they placed the first manned spacecraft into orbit about the earth on April 12, 1961. Since then, there have been many achievements stemming from the exploration of space. Bands of radiation have been discovered surrounding the earth, hundreds of miles above the equator. Mars has been photographed from spacecraft that passed within 2,000 miles of that planet's surface. On other occasions spacecraft have flown close to Venus and have relayed valuable information about that planet back to scientists on the earth. Of course, the most spectacular accomplishments so far have been the Apollo missions to the moon and back.

The achievements listed above are not the only ones that have been made through man's exploration of space. There is not enough room on this page to list all the achievements of space exploration. However, just from the achievements listed, you can understand that space exploration has been important in man's quest for knowledge. Thus, although man himself is still not able to travel at will throughout the universe, his achievements in space exploration have been remarkable, and they definitely represent a breakthrough in scientific achievement.

REVIEWING UNIT THREE

SUMMARY

1. The sun is enormous compared to other objects in the solar system and smaller than average when compared with other stars.

2. The sun supplies practically all the energy we use on the earth.

3. The sun's gravitational field controls the orbital motion of objects in the solar system.

4. The surface of the sun is very hot and is marked by regions of turbulence.

5. There are nine planets moving about the sun in elliptical orbits. Most of these planets have satellites of their own.

6. On the basis of size and density, the planets are easily divided into two groups.

7. In addition to the planets, other objects, including asteroids and comets, revolve about the sun.

8. Newton's law of universal gravitation and Einstein's theories of relativity give somewhat different concepts of gravity.

9. Several theories have been proposed to explain the origin of the solar system. However, no theory is completely acceptable.

QUESTIONS TO DISCUSS

1. Why does the sun look like a sphere with a clearly defined surface, although it is composed entirely of gaseous material?

2. What is the meaning of the term "frame of reference"? Why is it necessary to define your frame of reference when you attempt to describe the motion of another object?

3. Is a knowledge of Einstein's theories of relativity valuable to the average citizen? Give reasons for your answer.

4. What factors determine your weight on the earth? Would you weigh more or less on the moon? On Mars? On Jupiter?

UNIT TEST

Study the test below. On your paper write the numerals *1-10*. Beside each numeral write the correct response to that part of the test having the corresponding numeral.

1. Which of the following men performed the earliest experiments concerning the effect of gravity on motion? (a) Einstein, (b) Newton, (c) Galileo, (d) Ptolemy.

2. Which of the following men first thought that gravitational force controlled the orbits of the moon and all the planets? (a) Einstein, (b) Newton, (c) Galileo, (d) Ptolemy.

3. Which of the following men proposed that what we describe as gravitational force is really the curvature of space? (a) Einstein, (b) Newton, (c) Galileo, (d) Ptolemy.

4. Which of the following is not a factor in the weight of an object on the surface of the earth? (a) the object's mass, (b) the earth's radius, (c) the object's volume.

5. Which of the following observations is not explained by any theory for the origin of the solar system? (a) Bode's law, (b) some planets have moons, (c) the sun rotates on its axis once in about 25 days.

6. The magnetic field of the sun (*is very uniform, changes constantly, is not measurable from the earth*).

7. The largest planet is (*Saturn, Mercury, Pluto, Jupiter*).

8. The composition of the atmospheres of the other planets is (*like the earth's, not like the earth's, completely unknown*).

9. One attempt to relate gravitational, electric, and magnetic forces is (*the law of gravitation, Bode's law, the unified field theory*).

10. Near the earth's surface, the acceleration of a freely falling body due to gravity is (*9.8 m/sec, 9.8 ft/sec, 9.8 m/sec²*).

ENRICHING YOUR SCIENCE EXPERIENCES

INVESTIGATIONS TO CARRY OUT

1. Determine the fraction of the sun's energy which is received by the earth. Find the area of a sphere of radius 9.3×10^7 miles. Then find the area of a circle of radius 4×10^3 miles. Explain why the ratio of the area of the small circle to that of the large sphere is the fraction of the sun's energy which is received by the earth.

2. Find out when the next occultation of a star by the moon will occur. (An occultation is the passage of one heavenly body behind another so that the farther one is hidden from view.) Also, find out when the moon will occult a planet. Observe these occultations if possible. These observations can best be made with a telescope or with good binoculars. Record the exact time of the occultation for your locality. Does the time agree with the predicted time? If you are fortunate enough to observe the occultation of a star and of a planet, describe any differences you observe between the two occultations. From your observations of the occultations, what can you infer about the atmosphere of the moon? (See pp. 166–167.)

3. Investigate the phenomena of lunar and solar eclipses. Answer the following questions. What is an annular eclipse? Why is each total solar eclipse visible from only a small portion of the earth's surface? Which occurs most often, total solar eclipses or total lunar eclipses? What is the difference in meaning between the terms umbra and penumbra?

ADDITIONAL READING IN SCIENCE

Flammarion, Camille, *The Flammarion Book of Astronomy,* Gabrielle Camille Flammarion and André Danjon, editors. New York, Simon and Schuster, 1964. 670 pp.

Gamow, George, *Gravity*. Garden City, New York, Doubleday & Co., Inc., 1962. 157 pp.

Gardner, Martin, *Relativity for the Million*. New York, The Macmillan Company, 1962. 182 pp.

Mariner Mission to Venus. New York, McGraw Hill Book Company, Inc., 1963. 118 pp.

Nicholson, Thomas D., *The Sun in Action*. Garden City, New York, The Natural History Press, 1964. 32 pp.

Ohring, George, *Weather on the Planets*. Garden City, New York, Doubleday & Co., Inc., 1966. 144 pp.

Pickering, James S., *Captives of the Sun*. Garden City, New York, The Natural History Press, 1964. 32 pp.

Ronan, Colin A., *Man Probes the Universe*. Garden City, New York, The Natural History Press, 1964. 156 pp.

Whipple, Fred L., *Earth, Moon, and Planets*. Cambridge, Massachusetts, Harvard University Press, 1963. 278 pp.

THE NATURE OF THE EARTH

Chapters

Much of the effort of people involved in the earth-space sciences is spent in trying to find answers to seemingly simple questions. One such question is, "What is the earth?" Consider this question for a short time. As you do, you will probably realize that any complete answer to this question would require volumes of writing. You will probably realize, too, that finding out all there is to know about the earth is as impossible for you as writing all there is to know about it. Yet, it is important for you to know about the earth, its structure, its origin, and the changes it has undergone.

In the previous units, you have studied the universe—that collection of galaxies, stars, gases, and space which surrounds us and contains us. You have learned about the sun and the group of nine planets held in orbit around it by the force of universal gravitation. In UNIT 4 you will look upon our earth from this viewpoint. You will continue to view the earth as a member of a planetary system which is moving about a rather average star, the sun. The sun is one of billions of stars of the Milky Way Galaxy which, in turn, is one of billions of galaxies making up the universe.

From this point of view, the earth seems somewhat unimportant. However, it is our home in space, and our only home. Furthermore, it is the only object in space which is close enough for us to examine in detail. Thus, as both our home and as our natural laboratory, the earth has a very special importance to us. For these reasons, in UNIT 4 we will explore our home planet, the earth.

◄ Man, in his quest to discover the nature of the earth, makes use of man-made satellites.

Certain aspects of our planet could be studied by observing the earth from space.

CHAPTER 12

The Earth as a Planet

What we know of the earth is largely the result of investigations carried on at the surface or very near the surface of the earth. From such a perspective, the overview is somewhat limited. It would not be surprising if some of our information about the earth is affected by our closeness to the earth. It may well be that "we cannot see the forest for the trees."

Let us consider, then, a different approach. To begin our study of the earth, let us look upon the earth as a complete planet and consider its general characteristics. To gain this perspective we might imagine the point of view of visitors in a spaceship from some planet outside of the solar system.

Suppose these travelers note the solar system in space and change course to investigate it. As they approach the system, their attention is drawn first to the star at the center of the rotating system and then to one of the revolving objects. As they rapidly approach this planet—the third one out from the sun—their observations become more detailed. Their information about the planet being observed accumulates rapidly.

What information could be obtained about our earth? What shape does it have? What is its size? What is its makeup? What, if any, unusual features does it have? These and other questions about the earth will be explored in Chapter 12.

1. The Shape, Size, and Density of the Earth

Observations of the earth. Travelers from outer space approaching the earth in a spaceship would observe the earth differently at various distances. If they passed by the moon in their approach, their view of the earth would be like that in the picture taken by the satellite *Lunar Orbiter I. (Figure 12-1.)* The observations made by the visitors would include many made with their eyes and many more made with instruments. Their data and calculations would give these visitors information about the shape, size, and mass of the earth. These would be some of the most fundamental characteristics of the earth that the visitors would be interested in determining.

The earth's shape. The earth is very nearly a sphere, but not exactly so. A sphere, as you know, has all points of its surface the same distance from its center. The general shape of the earth differs from a sphere in that it is slightly squashed at the North and South Poles and slightly fat around the equator. Observe the diagram in *Figure 12-2* showing the shape of the earth. The name given to this shape is *oblate spheroid* (ob′lāt sfir′oid).

Figure 12-1. The spacecraft *Lunar Orbiter I* was 1,200 kilometers from the moon's surface when it took this picture of the earth. The moon's surface is in the foreground. Judging from this picture, what is the shape of the earth?

NASA

The flattening at the poles is very slight. How slight it is can be determined by comparing the distance through the center of the earth between the poles to that through the center of the earth in the plane of the equator. These distances have been determined. The distance directly through the center of the earth in the plane of the equator is 7,926.68 miles (12,756.77 kilometers). This measurement is taken at average sea level, between points on opposite sides of the earth. The distance from the North Pole to the South Pole through the center of the earth is 7,899.98 miles (12,713.82 kilometers).

Compared with the size of the earth, the difference between these two distances is small—about 26 miles or 43 kilometers. But, considered in another way, this difference is quite large. For example, the top of the highest mountain on earth is about 5½ miles or 9

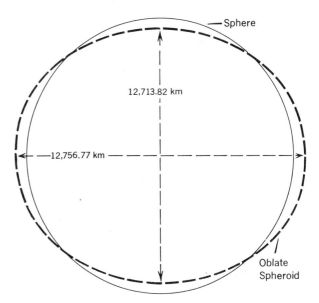

Figure 12-2. The earth's shape is more like that of an oblate spheroid than it is like that of a sphere. However, the flattening is very slight.

221

kilometers above sea level. The difference between the equatorial diameter and the polar diameter is, then, about 5 times as great as the height of earth's highest mountain.

Determining the shape. You may be wondering how the measurements of the polar and equatorial diameters could have been made. You are aware of one problem immediately. That is, there is no ocean at the South Pole. A continent—the mountainous and ice-covered Antarctica—is there. What does it mean, then, to give a measurement for the distance from the North Pole to the South Pole based on sea level? It means that the measurement was taken from the position which the surface of the ocean would have if the mountains and ice were not there. Of course, the determination of the actual distance from pole to pole has to be calculated from other measurements since it cannot be measured directly.

What problems would be encountered in any attempt to measure directly the distance between the poles of the earth? Which "next best" ways of determining this distance can you suggest?

The job of carefully measuring the earth is an extremely difficult task of surveying. Many measurements must be made over the continents of the earth, mile by mile. And then, many calculations must be made using these data to determine the shape of the earth.

In more recent years, the methods used previously have been improved upon. By carefully tracking artificial satellites which have been put in orbit about the earth, scientists have been able to improve the accuracy of measurements made of the earth. From these measurements, they have refined their ideas of the shape of the earth.

Measurements made with satellites have shown that the earth is not only flattened at

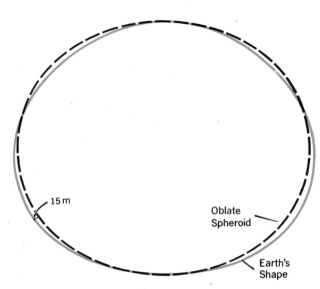

Figure 12-3. The earth's shape is indicated by the solid line. If you were to view the earth from outer space, do you think you could tell that the earth is not a sphere?

the poles. They show, also, that the earth is slightly fatter in the Southern Hemisphere than it is in the Northern Hemisphere. In *Figure 12-3*, a diagram representing the shape of the earth is shown. The dashed line shows the oblate spheroid, the shape determined from measurements made of the earth before satellites were launched. The solid line shows the slight correction which has been determined from measurements made with earth satellites. As you can see, the correction required is quite small. At most, the greatest difference between the sea level surface for the corrected shape and the oblate spheroid is only about 49 feet or 15 meters.

Determining the mass of the earth. A space traveler orbiting the earth in his spaceship could figure out the mass of the earth from his orbital period. We on earth have been able to determine the earth's mass by a different method. Newton's law of gravitation, as you observed in Chapter 10, says that the force of attraction between two objects depends on the mass of each. Of course, we can measure the gravitational force of the earth on any mass, but we need a standard of comparison to complete the calculation. A standard method was invented almost two centuries ago. It is a delicate pendulum with which scientists can measure the force of gravity between two standard weights. With this instrument the gravitational constant G, described in Chapter 10, can be determined. With this value known, the mass of the earth can be determined. From measurements of this type, scientists have de-termined that the mass of the earth is about 6.6×10^{21} tons. A more exact expression of the earth's mass is 5.98×10^{27} grams.

Determining the volume. Finding the volume of an oblate spheroid is somewhat more difficult than finding the volume of a sphere. However, the difference between the equatorial diameter and the polar diameter is quite small compared to these diameters. We can use an average value between these two and calculate the volume of the corresponding sphere. Rather accurate determinations of the volume of the earth have been made.

Find the average of the polar and equatorial diameters. Use one half of this value as the measure of the radius of the earth. Express this measure in centimeters. Then, using the formula $V = \frac{4}{3}\pi r^3$, calculate the volume of the earth. Express the volume in liters. Does this volume include the earth's atmosphere? Do you think this volume should include that of the earth's atmosphere?

Determining the density. Density is defined as mass per unit of volume. The density of a material can be useful in comparing one material with another material. You have probably been asked, "Which has more mass, 100 grams of feathers or 100 grams of lead?" In considering the problem, you would be comparing the mass of one material with the mass of the other material. The masses, you would say, are equal. However, the space taken up by each of these masses would not be the same. The feathers would take up more space than the lead. In comparing densities, both volume and mass of the materials are being considered in the comparison. Thus, although the masses are equal, the density of the lead is greater than that of the feathers. In studies of various materials in space and materials on earth, comparisons are often made of their densities.

Dividing the value determined for the mass of the earth by the value determined for its volume gives the value for the average density of the earth. The value that has been determined is 5.522 g/cm^3. This value indicates that, on the average, the mass of the earth is a little more than five and a half times that of an equal volume of water. This value is the first somewhat mysterious fact that we have learned about the earth. We are not ready to appreciate its mystery yet.

As we go more into a detailed study of the earth's surface, however, we will find that the average density of surface rock is considerably less than this value of 5.522 g/cm^3. The difference in these densities is important. The interior of the earth must be made of denser material than its surface. To become aware of this condition is an important discovery.

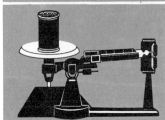

FIND OUT BY TRYING

Materials you will need: small tin can, iron ball, graduated cylinder, water, steel wool, balance

Obtain a small tin can from which the top has been neatly cut. Fill the can completely with water. Measure the amount of water the can holds. Record this amount of water as the volume of the can.

Press several pads of steel wool into the can until the can is about half full. Place the iron ball in the can. Fill the can with steel wool until the steel wool is even with the top of the can.

Place the can containing the steel wool and ball on the balance. Determine the mass of the can and materials within it. Record the value you determine.

Divide the value you find for the mass by the value you found for the volume. What is the average density of the can and its contents? Record this value.

Do you think the average density is the same as the density of the iron ball? If not, how would you compare these values? Do you think that the average density is the same as the density of the steel wool? As that of the can? If not, how would you compare these values? How might you test your ideas?

2. Oceans, Continents, and the Atmosphere

Observations of surface characteristics. Having established the general shape and size of the earth, it is important that we examine the earth in more detail. If we consider the earth as seen by visitors in a spaceship circling the earth, what would they see? They would see details of the earth's surface similar to those seen in *Figure 12-4*. In this view of the earth, three details stand out immediately. These are the oceans, the continents, and the clouds. These three characteristics are the same ones which are the most obvious to us who inhabit the planet earth.

The atmosphere. The clouds, of course, are the visible portion of a much more extensive feature of the earth—namely, its atmosphere. The visitors from another planet would be able to see a different aspect of the atmosphere

Figure 12-4. This picture was taken from an orbiting spacecraft. From this distance, three features of the earth—land, oceans, and clouds—are visible.

NASA

if they looked at the right time. As their space-ship carried them in orbit about the earth to the point where they were just passing into the earth's shadow, they could see a thin band of atmosphere illuminated by the sun. *(Figure 12-5.)*

The oceans and continents. From their observations, the orbiting visitors could make detailed maps of the earth below. They would, in a short time, create maps similar to those which surveyors on earth have been developing over the last several centuries. As the visitors studied their maps, they would discover that the oceans cover more than two thirds of the earth's surface. If they were to carefully measure the area of all of the earth's oceans, they would find the area to be about 1.39×10^8 square miles (3.61×10^8 km²). The area of the continents, they would find, is about 5.75×10^7 square miles (1.49×10^8 km²). Of course, to get the same values for these areas as surveyors on earth do, the visitors from space would have to realize that the ice at the North Pole is covering an area of ocean and not a continent.

Upon examining the earth's continents more closely, the visitors would note that the continents are marked by long chains of mountains interlaced with rivers. In some regions, they would observe, there are broad, flat plains having no mountains and very few hills. The visitors from space would probably be curious about these different surface features. They would probably wonder how high

Figure 12-5. Except for clouds, the earth's atmosphere is invisible from the earth. From space, however, an astronaut has this unique view of the atmosphere.

NASA

the mountains in the different ranges are. If they measured the heights carefully, they would find that some mountains rise many thousands of meters above the average level of the sea. The highest is Mt. Everest in the Himalaya Mountains. It rises 29,003 feet or 8,840 meters above the average sea level.

If the visitors had some way of measuring ocean depths from their spaceship, they would find that the depth of the water in the ocean varies from place to place. They would discover that the deepest part of the ocean, located just southwest of the island of Guam in the Pacific Ocean, is about 36,000 feet or 10,970 meters below sea level.

DO IT YOURSELF

Make a report

Use reference books, newspapers, and magazines to gather information about how far man has been able to penetrate the earth's surface, the ocean, and the atmosphere. Find out some of the conditions experienced by man in making these penetrations. From the data, do you think that man is best adapted to live in a certain zone about the earth?

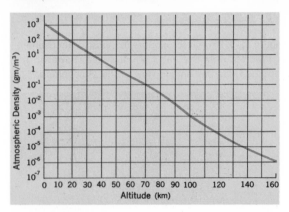

Figure 12-6. As indicated by the curve above, the density of the earth's atmosphere decreases as the distance above the earth's surface increases.

Characteristics of the atmosphere. The travelers in the spaceship circling the earth would have an easier time measuring the depth of the atmosphere than they would have measuring the depth of the ocean. By bringing their spaceship into closer and closer orbits about the earth, they would eventually begin to interact with the widely separated molecules at the outer reaches of the atmosphere. If their instruments were highly sensitive, they could detect molecules of gas at a height of 300 kilometers. If they moved to an orbit 150 kilometers above the surface, the earth's atmosphere would be dense enough to cause a noticeable drag on the motion of their spaceship and a decrease in their speed. If they descended below 100 kilometers, the drag effect of the atmosphere would be strong enough to bring their spaceship out of orbit and down to the earth. As they descended, they would observe the changes in density indicated in the graph in *Figure 12-6*.

Even if the graph were extended, there would be no point corresponding to a density of zero. Does this mean that the atmosphere of the earth never ends, but just extends out indefinitely into space? How might you proceed in order to decide where the "upper edge" of the atmosphere is in relation to the earth?

Changes at the earth's surface. Whether we are in a spaceship circling the earth or exploring on the earth's surface, the three features we observe most easily are the ocean, the continents, and the atmosphere. If we watched them over a period of time, we would see all of them change. The most rapid change occurs in the atmosphere, as your experience with constantly shifting patterns of clouds and continual change in weather would verify. As we would study the ocean, we would observe regular changes in the tide. We would also detect movements of great quantities of water in the huge system of ocean currents.

Changes, as a rule, take place much more slowly on the continents than they do in the atmosphere or in the oceans. The rate of most of these changes is so slow that we would have difficulty in detecting any change. But changes do take place. And, although they proceed at a slow rate, many of the changes on the continents are extensive. For example, consider the amount of change involved in the forming of the Grand Canyon. The change in only one year would not be noted. The difference after six million years, however, is very great and very easily noted.

3. Surface Chemistry

Investigating surface materials. If our imagined visitors from outer space succeeded in landing on earth, what kind of scientific

measurements might they make? In answering this question we might consider our own space program as an example. We can gain some

NASA

Figure 12-7. The device shown above, if sent to another planet, could detect life on that planet. If chemical reactions unique to living organisms were detected by this device, radio signals would be sent out, indicating a possibility of life existing on that planet.

idea of what visitors here would be interested in investigating by finding out what scientists here are planning for explorations on other large objects in space.

What determinations do scientists consider most important for spacecraft they send and land upon the moon or upon a nearby planet? The most important determinations to be made by such a spacecraft are chemical in nature. Even the search for life on Mars— one of the most important parts in the space program—will be carried out by an instrument designed to measure chemical reactions.

Since investigations into the chemical nature of distant objects in space are part of the project of space exploration, it is reasonable that in our study we turn to the chemistry of the earth, or *geochemistry*. To help organize our study of geochemistry, we can divide the earth into four separate zones. *(Figure 12-8.)* These zones are described below.

1. The *atmosphere* is the zone of gas that extends from the solid (or liquid) surface of the earth out into space. The density of the gas and particles within this zone is less and less at higher and higher altitudes, as shown in the graph in *Figure 12-6*.

ATMOSPHERE

HYDROSPHERE

LITHOSPHERE

BIOSPHERE

Figure 12-8. These pictures help us visualize each of the zones of the earth. There is no way that each zone can be observed in its entirety. For instance, the deep layers of the lithosphere cannot be seen. Even the surface of the lithosphere cannot be seen in many places because it is covered with water. The hydrosphere contains much water that we are not able to see, and the atmosphere—except for clouds—is invisible. The biosphere is the easiest zone to observe, but it is not usually included in a study of the earth.

2. The *hydrosphere* consists of all the water—either liquid or solid—that is distributed about the earth's surface, or within its crust.

3. The *lithosphere* consists of all the rest of the earth—that is, the rocks, soil, and interior of the oblate spheroid which we call our planet.

4. The *biosphere* (bī′ə sfir) is a very thin zone at the surface of the earth wherein living creatures exist. This zone extends for a short distance down into the earth's crust on the continents. It extends for a short distance up into the atmosphere. It also extends to varying depths in the oceans and other bodies of water upon the earth.

In order to make this division, some observations about the chemical nature of the surface materials are required. Also, to recognize the biosphere as something special and apart from the rest of the liquids, solids, and gases of the earth requires that the biosphere have some distinctive nature.

Living things are distinctively different from the rest of the earth, primarily in their chemistry. The nature of their chemistry—that is, the chemical elements and compounds of which they are composed and the chemical reactions that characterize life—sets them apart. Having established that the biosphere does exist and that it is distinctively different, let us leave the study of it to the biologists and continue with our investigation of the nature of the earth.

Relative amounts of materials about the earth. From the standpoint of mass, the atmosphere and the hydrosphere are unimportant parts of the earth. The mass of the gas in the atmosphere amounts to only 0.00009 per cent of the mass of the earth. The mass of the hydrosphere is somewhat greater, but it is still a small fraction of the total mass. It represents only 0.024 per cent of the earth's mass. From this information you can see that more than 99.9 per cent of the earth's mass is in the lithosphere. Therefore, in any study of the chemistry of the earth, a study of the solid portion, or lithosphere, is most important. It is by studying the lithosphere that we begin to get some idea about the composition of the planet earth.

DO IT YOURSELF

Make a calculation

The atmosphere is said to represent only 0.00009 per cent of the mass of the earth. This seems to be a very small amount, indeed. However, when considering the great mass of the earth, a very small part of such a large mass represents a vast amount of matter. Use your text or other reference books to find the mass of the earth. Use the value you find and calculate the mass of the atmosphere.

On the basis of your calculation, do you think that the atmosphere is a small amount of matter, in terms of your everyday experience?

Determining the chemical composition of the earth. Several thousand rocks, collected from all over the world, have been carefully analyzed. From these analyses it has been determined that the average density of surface rock is about 2.8 g/cm³. This value is only half the value determined for the average density of the whole earth.

228

Analysis of surface rocks also reveals which of the chemical elements the rocks contain, as well as the amounts of these elements. From a combination of all of these data, scientists have been able to determine values for the relative abundance of the various elements on the earth's surface. Values for some of the elements are given in the table in *Figure 12-9*. Note that the table includes three values for each element listed. You can see that in the first column of figures is given the fractional amount (by mass) of each element in the earth's surface. From these figures you can determine that oxygen accounts for nearly one half of the mass of the rocks at the earth's surface. Also, you can observe that eight elements account for nearly 99 per cent of the mass of these same rocks.

In the second column of figures is given the number of atoms of each element out of each 100 atoms in the rocks of the earth's surface. From these figures you can determine that nearly one fourth of the atoms in the rocks of the earth's surface are silicon atoms. Also, you can determine that the number of oxygen atoms in the surface is about thirty times that of iron atoms.

In the third column of figures is given the fractional amount (by volume) of each element in the earth's surface. From this information you can determine that nearly 92 per cent of the space within the surface rocks is taken up by oxygen atoms. Less than 1 per cent of the volume of the surface rocks is taken up by iron atoms.

In studying the table you can develop some interesting comparisons. For example, silicon atoms account for a little more than one fourth of the mass and about one fourth of the number of atoms in surface rocks. Yet, silicon atoms account for less than 1 per cent of the volume of these rocks. Also, studying the table leads to several questions. Some of

ELEMENT	MASS (Per Cent)	ATOMS (Per 100)	VOLUME (Per Cent)
Oxygen	46.60	62.55	91.97
Silicon	27.72	21.22	0.80
Aluminum	8.13	6.47	0.77
Iron	5.00	1.92	0.68
Magnesium	2.09	1.84	0.56
Calcium	3.63	1.94	1.48
Sodium	2.83	2.64	1.60
Potassium	2.59	1.42	2.14
All Others	1.41	< 0.005	< 0.005

Figure 12-9. The abundance of eight common elements in the earth's surface is shown above. What can you infer about the sizes of oxygen and silicon atoms?

these develop from the fact that only eight elements are named, although there are more than ten times that many elements that occur in nature. Why do these eight elements account for so great a part of the earth's surface rocks? Why are five of these eight elements metals? Why are the elements silicon and oxygen so much more abundant than the other elements? Attempting to answer such questions as these is one of the principal tasks of modern science.

Comparing chemical compositions. How the average chemical composition of a star's atmosphere can be determined has been described in Chapter 4. Such a determination has been made for the sun with considerable care. Determinations have been made, also, of the chemical composition of many other stars and, to some extent, of the clouds of gas between the stars. From the data obtained, scientists have tried to determine the average composition of all the material in the universe. How does the chemical composition of the earth's surface compare with the chemical composition of the universe? The table in *Figure 12-10* enables you to make such a comparison.

ELEMENT	UNIVERSE (Number of Atoms per 10,000 Atoms of Silicon)	EARTH'S SURFACE (Number of Atoms per 10,000 Atoms of Silicon)
Hydrogen	3.3×10^8	1,400
Helium	3.4×10^7	0
Carbon	38,000	27
Nitrogen	83,000	3
Oxygen	140,000	29,500
Neon	160,000	0
Sodium	490	1,250
Magnesium	11,000	870
Aluminum	870	3,050
Silicon	10,000	10,000
Sulfur	4,300	< 0.5
Potassium	66	670
Calcium	690	920
Titanium	26	133
Iron	5,400	910
Nickel	380	1

Figure 12-10. Shown above is a comparison of the amounts of various elements in the universe with the amounts of the same elements in the earth's surface.

In the table are listed numbers of various kinds of atoms occurring in the universe and in the earth's surface. The numbers of atoms are relative to a standard. In this instance the standard used is 10,000 atoms of silicon. To better understand what the table means, consider the number that is listed as the number of carbon atoms occurring in the universe. The number listed is 38,000. This means that if we analyzed a sample of material from the universe and found 10,000 atoms of silicon in it, this same sample would have 38,000 atoms of carbon. It would also have 5,400 atoms of iron. In other words, for every 10,000 atoms of silicon in a sample of the material of the universe, there are 38,000 atoms of carbon and 5,400 atoms of iron. On the other hand, if we analyzed an average sample of the earth's surface and found that it contained 10,000 atoms of silicon, the number of carbon atoms in this sample would be 27. The number of iron atoms would be 910.

From such comparisons as these, we very quickly come to the conclusion that something has happened to the chemistry of the earth. Some elements are relatively more abundant on the earth than they are in the universe as a whole. Other elements are much less abundant on the earth. Consider the abundance of the element potassium. In a typical rock of the earth's surface, 670 atoms of potassium would be found for every 10,000 atoms of silicon. In the universe as a whole, however, only 66 atoms of potassium occur for every 10,000 atoms of silicon.

The evidence would indicate that while the relative abundance of some elements such as carbon and iron has been depleted in the earth's surface, the relative abundance of others has been increased. The most striking examples of change are the differences in the amounts of hydrogen and helium. In the universe as a whole, these two elements are very common. In fact, they dominate the picture completely. In the average surface rock, however, hydrogen is not an unusually abundant element. Helium is present in such a low relative abundance that its abundance is indicated as zero in the table.

The elements hydrogen and helium are in the gaseous state, normally. Are all of the other elements which are less abundant in the earth's surface than in the universe in general also in the gaseous state normally? Do the elements which are relatively more abundant in the earth's surface have anything in common?

Theories to explain the differences. In Chapter 11 some of the theories for the origin of the earth were described. Some of the theories, it was pointed out, propose that such elements as hydrogen and helium were blown away from the condensing earth by light pressure from the sun. Perhaps this explanation is correct for those particular elements which would tend to stay in a gaseous form, even after much of the materials had condensed to form the solid earth. But what about other elements, such as nickel and iron? These elements are not elements which would remain in the gaseous state as the earth condensed. We would expect them to condense rapidly to solid particles in the early stages of planet formation since they are in the solid form, even at rather high temperatures. Certainly these elements would not be gases to be blown away by light pressure. But, examining the table of relative abundance of elements, we observe that both of these elements are much more abundant in the universe as a whole than they are on the earth's surface. What is the explanation for these differences?

There are many detailed observations of the variations in the chemical nature of the materials in space. Such observations must be explained by any scientist who wishes to develop a theory for the origin and history of the earth. Our observations are descriptions of what is. Our theories must be consistent with what we observe.

4. The Magnetic Field

An interesting observation. As the imaginary space travelers approached the earth, they probably would have detected a magnetic field long before they came into the earth's atmosphere. Their instruments would have detected the field and would have provided the visitors with data about the field. These data would be similar to the data scientists on earth have obtained from instruments in artificial satellites placed in orbit about the earth.

Characteristics of the field. Limited observations of the earth's magnetic field can be made at the surface of the earth by using a very simple instrument—the magnetic compass. The compass not only indicates the presence of a magnetic field. It also gives us information about the location of the magnetic poles. One pole is near the geographic North Pole, and the other is near the geographic South Pole of the earth. It is an interesting fact that the magnetic poles do not coincide with the geographic poles. We suspect that this difference is another detail of nature for which the theories about the earth and its formation will have to give an explanation. An even greater problem to be solved or explained is the presence of a magnetic field at all about the earth.

The magnetic field about the earth extends far out into space. This is one reason the visitors from space could detect and measure it far beyond the earth's atmosphere. We can obtain a partial picture of a magnetic field by drawing the magnetic lines of force. A magnetic line of force is the direction along which a magnetic needle, such as a compass needle, would become aligned. A diagram of a magnetic field as it would exist about an ordinary bar magnet is shown in *Figure 12-11*.

Figure 12-11. The magnetic field about a magnet is invisible. However, such a field is often represented by drawing lines of force.

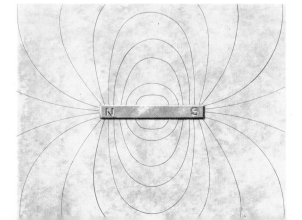

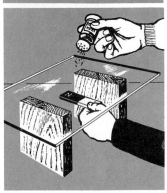

Materials you will need: piece of transparent glass or plastic, a bar magnet, iron filings, 2 large blocks

Place the glass or plastic upon the blocks as shown. Hold the bar magnet under the glass so that the magnet is parallel to the plane of the glass. Have a friend sprinkle iron filings on the glass. Observe what happens. Do the particles of iron move? Do they form a pattern above the magnet?

Now slowly move the bar magnet, keeping it below the glass. Slowly rotate the magnet so that one of the ends of the magnet is up against the glass and the other end is pointing down. Does the pattern of iron filings change as you move the magnet? Based on your observations, would you say that the magnetic field about the magnet is two-dimensional or three-dimensional? Which of these terms would best describe the earth's magnetic field?

Comparing the magnetic field and the gravitational field. Suppose you are in a situation in which there are no forces except magnetic forces—that is, no gravity, no air resistance, no light pressure, or anything else. Suppose, too, that in this situation, you release a small magnet and observe what happens. The magnet would be attracted to whichever magnetic pole is closer to it. The small magnet would move toward the pole, but not in a straight line. It would travel along a line of force. Thus, its path of motion would describe an arc, rather than a straight line.

Suppose, now, you are in a similar situation as before, except there are no forces except the gravitational forces. As you release the small magnet in this situation, the magnet is attracted to the object about which the gravitational field exists. The small magnet moves in a straight line and at an increasing speed into the gravitational field.

From these examples you see that the magnetic field is different from the gravitational field. And, although these fields produce some effects which are similar, the nature of each type of field is quite distinctive.

Figure 12-12. Before satellites were used in investigations of the earth's magnetic field, scientists assumed this magnetic field to be symmetrical. In this illustration, the earth is represented by the black circle and the magnetic lines of force by the white loops. The lines of force, as you can observe, continue through the interior of the earth.

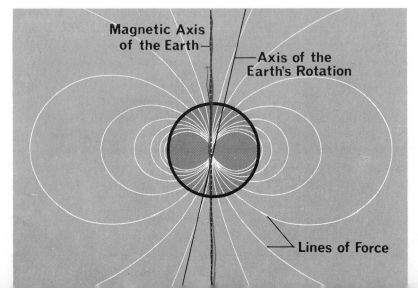

The form of the earth's magnetic field. Before satellites were launched to explore the regions of space about the earth, many scientists believed the form of the earth's magnetic field to be like that shown in *Figure 12-12*. Now, however, we know that the earth's magnetic field is not so symmetrical. Data obtained from instruments in solar satellites indicate the earth's magnetic field to be like that shown in *Figure 12-13*. Scientists have theorized that this particular form is due to the effects of charged electrical particles in the solar wind.

Effects of the solar wind. You will recall that in Chapter 8 a brief description was given of what happens when charged particles move in a magnetic field. First, since they are charged particles in motion, they make up an electric current. And, electric currents create magnetic fields. As these charged particles stream out from the sun into space, they create a magnetic field along their path. If these particles come near the earth, then their magnetic field interacts with the earth's magnetic field. This interaction causes the change in form indicated for the earth's magnetic field. As you can see, the charged particles streaming from the sun tend to squash the earth's magnetic field on the side toward the sun. These particles tend to pull the magnetic

field out from the earth and extend it into a long streamer on the side of the earth away from the sun.

In your study of Chapter 12, you have no doubt become aware of the role of satellites in enabling scientists to gather data about the earth in space. Three interesting facts have come to light. First, the average density of the whole earth is 5.522 g/cm³, whereas the average density of the rocks on the surface of the earth is only 2.8 g/cm³. Second, the relative abundance of various elements in the surface material of the earth is quite different from the relative abundance of these same elements determined for the sun and other stars. Third, the earth has a strong magnetic field.

So far, these are simply three, separate observations. However, as we continue our examination of the earth, we will find that these three facts are closely related. We will find that they are important basic pieces of information to be used in developing a general picture of the nature and history of our planet, the earth.

What reasons can you give for the long period of time between the discovery of the earth's magnetic field and the measurement of its intensity and form in space about the earth?

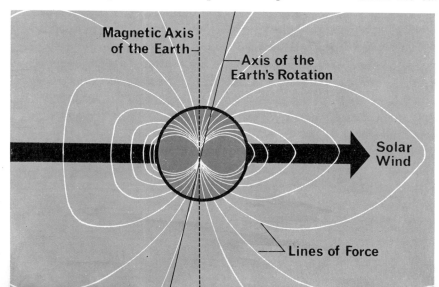

Magnetic Axis of the Earth

Axis of the Earth's Rotation

Solar Wind

Lines of Force

Figure 12-13. By using satellites in their investigations, scientists discovered that the earth's magnetic field is not symmetrical. On the side nearest the sun, the loops formed by lines of force are squashed. On the opposite side, the loops are extended. The solar wind is believed to cause the distortion. Within the earth—away from the effects of the solar wind—the magnetic field is assumed to be symmetrical.

Checking Your Knowledge

1. The earth, one of nine planets in the solar system, is our home in space.

2. The earth is nearly spherical, but not exactly so. It is slightly squashed at the poles and slightly bulging about the equator.

3. More than two thirds of the earth's surface is covered by the water of oceans. Approximately one third of the surface is land.

4. Scientists, for convenience in making their studies, divide the earth into zones called the atmosphere, the hydrosphere, the lithosphere, and the biosphere.

5. There are three facts scientists need to explain in their studies of the earth.

   a. The average density of surface rock is half the average density of the earth.

   b. The relative abundance of elements in the surface materials of the earth is quite different from that determined for the rest of the universe.

   c. The earth has a strong magnetic field.

USING NEW WORDS

Study the words listed below. On your paper write the numerals *1-4*. After each numeral write the words or statements to satisfy the instructions having the corresponding numeral.

atmosphere	biosphere
oblate spheroid	hydrosphere
lithosphere	geochemistry

1. Select and list those words which name zones of the earth. Look up each of these names in a dictionary to find its derivation. Write the word parts and their original meanings for each of the names you list.

2. Select the term used to name the study of the earth's composition and structure.

3. Give the term naming the earth's shape.

4. Tell how this shape is not a sphere.

TEST YOURSELF

Study the test below. On your paper write the numerals *1-10*. After each numeral write the correct response to that part of the test with the corresponding numeral.

1. The most accurate measures of the earth's size have been made through the use of instruments installed in _____.

2. The most abundant element in the sun is named _____.

3. The element which is second in abundance in the sun but nearly absent in the earth's surface rocks is named _____.

4. The zone which makes up the major portion of the earth is called the _____.

5. Through most of his history, man's greatest concern and interest has been in the zone which is called the _____.

6. The zone of the earth which has the least mass is the (*outermost, innermost*) zone.

7. Studies to determine relative abundance of elements in the earth's surface and in the universe as a whole indicate that, of the metals, (*sodium, aluminum, iron, potassium*) shows the greatest factor of change.

8. In approaching the earth, a visitor from outer space using visual means would first detect which of the following characteristics of the earth? (a) surface features, (b) shape, (c) magnetic field.

9. The same visitor, using other than visual means, would probably first detect which of the following characteristics of the earth? (a) surface features, (b) shape, (c) magnetic field.

10. The ratio of the density of the atmosphere at sea level compared to its density at an altitude of 100 km is closer to which of the following? (a) 10/1, (b) 100/1, (c) 1,000/1, (d) 1,000,000/1.

Extending Your Knowledge

1. In studying a globe, do you see any lack of uniformity in the distribution of land and oceans about the earth's surface? If so, how would you describe it to someone who had never seen a globe or map?

2. Why, do you think, is it important to know about the numbers of atoms of the various elements present in the earth's rocks and the numbers of those in the universe as a whole?

3. What reasons can you think of for scientists using silicon as the basis for comparing the abundance of elements in the universe? Would hydrogen serve just as well as a basis of comparison? If not, why not?

4. Scientists, at one time, considered the earth to be a magnetized sphere. What facts can you give to show that the concept of a magnetized sphere is not an adequate concept in light of what is known now?

5. What possible reasons can you suggest for the differences between the relative abundance of various elements in the earth's surface and that of these elements in the universe at large?

SOME THINGS TO DO

1. Determine the mass and volume of specimens of several types of surface rocks. Calculate the average density of each type. Find the average density for all of the different types of rock samples. Compare this value with that given in the text. Are the two values the same? How might you explain any difference?

2. The formula for the area of a sphere is $A = 4\pi r^2$. Calculate the area of the earth. How does the value you find compare with the sum of the values given in the text for the area of land and the area of ocean? Using these data, find what percentage of the area is land. Also, find what percentage of the area of the earth is water.

CHALLENGES IN SCIENCE

1. On page 232 of the text, the statement is made that a freely suspended magnet would move toward one of the earth's poles. How might you be able to demonstrate to the class the truth or falsity of this statement?

2. Imagine that you are a visitor from outer space, observing the earth for the first time. What interesting and probably surprising information could you send back to your home from your orbit 100 miles out from the earth? Use your imagination and write such a report. What additions to your report could you make if you landed your spacecraft on the earth?

3. Not all of the elements which are known to exist are found in the surface rocks of the earth. Try to find out those elements which are not found in surface rocks. Also, try to find out explanations for these elements not being found in the surface rocks.

4. Carefully study the tables in *Figure 12-9* and *Figure 12-10*. After such a study, do you think that silicon occurs on the earth in about the same abundance as, in greater abundance than, or in less abundance than it does in the universe as a whole? What reasons or evidence can you give to support your answer?

5. Make an investigation in order to determine what the range is in the density of rocks. Make a table or chart representing this range. Do you find that the density of some rocks is so low that a specimen of the rock could float in water? How could you explain such a phenomenon?

When the earth's crust shifts, the results may be devastating.

CHAPTER 13

Changes About the Earth's Crust

We usually think of the earth as very solid and permanent. But, the earth's crust is continually in motion as a result of the many forces acting upon it. Although the changes in the earth's crust that result from such forces are continual, they almost always happen very slowly.

Sometimes, however, the crust stirs like a waking giant, producing sudden changes that may devastate large portions of the countryside or cause disastrous ocean waves. These sudden shifts in the earth's crust are called earthquakes. Earthquakes are sudden and spectacular changes that result when forces affecting the crust of the earth build up too rapidly to be relieved by the small tremors that are continually occurring.

It is difficult to realize that man knows less about the conditions that exist only a few miles beneath his feet than he does about conditions thousands of miles above his head. One way scientists learn about the interior of the earth is to study the effects which earthquakes produce. Chapter 13 is about earthquakes. In your studies of earthquakes, you will discover some of the effects produced by earthquakes. You will also find out how scientists detect and measure these effects. Then, you will discover how scientists use and interpret these effects in order to add to man's knowledge of the earth on which he lives.

1. Observing Changes Which Occur

The weather and the oceans. The atmosphere and the hydrosphere are in a state of constant change. We have come to expect changes in the weather from season to season, from day to day, and even more frequently. As we shall see in later chapters, we have a fairly good understanding of the reasons for these changes.

We are also accustomed to changes in the sea. The tides rise and fall, the currents seem to flow endlessly, and the patterns of the waves are always changing. Scientists also have a fairly good understanding of the causes for these changes in the oceans. In fact, changes in the ocean are closely related to happenings in the atmosphere.

However, we are not so accustomed to changes in the solid surface of the earth. We usually think of the earth as constant and unchanging—a permanent fixture in our lives. Of course, if we watch the side of a hill during a rainstorm, we will see the water running down the hill. As the water moves, it washes away a little bit of dirt. We can imagine how, after millions of years, the whole hillside might be washed away. In most cases, however, this change in the earth's surface is a rather slow change compared with the dynamic changes in the weather.

What changes, other than those of currents and weather, can you think of that are brought about by the forces of the atmosphere? By forces of the hydrosphere?

Volcanoes. There are other changes in the surface of the earth that are more violent. Few of us have ever seen an active volcano spurting smoke and ash into the air and having streams of lava pouring down its sides. But many of us have seen movies of volcanoes, and we can imagine how terrifying such an event would be if we were close beside it. With fire and smoke and molten rock, a volcano is certainly one of nature's most impressive displays.

Terrifying though it is, a volcano still seems to be within our understanding. We might compare it to a thunderstorm, complete with flashes of lightning, or to a bonfire throwing hot sparks up into the sky. Perhaps it is because a volcano is so noisy and spectacular that it does not seem terribly mysterious, regardless of how frightening it might be.

Earthquakes. There is another way in which the earth changes itself that seems to be more mysterious and terrifying than volcanoes. This is the earthquake. People who have been through a major earthquake have reported that an earthquake is by far the most frightening experience they have ever had. Quite often there is a definite uproar which accompanies the violent shaking of the earth. Some have compared it to the rumbling of thunder, to the roaring of the wind, or to gunfire and explosions. The noises that accompany an earthquake can often be heard hundreds of miles from the center of the earthquake.

In an earthquake the surface of the earth begins to move like the surface of the sea, in waves. Sometimes the waves are about a foot high and about fifty feet apart. Quite often the motion of the earthquake causes a complicated pattern of surface waves to be generated. As one group of waves moves in one direction across the surface of the earth, another group may be moving in a different direction. Where these groups of waves cross, the interaction causes a series of bumps and hollows to rise and fall. In the area where the waves cross, the surface of the earth looks like the storm-tossed sea.

Figure 13-1. Various effects of earthquakes can be observed in these pictures. The picture in the upper-right corner is of a large area of ocean floor that has been uplifted and is now dry land. The upward shift was measured to be 33 feet. The other pictures show the effects of earthquakes on man-made structures, such as buildings, roads, and railroads. Four of these pictures were taken in Alaska, after the 1964 earthquake. The other picture (lower right) shows damage resulting from an earthquake in Morocco in 1960.

In the midst of this violent motion, structures are crashing to the ground. Long cracks open in the earth, only to slam closed again a short time later. Trees swing back and forth, thrashing their branches. Some trees fall.

When the violence has finally subsided, the surface of the earth is no longer the same. A portion of the earth has been moved. Perhaps the movement has been up and down. Perhaps it has been from side to side. Usually, it is a combination of the two. Roadways are displaced. New cliffs are formed. In the Alaskan earthquake of March, 1964, large areas of sea bottom—complete with seaweed and shellfish—were raised to become dry land. If the earthquake happens near a city, the destruction and loss of life can be terrible. In 1960 an earthquake near the city of Agadir, Morocco, killed thousands of citizens and destroyed most of the city.

If a severe earthquake occurred near your home, what serious results might you expect?

DO IT YOURSELF

Study pictures of earthquakes

Obtain as many pictures as you can of places where earthquakes occurred. Observe how the earthquake has changed the surface of the earth. How many different types of changes can you identify? What changes, other than those shown in the pictures, could be caused by earthquakes? Select the most dramatic and spectacular pictures and prepare a bulletin-board display of the effects of earthquakes.

Distribution of earthquakes. In studying earthquakes, one of the first steps is to determine where earthquakes frequently occur. Maps showing the locations of all known earthquakes have been prepared. Two such maps are shown in *Figure 13-2*. From your own observations of these maps, you can tell that earthquakes do not occur with the same frequency all over the world. Rather, they occur most often within comparatively narrow zones. What is so special about these particular zones? Scientists, of course, would like to know the answer to this question.

So far, the answer is not known. There are, however, some clues which scientists have to work with. The region of most frequent earthquakes, sometimes called the earthquake belt, is also the region in which most of the world's active volcanoes are located. Furthermore, many of the world's young mountain ranges are near the earthquake belt. Naturally, scientists try to relate these observations when formulating theories about the causes and distribution of earthquakes.

Earthquakes under the ocean. The maps in *Figure 13-2* reveal that some regions where earthquakes frequently occur are in the ocean. Later in your study of this chapter, you will find out how scientists determine where the center of an earthquake is located. Right now, however, it is worth pointing out that an earthquake in the floor of an ocean quite often causes destructive effects on land. This occurs because the ocean floor has been so disturbed as to cause the ocean itself to react. Waves, starting from the center of the disturbance, move outward across the sea.

In the open ocean, the waves will not be very high. Furthermore, these waves will be far apart. If you were in a ship, you might not even notice their passage, since there would be only a very gentle rise and fall over a period of several minutes. Perhaps the total movement would be no greater than two feet. But, in spite of that, there is a tremendous amount of energy and a tremendous amount of water involved in each wave. As long as the waves are in deep water, however, this energy is spread out over a large area, like a very broad ripple pattern.

As the waves begin to approach the shoreline, the water through which they are moving

Figure 13-2. These maps show the locations of the major earthquakes which occurred from 1904 through 1952. The map at the left indicates earthquakes which occurred within 70 km of the earth's surface. The map at the right indicates earthquakes which occurred deeper than 70 km below the earth's surface.

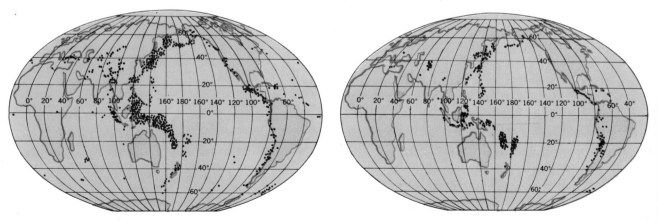

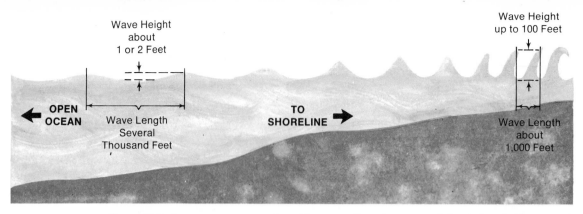

Figure 13-3. As ocean waves produced by an earthquake approach land, the shallowness of the water causes the energy of the waves to become concentrated in a few, very large waves.

Wave Height about 1 or 2 Feet

OPEN OCEAN

Wave Length Several Thousand Feet

TO SHORELINE

Wave Height up to 100 Feet

Wave Length about 1,000 Feet

becomes more and more shallow. This change in depth begins to affect their motion, just as the beach affects the motion of ordinary waves by causing them to break and form the familiar surf. Waves from an earthquake in the ocean are usually much longer in wave length (the distance from one crest to another) than ordinary ocean waves. Because of their long wave length, these waves begin to react to the bottom of the ocean in much deeper water than ordinary waves would. The ocean waves produced by earthquakes begin to turn into breakers far out from shore. All the energy which may have been spread out over miles of surface in the open ocean becomes concentrated into a few very steep waves, as diagramed in *Figure 13-3*.

In many cases, the first visible sign of the approach of these waves is that the water moves out to sea, like a huge undertow, exposing long stretches of sea bottom. Then the main train of waves moves in with tremendous speed. The largest wave in this train may be as high as 100 feet when it finally breaks. It may crash against the shore at a speed of more than 400 miles an hour. It is no wonder that these waves have become legendary.

Many years ago, no one knew where these devastating ocean waves came from or how they originated. Thus, the names that have been given to these waves give no hint as to the waves' origin. Sometimes, these waves are called tidal waves. This is a mistake, however, since these waves have nothing at all to do with the tides. Such a wave is most commonly called a *tsunami* (tsü nä′mi), a name derived from the Japanese language. One meaning of the word tsunami is "storm wave."

Often, Greek or Latin words are used by scientists as the basis for naming objects or phenomena. Why, do you suppose, is a Japanese name given to the destructive waves which are caused by earthquakes?

Figure 13-4. The men in this picture are standing amid the debris left by a tsunami which struck the Hawaiian Islands in 1960, killing 61 people.

ESSA

Materials you will need: 3 boards, large puddle of water about 2 inches deep

Place one of the boards on the water. To generate waves, push the board down into the water and then allow it to come back up. Repeat this procedure so that a series of waves are produced. Place the other two boards on edge in the water, so they are parallel to each other and parallel to the direction in which the waves are moving. Do the parallel boards affect the waves? If so, how?

Now place the boards in the form of a V, but have both ends of the V open. Generate a series of waves so that they enter the wide part of the V. How are the waves affected as they travel through the V? How would a tsunami be affected as it enters an inlet or a bay?

2. Detecting Movements in the Earth's Crust

Seismology. Earthquakes can be very dramatic, very sudden, and very dangerous. More complete knowledge of earthquakes would be beneficial to mankind. For example, many lives might be saved and much damage averted if earthquakes could be predicted and controlled. Therefore, it is not surprising that scientists have devoted much attention to the study of earthquakes and the waves produced by earthquakes. This study is called *seismology* (sīz mol′ə ji). A scientist involved in this study is a *seismologist* (sīz mol′ə jist). The first part of the words comes from the Greek word *seio,* which means "to shake."

Figure 13-5. The work of seismologists is varied. In the picture on the left, you see a seismologist with instruments which will detect and record vibrations of the earth's crust. The seismologist in the picture on the right is using seismic wave data to determine the location of the center of an earthquake.

ESSA

ESSA

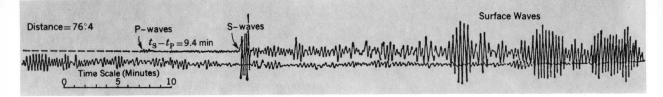

Distance = 76°4

P-waves
$t_S - t_P = 9.4$ min

S-waves

Surface Waves

Time Scale (Minutes)
0 . . . . 5 10

Figure 13-6. This seismogram represents a record of an earthquake which occurred in Chile. It was recorded at the Harvard Seismograph Station.

Scientists estimate that from 1,000 to 5,000 earthquakes occur every day. Of course, most of these earthquakes are very minor and are detected only by sensitive equipment. Such minor earthquakes have little effect on the regions in which they occur. They may be important to scientists, however, since studying even small earthquakes adds to our knowledge of all earthquakes. Although seismologists still cannot accurately predict earthquakes, through seismology man has gained a better understanding of the nature of the earth.

Instruments used. An instrument which detects and measures the motion of the earth's crust in an earthquake is called a *seismograph* (sīz′mə graf). The record of data from such an instrument is called a *seismogram* (sīz′mə gram). In *Figure 13-6* you see an example of a seismogram, showing a record of the waves produced by a particular earthquake.

On the seismogram in *Figure 13-6,* there appear to be two lines. Actually, the lower line is simply a continuation of the line above it. As much information as possible is recorded on each piece of paper. The paper on which the data are recorded is wrapped around a drum, as shown in *Figure 13-7*. The drum is turned by a clock. The clock can be set to turn the drum at different speeds, but usually the drum takes several minutes to turn around once. Resting on the paper is a pen or some other marking instrument which makes a mark on the paper wrapped around the rotating drum. As the drum is rotating, the marking pen

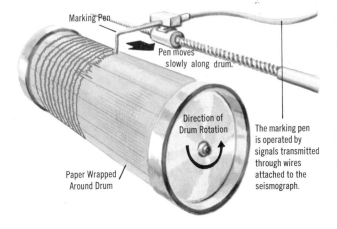

Marking Pen

Pen moves slowly along drum.

Direction of Drum Rotation

The marking pen is operated by signals transmitted through wires attached to the seismograph.

Paper Wrapped Around Drum

Figure 13-7. As the drum rotates, the marking pen moves slowly down the length of the drum, producing a continuous mark on the paper wrapped around the drum.

slowly moves down the length of the drum. Thus, a long, spiral mark is made on the paper wrapped around the drum. Of course, when the paper is taken off the drum and flattened out, the mark appears as a series of lines across the paper.

When the seismograph which controls the marking pen detects a vibration, the marking pen moves, drawing an exact record of the motion of the earth's crust. Of course, if vibrations are to be detected and recorded, the device must operate continuously because it is impossible to know ahead of time when the vibrations will occur. Therefore, the lines (which go together to form a spiral when the paper is on the drum, but which are separate lines when the paper is flattened out) are close together. During a vibration, when a portion of one line becomes wavy, the wavy line may overlap some of the neighboring lines on the seismogram and cause the final record to look rather complicated. Nevertheless, it is a simple matter to determine the path taken by the marking pen and so analyze the vibration.

The seismograph which detects the vibration and controls the operation of the marking pen is basically a very simple instrument. It consists of a large mass suspended like a pendulum, as shown in *Figure 13-8*. The mass detects earthquakes by standing still! If the portion of the earth to which the seismograph is attached vibrates, the inertia of the large mass holds it steady, while the support and the platform below the mass move.

Now, imagine that a pen is rigidly attached to the mass. One end of the pen rests lightly on the platform underneath. If an earthquake were to move the platform and the mass were to remain still, the pen would draw a line back and forth on the moving platform. If a piece of paper were to be pulled steadily between the pen and the platform, this back-and-forth motion would show up as a wavy line, and the result would be a seismogram.

Figure 13-8. A large mass is used as a means of observing seismic waves. As the earth vibrates, the large mass remains stationary because of its inertia. Although this diagram illustrates the basic principle of a seismograph, the device would have to be refined before it would be useful.

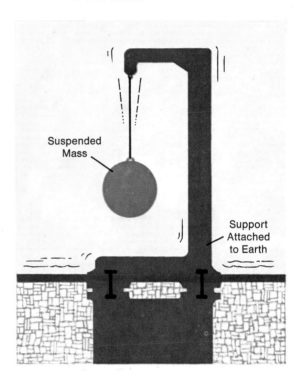

Suspended Mass

Support Attached to Earth

FIND OUT BY TRYING

Materials you will need: ring stand, burette clamp, 1-kg weight, string, pencil, paper

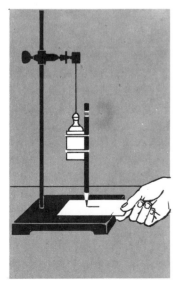

Using string, suspend the 1-kg weight from the burette clamp as shown. Then tie a pencil to the weight so that the pencil point just touches a piece of paper placed on the base of the ring stand.

When the weight is hanging motionless, slowly pull the paper out from under the suspended weight. What type of figure does the pencil mark make on the paper? Repeat the experiment. This time, however, as you slowly pull the paper, have someone pound on the table or stomp on the floor. What does the pencil mark on the paper look like this time? When the table is pounded or the floor shaken, does the suspended weight move back and forth? Does the base of the ring stand move back and forth? Could this instrument be used to detect earthquakes? Why or why not?

Amplification. Of course, for a simple seismograph to give useful data, the motion of the earth would have to be great enough to produce a wavy line on which the waves are wider than the width of the pen line. Any smaller vibration would be very difficult to see on the seismogram.

Seismologists have devised instruments which enable them to record very small vibrations of the earth's crust. One instrument is diagramed in *Figure 13-9*. A pointer attached to the bottom of the mass rests against the top edge of a mirror. The bottom edge of the mirror is hinged to the platform underneath. If the ground vibrates only slightly, the platform would move back and forth very slightly. The mass, because of its inertia, would remain still. As a result, the mirror would be tilted back and forth only slightly. If a narrow beam of light were being reflected off the mirror, the other end of the reflected beam

Figure 13-10. Modern seismographs are very sensitive. Complex electronic circuits are used to amplify seismic wave effects. East-west, north-south, and vertical vibrations are each detected by separate instruments.

would be moved back and forth a much greater distance than the mirror would move. The longer the reflected light beam, the greater would be the back-and-forth motion of the spot of light cast by the reflected beam. With this type instrument, photographic film is used to record the changing position of the spot of light.

A technique such as this is called *amplification* (am′plə fə kā′shən). Through this technique the motion that is recorded is a much larger, or amplified, record of the original motion. In modern seismographs, there are many techniques used to amplify the motion of the earth's crust. Most of the modern techniques rely upon electronics. Some of the methods of amplification used on seismographs are rather complicated, but the fundamental instrument itself is still simple—a mass supported as a pendulum.

In most seismographs, the mass is supported in such a way that it can move back and forth in only one plane. Separate records are made for north-south vibrations and east-west vibrations. Furthermore, in most earthquakes, the vibration of the surface is up and down as well

Figure 13-9. One way to amplify the motion of seismic waves as they appear on a seismogram is illustrated below. As the tilt of the mirror changes slightly, the spot of light from the reflected beam moves up and down on the rotating drum.

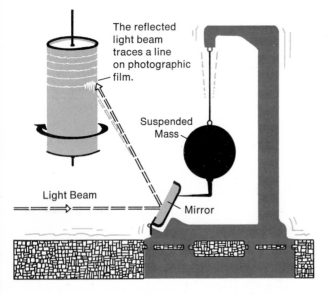

The reflected light beam traces a line on photographic film.

Suspended Mass

Light Beam

Mirror

as side to side. Thus, a seismograph is needed to record this motion, too. A typical modern seismograph is shown in *Figure 13-10*.

Why is more than one seismograph required to accurately record movements of the earth's crust during an earthquake?

3. Seismic Waves

Types. In the 19th century, the seismographs in use were not sensitive enough to accurately measure earthquake waves. However, the mathematicians and physicists of that time had determined what kind of vibrations should move through the earth from any sudden disturbance such as an earthquake. They had determined that three general types of vibrations would occur. These vibrations are called *seismic* (sīz′mik) *waves.*

The waves in one of the types of seismic waves are called *P-waves*. The *P* stands for primary. Because these waves travel through the earth faster than the other types, they arrive at the seismographic stations first. That is why they are called primary waves. They are also waves of compression—similar to sound waves—and might be called pressure waves. So it is convenient to think of *P* as standing for pressure as well as for primary.

As P-waves move through the earth, the particles that make up the earth vibrate back and forth. The direction of the vibration is parallel to the direction in which the wave is moving. See *A* in *Figure 13-11*. In a similar manner, when a sound wave passes through the air, particles of the air move back and forth, and the direction of their motion is parallel to the direction in which the wave is traveling.

The waves in a second type of seismic waves are called *S-waves*. The *S* stands for secondary. S-waves travel slower than P-waves and arrive at seismographic stations later than P-waves. Hence, they are secondary waves.

In S-waves, as in P-waves, the particles that make up the earth also vibrate back and forth. However, in the S-waves the direction of the vibrating motion is perpendicular to the direction in which the wave is traveling. See *B* in *Figure 13-11*. This type of motion is called shearing motion, so it is convenient to think of *S* as standing for shear as well as for secondary.

Figure 13-11. As a P-wave goes through the earth, particles of the earth vibrate back and forth, parallel to the direction in which the wave travels. This is illustrated in A. As an S-wave—illustrated in B—passes through the earth, the vibrations are in any direction on a plane perpendicular to the direction in which the wave travels. As surface waves move along the earth's surface, the movement of individual particles is in an elliptical path—illustrated in C.

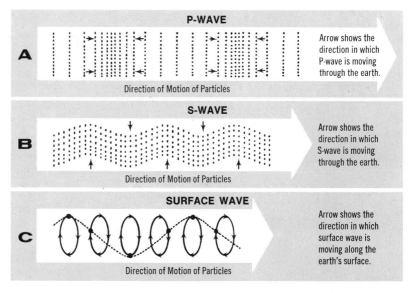

P-WAVE

A

Direction of Motion of Particles

Arrow shows the direction in which P-wave is moving through the earth.

S-WAVE

B

Direction of Motion of Particles

Arrow shows the direction in which S-wave is moving through the earth.

SURFACE WAVE

C

Direction of Motion of Particles

Arrow shows the direction in which surface wave is moving along the earth's surface.

P-waves and S-waves travel through the interior of the earth. A third type of wave travels only along the surface. These *surface waves* are similar to the waves on the surface of the ocean. In a surface wave, most of the motion of the particles is up and down, but there is a slight back-and-forth motion at the same time. See C in *Figure 13-11*. You could observe these motions by watching a floating object as it bobs on the rippling surface of a lake or pond.

These three types of waves—P-waves, S-waves, and surface waves—were predicted by theory before instruments were accurate enough to detect them. However, there is a fourth type of wave that was first discovered by using seismographs. Careful theoretical work was required in order to explain this fourth type of wave, which is a somewhat different type of surface wave. These waves are called *Love waves* after the scientist A. E. H. Love, who finally succeeded in explaining them. In Love waves, the vibrating motion of the earth's surface is perpendicular to the direction in which the wave travels. However,

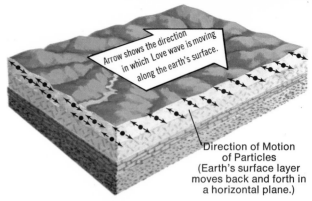

Arrow shows the direction in which Love wave is moving along the earth's surface.

Direction of Motion of Particles (Earth's surface layer moves back and forth in a horizontal plane.)

Figure 13-12. Love waves occur where the material near the earth's surface is layered. Only the topmost layer vibrates, as illustrated above.

the vibrating motion is only in a horizontal plane. Thus, Love waves are somewhat like shear waves and quite different from waves that occur on the surface of the ocean.

Love waves are observed only in regions where the earth has a layered structure. However, a large fraction of the earth's surface is layered with different types of rock, or a layer of soil on top of bedrock. Therefore, after the occurrence of an earthquake, Love waves are observed quite commonly.

DO IT YOURSELF

Observe various types of waves

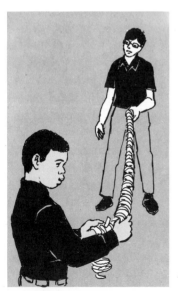

A simple toy called a "Slinky" is ideal for demonstrating some types of wave motion. Have someone hold one end of a long "Slinky" while you hold the other end. Stretch the spring, but be careful not to stretch it so far that it will not return to its original size.

While the spring is stretched, attach a small piece of masking tape to one coil. Then compress several coils of the spring and release them. As the wave travels along the spring, observe the motion of the piece of tape. What kind of wave have you demonstrated?

Then, while one end of the spring is held in place, move the other end up and down. Again observe the motion of the tape as the wave travels along the spring. What kind of wave have you demonstrated?

The "Slinky" is not very useful in demonstrating surface waves or Love waves. Try to design and conduct demonstrations which illustrate these types of waves.

Speed of waves. One of the most important characteristics of the various kinds of waves is that each of them travels at a different speed. The P-waves travel fastest and the surface waves travel slowest. You may wonder why this difference in speed is important to seismologists. Suppose an earthquake happened several hundred miles away from a seismograph. The first indication of the earthquake on the seismogram is the record of the P-waves. Second come the S-waves, and finally, the surface waves. Such a seismographic record is shown in *Figure 13-6*.

The exact speed at which each type of wave travels depends on the nature of the material through which it is passing (or along which it is moving, in the case of surface waves). One important characteristic in determining this speed is the compressibility of the material. Compressibility is the amount of change in volume that results when a material is subjected to a standard pressure. Another important characteristic in determining the speed of waves through a material is the rigidity of the material. Rigidity is the tendency of the material to resist bending or twisting.

These characteristics are different for different materials. One kind of rock is different from another. And, of course, rock is different from soil, and soil is different from sand. Thus, the precise time at which a seismic wave arrives at a seismograph depends not only upon the distance between the seismograph and the earthquake, but also upon the nature of the rock and other material through which the seismic wave traveled.

Locating earthquakes. As you can guess, information about the materials in the earth is very important to scientists studying the earth. By carefully noting the times when earthquakes occur and the times when waves are recorded by various seismographs, seismologists have been able to determine something about the characteristics of the materials through which the waves travel deep beneath the surface of the earth.

This information can then be used in another way. Suppose an earthquake happens in a part of the world where no one lives, or perhaps under the sea. Seismologists in different locations will observe the record of the waves which reach their seismographs. Ordinarily the P-waves arrive first, since they travel fastest. The P-waves will be followed first by the S-waves and then by the surface waves. By noting the intervals of time between the arrival of various types of waves and using the information about speed of wave travel through rock, the seismologist can determine how far the earthquake was from his station.

For example, through rock near the surface of the earth, P-waves travel at an average speed of 7.75 km/sec. The S-waves travel with an average speed of 4.35 km/sec. Since speed equals distance divided by time, the seismologist can use the algebraic equation shown below to figure out the distance from his station to where the earthquake occurred.

$$\frac{d}{v_\text{S}} - \frac{d}{v_\text{P}} = t_\text{S} - t_\text{P}$$

In this equation d is distance, v is speed, and t is time. The subscripts S and P refer to to S-waves and P-waves. By substituting the average values for v_S and v_P into the equation and then solving the equation for d, we obtain the following.

$$\frac{d}{4.35} - \frac{d}{7.75} = t_\text{S} - t_\text{P}$$

$$\frac{7.75d - 4.35d}{33.7} = \frac{3.4d}{33.7}$$

$$.101d = t_\text{S} - t_\text{P}$$

$$d \text{ (in km)} = \frac{t_\text{S} - t_\text{P}}{.101} = 9.91 \, (t_\text{S} - t_\text{P})$$

Suppose the seismologist found that the P-waves arrived at the seismograph 14.1 seconds before the S-waves. That is, $t_S - t_P = 14.1$ seconds. By using 14.1 seconds instead of $t_S - t_P$ in the final equation on the preceding page, he can write the following equation.

$$d = 9.91 \times 14.1$$
$$d = 140 \text{ km}$$

Then, on a map, he draws a circle with a radius of 140 km centered at his location. Suppose his seismograph is at the position marked 1 in *Figure 13-13*. He knows the center of the earthquake is somewhere on this circle, but he does not know exactly where.

But now, suppose a seismologist at another location has also observed the waves from this same earthquake. This seismologist is at the location marked 2 on the diagram in *Figure 13-13*. At this location, the S-waves arrived 28.3 seconds later than the P-waves. This second seismologist can use the same equation to determine the distance from his station to the earthquake. He determines the distance to be 280 km. He can get in touch with the first seismologist and pass on this information. Now the first seismologist can draw another circle on his map with a radius of 280 km centered at the location of the second seismographic station. The earthquake must be where these two circles intersect, that is, at Point A or Point B.

If there is a third seismologist observing the waves from the location marked 3 in *Figure 13-13*, he can contribute his information to complete the picture. If he determines that the earthquake is 485 km from his location, the third circle intersects the other two at Point B.

This technique of locating the center of an earthquake is quite reliable and simple if three seismographic stations are within a few hundred kilometers of the earthquake's center.

When an earthquake is very far away from any seismographic station, however, the problem becomes more difficult. The increase in difficulty results from the complex structure of the earth. The complex structure of the earth causes reflections and refractions which complicate the seismogram.

In what circumstances would information from only two seismographic stations be sufficient to locate an earthquake?

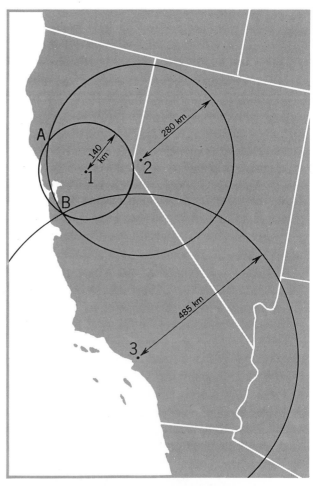

Figure 13-13. Usually, data from three seismographic stations must be combined to determine the location of the center of an earthquake.

DO IT YOURSELF

Determine the location of the center of an earthquake

Use the equation on page 247, a map of the United States, and the data shown below to find the location of an earthquake's center.

LOCATION OF SEISMOGRAPH	$t_S - t_P$
San Francisco, California	45 sec.
Tucson, Arizona	148 sec.
Bismarck, N. Dakota	184 sec.

Factors affecting wave motion. As waves travel through a material which is the same throughout, they move in a straight line at a constant speed. But, if the properties of the material differ from one place to another, then this difference affects the motion of the waves. For example, the material deep beneath the surface of the earth is different from the material near the surface. The deep material is denser, hotter, and under greater pressure. These differences affect the speeds at which seismic waves travel. Until they reach a depth of 2,900 km, the deeper the seismic waves penetrate into the earth, the faster the waves travel.

How does this difference in speed affect the direction in which the seismic waves travel? Suppose we use a diagram—*Figure 13-14*—to illustrate the direction followed by the seismic waves as they move away from the point where the earthquake occurred. Keep in mind that the earth is 3-dimensional, not 2-dimensional like a page in a book. Thus, *Figure 13-14* shows only a cross section of the earth. You will also have to keep in mind that the seismic waves travel in all directions, not

Figure 13-14. On this cross section of the earth, the arrows show the direction in which seismic waves travel through the earth. The white lines represent successive positions of the forward edge of the wave as it moves through the earth.

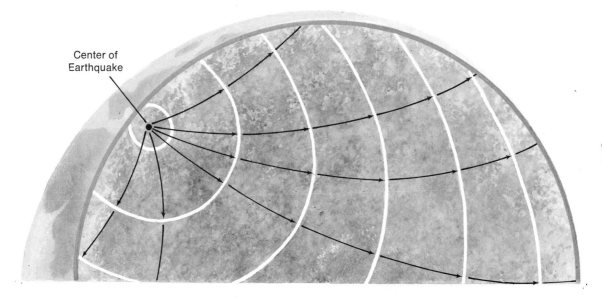

Center of Earthquake

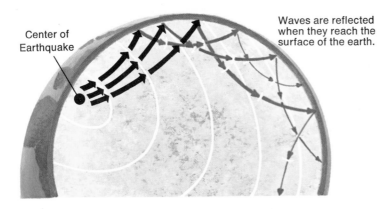

Center of Earthquake

Waves are reflected when they reach the surface of the earth.

Figure 13-15. When the curved path of a P-wave or an S-wave brings the wave to the surface of the earth, the wave is reflected back into the earth. The reflected wave eventually curves upward and comes to the surface of the earth again, producing another reflection. This process can be repeated several times. However, the wave becomes weaker with each reflection.

just those directions that can be shown in the plane of this page.

The arrows show the direction in which the waves travel. Because the speed of the wave is greater at greater depths, the direction of wave travel changes. The path of the wave curves upward until the wave is directed toward the surface.

Another interesting change occurs whenever one of the P-waves or S-waves reaches the surface of the earth. The wave is reflected from the surface and starts back down again into the earth, as shown in *Figure 13-15*. Once again, its path is gradually bent until it is again heading toward the surface. It can be reflected many times, but the farther the wave travels, the weaker it gets.

A sudden change in the nature of the material through which the wave passes is another factor that affects the waves. An example of such a change in materials would be the boundary between a layer of limestone and the granite beneath it. Another change of this type might be that between loose soil that has washed down off a mountainside and the bedrock which lies underneath the loose soil.

Whenever earthquake waves meet such a boundary, part of their energy is reflected while the rest goes on through the boundary. The portion of each wave which goes through the boundary will change its direction of travel. Such a change of direction is called *refraction*. Refraction is illustrated in *Figure 13-16*. Here the source of the waves is an earthquake occurring in one type of rock close to the surface of the earth. The waves move down toward a boundary between the surface rock and the second type of rock which lies beneath it. At the boundary, part of the energy of the waves is reflected. The remainder continues on through the boundary, but in a slightly different direction.

Figure 13-16. When a seismic wave reaches a boundary between two different types of rock, part of the wave's energy is reflected. Part of the wave's energy goes through the boundary and is refracted. What affects the direction in which the wave is refracted?

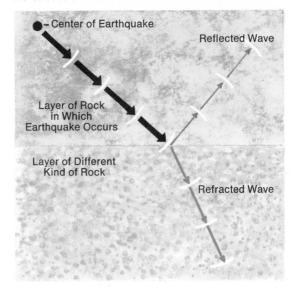

- Center of Earthquake

Reflected Wave

Layer of Rock in Which Earthquake Occurs

Layer of Different Kind of Rock

Refracted Wave

4. Interpreting Seismic Waves

Obtaining information. The generally curving direction of wave travel, together with the refraction and multiple reflection of seismic waves within the earth, makes the task of interpreting a seismogram quite difficult. The first waves which a seismograph detects have arrived at the seismograph by the most direct route. Waves that arrive later may represent reflections or refractions through different kinds of materials. These later-arriving waves may be difficult to interpret. But the first waves, at least, can be understood without too much trouble.

Suppose we talk about the seismograms we might observe after a very severe earthquake. Suppose these seismograms come from a number of different seismographic stations located at different places around the earth. *Figure 13-17* gives an example of where such stations might be located compared to the earthquake.

By checking with people who lived near the earthquake, seismologists can find out precisely when the earthquake occurred. Then, looking at the seismograms from each station, they can determine how long it took for the waves to travel to any particular station. The seismologists can put all of these points on a diagram called a travel-time diagram, such as the one in *Figure 13-18*.

There are several things to notice in this diagram. First, travel times for P-waves, S-waves, and surface waves are all shown. Second, the distance is not measured in miles but in degrees. These are like degrees of latitude around the earth. They represent the angle between two lines drawn from the center of the earth, one to the point of the earthquake and the other to the recording station. For example, in *Figure 13-17* the distance from the earthquake to Station 2 is 60°.

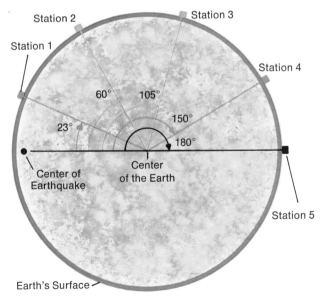

Figure 13-17. In locating earthquakes, the position of a seismographic station, relative to the center of the earthquake, is expressed in degrees.

Figure 13-18. A travel-time diagram for seismic waves is based on data from several seismographic stations.

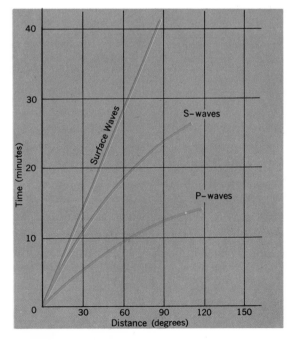

As you can see, the graphs for both P-waves and S-waves are curves, whereas the graph for surface waves is a straight line. The reason for this is that P-waves and S-waves travel through the earth, whereas the surface waves travel only along the surface of the earth.

As scientists continued to obtain information from various seismographic stations, they noticed something that seemed very strange. Stations located more than 105° but less than 142° from an earthquake recorded no S-waves or P-waves. At angular distances greater than 142°, P-waves were again detected, but no S-waves. The region in which no waves are observed is called the *shadow zone*. See *Figure 13-19*. (Actually, there are some very weak waves detected in the shadow zone. However, careful study has revealed that these weak waves are reflections.)

Figure 13-19 also shows the interpretation that scientists have made of their observations. The interpretation is this. First of all, there must be some sort of discontinuity, or boundary, between two different kinds of material deep in the earth. This boundary causes seismic waves to bend, just as the boundary between the two types of rock in the diagram of *Figure 13-16* causes the waves to bend. A wave just grazing this boundary deep in the earth—at A for instance—would continue on and be detected at the earth's surface 105° away from the earthquake. A wave encountering the boundary at B, however, would be bent inward and would strike the other side of the earth at some distance from the 105° point. Some waves would strike the boundary at C. These waves strike the boundary at just the right angle and come out the other side at just the right angle to be detected 142° from the earthquake. Waves entering the core at D—that is, perpendicular to the boundary—travel directly through the layers of the earth without being refracted.

Materials in the earth's interior. The discovery of the shadow zone has led scientists to some very important information about conditions deep in the interior of the earth. In order to cause the observed effects, the materials deep within the earth must have special properties. Using their knowledge of physics and mathematics, scientists have been able to infer some of the properties of the material deep within the earth. They have been able to determine that a boundary between two different materials is located at a depth of 2,900 km below the earth's surface. Furthermore, they have been able to determine that the material beneath this boundary is quite different from the material above it. The region which lies beneath the boundary is called the *core*. The region directly above it is called the *mantle*.

Two kinds of information have helped scientists discover the nature of the material in the core. First of all, the existence of the shadow zone indicates that the speed with which P-waves travel is slower in the core than it is in the mantle. One of the things which affects the speed with which waves travel is the density of the material through which they are traveling. Thus, the discovery of the shadow zone for earthquake waves gave a hint that the material deep within the earth might have a different density from that nearer the surface.

It was pointed out in Chapter 12 that the average density of the earth is almost twice as great as the density of the material near the surface. Somehow this difference has to be accounted for, and the discovery of a core at the center of the earth might be used to account for the difference.

The second observation which gave information about the core was that no S-waves are transmitted through the core. What does this observation mean? If you think about

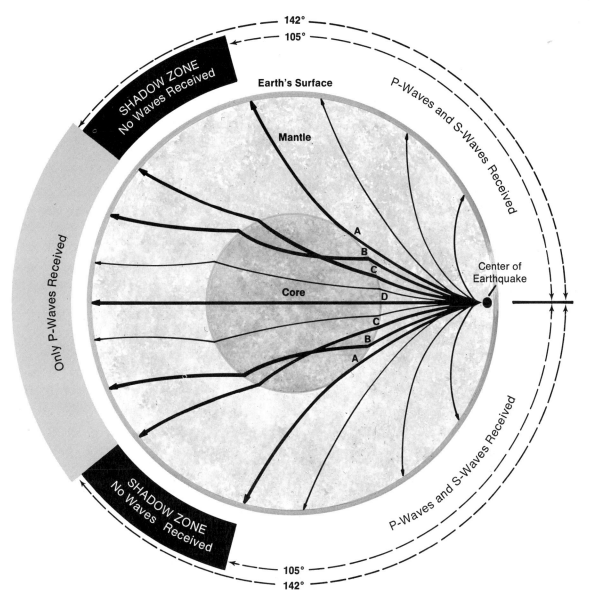

Figure 13-19. A boundary between two different materials exists 2,900 km below the earth's surface. The effect of this boundary on P-waves and S-waves causes the shadow zone.

S-waves, you will realize they cannot be transmitted through a liquid. S-waves will travel through a solid, like a piece of rope, but not through a liquid, like the water in a tank. P-waves can be transmitted through a liquid, since these are like sound waves, but S-waves will travel only through solids. The fact that no S-waves are transmitted through the core implies that the core is in a liquid state.

What are some reasons for believing the core to be more dense than the mantle? Does any evidence indicate that the core is less dense than the mantle?

Conclusions. Scientists have combined the information about seismic waves as recorded at various seismographic stations. They have carefully noted the distances between the earthquake's location and the recording seismographs. Scientists have noticed that there is always a shadow zone within which very weak P-waves, or perhaps no waves at all, are observed. They have also noticed that beyond a certain distance from an earthquake, no S-waves are observed. Of course, in making these observations, scientists had to make sure they were observing the waves transmitted directly from the earthquake to their stations, and not waves that had been reflected many times from the surface of the earth. In order to be certain that only the first arrivals were being observed, scientists were careful to check the travel time of each wave observed on the seismograms.

By combining all this information, scientists have been able to determine that the earth has a sharp boundary in its interior. Below this boundary, in the core of the earth, the material is quite different from the material above the boundary. The material of the core appears to be in a liquid state and may be of a different density than the other materials of the earth.

As far as we know, there will never be a way to look into the core of the earth. As far as direct observation goes, the interior of the earth is more remote than the surface of Mars. And yet, by carefully analyzing the vibrations which the earth itself creates, scientists are beginning to probe these invisible depths and to learn the nature of the materials deep within the earth's interior.

What are some reasons you can give in support of the statement ". . . the interior of the earth is more remote than the surface of Mars"?

INFORMATION DERIVED FROM LABORATORY INVESTIGATIONS AND THEORETICAL STUDIES

Three types of seismic waves were predicted by scientists before seismographs were perfected.

1. Compression waves—similar to sound waves—were predicted. In these waves, each particle of the medium (the material through which the waves travel) vibrates back and forth, parallel to the direction in which the wave travels.
2. Shear waves—similar to waves formed by shaking one end of a rope—were predicted. In these waves, each particle of the medium vibrates in a plane perpendicular to the direction in which the wave travels.
3. Surface waves were predicted. These waves affect only those materials near the earth's surface. Each particle of the medium moves in an elliptical path, but the motion is only in a plane parallel to the direction in which the wave travels.

Scientists have investigated many of the properties, including density and chemical composition, of various types of rock occurring near the earth's surface. The speeds at which various waves travel through this rock have also been determined. After taking into account the extreme pressure and temperature within the earth (to the limits of their knowledge), scientists can state what materials are likely to be present in the earth's interior.

Figure 13-20. These three columns represent a brief summary of what has been observed and inferred about the earth's interior from investigations using seismic waves.

INFORMATION OBTAINED FROM STUDIES OF SEISMIC WAVES AND SEISMOGRAMS	INFERENCES MADE ON THE BASIS OF ALL AVAILABLE INFORMATION
Four types of seismic waves have been observed. 1. P-waves are compression waves. They travel at a faster rate of speed than any other type of seismic wave. Thus, P-waves from an earthquake reach seismographic stations first. The P is an abbreviation for primary or for pressure. 2. S-waves are shear waves. Because they travel more slowly than P-waves, S-waves arrive at seismographic stations after P-waves do. The S is for secondary or for shear. 3. Surface waves travel more slowly than P-waves and S-waves and affect only those materials near the earth's surface. 4. Love waves—surface waves of a special type—occur where the materials near the earth's surface are layered. Each particle of the medium vibrates perpendicularly to the direction of wave travel, but only in a horizontal plane.	Wave motion is a natural phenomenon. This phenomenon has been studied in great detail. In general, the waves produced by earthquakes—that is, seismic waves—are similar to other types of waves that have been studied by scientists. Love waves are an exception. The complex nature of the materials near the earth's surface probably helps to account for the fact that Love waves were not predicted as the other types of seismic waves were.
Curves relating speed of waves to depth within the earth indicate that the speeds of P-waves and of S-waves change as they travel through the earth. The speeds of both P-waves and S-waves increase—but not in a regular manner—as the depth increases. At a depth of 2,900 km, the S-waves stop. At this depth the speed of the P-waves suddenly decreases, then begins to increase again. Evidence indicates that a sudden increase in speed occurs at a depth of 5,000 km.	Using their knowledge of physics and mathematics, scientists have been able to make inferences about the nature of the materials deep within the earth. Changes in wave speed indicate that a definite boundary between two different materials is located at a depth of 2,900 km. At a depth of 5,000 km, another boundary—this one not quite so clearly defined—is suspected.
Seismographs located at distances up to 105° from the center of an earthquake detect both S-waves and P-waves. At distances greater than 142° from the center of the earthquake, P-waves are recorded, but S-waves are not recorded. Between 105° and 142° from the earthquake's center, no S-waves are recorded, but some very weak P-waves are recorded.	The central portion of the earth's interior must be in a liquid state. This accounts for the fact that S-waves do not travel through the center of the earth. The outer edge of this liquid portion must be 2,900 km beneath the earth's surface. The material surrounding the liquid core is solid. In this case, solid means rock that has rigidity when subjected to sudden twists and bends, but that might flow slowly under the influence of intense, steady pressure.

Checking Your Knowledge

IMPORTANT IDEAS

1. The earth's surface is not completely stable. It changes and moves as different forces act upon it.

2. Earthquakes are more common in some places than in others. Some areas of the earth where earthquakes are common are land areas. Others are under the ocean.

3. Undersea earthquakes often cause great, destructive ocean waves called tsunamis.

4. There are four types of seismic waves. Each type has certain characteristics and travels in a particular manner.

5. By examining seismograms from several recording stations, seismologists can determine the location of an earthquake's center.

6. The speed and direction of a seismic wave depend, to a great extent, upon the material through which the wave is traveling.

7. Seismology has yielded much information about the interior of the earth.

USING NEW WORDS

Study the words listed below. Write the numerals *1-4* on your paper. After each numeral write words or statements to satisfy the instructions given.

seismograph	P-waves
S-waves	refraction
seismogram	Love waves
tsunami	seismology

1. Which of the above terms refers to a wave in the ocean?

2. List the terms which refer to types of earthquake waves. Tell how each type differs from the others.

3. List the differences in the meanings of the three words beginning with *seis*.

4. Which word refers to a change in the direction in which a wave travels?

TEST YOURSELF

Study the test below. Write the numerals *1-10* on your paper. Beside each numeral write the correct response to that part of the test having the corresponding numeral.

1. A tsunami does its greatest damage *(in the open ocean when it strikes a ship, when it reaches the shore)*.

2. The study of movements of the earth's crust is called _____.

3. A _____ is an instrument which detects and records movements of the earth's crust.

4. When a wave passes from one material into another material with different properties, there is a change in the direction in which the wave travels. This change is called _____.

5. The fact that S-waves do not travel through the center of the earth indicates that the core of the earth is _____.

6. The _____ is the name given to that portion of the earth's surface where the P-waves and S-waves produced by a particular earthquake are not observed.

7. Which of the following types of seismic waves travels fastest? (a) Love waves, (b) surface waves, (c) P-waves, (d) S-waves.

8. Which of the following types of seismic waves travels through the core? (a) Love waves, (b) surface waves, (c) P-waves, (d) S-waves.

9. In which of the following states is an earthquake most likely to occur? (a) Michigan, (b) Texas, (c) California, (d) Florida.

10. In order to determine the distance from a seismographic station to an earthquake, you must know which of the following? (a) the exact time at which the earthquake occurred, (b) how severe the earthquake was, (c) the time interval between the arrival at the station of the P-waves and the S-waves.

Extending Your Knowledge

QUESTIONS TO EXPLORE

1. What suggestions could you make that might be helpful in lessening the loss of lives from earthquakes?

2. What are some examples of unwise practices in the design, construction, or location of buildings that might make them unsafe to occupy during an earthquake?

3. What are some examples of man-made earthquakes? Are man-made earthquakes useful? If so, what are they used for?

4. How do the four types of seismic waves differ from each other? How do seismologists use these differences in their studies of earthquakes and of the interior of the earth?

5. Why is the direction in which a seismic wave travels changed when the wave passes from one material into a different material?

6. How do scientists explain the fact that S-waves do not pass through the earth's core?

7. If you know the length of the time interval between the arrival of the P-waves and the S-waves from a certain earthquake, what else can you determine about that earthquake?

SOME THINGS TO DO

1. Prepare and present to the class a detailed report of a major earthquake that occurred within the last 10 years. Explain such factors as the magnitude of the earthquake, how far under the surface it occurred, and how the surface of the earth was changed by the earthquake. Use a globe to illustrate those areas of the earth which were in the shadow zone for this earthquake. Find out if this earthquake produced any tsunamis. If so, where did they strike and with what effect?

2. Build a small seismograph and see what vibrations you can record with it. Even though you may not record an earthquake, you may

be able to record earth tremors that result from traffic or other causes.

3. Study the refraction of light that is passed through the water in an aquarium. How is this refraction similar to, and how does it differ from, the refraction of seismic waves?

4. Make a display in which you compare earthquakes, volcanoes, and thunderstorms. Show their effects, how they can be predicted (if they can be), what they have in common, and how they are unique.

5. What, do you think, are some characteristics of the earth's mantle? Keep a record of your ideas and see if they are in agreement with what you will learn when you study about this region in later chapters.

CHALLENGES IN SCIENCE

1. Prepare a series of sketches to show how the region near your home has changed with time. Show how it appears today, how it may have appeared 50 years ago, 500 years ago, and 5,000 years ago. Show what you think the region near your home might look like 500 years in the future.

2. One of our handicaps as humans is that our eyes cannot detect very slow or very rapid changes. How can such changes be recorded so that they may be studied?

3. Make a study of tsunamis. Find out how many tsunamis of major proportions have occurred in recent years. How would you explain less loss of life from tsunamis in the past decade or two than there was during the earlier part of the century?

4. Try to find accounts in ancient literature of earthquakes. To what did the people of ancient times attribute the occurrence of an earthquake? According to modern theories, what causes earthquakes?

Rock layers such as these may contain clues to the mystery of the earth's interior.

The Structure of the Earth

Although man has climbed the tallest mountains and descended into the deepest parts of the sea, he still does not know everything he would like to know about the earth. Even with the information he has gained—through drilling holes as deep as three miles into the earth, for example—he has not gained a thorough knowledge of the structure of the earth.

If he is to know the earth's structure, man must first determine the nature of the interior of the earth. But how can he determine what conditions and materials exist 50 km, 500 km, or 5,000 km beneath the earth's surface? There is no way that he can travel to these depths to observe the conditions. There is no way for him to even obtain samples of materials from deep within the earth.

Nevertheless, scientists have been able to gather a surprisingly great amount of information about the internal structure of the earth. As you study Chapter 14, you will find out what modern geophysicists believe the structure of the earth to be. You will also discover some of the information upon which they have based their beliefs about the earth's structure. Of course, modern concepts of the earth's structure are only theories. There is evidence to support these theories. There are also many aspects of these theories which still must be checked. How scientists reach conclusions about the earth's structure is a classic example of how indirect observations and reasoning can be combined to formulate a theory about something which has never been observed directly.

1. The Core

Obtaining information. In Chapter 13 you learned how seismologists, by observing the vibrations created by earthquakes, discovered that the earth has a core which is quite different from the rest of the earth. The material in the core probably has a greater density than the material in the outer portions of the earth. Observations have revealed that P-waves travel more slowly through this central core than they do through regions outside of it. Scientists have also observed that S-waves do not travel through the core at all. These observations indicate that the material in the core is a liquid. But there is still more information that can be used to tell us about the earth's core. This information concerns the average density of the earth.

If you divide the earth's total mass by its total volume, you find that the average density of the earth is about 5.5 g/cm³. On the other hand, the average density of rocks near the surface of the earth is about 2.8 g/cm³. In order for the earth to have an average density of 5.5 g/cm³, the material deep within the earth must be of much greater density than that near the surface.

Of course, this is what we expect. Pressures which are squeezing the material located deep in the earth are very great. Although it is very hard to squeeze a solid, we would expect the interior of the earth to be somewhat denser than rocks near the surface.

How much would the materials near the earth's center be compressed? The pressures inside the earth are so great that it is impossible to reproduce them in a laboratory. Thus, scientists are not able to get laboratory measurements to answer this question. Nevertheless, scientists can use the laws of physics and chemistry to reveal something about the rules of compression. Scientists can also obtain information about materials within the earth by measuring the speed of earthquake waves traveling through the depths of the earth. Combining the rules of compression with the measurements made by seismologists, scientists have reached a very important conclusion. The material deep in the interior of the earth cannot possibly have the same chemical composition as the material near the surface.

Still another piece of evidence must be considered. This evidence also has to do with the chemical composition of surface rocks. When the composition of surface rocks is compared with that of meteorites or with that of the atmospheres of stars, some important differences are apparent. One important difference is the proportion of iron compared to the proportion of the other elements. For average rocks on the surface of the earth, this proportion is less than that in average meteorites or in the atmospheres of many stars. It seems that iron is a much more common element in the universe as a whole than it is in the surface materials of the earth.

Combining the information. There are four types of evidence we can use to make inferences about the interior of the earth. First, from seismology we know that 2,900 km below the surface of the earth there is a boundary. Beneath this boundary, seismic waves behave in quite a different way than they do above the boundary. Second, the average density of the whole earth is much greater than the average density of its surface rocks. Third, in light of scientists' present knowledge of chemistry and physics, calculations of density and observations of seismic waves indicate that the deep rocks must be different from the rocks near the surface. This difference is more than just a difference in pressure. There probably is also a difference in chemical composition. Fourth, surface rocks contain much less iron in proportion to other elements than do meteorites and stellar atmospheres.

Putting all of these pieces of information together, scientists have concluded that the core of the earth below the depth of 2,900 km consists of molten iron. In addition, since a certain amount of nickel is found with iron in meteorites, it is believed that a small percentage of molten nickel is mixed with the molten iron in the core.

Although the concept of a core of molten iron and nickel is the best conclusion reached so far, we must admit that this conclusion may be wrong. Discoveries in the future may reveal that this is not the correct explanation after all. It cannot be proved that the overall chemical composition of the earth should be like that of meteorites. For example, we know that the average density of the moon is about 60 per cent that of the earth. This seems to show that the moon has a different chemical composition than the earth. If the earth is different from the moon, why can't the earth be different from the meteorites?

Furthermore, our theories about the behavior of material under very high pressures may be wrong. Man's knowledge of how materials behave under increased pressure is limited to amounts of pressure which can be produced in a laboratory, and pressures in the earth are very much greater than this. The pressure in the center of the earth must be about 3 million times greater than atmospheric pressure. Laboratory equipment can produce pressures much greater than atmospheric pressure, but not millions of times greater.

We can arrange our theories about the earth's interior in order, depending upon how certain we are of their correctness. Such an arrangement follows.

1. The interior of the earth is much denser than the surface.

2. There is a boundary about 2,900 km beneath the surface of the earth. Below this boundary the material is quite different from that above it. Below this boundary, in the region called the core, the material is of high density and behaves like a liquid.

3. The material of the core is molten iron, with a small percentage of nickel.

Of course, new data are continually being gathered. Scientists must be open-minded and ready to modify, or even discard, any of these theories if new evidence indicates these theories to be incorrect.

What is the ratio of the core's radius to that of the earth? What is the ratio of the core's volume to that of the earth?

A structure within the core. Recent measurements by seismologists indicate that there may be a complex structure within the core.

Figure 14-1. The diagram below represents a cross section of the earth. The core is represented by the shaded area. You can see the relative sizes of the core, the inner core, and the earth itself.

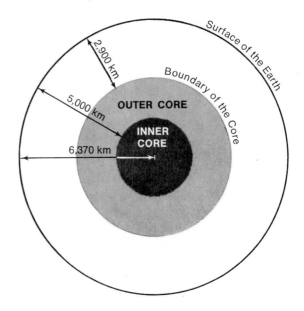

So far, there is no very good evidence for this, and scientists today are arguing about it. One theory is that below a depth of 5,000 km the core is solid. In this solid portion—called the *inner core* by some geophysicists—the density of the material is 16 to 20 g/cm³. The remainder of the core—supposedly liquid iron and called the *outer core*—has a density of about 11 to 12 g/cm³. (*Figure 14-1.*)

One hypothesis is that the inner core is crystalline iron. According to the hypothesis, this is a form of iron completely unknown on the surface of the earth. It is thought that such iron is able to exist as a solid (even though it is surrounded by liquid iron) because of the very high pressures in this region. But, as you can judge, this hypothesis is little more than a guess, and the scientists who have suggested

that the inner core may be crystalline iron are perfectly willing to admit this.

The inner core is a region of the earth about which little is known. In such a situation, an intelligent guess can be important. It can serve as a guide to further calculations and experiments. These calculations and experiments may eventually lead to a better understanding of the earth's interior.

Is there any similarity between the structure of a baseball and the structure of the earth? How much information about the interior of a baseball can you gather without damaging the ball? Could you learn more about a baseball if part of the cover were torn off? If you cut the ball in two with a hacksaw?

2. The Mantle

Figure 14-2. The diagram below represents a cross section of the earth. The mantle is represented by the shaded area. Compare this diagram with *Figure 14-1.* Which has the greater volume, the mantle or the core?

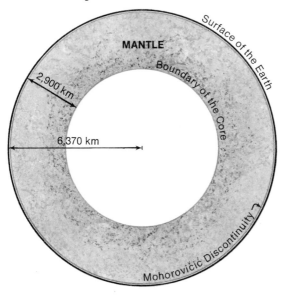

The Mohorovičić discontinuity. A great percentage of the total volume of the earth is occupied by a thick layer called the mantle. This region extends from the boundary of the core almost to the earth's surface. (*Figure 14-2.*) You have already studied the lower boundary of the mantle. The upper boundary of the mantle has a very complicated name. It is called the *Mohorovičić discontinuity* (mō hō rō' və chich' dis'kon tə nü' ə ti). This boundary is named after the scientist who first found evidence to show that this boundary exists. He discovered this boundary as a result of the way it affected the reflection of P-waves. The Mohorovičić discontinuity is of great interest to geologists. They would like to study the Mohorovičić discontinuity and the composition of the mantle directly beneath it.

Sources of information. Our knowledge about the mantle, like our knowledge about the core, is based upon seismology, laboratory experiments, and theory. Seismology has provided information about the speed of earthquake waves as they move through the mantle of the earth. In a laboratory, scientists can measure the speeds of waves as the waves move through samples of different kinds of rock. By using the information obtained in laboratories and the observations of seismologists, scientists have learned something about the density of the rocks in the mantle.

Of course, laboratory equipment cannot produce the high pressures which are characteristic of the mantle. Therefore, scientists must combine the results of the laboratory work and theoretical studies in reaching the best judgment about the nature of the material in the mantle.

DO IT YOURSELF

Observe differences in the speeds of sound waves in different materials

Hold your ear close to a concrete sidewalk while another person some distance away strikes the sidewalk with a stone. Can you detect any difference in the time it takes the sound to reach you through the concrete and through the air? Try the same experiment using different materials such as iron or water. Think of ways to measure the difference in time required for the sounds to reach your ear. Does the density of the material through which the wave passes seem to have any effect on the wave's speed? What kind of seismic wave travels in the same manner as a sound wave? How could seismic waves be used to determine the density of the materials through which they travel?

Rocks and minerals of the earth. Geologists and mineralogists are familiar with many different types of minerals and rocks found near the surface of the earth. In general, a mineral is an element or compound—usually a solid of inorganic origin—which occurs within the earth. Often, minerals occur as crystals. A rock is a mixture of minerals. In most rocks, the separate minerals occur as tiny crystals or particles. A large crystal is a rare and beautiful discovery.

Minerals and rocks similar to those found on the earth's surface may occur deep in the mantle, but we cannot be certain of this. In the high temperature and high pressure environment of the mantle, quite different mineral forms may be present. Thus, familiar minerals may exist in the mantle, but in forms never seen on the earth's surface.

Comparing surface rocks with mantle rocks. The results of laboratory work and theoretical studies give some indication of the nature of the minerals and rocks which compose the mantle. The speed with which seismic waves travel through the earth is one source of information about the earth's interior. Three known types of rock have properties that correspond to the observed data on wave speed. These three rock types have the names *dunite* (dun′īt), *peridotite* (per ə dō′tīt), and *eclogite* (ek′lə jīt). Each of these rock types is a combination of several different minerals. However, these three types of rock have one thing in common. Each contains a large percentage of *silica* (sil′ə kə). Silica is a combination of the elements silicon and oxygen. Pure silica is sometimes called *quartz*. It has the chemical formula SiO_2. Two other minerals

MINERAL	CHEMICAL FORMULA	DENSITY (g/cm³)	PERCENTAGE IN TYPICAL GRANITE	PERCENTAGE IN TYPICAL DUNITE
Quartz	SiO_2	2.6	70.2	40.5
Alumina	Al_2O_3	4.0	14.4	0.8
Iron Oxides	$\{$ Fe_2O_3 FeO	5.2 $\}$ 5.7	3.4	8.3
Periclase	MgO	3.6	0.9	46.3
Lime	CaO	3.3	2.0	0.7
Sodium Oxide	Na_2O	2.3	3.5	0.1
Potassium Oxide	K_2O	2.3	4.1	0.04
Water	H_2O	1.0	0.8	2.9
Others			0.7	.36

Figure 14-3. The mineral content of granite (a common rock in the surface materials of the earth) and that of dunite (believed to be a common rock in the mantle) are shown above. In addition, the chemical formulas and the densities of some common minerals are given.

which occur in large percentages in these three types of rock are the oxides of magnesium and iron.

Of course, geologists do not know that the mantle of the earth is composed of these rocks (dunite, peridotite, and eclogite). However, if the mantle is assumed to be made up of dunite and if granite is chosen as a typical surface rock, a comparison can be made between the chemical composition of the mantle and that of the rocks near the surface. Such a comparison is shown in the table above. (*Figure 14-3.*)

Notice that each of the minerals listed is an oxide—that is, an element combined with oxygen. Many minerals are combinations of these oxides. Although we do not know precisely what these combinations might be, we can be pretty certain that most minerals are combinations of other elements and oxygen. Not only is oxygen a very plentiful element, oxygen also combines readily with each of the other elements included in the table.

What can we learn by examining *Figure 14-3*? First of all, there are several important differences to be noted between dunite and granite. Although quartz is in both of these types of rock, it is more abundant in granite.

Other minerals more abundant in granite than in dunite are the oxides of aluminum, calcium, sodium, and potassium. Dunite, on the other hand, contains a large percentage of *periclase* (per'ə klās) and a relatively large percentage of iron oxides.

Implications. These differences in the chemical composition of granite and dunite result in a difference in the density of granite and the density of dunite. The most abundant mineral in dunite has a density of 3.6 g/cm³, while the most abundant mineral in granite has a density of only 2.6 g/cm³. Furthermore, dunite contains a relatively large percentage of iron oxides. These iron oxides are more dense than the oxides which are abundant in granite—that is, the oxides of aluminum, calcium, sodium, and potassium.

As a result of the differences in chemical composition, dunite has a greater density than granite. This result fits properly into our theory, since we expect the mantle to have a greater density than that of the earth's surface rocks. Although the difference in density fits into our theory, we still do not know for sure that the mantle is composed of dunite, but we do have some evidence that indicates the mantle might be composed of dunite.

FIND OUT BY TRYING

Materials you will need: samples of granite and dunite, balance, graduated cylinder

Determine the density of granite and dunite. The density of a substance, as you know, is the mass of a unit volume of the substance. Density is determined by dividing the measure of the mass of the substance by the measure of the volume of the substance. Of course, the balance is used to measure the mass of each sample. But how is the volume of an irregularly shaped object measured? One way is to put a given amount of water into a graduated cylinder, and then immerse the object in the water. The level of the water rises. The apparent increase in the amount of water is equal to the volume of the object immersed in the water. Can you think of some instances in which you could not use this method? Could liquids other than water be used? What other ways can you think of to measure the volume of an irregularly shaped object?

According to your measurements, what is the density of granite? Of dunite? How closely do your determinations agree with accepted values for the densities of these minerals? Which of these types of rock would you expect to be most abundant in the mantle? Which would you expect to be the most abundant near the earth's surface?

Variations within the mantle. It would be surprising if such a thick layer of the earth as the mantle should be everywhere the same. It seems logical that there would be variations from one place to another. For many years, scientists searched for evidence of such variations. Finally, after many seismograms had been obtained and studied, some evidence of variations within the mantle did show up. So far, however, the evidence is very fragmentary.

Seismograms are studied to determine the speed of seismic waves at various depths. The results are given in curves such as those in *Figure 14-4.* Following a detailed examination of these results, scientists have concluded that there are three regions within the mantle. One region extends from the Mohorovičić discontinuity to a depth of about 413 km below sea level. The second region extends

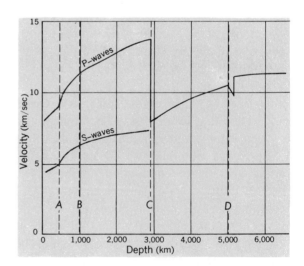

Figure 14-4. The above curves indicate the speeds of seismic waves relative to their depth within the earth. Changes in wave speed (indicated by changes in the curves' slopes) occur at boundaries between different materials. The locations of probable boundaries are indicated by the broken lines *A, B, C,* and *D.*

264

from 413 km below sea level to a depth of 984 km below sea level. The third region extends from 984 km below sea level to a depth of 2,900 km below sea level. See *Figure 14-5*.

It is impossible to know how each of these regions differs from the other two. Perhaps the mineral content in one region is different from that in the other regions.

One theory is that the *upper mantle* (the outermost region of the mantle) is made up primarily of rocks similar to dunite. This same theory states that the minerals in the *inner mantle* (the innermost region of the mantle) are magnesium and iron silicates, together with some uncombined iron. Thus, the inner mantle would have a composition similar to that of a mineral found near the earth's surface. This mineral—called *olivine* (ol′ə vēn), because of its olive-green color—is a mixture of magnesium silicate and iron silicate. In this theory, the *intermediate mantle* (between the upper and inner mantles) is composed of a material that is a blend of the materials of the upper and inner mantles. The intermediate mantle, then, is composed of rock similar to dunite, except that some olivine and some iron would be mixed in with it.

Keep in mind, however, that the pressure deep in the earth is extremely great. Such extreme pressure might affect the properties of the materials there. Therefore, the materials deep in the earth, although they have the same chemical composition as materials near the earth's surface, may exist in an entirely different form than we are familiar with.

Other geophysicists disagree quite strongly with this picture. For example, one theory is that, except for its outermost layer, the earth is almost completely olivine. According to this theory, even the core is made up of this mixture. The change in density at greater depths is simply a result of higher pressures forcing a change in the structure of the olivine. This

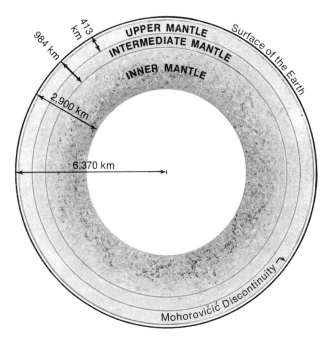

Figure 14-5. The diagram above represents a cross section of the earth. The mantle is represented by the shaded area. The locations of the boundaries between various regions within the mantle are shown, along with the radius of the earth.

theory says that the core is olivine in liquid form because of the very high pressure in that region. As you can see, this theory is quite different from the theory which states that the core is iron and nickel.

As you have just read, there is some disagreement among geophysicists as to which theory provides the most accurate description of the earth's interior. However, most scientists agree that they cannot reach any firm conclusions about the nature of either the mantle or the core at the present time. Instead, they must devote their attention to looking for more evidence which may help to resolve the problem. As more and more data are obtained, geophysicists will be better able to decide which of the present theories is more likely to be correct. Perhaps the new evidence will result in the formulation of an entirely new theory.

3. The Crust

Thickness and mineral content. The *crust* is the outermost layer of the earth's structure, or the solid portion of the earth above the Mohorovičić discontinuity. Since the crust is that portion of the earth on which we live, scientists have been able to learn more about the crust than they have about the mantle or the core. The continents, which make up almost all of the dry-land portion of the earth, form a crust which is more than 30 km thick in most places. The crust of the ocean basins is only about 5 km thick.

The crust of the ocean basins is different from the crust of the continents in ways other than just thickness. The mineral content of the material under the oceans appears to be different from that of the material in the continents. The table in *Figure 14-6* provides a comparison of certain properties of the rock in these two crustal regions.

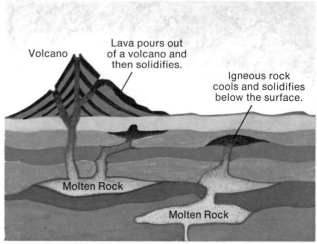

Figure 14-7. Deep within the crust or in the mantle, pockets of rock are somehow heated until they become molten. If these pockets are less dense than the surrounding rock—for example, molten granite surrounded by olivine—the molten material tends to rise through cracks and weak spots in the rock above it. A stream of such rock may break through the surface to form a volcano. In another region, such rock may be trapped beneath a strong overlying layer and slowly cool without ever breaking through to the surface.

Figure 14-6. The table below indicates some differences between the crust which makes up the continents and the crust which makes up the ocean floor.

PROPERTY BEING COMPARED	CRUST OF BASINS	CRUST OF CONTINENTS
Percentage of quartz	lower	higher
Percentage of less dense metals (Al, Ca, Na, K)	lower	higher
Percentage of more dense metals (Fe, Ni)	higher	lower
Average thickness	5 km	30 km

Types of rock. There are important characteristics of the crust in addition to the chemical composition of its rocks. A study of types of rock shows that the origin of some rock is quite different from the origin of other rock. For example, some rock shows clear evidence

of having been molten at some time in the past. Perhaps it solidified from lava pouring out of a volcano. Or, perhaps it solidified from molten material working its way up from deeper within the earth, but cooling and hardening before it broke through the surface. (*Figure 14-7.*) Rock of this type is called *igneous* (ig'ni əs) *rock,* which means "formed by heat." Granite is the most common igneous rock.

Another type of rock is called *sedimentary* (sed'ə men'tər i) *rock.* Rock of this type appears to have formed on the bottom of oceans, lakes, or on large, flat plains. In most cases, the materials from which this type of rock formed were transported by rivers and streams. As running water moves, it can carry particles of rock or soil with it. When a river or stream empties into a large body of water or onto a dry plain, the moving water slows or stops its motion. Then the bits of rock or soil, which were being carried by the water, settle. When the settled material becomes cemented together, sedimentary rock is formed.

Of course, the characteristics of the sedimentary rock which is formed depend on what materials settle to the bottom. Sandstone is a sedimentary rock formed by the settling and cementing together of tiny pieces of sand. Shale is a sedimentary rock formed by the settling and cementing together of clay particles. Some sedimentary rocks form from the

Figure 14-8. The igneous rocks shown are (top to bottom) granite, lava, and obsidian. These rocks obviously were molten at some time in the past. The sedimentary rocks are (top to bottom) sandstone, limestone, and shale. These rocks formed as particles of various materials settled to the bottom of a lake or ocean and became cemented together. The metamorphic rocks are (top to bottom) gneiss, marble, and slate. These rocks have been changed in form. For example, granite—when subjected to extremely high temperature and/or pressure—becomes gneiss.

| IGNEOUS ROCK | SEDIMENTARY ROCK | METAMORPHIC ROCK |

bones and shells of dead marine creatures accumulating on the ocean bottom. Over hundreds of millions of years, certain chemical and physical changes occur, resulting in the formation of rock. Limestone is a rock of this type. Fossils, the remains or evidence of plants and animals that lived many years ago, can often be found in sedimentary rock.

Would you expect to find as many fossils in igneous rock as in sedimentary rock? Why or why not?

There is a third type of rock, called *metamorphic* (met′ə môr′fik) *rock*. See *Figure*

14-8. The term metamorphic means that rock of this type has been changed in form. The origin of metamorphic rock cannot be clearly determined. Such rock may once have been either sedimentary or igneous. Apparently, metamorphic rock has been subjected to very high pressures and/or temperatures at some time. Marble is a metamorphic rock.

These three classes of rock—igneous, sedimentary, and metamorphic—and the tremendous variety of minerals which exist within them are all found in the earth's crust. These rocks and minerals will be studied in more detail in later chapters.

DO IT YOURSELF

Collect rocks

If possible, locate at least one specimen of each of the three major classes of rock—igneous, sedimentary, and metamorphic. Examine each rock carefully. Try to identify some of the minerals in each one. Does the presence (or absence) of a certain type of mineral indicate anything about the past history of the locality in which you found the rock? If so, what does it indicate?

The structure of the crust. On the earth's crust, the occurrence of continents and ocean basins is a rather surprising feature. It is one of the details of nature which does not appear to be accidental. Ocean basins and continents are not all mixed together in some sort of rocky soup. Instead, the continents are distinct, large masses. Separating the continents are large ocean basins. The continents seem to be composed of one type of rock and the ocean basins of another. In the ocean basins, there are no rocks of the type found in the continents. Even islands in the middle of the Pacific, such as Hawaii, consist of rocks typical of the ocean basins, and not of rocks typical of the continents.

The igneous rocks that are most abundant in continents are composed predominantly of

light-colored and relatively lightweight minerals. These are *granitic* (grə nit′ik) *rocks*. The igneous rocks which compose the crust beneath the oceans are composed largely of dark-colored and relatively dense materials. This dark-colored, dense type of rock is referred to as *basalt* (bə sôlt′).

The depth of the crust forming the continents and the depth of the crust under the oceans have been determined by seismologists. Many studies of the thickness of the earth's crust have depended upon the analysis of seismic waves generated by earthquakes. But a number of other studies have used waves generated by man-made explosions. See *Figure 14-9.*

Vibrations from an explosion on the surface travel down through the crust and are

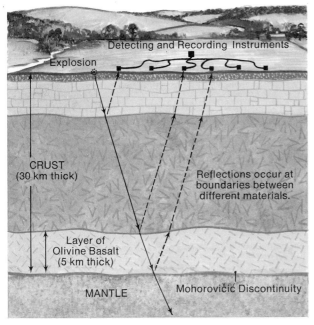

Figure 14-9. Man-made seismic waves are used to study the earth's crust. Various boundaries, including the Mohorovičić discontinuity, reflect the waves.

reflected at the Mohorovičić discontinuity. By making many measurements, scientists can determine both the depth of the reflecting layer and the speed of the waves through the rock. With measurements such as this, an interesting piece of information has been gained. It seems that a layer of dense rock, five kilometers thick, lies not only under the ocean basins, but also under the continents. Thus, the less dense rocks of the continents do not rest directly upon the mantle. Instead, they rest upon an intervening layer of dense rock. This thick layer of dense rock is believed to be made up mainly of a material called *olivine basalt*. This material contains a large percentage of olivine (iron silicate), which was described in the previous section. It appears that this layer completely covers the earth like a thin skin. Resting on top of it are extended layers of granitic rocks which make up the continents.

Around the edges of the continents and stretching in a thin layer over the ocean floors are those sedimentary rocks compacted from particles which have been washed down off the mountains of the continents. If we were to slice through a section of the crust where a continent meets an ocean, it would look like the diagram shown in *Figure 14-10*.

The lightweight granitic rock almost seems to be "floating" on the heavier basalt rock, the way oil floats on water. Of course, rock is solid, so this process of floating cannot be exactly the same as oil floating on water. However, imagine a layer of basalt, five kilometers thick, completely covering the earth. Then, suppose that somehow the lighter rock of the continents was spread over certain regions of the surface of the earth on top of the

Figure 14-10. As shown in the diagram below, the earth's crust is not the same everywhere on the earth's surface. Under the ocean, the crust consists of a layer of basalt covered only by a thin layer of sediments washed down from the continents. In the area of the continents, masses of granitic rock seem to be floating on top of the layer of basalt. The weight of the granitic rock is believed to have pushed the layer of basalt down into the mantle.

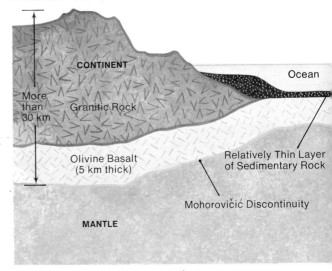

layer of basalt. Over billions of years, even rock will gradually give way, and the granitic rock in the continents will gradually sink, pushing the basalt layer beneath them ever deeper into the earth.

How long will this sinking process go on? It will go on until the downward force (the weight) of the granitic rock is balanced by the upward force exerted by the mantle. In a similar manner, a piece of wood will sink down into water until the buoyant force pushing up equalizes the weight of the wood pushing down. The piece of wood floating on water is an illustration of Archimedes' principle, which states that a floating object displaces an amount of fluid equal to its own mass.

If Archimedes' principle can be applied to the rock on the continents, then this rock will sink down until it has displaced an amount of the denser mantle rock equal to its own mass. Since the continental rock is less dense than the mantle rock, a portion of the continental rock will stick up above the average level, just as the top of a floating block of wood sticks up above the surrounding water. See *Figure 14-11.*

Calculations of the mass of the continental rock and the depth of the continental layer indicate that apparently Archimedes' principle

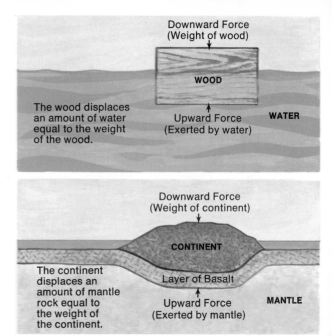

Figure 14-11. Wood sinks into water until the buoyant force of the water equals the weight of the wood. Continents sink into the mantle until the upward force exerted by the mantle equals the continent's weight.

can be applied to the case of granitic rocks "floating" on the basalt layer. Thus, we can understand why the continents extend several kilometers above the ocean basins. But why should the continents be limited to certain areas? Why are these rocks not spread uniformly around the surface of the earth?

FIND OUT BY TRYING

Materials you will need: overflow can, water, detergent, various small objects having different masses (but which will float on water), balance, beaker

Record the weight of each of the small objects. Fill the overflow can with water and add one or two drops of detergent. Then place one of the small objects into the water in the overflow can. Catch the water which overflows, and record its weight. Repeat this procedure for each of the floating objects. What is the purpose of adding detergent to the water in the overflow can? How does the weight of each object compare with the amount of water it displaces? How can such a relationship be applied to the crust of the earth?

Unsolved problems. As you can see, geophysicists have managed to discover a great deal about the structure of the earth. Theories, data from seismograms, and laboratory experiments have helped geophysicists build up a reasonable picture of those interior layers which are impossible to see directly. (*Figure 14-12.*)

Now, the major problems which confront earth scientists are problems of explanation. How did the earth acquire the structure that it has? How can the variations in the chemical composition of the earth be explained in a manner consistent with what we know about the surface of the earth, the meteorites, and the stars? How were continents formed? Why were continents formed just in certain special places?

Answering questions such as these is the task of modern scientists. As you can understand, there is still much to be learned about the earth. In the next chapters you will find out more about geological research and the results and ideas which have come from it.

Is it a part of the scientist's method to guess about the earth's interior when his only observations have been made from the earth's surface? If so, what is the purpose of such a guess?

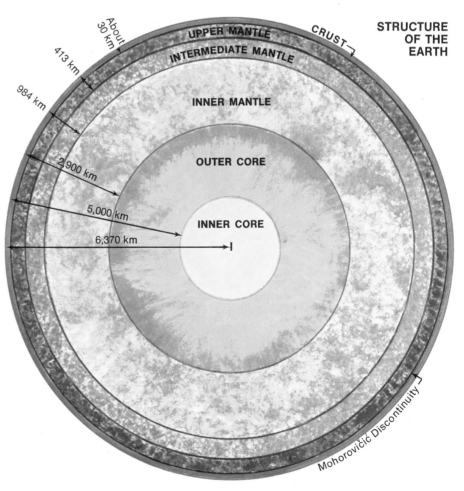

STRUCTURE OF THE EARTH

Figure 14-12. According to present-day interpretations, the structure of the earth is as shown at right. The thickness of each of the layers, except for the crust, is shown in the proper proportion. If the earth were somehow reduced to the size of this diagram, how thick would the crust be?

Checking Your Knowledge

IMPORTANT IDEAS

1. The earth consists of several distinct layers. These include the core, the mantle, and the crust.

2. Scientists have reasoned that the materials in the earth's core are much more dense than any rocks on the surface of the earth.

3. Many geologists believe that the earth's core is composed chiefly of molten iron mixed with a small amount of molten nickel. A solid, inner core may be present within the core.

4. Little is known about the chemical composition of the earth's mantle. It may be composed of a material similar to dunite.

5. The core is thought to be composed of two layers, and the mantle is thought to be composed of three layers.

6. The crust is thicker and less dense in the areas of the continents than it is in the areas beneath the oceans.

7. Minerals are chemical substances—either elements or compounds—which occur in the earth. A rock is a mixture of minerals.

8. Surface rocks are classed as igneous, sedimentary, or metamorphic.

9. The Mohorovičić discontinuity is of great interest to scientists.

USING NEW WORDS

Study the five groups of words below. Write the letters *a* through *e* on your paper. Following each letter, explain the similarities and differences in the meanings of the words in the group designated by that letter.

   a. core—mantle—crust
   b. sedimentary—igneous—metamorphic
   c. rock—mineral
   d. quartz—periclase—water
   e. Mohorovičić discontinuity—earth's surface

TEST YOURSELF

Study the test below. Write the numerals *1-10* on your paper. After each numeral, write the correct response to that part of the test having the corresponding numeral.

1. Much of man's knowledge of the structure of the earth has been derived through a careful study of _____ waves.

2. Scientists think that, below a depth of 2,900 km below sea level, the earth consists mainly of _____.

3. The layer of the earth that lies between the Mohorovičić discontinuity and the core of the earth is known as the _____.

4. The density of the rock in that part of the crust which forms the continents is (*greater than, less than, about the same as*) the density of the rocks which form the crust beneath the ocean.

5. The pressure on the materials in the core of the earth is believed to be (*thousands, millions, billions*) of times greater than atmospheric pressure.

6. The rocks which make up the continents extend (*to a greater depth, to a lesser depth, about the same depth*) below sea level than they do above sea level.

7. The light-colored and relatively lightweight igneous rock that is abundant in the continents is (*basalt, olivine, granite*).

8. Rock formed by the cooling and hardening of hot, molten material from within the earth's crust is called _____ rock.

9. Rock that has been formed by the accumulation and hardening of sediments is called _____ rock.

10. Rock that has undergone a change in structure and in texture as a result of being subjected to great pressure and/or high temperature is called _____ rock.

Extending Your Knowledge

QUESTIONS TO EXPLORE

1. What effects do you think high pressures and high temperatures might have on solids? What are some examples of ways in which high pressures and high temperatures are used commercially to change materials?

2. Geologists sometimes state that certain rocks are volcanic rocks. How, do you think, can it be determined that these rocks are volcanic in origin?

3. How would you explain the difference between a rock and a mineral?

4. What are fossils? Why are they most often found in sedimentary rocks?

5. What are some factors which would affect the size of the crystals formed in a particular kind of rock?

6. How does shale differ from sandstone? How does sandstone differ from limestone?

SOME THINGS TO DO

1. Investigate the differences between cold tar and warm tar. How does tar react when struck a sharp blow with a hammer? When subjected to steady pressure? How does temperature difference affect this behavior? How can your observations help you understand the nature of the earth's mantle?

2. On the chalkboard, draw a circle to represent the earth. Use a scale so that the circle will be nearly the size of the chalkboard. Then, using this scale, draw concentric circles to represent the boundaries between the various layers within the earth. Label each layer. In the label, tell what the composition of each layer is believed to be.

3. Try to locate some feature in your community where various layers of rock are exposed. Road cuts through hills and deep excavations such as quarries are two examples of such features. From your observations, is the material of the earth's crust uniform in chemical composition, physical makeup, and distribution?

4. List all the arguments you can against the idea that the earth is a molten mass covered by a thin crust of solid rock.

5. Make a list of the unknown characteristics of the earth's interior which scientists are trying to determine. Keep the list. Before the end of the school year, try to find a report of the discovery of any information concerning these characteristics.

CHALLENGES IN SCIENCE

1. Calculate the volume of the earth. Then calculate what percentage of the earth's total volume is represented by each of the following: the core, the mantle, and the crust.

2. Make a chart in which the name, chemical composition, density, and melting point of each of the minerals listed in this chapter are given. Add any other minerals as they are studied in later chapters.

3. Make a study of *Project Mohole*. How did this project come to be proposed? What obstacles did its supporters encounter? What outcomes of the project were benefits? Make a report to the class in which you describe the project and its objectives.

4. Scientists often make comparisons between the average density of the earth and the average densities of the moon and the planets. From these comparisons, what conclusions can be drawn concerning the interiors of the objects involved?

5. Suggest a hypothesis which explains the observed differences in the composition of the rock in the continents and the composition of the rock beneath the ocean.

The earth's unique chemical composition may be a clue to the earth's origin.

CHAPTER 15

The Origin and History of the Earth

So far in UNIT 4, your attention has been focused on finding out about the earth as it is. You have studied some of the data scientists have gathered about the earth. You have discovered how scientists, in making use of the data, have made inferences about the nature of the earth's interior. Now, you are ready to turn your attention to investigating the problem of what the earth's beginning was.

Any study of the earth's beginning must, of course, be closely tied to the origin of the solar system and, indeed, to the origin of the whole universe. Since the earth is the one body in space which we can study in considerable detail, the study of the planet earth may provide valuable clues about the earth's beginning and about the beginnings of various other bodies in space, as well.

You are already aware of some of the unique aspects of the planet earth. One of these is the large amount of free oxygen in its atmosphere. Another is the great amount of water about its surface. Perhaps these unique aspects are clues to the earth's origin. What significance do these aspects have? What was the origin of the earth? These and other similar questions about the beginning of the earth are explored in Chapter 15.

1. Explaining the Earth's Beginning

Using theories to explain the earth's origin. In Chapter 11, you studied various theories which have been proposed to explain the origin of the solar system. As you found out then, such theories must also explain the origin of the earth. Of course, a theory proposed to explain the origin of a planet carries within it certain implications about the nature of that planet. If these implications are in agreement with the observations made by scientists about the nature of that planet, then the theory is supported, although not proved. However, if the observations of the condition of the planet are contrary to the implications of a particular theory, then that theory must be discarded or revised.

It would seem that formulating an acceptable theory about the origin of a planet is a pretty simple task. To perform it, scientists have only to work out the theory in detail and then check it against observations. But this, as we shall see, is considerably easier said than done.

Under what conditions might a scientist continue to use a theory, even after an observation seems to contradict one or more of the implications of the theory?

Reviewing theories of the origin of the solar system. Suppose we review, briefly, the various theories described in Chapter 11. Let us consider first the two-star theories—that is, those theories which involve interactions between two stars. The basis of one of these theories is that two stars accidentally passed close by each other. One of the two stars was the sun. Gravitational attraction between the two stars raised tides so huge that streamers of material were pulled away from the surfaces of the two stars. Much of the material which formed these streamers was left orbiting the

separate stars after the two stars had passed each other and gone on their separate ways. (*Figure 11-2.*)

According to this theory, the planets of the solar system condensed out of the material that had been pulled from the two passing stars. However, as you will recall, there is a serious difficulty with this theory. Calculations have been made which indicate that material torn from stars in this way would not condense into planets. Instead, the material would expand rapidly into a large, hot cloud. The mass of such a cloud would not be great enough for the gravitational forces within it to cause the cloud to condense. Thus, planets would not have been formed in this way. Because the impossibility of planet formation is such a serious difficulty, we are probably safe in disregarding this particular theory.

Another two-star theory suggests that the sun was once a member of a double-star system. At some time, the sun's companion exploded and became a supernova. According to this theory, some material from the exploded star continued to move about the sun as a huge cloud of dust and gas. Eventually, this cloud condensed at various points, forming the planets.

Other theories that have been proposed are sometimes called nebular theories or condensing-cloud theories. All of these theories start with a large cloud of dust and gas. Some such theories suggest that the sun was formed first, and the remainder of the cloud continued to swirl about it like a gigantic ring. Then, in a few hundred million years or so, the cloud began to condense here and there as a result of gravitational forces. Thus, the planets were formed, revolving about the sun.

Other condensing-cloud theories suggest that the sun and planets were all made at about the same time from a rotating cloud of gas and dust. A central concentration of material, compacted by gravitational force, formed the sun. As the sun formed at the center of the rotating cloud of gas and dust, other zones of concentration developed and compacted within the cloud. These other zones of concentration eventually became the planets.

You will note that all of these theories, except the first one which we discarded, suggest that the planets formed within a condensing cloud of dust and gas. Thus, all of the materials in the planets must be related to the original materials in this condensing cloud. As you may remember, it is this conclusion that led us to one of the faults of this theory. From observations that have been made, it seems unlikely that the planets are all composed of the same material. For example, Jupiter has an average density very nearly the same as that of water, while the average density of the earth is more than five times as great as that of water.

DO IT YOURSELF

Investigate common properties of objects within the solar system

Use various references to find out the density that has been estimated or determined for different objects in the solar system. Using the data, determine whether or not any objects in the solar system have a density approximately the same as the density of Jupiter. If you discover some objects that have this density, describe how Jupiter is similar to these objects. Also, tell how Jupiter is different from these objects. Judging from the results of your investigation, would you say that the objects of the solar system are made up of the same materials?

Explaining the separation of elements. The evidence indicates that some separation of substances must have taken place during the formation of the planets. In this separation the heavier elements seem to have been concentrated in the planets nearer the sun and the lighter elements in the planets farther away. This separation might have taken place in the original cloud before formation of the planets began. Or, the separation might have taken place during the process of planet formation, or even later, when the planets were almost complete. Of course, it is also possible that a separation process was going on continuously from the time before the planets began to form until they were almost complete.

What do the various theories say about this process of separating the elements? The theories which seem to offer the best explanation suggest that each planet was formed as the central part of a gigantic protoplanet. The protoearth, for example, was several hundred—perhaps even one thousand—times greater in mass than the earth of today. Most of the mass of the protoearth was in the form of hydrogen and helium, just as most of the material of the universe is hydrogen and helium. Eventually, light from the sun began to strike the huge cloud of gas and dust. Light pressure pushed away most of the enveloping cloud about the protoearth, leaving only the small, solid core at the center. This core became the earth as we know it today. See *Figure 15-1*.

The pressure of sunlight would decrease as the distance from the sun increased. This decrease in the pressure of light would account for the fact that the outer planets—Jupiter, Saturn, Uranus, and Neptune—have kept

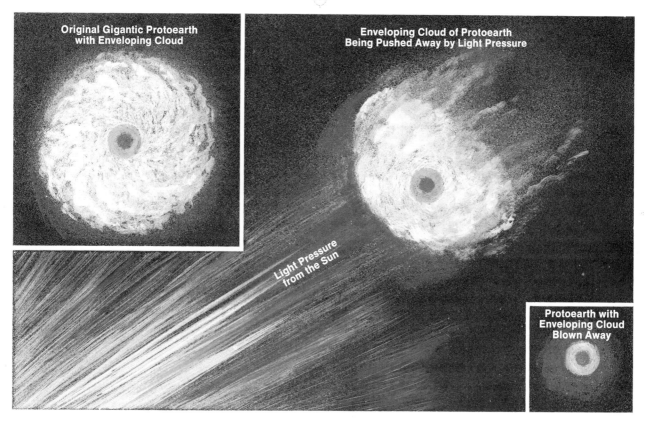

Figure 15-1. Originally, hydrogen and helium represented a large percentage of the mass of the protoearth. Eventually, however, the pressure of the sun's light pushed these gases away, leaving only the small, solid core at the center of the protoplanet.

much of their enveloping cloud of hydrogen and helium. It would also account for the fact that these planets are both larger and less dense than the earth and the other planets nearer the sun. Pluto is not mentioned here because little is known of this distant planet.

So far, theory and observations seem to be in agreement. But suppose we examine more closely what we have learned. First of all, we know that the density of the earth is greater than the density of the moon or of the meteorites. The earth's density is also greater than the density of Mars. What is to account for this?

The theory just described tells how the gases hydrogen and helium were lost from the earth. Theoretically, the gases hydrogen and helium were lost from around the moon, Mars Venus, and Mercury in the same manner. But then, why shouldn't all of these bodies have about the same density? Clearly, some additional separation process took place. Can any theory account for this? In order to answer this question, we must look again at what we know about our own planet. Furthermore, we must examine our knowledge of the rest of the material in the universe. In short, we must review our knowledge of (1) the densities of the planets, (2) the chemical nature of meteorites, and (3) the atmosphere of stars. Then, we can try to explain their varied compositions.

2. Observations of the Earth's Chemical Composition

The presence of iron. Seismologists have discovered that the earth has a dense core that behaves like a liquid. A theory most scientists accept is that this core is made up of molten iron with some molten nickel mixed with it.

Why do geophysicists believe that nickel is mixed with iron in the earth's core?

We must remember that there is no known way to determine the chemical nature of the core. Thus, it is only a theory that the core is mainly iron, with only a small amount of nickel mixed in. But suppose this theory is correct. Iron, then, represents a very large percentage of the earth's overall composition. In fact, even without any iron at all in the mantle of the earth, 31 per cent of the earth's mass is iron. (We can neglect the crust for now, since it represents such a small percentage of the earth's total mass.) A more reasonable assumption, however, is that the mantle has at least a small percentage of iron in it, perhaps 15 per cent. Let us assume, then, that the earth has a mantle containing 15 per cent iron and a core composed of nearly pure iron. Calculations based on this assumption indicate that the amount of iron in the earth is about 40 per cent of the earth's total mass. How does this percentage compare with what we know about other bodies?

Cosmic abundance of elements. In previous chapters, we have tabulated relative abundances of various elements. Such tables can be made for relative abundances of elements in the atmospheres of stars, in meteorites, and in the crust of the earth. Suppose an object can be brought into the laboratory to be analyzed, or perhaps it can be analyzed by spectroscopic means. Then, the relative amounts of the various elements in that object can be determined with some degree of accuracy.

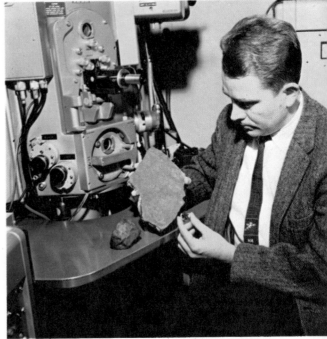

NASA, AMES RESEARCH CENTER

Figure 15-2. Several types of meteorites have been analyzed by scientists. The results, when combined with information about other objects in the universe, have enabled scientists to prepare tables representing the composition of the universe as a whole.

Scientists have analyzed many different objects in an attempt to make a table that would represent the composition of the universe as a whole. *Figure 12-10* on page 230 is one such table. As you can readily imagine, it is impossible to be sure that such a table is correct. After all, we can get samples of only a very small portion of the universe. Therefore, scientists who make these calculations always allow for some uncertainty. Of course, different scientists have different ideas as to which particular meteorite or which particular star is more representative of the average. Thus, there is always some disagreement among the scientists who work on this problem. But, taking all factors into account, there is fairly good agreement between the various tables of relative abundance.

Comparing abundances of elements. Suppose we compare a table of cosmic abundances with the relative abundances of various important elements on the earth. First of all, we will have to disregard hydrogen and helium in our comparison, although these are the two most abundant elements of the universe. We can easily understand why the gases hydrogen and helium would no longer be part of the earth. These gases are so light that they easily escape from the atmosphere of the earth and move out into space. Then, the pressure of the sun's light blows these gases away. There are, in fact, many other gases that would escape

Figure 15-3. If the kinetic energy of the particles of a substance is great enough that they escape from the substance, the substance evaporates. How could a nonvolatile substance be made to evaporate?

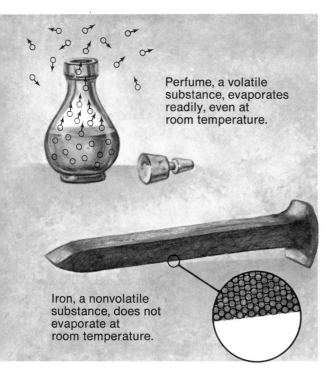

Perfume, a volatile substance, evaporates readily, even at room temperature.

Iron, a nonvolatile substance, does not evaporate at room temperature.

from the earth in the same way, only much more slowly. But there are many more elements that are solid, at least at the temperatures at the surface of the earth. Once the earth was formed, these solid elements would not escape, and so they are still present in the earth.

Substances that evaporate and form gases readily at ordinary temperatures are said to be *volatile* (vol′ ə təl). Those substances that do not are said to be *nonvolatile*. Of course, a nonvolatile substance will evaporate when it gets hot enough. But, considering the average temperature near the surface of the earth, we can easily divide the elements into two classes —those that are volatile and those that are nonvolatile. At the ordinary temperatures of the earth's surface, hydrogen is a volatile element. Iron is a nonvolatile element. Considering only the nonvolatile elements, how does the earth's composition compare with that of the universe as a whole?

If the core of the earth is mostly iron, as most scientists believe, then the earth is about 40 per cent iron. In considering the nonvolatile elements in the composition of the rest of the universe, scientists have discovered that iron makes up between 22 and 28 per cent of this portion of the universe. If all of our information and theories about relative abundances are correct, the earth has somehow acquired a percentage of iron greater than the percentage of iron present in the average material of the universe.

Many scientists like to look at this relationship the other way around. They express it this way. Somehow the earth has lost many of the lighter elements compared to the matter in the universe in general. In referring to lighter elements, these scientists are not considering just hydrogen and helium. They are also considering certain elements that ordinarily are nonvolatile, such as magnesium, phosphorus, and sulphur.

Figure 15-4. Man uses great quantities of iron and aluminum. Fortunately, these elements are more abundant in the earth than they are in the universe as a whole. The mining of taconite—an ore of iron—is shown in the picture at the left. In the top picture on the right, bauxite—aluminum ore—is shown being mined. Not every abundant element is so sought after by man. Silicon, for example, represents more than 46 per cent of the mass of the sand dunes shown. But, today, man does not use or need huge amounts of silicon. Thus, he has not developed an economical way to separate silicon from sand.

Some of these elements are very common in the universe as a whole. For example, magnesium is as common as silicon. One calculation of relative abundances—*Figure 12-10* on page 230—shows that, for every 100 atoms of silicon in the universe as a whole, there are 110 atoms of magnesium. However, on the surface of the earth, for every 100 atoms of silicon there are only 9 atoms of magnesium. The relative abundance of magnesium in the universe is more than 12 times as great as it is in the earth's surface materials.

On the other hand, there are some lighter elements that seem to be more common in the earth's surface rocks than in the universe as a whole. For example, consider aluminum. In the universe as a whole, there are about 9 atoms of aluminum for every 100 atoms of silicon. On the surface of the earth, this ratio is 30 to 100. Thus, aluminum is more than 3 times as abundant at the earth's surface as it is in the universe as a whole.

Even more surprising is the comparison of the abundances of the very light element lithium. In the universe as a whole, there is 1 atom of lithium for every 10,000 atoms of silicon. But on the surface of the earth, this ratio is 9 to 10,000. That is, the relative abundance of lithium is 9 times greater here on the earth's surface than it is in the universe in general. We must realize that these comparisons (except for iron) are based on the composition of the surface materials of the earth, rather than the earth as a whole. The composition of the interior may be quite different. Nevertheless, these observations of the earth's surface material must somehow be explained.

From their observation of the relative abundances of elements, scientists have come to some rather surprising conclusions. Compared to the universe as a whole, the earth has a higher concentration of iron and a lower concentration of certain of the lighter elements. However, for the surface material at least, this general rule is not applicable for every element, but only for some of them. Thus, whatever process is responsible for the differences in composition between the earth and the rest of the universe, the process must have gone on in a very unusual manner. If iron were heavily concentrated and everything else were low in concentration, then we might hope to find some simple explanation. But nature has not given us such an easy task.

In what way might the earth have lost some of its lighter metals without losing all of its gases?

3. Possible Methods of Separating Elements

Defining differentiation. Astronomers observe clouds of gas and dust that exist now in our galaxy. These are the gaseous nebulae. It is difficult to determine the chemical composition of these nebulae, since most of the light observed from them is reflected light from nearby stars. Whatever the composition of these clouds is, most scientists believe that the gases and dust particles in the clouds are very well mixed. Thus, they believe the percentage of a particular element in one part of the cloud is pretty much the same as it is in all other parts of the cloud.

If such a cloud were the starting point for the origin of the solar system, then originally all of the elements should have been uniformly mixed. But, an examination of the earth as it exists today reveals that somehow the elements have become separated from one another. For example, the iron in the earth seems to be concentrated in the core. The silicate rock in the earth seems to be concentrated in the crust. The process by which certain chemicals become separated from other chemicals in a planet is called *differentiation* (dif'ə ren' shi ā'shən).

In the development of the planet earth, differentiation has done more than simply separate the silicate rock from the iron. Somehow, the amounts of many of the lighter elements present in the earth have been greatly reduced compared to the amount of iron present. Scientists would like to be able to explain such examples of differentiation.

Differentiation in the protoearth. Suppose, in order to explain differentiation, we refer to the protoplanet theory of the formulation of the earth. If we start with a condensing dust cloud, then, at some point in the process, the protoearth was formed. According to the theory, the protoearth was a huge mass of dust and gas having a mass about 500 to 1,000 times greater than that of the present earth. Its radius was several hundred times greater than the radius of the present earth. In the center of the condensing cloud, the gases were compact and very hot. Gravitational force had compressed the gases in the central portion of the cloud. As a result of the compression, the gases had heated up. Temperatures near the center of the protoearth probably reached several thousand degrees Kelvin.

There are two factors that determine the temperature at the center of a protoplanet and, in fact, the temperature of the whole cloud. One factor is the gravitational force which compacts the gas, causing the gas to heat up. A second factor is radiation. The hot gas emits infrared radiation and, in the process, loses heat. The balance between these two factors—heat generated by gravitational force and heat lost through infrared radiation—determines

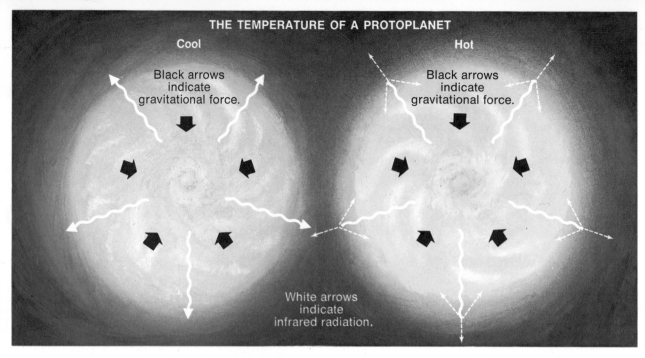

Figure 15-5. Heat resulting from compression in a protoplanet is radiated away as infrared radiation. If the radiation escapes, the protoplanet does not heat up. If the gases in the outer part of the protoplanet absorb some radiation and reflect some back to the center, the temperature of the material inside the protoplanet continues to rise.

the temperature. If the infrared radiation escapes out into space, the center of the cloud will lose heat quickly. Therefore, even though the compression caused by gravitational force continues to generate heat, the temperature at the center of the cloud will not become very high. On the other hand, suppose the gases at the outer edges of the cloud absorb infrared radiation and reflect some of it back in toward the center. Then the center of the cloud will lose heat very slowly. (*Figure 15-5.*) In this case, heat resulting from the compressing effect of gravitation will cause the center of the cloud to continue to heat up. Eventually, an equilibrium will be reached. The amount of heat being generated through compression will be the same as the amount being lost by radiation.

It is impossible to calculate what the temperature at the center of the protoplanet would be when this equilibrium is reached. It depends upon how rapidly the gas is being compressed by gravitational force. The rate of compression also depends upon how rapidly the gas is swirling around. The faster the swirling motion is, the longer it takes the gas to get into the center. Thus, the rate of compression and heating will be slower. The rate at which heat is lost by radiation depends on the details of the composition of the gas cloud. Different elements absorb and reflect infrared radiation at different rates. In order to calculate the rate of absorption and reflection, it is necessary to have some knowledge of the distribution of the elements in the cloud.

Calculating the rate of absorption and reflection is very difficult. The calculation is difficult even if we assume that all the elements would be uniformly mixed in the condensing gases of the protoplanet, just as they were in the nebula before the process of solar system formation began. Remember, however, we are looking for an explanation of differentiation. Therefore, we cannot assume ahead of time that all of the elements are uniformly mixed through the cloud. As the process of compaction and planet formation continues, some elements will be more concentrated in the center of the protoplanet. Other elements will be scattered to the edges. Only through such a process of separation could a planet eventually be formed.

Of course, calculations have been made in an attempt to determine the temperature in such a cloud. However, scientists are not at all certain as to how far the calculations should be trusted. Determining the temperature in a protoplanet is a more difficult problem than trying to predict the weather for next week, and we all know what an uncertain process that is. About all scientists can say is that the temperature would probably be a few thousand degrees Kelvin.

How would you explain the rate of compression being slower for a rapidly rotating mass of gas than it is for one which rotates slowly?

Conditions inside the protoearth. Suppose we take a more detailed look at what is going on inside a condensing protoplanet. Remember, this is a cloud of dust and gas. Dust implies small, solid particles. Thus, the dust would consist of those elements or molecules that would be nonvolatile at the temperature of the cloud. In other words, unless the temperature was extremely high, the dust would be composed of the nonvolatile elements and compounds, such as iron and silicate minerals. The gas would consist of the volatile elements and compounds, such as hydrogen, helium, nitrogen, oxygen, ammonia, methane, and water vapor.

Water is a very important substance in such a condensing cloud, and water molecules must have been very abundant in the cloud. Hydrogen and oxygen are very common elements in the universe as a whole, and, as you know, it is these two elements which make up water. Where the cloud was warm, the water in it would be a gaseous form. Where the cloud was cold, the water in it would be a solid form —that is, crystals of ice.

Theoretically, such a cloud is cold at its outer edge. At its center, the cloud is hot. Near the outer edge of the cloud, hydrogen and helium would be in a gaseous form, but water would probably be crystallized into snowflakes. Thus, we might imagine that the outer region of the cloud was really a cloud of "dirty snow"—that is, snow with other solid particles scattered through it.

At what other place in the universe might such a cloud of "dirty snow" be found?

Separation of solids and gases. As we consider what would happen in a condensing cloud, we must take account of an important difference between a gas molecule and a solid particle. According to the protoplanet theory, the pressure is greater near the center of the protoplanet than it is near the outer edges. If a gas molecule were to move closer to the center of the cloud, the higher pressure there would tend to force the gas molecule out again. Although gravitational force would be pulling the molecule inward, the higher pressure near the center would tend to force the gas molecules outward.

On the other hand, solid particles do not behave in the same way that gas molecules do. As a solid particle starts falling toward the center of the condensing cloud, it would be slowed down by friction with the gas through which it was traveling. It would, however, not be pushed away. This difference in the behavior

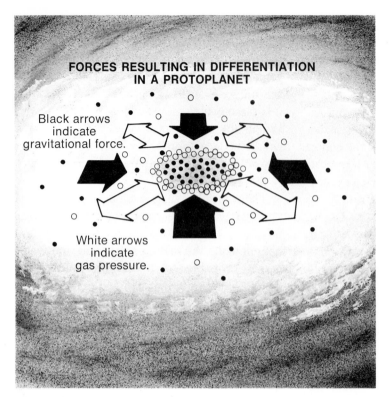

FORCES RESULTING IN DIFFERENTIATION IN A PROTOPLANET

Black arrows indicate gravitational force.

White arrows indicate gas pressure.

Figure 15-6. Solids and gases are drawn toward the center of the condensing cloud by gravitational force. Although the solids are slowed somewhat by friction as they move, they do keep moving toward the center. Gases, on the other hand, move toward the center only until the increased pressure in the region near the center balances the gravitational force on the gas molecules. Thus, gases become separated from solids in the first step of differentiation.

of the solid particles and the gas molecules enables us to have a better idea of the processes within the cloud. The gravitational force slowly compresses the gas, and slowly the gas particles are drawn closer together. But gas pressure within the cloud is constantly resisting this inward motion. Thus, compression of the gases is a slow process. In the meantime, the solid particles are falling in toward the center more rapidly. The result is that the solid particles become concentrated in the center, while the gas particles tend to remain outside. This is the first step of differentiation.

The solid particles would begin their motion toward the center as small, dirty clumps of snowflakes. Most of the material in these clumps would be crystals of ice. Mixed with the ice would be small amounts of silicate rock and iron. Also mixed into the clump would be small amounts of all of the other elements in the universe. This is the sort of particle that would begin its fall from the outer edge of the cloud toward the center.

Effects of increasing temperature. The nearer a particle would get to the center of the protoplanet, the hotter it would become. Since the particle would be moving into a region of hotter and hotter gas, it would soon reach a point where the ice would melt. Still, the particle would keep falling, but now it would be a drop of dirty water.

As the drop moved closer to the center of the cloud, the drop would reach a point in the cloud where the temperature was great enough so that the water would change to a vapor. From this point to the center of the cloud, water could exist only as a vapor. The water—because it is now a vapor—falls no farther.

The solid particles, however, would continue their fall toward the center of the cloud.

The nearer to the center these solids got, the hotter they would become. Finally, a point would be reached at which silicate rock would melt. A little farther on, the iron would melt. Now the particles falling toward the center would be drops of liquid, like drops of lava. At the center of the protoplanet there would be a rain of fiery drops of molten rock and iron.

Scientists would like to know how high the temperature is at the center of a protoplanet. The temperature is very important since it is a factor in determining the final nature of the planet. If the temperature were great enough, then silicate rock would be vaporized and, as a gas, would not continue its fall toward the center of the protoplanet. If the temperature were not great enough to vaporize the silicate rock, drops of liquid silicate rock would continue,

together with the drops of iron, to fall to the center.

In the center of this protoplanet, we might imagine that molten rock and liquid iron have finally found a resting place. But liquid iron is much more dense than liquid silicate, so the iron would quickly settle to the center and be surrounded by an envelope of liquid silicate rock. More such material would fall, and the center of the protoplanet would grow larger. Gravitational force would continue to compress the entire protoplanet. This compression would tend to cause the temperature of the protoplanet's interior to rise. Of course, the growing ball of molten iron and rock in the center would radiate heat from its outer surfaces, and gradually the outer regions of the molten ball would become cooler. Currents

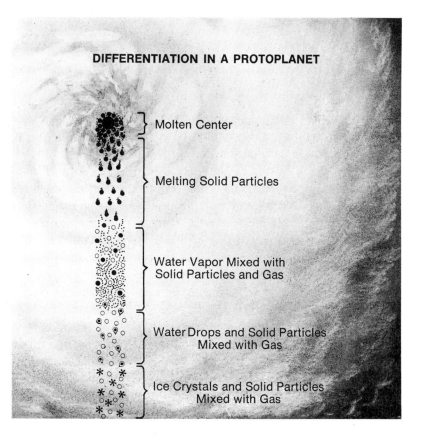

Figure 15-7. As materials are drawn closer and closer to the center of a protoplanet, the temperature becomes higher and higher. When the temperature is high enough to vaporize a substance, the vapors do not continue to fall in toward the center of the protoplanet. Thus, temperature is a factor in the differentiation of volatile and nonvolatile substances.

DIFFERENTIATION IN A PROTOPLANET

Molten Center

Melting Solid Particles

Water Vapor Mixed with Solid Particles and Gas

Water Drops and Solid Particles Mixed with Gas

Ice Crystals and Solid Particles Mixed with Gas

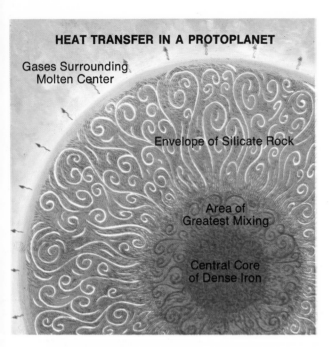

HEAT TRANSFER IN A PROTOPLANET

Gases Surrounding
Molten Center

Envelope of Silicate Rock

Area of
Greatest Mixing

Central Core
of Dense Iron

Figure 15-8. Heat resulting from compression in a protoplanet is transferred from the central region of the molten ball to the outer edge by convection currents. These currents produce some mixing of the molten material. The heat is then radiated from the outer edge of the molten ball out into space.

would begin to move in this molten ball. The hot material in the interior would rise toward the surface. Then, having radiated some heat away, cooled, and contracted, the material would sink toward the center of the ball as other hot material replaced it at the surface. During this process, some mixing of materials would occur. The iron, however, being much heavier than other materials in the center of the protoplanet, would tend to stay in the center of the growing planet.

The description just given is a more detailed picture of the formation of a protoplanet than was given in Chapter 11. However, even this detailed picture does not explain what we see on the earth today. There is not as much silicate rock on the earth as might be expected

from the relative abundances of elements in average universe material. Thus, there must have been some sort of differentiation in the earth by which much of the silicate rock has been lost. So far, our explanation does not account for this loss of silicate rock.

Why do scientists think that gravity is not the only factor in the process of differentiation? What factors, other than gravity, might be important in the process of differentiation?

Temperature as a factor in differentiation. One explanation for the earth's unique chemical composition is that the temperature in the center of the protoearth eventually became very great. According to this explanation, the temperature in the central portion of the protoearth became great enough to boil away some of the silicate rock around the outer edges of the protoearth's central portion. Perhaps that is what happened. However, only certain ones of the lighter elements appear to be missing from the earth. Other light elements appear to be more concentrated in the earth than they are in average universe material. According to many scientists, if the temperature had been high enough to boil away silicate rocks, all the less dense elements would also have boiled away. Had this happened, the distribution of elements on the earth would be quite different from what we now know the distribution to be.

Differentiation by collision. Another explanation has been offered to account for the distribution of the elements on the earth. This explanation is fairly recent and somewhat complicated. So far, scientists have not had an opportunity to study it in detail to see whether or not it explains all of our current observations. At present, however, it appears to be the best explanation.

In this new theory, developed by Professor Harold Urey, a planet would not form from a

DIFFERENTIATION BY COLLISION

Protoasteroids Colliding

Center of
Condensing
Cloud

Protoasteroid

Figure 15-9. According to one theory, protoplanets formed as a result of protoasteroids colliding within a condensing cloud of gas and dust. The collisions shattered the solid outer regions of the protoasteroids. Some fragments were pushed away by the pressure of light, leaving the newly formed protoplanet with an unusual distribution of elements.

single protoplanet. Instead, Urey suggests that there would be several centers of condensation and compaction. A number of small *proto-asteroids* would form within a condensing cloud. In each of these protoasteroids, the temperature would be high enough to melt the iron and rock, but not high enough to boil them away. The liquid iron would settle to the center of such protoasteroids, and the melted rock would remain as a shell around the outside. These bodies would be anywhere from a few miles to a few hundred miles in diameter.

According to this theory, as the bodies continued to grow and as the gas cloud continued to compact, the bodies would eventually run into each other. When this happened, some of the outer shells of silicate rock would be broken up and scattered out into space. It would be a matter of chance as to which pieces of rock were broken loose and which ones stayed. Thus, it would be a matter of chance as to which elements were lost from the outer rocks of the colliding bodies and which were left behind.

This theory suggests that, eventually, many of the smaller bodies—what we might call asteroids today—finally combined to form planets, such as the earth. In the meantime, pressure from the sun's light had pushed away the gas and dust particles remaining in space about the newly formed planet. The material pushed away would include not only hydrogen and helium but also much of the powdered silicate rock that came from the collisions between the asteroids. In this theory, the pieces which eventually combined to form the earth would have a very unusual distribution of elements. Thus, the earth would have an unusual distribution of elements. Since the earth does have an unusual distribution of elements, this theory may be the correct explanation for the origin of the planet earth.

As you probably realize, although this theory gives an explanation, it is not a completely satisfactory theory. It is difficult to believe that an accidental occurrence accounts for something as important as the distribution of elements in the earth. Of course, Professor Urey's theory could be right. Nevertheless, scientists are still searching for a better explanation which does not rely on this sort of accidental occurrence.

Why do scientists dislike using an "accidental" event in attempting to explain natural phenomena?

4. Explaining the Earth's Magnetic Field

The earth's early stages. In its initial stages, the temperature of the interior of the earth must have been very high. The temperature would have been high whether the earth was formed as a single protoplanet or was formed by the accumulation of protoasteroids. In the beginning, at least the core of the earth must have been molten. Perhaps a considerably larger portion than the core was molten. If the center of the forming earth were molten, it is easy to understand why the more dense iron would sink to the center of this molten ball, leaving the less dense silicate rock on the outside. Rock of intermediate density, such as dunite, would form the mantle above the core. Thus, any of the theories described here would account for the fact that the earth formed in layers. This fact has been observed by seismologists. A core of iron is in the center, surrounded by a thick mantle of dense rock. The mantle is covered by a thin skin of relatively lightweight rock. The separation into layers may simply have been the result of dense material sinking to the center and less dense material rising to the top while the earth was molten.

But this whole process took place about 4 billion years ago. Why is the center of the earth still molten today? There are two reasons. First, rock is a very good insulator. It is very difficult for heat to penetrate thousands of miles of rock to the earth's surface where it can be radiated away. Even in 4 billion years, the amount of heat lost would be small, and the center of the earth would cool only slightly. Second, there has been a continual source of heat within the earth ever since it formed. A small fraction of the material which formed the earth consisted of radioactive elements, such as uranium. Over hundreds of millions of years, these radioactive elements decay—that is, they change to different elements. Each time the nucleus of an atom of uranium changes into different types of atomic nuclei, a small amount of heat is released. On the average, an atom of uranium will exist for about 4.5 billion years before it decays and breaks apart into a helium particle and an atom of thorium.

Figure 15-10. Radioactive elements were present in the materials from which the earth formed. Whenever a nucleus of such an element decomposes, energy is released. This energy has been a constant source of heat which many scientists believe has kept the earth's interior very hot. Scientists have devised a new way to study this radioactivity. When a nucleus decomposes, the nearby rock is damaged. The cones and circles in this picture show sites of such damage. By treating these tiny damage sites with chemicals, scientists have enlarged the sites for study. Further enlargement is obtained photographically. With this new technique, scientists hope to increase their knowledge of the amounts of radioactive elements present when the earth formed.

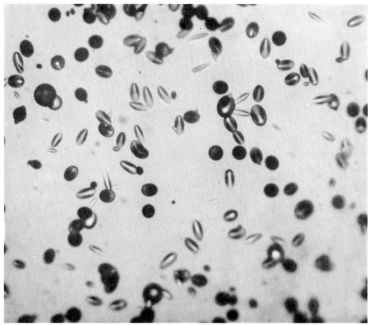

But in any quantity of uranium, some atoms are decaying all the time. With each decay of a uranium atom, some heat is given off by the atom and absorbed into the earth. Other radioactive elements in the earth also decay and also give off heat. Thus, decay of radioactive elements is a constant source of heat which keeps the core molten and the mantle hot.

Convection in the earth's core. Of course, the outer surface of the earth is much colder than the interior. Since heat always flows from a hot region to a colder one, there must be ·a steady flow of heat from the center of the earth, out toward the surface, and away into space. How is this heat transferred? To some extent it is transmitted by conduction directly through the rock. In solid rock, such as the mantle, this is the only way heat could be transferred. But the core is thought to be liquid, and in liquids there is another way to transfer heat.

Have you ever observed water boiling in a glass coffeepot or in a glass beaker? If so, you have seen bubbles rise from the bottom of the

Figure 15-11. Volcanism is one indication that the earth's interior is very hot. Furthermore, continued volcanic activity throughout the earth's history indicates that some process—perhaps radioactivity—is continually adding heat to the earth's interior.

D. APPENBRINK

Figure 15-12. What supplies energy to heat the water in a geyser such as the one shown above? An answer to this question would represent great progress in solving the mysteries of the earth's interior.

container to the top. But, if you observed boiling water carefully, you would see that the bubbles do not go in a straight line. You would see a slight swirling motion. If you had some way of watching the water alone, without the bubbles, you would be able to see that the water was indeed swirling. The swirling occurs as water near the bottom of the container is heated and rises to the top. Cooler water from the top sinks down to the bottom.

This turbulent motion of hot, liquid material is an example of *convection* (kən vek'shən). Convection—that is, the actual motion of the hot material from one place to another—is another process by which heat can be transferred. It is very likely that the molten iron core of the earth is moving right now, due to convection. If so, there are huge, slowly moving eddies of molten iron in the earth's core. We know that iron conducts electricity. Thus, a swirling mass of molten iron—with its free electrons—would probably constitute an electric current.

In Chapter 8 we described some of the unusual occurrences on the surface of the sun. We talked about swirling columns of hot, ionized gas. You learned that the motion of ionized gas was actually an electric current and that this motion would create a magnetic field. Magnetic fields are observed on the sun. These magnetic fields appear to be related to the swirling columns of ionized gas.

What might happen in the center of the earth as a swirling mass of molten iron circulates slowly? Is it not possible that this, too, would be a huge electric current which would create a magnetic field? As you have probably guessed, this is the way scientists now explain the magnetic field of the earth.

Before you give the theory much thought, it may seem to be a very good explanation. But, if we think about this explanation a while, we realize that the swirling currents of iron in the core might as easily go in one direction as another. And yet, the magnetic field of the earth seems very stable. The earth's magnetic field is like that of a simple magnet. One pole is in the northern region of the earth, and the opposite pole is in the southern region. It is not at all like the complicated magnetic fields on the surface of the sun. There, as you may recall, north and south poles vary in strength and even reverse rapidly as the swirling gas storms move from one place to another. Why should the swirling motion of the iron in the earth create a stable magnetic field, while the swirling gases on the sun create a rapidly changing, unpredictable magnetic field?

Scientists have worked on this problem for a long time. They have concluded that the combination of the earth's spin on its axis and the convection currents in the core would result in an organized, swirling motion, rather than a haphazard or random motion of the iron. The organized motion of the iron would account for a stable magnetic field. Of course, the magnetic field does change somewhat.

Each year the positions of the earth's magnetic poles move a little bit. This slight motion gives support to the idea of a slowly moving core. Even though the swirling motion of the core is organized, the motion changes a little bit year by year. Perhaps in the distant past, the motion of the molten iron in the earth's core and the resulting magnetic field were quite different from the way they are today. Some evidence seems to indicate such a difference.

What factors can you think of which might affect the strength of the earth's magnetic field?

Figure 15-13. The diagram on the left may be considered as a map of a small area near the geographic North Pole—the point where the earth's axis of rotation intersects the earth's surface. The red line indicates that in a 4-year period, this pole wandered about in an area approximately the size of the infield of a baseball diamond. In the diagram on the right, some positions are indicated for the geomagnetic North Pole—the point toward which a compass needle is directed. The large shifts in position over the last 600 million years may be the result of changes in the positions of the continents. If the earth's rotation is the major cause of the earth's magnetism, the geomagnetic pole has never been very far from the geographic pole. Today, these poles are about 17° apart.

POLAR WANDERING

Geographic

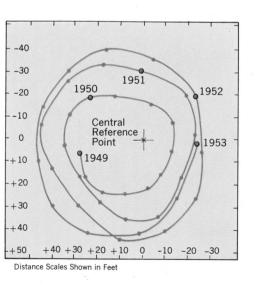

Distance Scales Shown in Feet

Magnetic

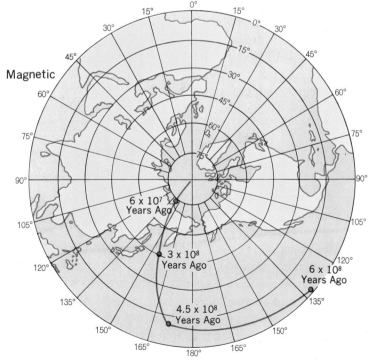

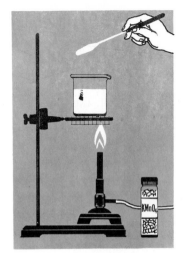

*Materials you will need: water, beaker, ring stand, Bunsen burner,
potassium permanganate, wire gauze*

Fill the beaker two-thirds full of cold water. Place it on the ring stand. Place the lighted Bunsen burner under one edge of the beaker. Drop a small crystal of potassium permanganate into the water so that the crystal settles on the side opposite where the burner is. CAUTION: Potassium permanganate is poison, so you should avoid contact between potassium permanganate and your skin. Observe what happens as the water heats more on one side of the beaker than on the other. Does the water circulate within the beaker? If so, describe the circulation. Why is heat applied to only one side of the beaker? What is the purpose of adding the potassium permanganate?

Increasing man's knowledge of the earth. From combinations of observation and theory, scientists are beginning to develop a reasonably good picture of how the earth began and how it developed to its present condition. Scientists have theories about the interior of the earth, although they have never seen it. Scientists also have theories about the origin of the solar system, although it happened very long ago. To support these theories, scientists use observations about the condition of the earth as it is today. These observations of the earth include the chemical nature of its surface material, the movement of seismic waves through its interior, and the strength and position of the poles of its magnetic field. In relating these observations to theories, scientists have used the laws of physics and chemistry.

This combination of theories, observations, and physical laws has turned out to be extremely useful. In spite of all of the uncertainties of our present ideas, scientists have a right to be proud of how far they have progressed in acquiring knowledge of the earth. In ancient times, man had to be content with myths and legends to account for the nature and origin of the earth. But now, scientists not only construct reasonable theories about such phenomena, but actually check the theories against careful observations. There is still much that is not known. However, the general picture of how the earth formed is definitely beginning to make sense.

Figure 15-14. Early theories of the earth were often imaginative, but not very logical. Today, theories are checked through experimentation and observation.

Some Hindus believed the earth rested on the backs of elephants, whose shiftings caused earthquakes. The elephants stood on a huge turtle. The turtle rested on a coiled cobra. Each animal had symbolic meaning.

The Sumerians visualized a universe containing a flat earth over which the dome of heaven was somehow suspended. The atmosphere between contained the sun, moon, planets, and stars. The universe was surrounded by the eternal sea.

One Greek concept held that a drum-shaped earth, surrounded by a mist which contained the heavenly bodies, floated freely in a universe bounded by a fiery sphere.

Checking Your Knowledge

IMPORTANT IDEAS

1. Acceptable theories of the origin of the universe, the solar system, and the earth must explain all the related facts. The theories must also agree with one another.

2. The most acceptable theories of the earth's origin assume that the earth and the rest of the solar system condensed from a huge cloud of gas and dust.

3. A process of differentiation took place during the formation of the solar system.

4. An acceptable theory must account for (1) differences between the earth's composition and that of the rest of the universe and (2) variations in composition at different depths within the earth.

5. Usually, scientists do not favor a theory which is based on some accidental event. Instead, they search for explanations that involve occurrences that take place regularly and repeatedly.

6. Convection currents in the earth's core might account for the earth's magnetic field.

USING NEW WORDS

Study the words listed below. Write the numerals *1-6* on your paper. After each numeral write words or statements to answer the questions having the corresponding numeral.

protoearth	uranium
convection	protoasteroid
differentiation	volatile

1. Which word is the name given to a method by which heat is transferred?

2. Which word is used to describe the process of separating substances?

3. Which word is related to evaporation?

4. Which word names an element?

5. What does the prefix "proto" mean?

6. Define protoearth and protoasteroid.

TEST YOURSELF

Study the test below. Write the numerals *1-10* on your paper. After each numeral write the correct response to that part of the test having the corresponding numeral.

1. The presently accepted theory of the origin of the earth states that the earth was formed from _____.

2. Some scientists think that during the formation of the earth, many lighter elements were lost because of the effect of _____.

3. In the early stages of the formation of the protoearth, scientists think that water existed in the outer regions of the protoearth in the form of _____.

4. Two elements that are present in much smaller percentages on earth than in the rest of the universe are hydrogen and _____.

5. Volatile substances are those substances which _____ readily at temperatures common to our everyday environment.

6. One element that occurs in a greater percentage on the earth than it does in the rest of the universe is _____.

7. The process of chemical separation in a planet, together with the loss of some elements and compounds during the formation of the planet, is called _____.

8. Many scientists believe that the earth's present magnetic field is caused by _____ believed to be occurring in the molten iron of the earth's core.

9. The temperature of the core of the earth is very high. An important factor in maintaining this high temperature is the presence of _____ elements deep within the earth.

10. A theory which states that the formation of the earth and of the other planets resulted from multiple collisions of asteroids was recently proposed by the scientist _____.

Extending Your Knowledge

QUESTIONS TO EXPLORE

1. Why does a small crystal of a substance fall in a gravitational field, while molecules of the same substance will stay suspended if the substance is in the gaseous state?

2. Each layer of the earth has an average density different from the average density of the other layers. The crust is the least dense, and the core is the most dense. From these different densities, what can be inferred about the temperature of the earth at some time in the past?

3. What differences would there be on the earth if the north and south magnetic poles were reversed? If there were no magnetic field about the earth?

4. Oxygen is more dense than nitrogen. Why doesn't the oxygen in the atmosphere settle to the bottom of the atmosphere?

5. If a radioactive material is wrapped in a very good heat insulator, the temperature of the radioactive material will rise. How would you explain this phenomenon?

SOME THINGS TO DO

1. Demonstrate that compression of a gas results in an increase in temperature. Tape a thermometer to a tire pump. Read and record the temperature. Then wrap the pump and the thermometer with a towel. Pump air into a tire. Unwrap the pump enough to read and record the temperature. How could you determine what part of any change in temperature was due to compression? What part of any change was due to friction?

2. Dr. Harold Urey, the author of a modern theory of the origin of the earth, is not a geophysicist—that is, his education and his profession are not primarily concerned with geophysics. Dr. Urey has made notable contributions in several different fields of science. His career is an excellent example of the fact that a successful person is constantly learning new things. Find out about his background. See if you can find out how he became interested in the earth-space sciences.

3. Find out and then record the melting point of each of the eight most abundant elements (other than hydrogen and helium) in the universe. Also do this for some of the earth's common compounds. Based on your data, which of these elements and compounds would be volatile at $300°K$? At $3,000°K$? At $5,000°K$? Based on these data, suggest ways to account for the loss of some elements during the formation of the earth.

CHALLENGES IN SCIENCE

1. Suggest several hypotheses to account for the fact that the earth has "more than its share" of iron. Let your classmates try to disprove these hypotheses by citing examples of observations which contradict the implications of the hypotheses.

2. One theory of the origin of the moon is that the moon was once part of the earth but was somehow pulled apart from the earth. What evidence can you find to support this theory?

3. The text states that uranium atoms decay, forming atoms of thorium and helium. Are these the final products of the decay? If not, what are the final products?

4. Study a table which lists the densities of the planets in the solar system. Explain how the observed densities of the planets can be used to support or contradict the theory that the pressure of light from the sun removed the hydrogen and helium from the atmosphere of some of the planets.

BREAKTHROUGHS IN SCIENCE

In the 18th century, geology was mainly an applied science. Geologists were interested in the immediate, practical results obtained through a study of the earth's crust. How to locate and mine the deposits of metals and other commercially important minerals was the main concern of most geologists of that period. But even then, there were some scientists who wondered about the origin of the rocks of the earth's crust. Theories were developed to suggest answers to questions such as the following. Why are there so many kinds of rocks? How did the rocks become distributed the way they are? Where did rocks come from in the first place?

By the late 18th century, a theory called the Neptunian Theory was widely accepted. Naturally, the complete theory and all its implications cannot be stated in one sentence. However, this particular theory assumed that the earth, at one time, was completely covered by a deep ocean. According to the theory, this original ocean contained all the materials of the earth. All the rocks of the earth were said to have precipitated from this ocean. Of course, not all geologists agreed. The dissenters, called Plutonists, argued that the main factor in the crust's formation was the outpouring of volcanoes, both past and present.

In the midst of the controversy between the Neptunists and Plutonists, James Hutton was quietly studying and observing various features of the earth's crust. In his book, *Theory of the Earth*, Hutton presented many brilliant ideas and conclusions. Compared with other theories of the time, Hutton's theory was far superior for its strictly inductive approach. Each conclusion was based on careful observation, and the events of the past were explained by comparing them with present-day phenomena. His book marked a turning point in our understanding of the earth. But Hutton's style of writing was difficult. Not until a more readable book—*Illustrations of the Huttonian Theory of the Earth*, by John Playfair—was published, did Hutton's ideas begin to have some influence among geologists.

Not all of Hutton's ideas were correct. For example, he made errors concerning the origin of certain rocks. However, Hutton was the first to demonstrate that geologic processes often span extremely long intervals of time. He did not believe that the condition of the earth was the result of a few disastrous events, such as imaginary floods which dug deep canyons and valleys in an hour or two, or moved huge boulders from the mountains to the plains. He believed that the earth is changing now, just as it changed long ago. To understand what happened in ancient times, we must learn what is happening today. He reasoned that seemingly small natural forces can, if they act over long periods of time, produce changes on a gigantic scale. The Huttonian concept of the importance of small, accumulative changes had a far-reaching influence, not only on geology, but on other natural sciences. Many of Hutton's ideas were adopted and extended by geologists of more recent times. Thus, Hutton's work may be considered as one of the foundation stones of modern geology and a significant breakthrough in scientific thought.

REVIEWING UNIT FOUR

SUMMARY

1. The earth is nearly spherical with a diameter of about 8,000 miles (12,800 km).

2. The density of the earth as a whole (5.52 g/cm³) is nearly twice the average density of surface rock.

3. The earth has a magnetic field about it.

4. The earth's average chemical composition is not the same as that of the universe.

5. Earthquakes cause vibrations—called seismic waves—which travel through the earth and along the earth's surface.

6. Most of man's theories about the nature of the earth's interior are based on studies of seismic waves.

7. The solid portion of the earth consists of three distinct layers—the core, the mantle, and the crust. Each of these layers is believed to have its own layered structure.

8. Although a completely satisfactory theory of origin has not been formulated, geophysicists feel that progress is being made toward arriving at a true picture of the origin of the earth.

QUESTIONS TO DISCUSS

1. What are fossils? What are some ways in which fossils form? Are fossils found only in sedimentary rock?

2. What is the difference between a mineral and a rock? How are rocks and minerals of economic importance to us?

3. In general, as we consider materials deeper and deeper in the earth, do their densities become greater or lesser? Explain.

4. What, do scientists think, is the cause of earthquakes? In what ways have earthquakes been useful to man?

5. What evidence is there to indicate that the core of the earth is liquid?

UNIT TEST

Study the test below. Write the numerals *1-20* on your paper. Beside each numeral write a term from the list below. Make certain the term you write is closely related to the statement having the corresponding numeral.

volatile	earthquake	differentiation
mineral	atmosphere	lithosphere
magnetic	geochemistry	nonvolatile
tsunami	protoearth	seismograph
uranium	seismogram	hydrosphere
core	convection	oblate spheroid
igneous	refraction	sedimentary
crust	seismology	biosphere

Mohorovičić discontinuity

1. The outermost layer of the solid earth
2. Rocks formed by heat
3. A method of heat transfer
4. A radioactive element
5. The true shape of the earth
6. The boundary between the mantle and the crust of the earth
7. The gases surrounding the earth
8. The study of earthquake waves
9. Process by which elements and compounds are separated during planet formation
10. Instrument to detect earthquake waves
11. A change in a wave's direction of travel
12. Includes all the waters of the earth
13. The innermost portion of the earth
14. Ocean wave caused by an earthquake
15. A sudden movement in the solid portion of the earth
16. The solid portion of the earth
17. Possibly, a very early stage in the formation of the earth
18. A record of earthquake waves
19. A study of the chemistry of the earth
20. Evaporates at room temperature

ENRICHING YOUR SCIENCE EXPERIENCES

INVESTIGATIONS TO CARRY OUT

1. Study the practices followed in the design and construction of buildings in those areas of the earth's surface where earthquakes occur frequently. Demonstrate some of these construction techniques. For example, on a card table, build two identical model buildings with plastic toy bricks. Then add decorative features, such as large chimneys or cornices of clay or wood to one of the buildings. Shake the table slightly. Observe the effect on the two models. Then build two models, using different methods of construction (for example, use cross braces in one and not the other). Observe what happens when the table is shaken. Devise and conduct a demonstration to show the difference in the effect of an earthquake on a house built on solid rock and one built on loose soil.

2. Place several wooden blocks of various thicknesses in a large pan of water. Assume that these blocks represent continents "floating" on the mantle. Do all blocks extend the same distance above the water level? Below the water level? Pour sawdust onto one block. Does the block float at the same level in the water? Measure the height of the wooden block above the water and measure the height of the top of the sawdust pile above the water. Remove some sawdust from one block and place it on an adjacent block. This could correspond to erosion of material from one place and its deposition in another place. What happens if the sawdust is not placed on the center of a block? Could this happen on a continent?

ADDITIONAL READING IN SCIENCE

Dunbar, Carl O., *The Earth*. Cleveland, Ohio, The World Publishing Company, 1966. 252 pp.

Earth Science Curriculum Project, *Investigating the Earth*. Boston, Massachusetts, Houghton Mifflin Company, 1967. 594 pp.

Editors of Scientific American, *The Planet Earth*. New York, Simon and Schuster, Inc., 1957. 168 pp.

Gamow, George, *Matter, Earth, and Sky*. 2nd ed. New York, Prentice-Hall, Inc., 1965. 624 pp.

Hurley, Patrick M., *How Old Is the Earth?* Garden City, New York, Doubleday & Co., Inc., 1959. 160 pp.

Mason, Brian, *Principles of Geochemistry*. 2nd ed. New York, Wiley, John, & Sons, Inc., 1962. 310 pp.

Rapport, S., and Wright, H., *The Crust of the Earth*. New York, The New American Library, 1955. 224 pp.

Shelton, John S., *Geology Illustrated*. San Francisco, California, W. H. Freeman and Company, 1966. 434 pp.

Strahler, Arthur N., *The Earth Sciences*. New York, Harper & Row, Publishers, 1963. 681 pp.

THE EARTH'S SURFACE

The surface of the earth is man's home in a vast and alien universe. Scientists are fairly certain that within our own solar system, no other place but the surface of the earth is habitable for man. Perhaps, as many theories suggest, there are other planets which are habitable near other stars of the universe. So far, however, none has been detected. That conditions on the earth's surface are unique (as far as we know) and that we live on the earth are two very good reasons for studying the earth's surface in detail.

You have already learned something of the earth's surface. You know that from a geologic standpoint, the earth's surface is constantly changing. You also know that a large percentage of the earth's surface is covered by the oceans. You know that the earth is enveloped by an atmosphere composed of various gases. You know that scientists have found evidence of changes that have occurred in the earth's surface, in its oceans, and in its atmosphere.

In UNIT 5 you will study about the changes which have taken place and are taking place near the earth's surface. You will discover how the continents, the oceans, and the atmosphere have changed in the eons of time since the earth formed. More important, you will find out what scientists think brought about these changes which have occurred at the earth's surface.

◀ The earth's surface is where the earth's land, water, and enveloping atmosphere meet.

AUTHENTICATED NEWS INTERNATIONAL

The highest point on earth is the peak of Mt. Everest.

CHAPTER 16

Surface Features of the Earth

The earth's highest mountain peak is more than five miles above sea level. Imagine the earth being represented by a globe five feet in diameter, and then imagine the highest mountain peak being represented on this globe. On the globe, the highest mountain peak would be less than 0.04 inch above sea level! Compared to the earth itself, the mountains (and other features of the earth's surface, such as river valleys) would seem rather insignificant.

In reality, however, these surface features—or land forms—are very significant. Land forms are vital to our existence. They provide the soil and water necessary for the crops man needs. In some parts of the world, land forms control the climate. The study of the earth's surface features can yield clues to the origin of the earth and other planets. Not the least important aspect of land forms is the beauty and grandeur they often provide for man's enjoyment.

Studying Chapter 16 will give you a broad overview of some important land forms. Processes of mountain building are described briefly. The role of rivers and glaciers in shaping the land is also described. Also, throughout the chapter, time is an important consideration. The forces that shape the earth seem to act slowly. However, these forces are at work constantly. During the extremely long time intervals involved in the shaping of the earth's surface, these forces produce changes on a gigantic scale.

1. Mountains

Distribution and characteristics of mountains. To many people, mountains are the most impressive of all the land forms on the earth's surface. As you probably know, a mountain may be defined as any portion of the earth's surface that is considerably higher than its surroundings. In general, the term mountain is applied to a very high elevation, while lesser elevations are called hills.

On all the continents of the earth, there are hills and mountains, and valleys and rivers. Measurements made of the ocean depths show that there are mountains and valleys even beneath the sea. Although no two mountains are identical, mountains do have many characteristics in common. These common characteristics have allowed scientists to classify mountains and to organize the study of the nature and development of mountains.

In general, mountains occur in groups. The names of many of these mountain groups are familiar to practically everyone. The Rockies, the Andes, the Himalayas, and the Alps are all familiar names to people everywhere.

The mountains of some groups are very high and very rugged. The Himalayas, on the northern border of India, are in this category. In contrast, the mountains of some groups, such as the Appalachians in the eastern United States, are comparatively low and gently rolling. The action of volcanoes and/or the upward movement of material in special regions of the earth's crust accounts for the elevation, or raising, of mountains. There is good reason to believe that high, rugged mountains have recently been raised or are still rising. On the other hand, low, rolling mountains appear to have stopped rising many millions of years ago. Apparently, these low mountains have been gradually worn down by the constant eroding action of rainfall, streams, rivers, and glaciers.

How long, do you think, would it take for the Himalayas to be raised? How long to become worn down? Could either raising or wearing down take place more quickly? If so, how?

Figure 16-1. The Himalayas (left) are high, rugged mountains. They are relatively young. The Appalachians (right) are lower and gently rolling. They are old mountains and have been undergoing erosion for a much longer period than have the Himalayas.

MONKMEYER   GRANT HEILMAN

Figure 16-2. Stone Mountain is not a typical mountain in that it is not part of a mountain range. Stone Mountain is a single, elevated portion of the earth, surrounded by fairly level land.

Mountain systems. Some mountains, such as Stone Mountain in Georgia and Mt. Etna on the island of Sicily, stand alone. Most mountains, however, are connected to form a group. A *mountain range* is the basic mountain grouping. A mountain range is usually defined as a row of mountains which forms a continuous pattern. Sometimes, however, a range of mountains consists of a series of rows, provided the rows are clearly related to one another.

There are many areas of the world in which several mountain ranges seem to be related to each other, although the ranges are separated by distinct valleys. When several mountain ranges are roughly parallel, consist of the same type of rock, and have the same general structure, the whole group of mountain ranges is called a *mountain system.* The Rocky Mountains consist of one such group of ranges. The Himalayas also consist of a group of mountain ranges. In the Himalayas there are several ranges of mountain peaks, like folds in a piece of cloth, but all the ranges are clearly related to each other. Therefore, the Rockies and the Himalayas are mountain systems. If you inspect a map of the earth, you can locate other mountain systems, such as the Mediterranean system of mountains which extends across southern Europe and the Andes

Mountain system along the west coast of South America.

If we observe the many mountain systems on a map of the earth, we can see relationships between them. *(Figure 16-3.)* For example, look at the American continents. There are mountain systems which extend from Alaska down through western Canada, through the western part of the United States, continuing on through Mexico, and into Central America. It would appear that these mountains of North America are closely related to the Andes Mountain system that extends from Central America on down to the tip of South America and even to the continent of Antarctica.

Now observe the Mediterranean mountain system. It seems closely related to mountain systems in Iran and Afghanistan. These systems, in turn, are connected to the Himalayan system in southeast Asia and to the mountains of the various islands of Indonesia.

There are several names for these groups of related mountain systems. Sometimes they are called *mountain belts,* sometimes *mountain chains,* and sometimes *cordilleras* (kôr′dəl yär′əz). The particular group that extends through North and South America, from Alaska to Cape Horn, has the name American cordilleras.

Mountain belts have also been discovered to exist under the ocean, but scientists have very little detailed knowledge about their structure. However, the studies that have been made reveal the presence of a group of mountains near the center of the Atlantic Ocean. This group of mountains is called the Mid-Atlantic Ridge. The Mid-Atlantic Ridge extends in a generally north-south direction, extending from the Northern Hemisphere to the Southern Hemisphere. There are also a number of mountains in the Pacific Ocean. In fact, some scientists believe that the floor of the Pacific Ocean, like that of the Atlantic

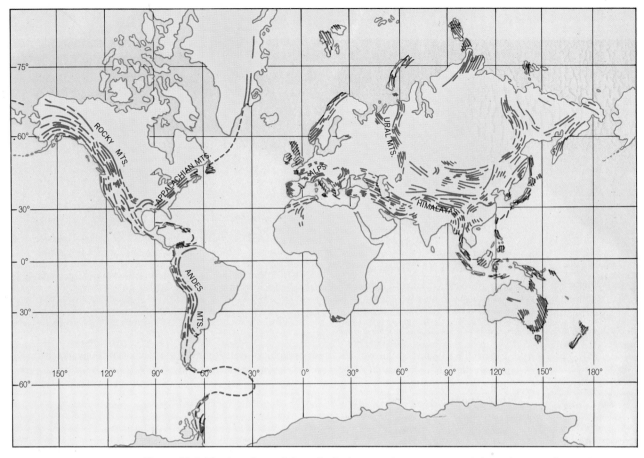

Figure 16-3. The locations of the principal mountain ranges, mountain systems, and mountain belts are shown on this map. When the world-wide distribution of mountains is viewed in this way, relationships between ranges, systems, and belts can be more easily recognized.

Ocean, has a belt of mountains in its central region. They believe that this mountain belt lies in a generally north-south direction. So far, however, not enough is known about the floor of the Pacific Ocean to be sure of this.

What factors would scientists consider in deciding whether or not the mountains in the Pacific Ocean should be grouped into a mountain belt? Why has this decision not been made as yet?

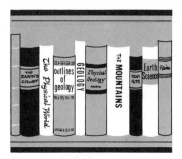

DO IT YOURSELF

Study mountain systems and individual mountains

Use reference materials to find out how scientists account for the fact that mountains usually occur in ranges, systems, and belts. How do scientists account for instances where one mountain is by itself? The examples of single mountains given in this book are Stone Mountain in Georgia and Mt. Etna on the island of Sicily. How were each of these two mountains formed?

FEILY FROM MONKMEYER · PHILCAROL FROM MONKMEYER

Figure 16-4. Many of the world's great mountains were created by volcanism. Fujiyama in Japan (left) is more than 12,000 feet high. Having erupted last in 1707, it is now considered dormant. Kilimanjaro, a great, snow-capped mountain in Africa, is more than 19,000 feet high. It has not erupted within historic time and is considered extinct.

Mountain building. From knowledge gained in studies of several mountain systems, geologists have determined three general ways in which mountains are formed. One of these is *volcanism* (vol′kə niz əm). Volcanism is the movement of melted rock. This movement may be either deep within the earth or over the earth's surface. Many volcanic mountains, such as Fujiyama in Japan and Kilimanjaro in central Africa, are famous. See *Figure 16-4*. In some cases, volcanoes occur quite near each other, and the melted rock, or lava, from the volcanoes builds up into a large mountain range. For example, the San Francisco Mountains south of the Grand Canyon in Arizona were formed in this way.

Some mountains are formed because of *plateau erosion*. A plateau is a generally flat region of the earth's surface. Usually a plateau is several hundred or several thousand feet

DE WYS INC.

Figure 16-5. The Catskill Mountains are an example of plateau erosion. The region was once a plateau. Erosion carved deep valleys, leaving peaks between them.

above sea level. A plateau may cover a large area—often several thousand square miles. Erosion, as you know, is a gradual wearing away. As time goes by, streams and rivers wash away soil and rock from the plateaus, carrying the soil and rock to lower plains or to the ocean. In so doing, the streams and rivers carve deep valleys into the plateau. The material of the plateau left standing between the river valleys then forms a series of mountains. The Catskill Mountains in New York are mountains formed by plateau erosion.

The highest mountains now in existence were formed in still another way. They were formed because of *crustal movement*. As the name implies, this process involves a shift in the position of a portion of the earth's crust. This shift in position can occur in several ways. A block of the crust can rise straight up above the surrounding plain, as shown in *A* of *Figure 16-6*. Or, a block can tilt, so that one edge

rises higher than the other. Such tilting accounts for the Sierra Nevada Mountains in California. A large block of the crust has tilted, so that the eastern edge of the range is steep and rugged, while the slope of the western edge is much more gentle. See *B* of *Figure 16-6*. Mount Whitney, the highest mountain in California, is on the eastern edge of this range.

Sometimes the crust has moved from side to side, rather than up and down. In this case, the crust is often compressed and folded, just as a piece of cloth would be if you spread the cloth out on a table and then slid two sides of the cloth together. The Appalachian Mountains of North America show clear evidence of such folding.

The bending, or folding, of rock layers might happen as shown in the series of diagrams in *Figure 16-8*. In *A,* a great thickness of sediments has been deposited in a valley.

Figure 16-6. Crustal movement can produce mountains. All sides of a huge block of the earth's crust may be raised above their surroundings, or one side of a block may be raised higher than the others.

Figure 16-7. The Sierra Nevada Mountains were formed as one edge of a huge block of the earth's crust was raised. The eroded face of the raised edge of the block is shown in this picture.

A

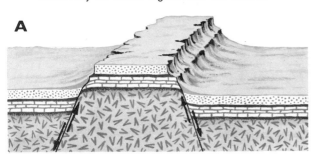

B

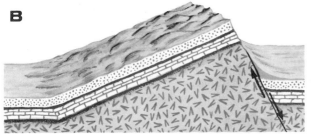

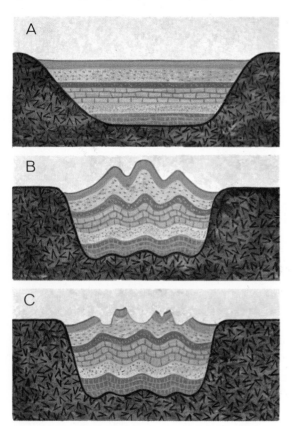

If the earth's internal forces compress the valley laterally—that is, from the sides—the layers of sediments will be folded as shown in *B*. The same folded sediments are represented in *C,* only now erosion has carved mountains and valleys out of the sediments.

Usually, a mountain range contains evidence of all of these separate mountain building processes. Thus, in the Rocky Mountains there is evidence of volcanism, of plateau erosion, and of crustal movement—both vertical and horizontal. If one process, such as volcanism, has clearly dominated the formation of a mountain range, then we can easily identify the mountain range as being volcanic in origin. However, when many processes have worked together to build the mountain range, we use the term *complex* to describe the origin of the mountain range. You can easily understand why.

What evidence would geologists use in determining whether a mountain was formed by volcanism, by plateau erosion, or by crustal movement? What factors might complicate the gathering of this evidence?

2. River Valleys

Rivers, river valleys, and man. Throughout man's history, rivers and their valleys have played an important role in human activity. Scientists believe that prehistoric men built their primitive communities on the banks of rivers. The earliest recorded civilizations developed in river valleys. The largest cities in the world today are on the banks of rivers—usually, at the point where a large river meets the sea in such a way as to form a good harbor. For centuries the produce of the land was

transported primarily on rivers, and at a large harbor, the commerce of the sea could meet the commerce of the land.

Just as rivers have been vital in the history of man, they have been vital in the history of the earth. As forces deep within the earth have formed mountains, the rivers on the surface have steadily worn the mountains away. The mountains which are young in terms of geologic time are still being forced upward today. Compared with the rates of movement we are accustomed to, the raising of mountains by the upward movement of the earth's crust is very slow—perhaps only a fraction of an inch per century. But, as the upward movement continues to build mountains, the rivers that wind through these mountains constantly wear away material from the mountains and carry it to lower levels.

Old mountains which ceased their growth millions of years ago have been worn down to a fraction of the height they once had. Some have disappeared entirely. Every continent (except Antarctica, where the water is all frozen) has a number of river systems through which rock, soil, and water move to low plains and to the sea. The larger rivers of these systems are well known. You undoubtedly have heard of the Nile and the Congo in Africa, the Mississippi in North America, the Amazon in South America, the Ganges in India, and the Volga in Russia. You could probably name others. These rivers have been important in shaping the land through which they flow.

Would you expect the volume of water transported by a river to become larger or to become smaller as the river approaches the sea? Give reasons for your answer. What exceptions, if any, can you think of? How would you explain the exceptions?

The nature of river systems. Every large river has a number of *tributaries*—that is, other rivers that carry water from the surrounding land to the main river. The Mississippi River is a good example of this. Its largest tributary, longer in fact than the Mississippi itself, is the Missouri River. The Mississippi has other large tributaries, such as the Ohio, Arkansas, and Red rivers. *(Figure 16-9.)*

Each of these large tributaries has tributaries of its own. For example, the Ohio River is formed by the junction of the Allegheny and Monongahela rivers. Along its course the Ohio is joined by other rivers, such as the Muskingum, Kanawha, Scioto, Wabash, and Tennessee rivers. See *Figure 16-10.*

Figure 16-9. The Mississippi River and some of its tributaries are shown in the diagram below. They are the larger streams in this particular river system.

Figure 16-10. The Ohio River is one of the large tributaries of the Mississippi. It has tributaries of its own, some of which are shown below.

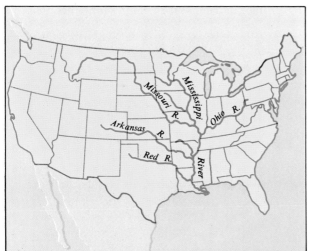

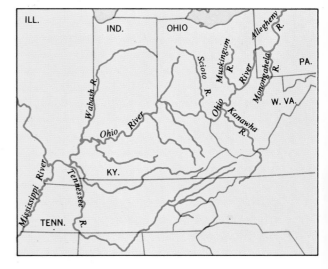

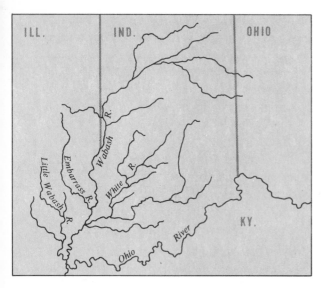

Figure 16-11. The Wabash River is a small river in the Mississippi River system. Its tributaries are streams which drain the surrounding countryside.

Each of these tributaries has still smaller tributaries. The Wabash, which forms the southern portion of the boundary between Illinois and Indiana, has tributaries such as the Embarrass, White, and Little Wabash rivers. *(Figure 16-11.)* Small streams lead into each of these, and even smaller creeks bring water to the streams. From these observations, you can see that a river system is a complex network of waterways, each one contributing its portion of water and of soil which has washed away from the land through which it flows.

Erosion and deposition along the course of a river. The path, or course, followed by a river is determined by the land through which the river flows. In a mountainous region, the course of a river is determined by the mountains themselves. The river flows in valleys between mountain ranges or between separate mountain peaks. Thus, many rivers flowing through the Appalachian Mountains run parallel to the direction of that mountain range. Occasionally, however, a river cuts directly across the mountains. For example, the Delaware River cuts directly through Kittatinny Mountain. *(Figure 16-12.)*

Rivers which flow through the valleys between mountains act to enlarge these valleys. The valleys are cut deeper and wider as rivers and streams wear away the surrounding soil and rock. The wearing away of rock and soil by running water is one form of erosion.

Running water is capable of moving enormous amounts of soil and rock. One spectacular example of the earth-moving capability of moving water is the Grand Canyon. Over a period of millions of years, the Colorado River has cut a canyon 217 miles long through

Figure 16-12. Usually, rivers flow in valleys between mountains. Sometimes, however, a river cuts directly through a mountain, as is shown in the picture at the right. In the picture you can see the Delaware River cutting directly through Kittatinny Mountain, forming the Delaware Water Gap.

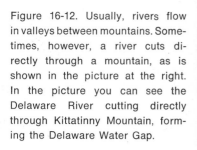

Figure 16-13. Running water is capable of wearing away and removing all kinds of earth material, even solid rock. Nowhere is this capability of moving water more evident than in the Grand Canyon.

MONKMEYER

the high plateau of northern Arizona. At the deepest point of the canyon, the river is a mile below the upper edge of the canyon.

The deposits of sediment, or *deltas,* which form at the mouths of certain rivers are also evidence of the earth-moving capability of rivers. Usually, as a river empties into the ocean, the motion of the water is slowed. The solid material that has been carried by the river settles. As the settling-out process, or *deposition* (dep′ə zish′ən), continues, a delta is formed. The delta of the Mississippi River is a well-known example of deposition. This delta consists of an extensive mass of swampy land formed from soil carried to the sea from a large area of the United States.

Some rivers, in spite of the fact that they are carrying large amounts of solid material

to the sea, do not form deltas. For instance, the Amazon River carries a load of sediment to the ocean, just as most rivers do. However, the tides and currents of the ocean near the mouth of the river carry the particles of solid material away from the mouth just as fast as they are brought to the sea. But at the mouths of other rivers, where the ocean's tides and currents are weaker, the solid material will be deposited when the river reaches the quiet ocean water. So the delta of the Mississippi River is formed in the Gulf of Mexico, and the delta of the Nile River is formed in the Mediterranean Sea.

Shaping the land. Throughout the geologic history of the earth, the earth's river systems have been in competition with the mountain-building forces which originate deep within the earth. As the crust of the earth is raised by internal forces, the rivers immediately begin

ESSA PHOTO

Figure 16-14. A delta, such as that shown above, results when the solid material being carried by river water is deposited at the mouth of a river.

to wear the crust down. Thus, the competition between the forces which build mountains and the action of rivers tends to produce an equilibrium in the continents of the earth. The growing mountains and the rivers which erode the mountains give shape to the surface of the land.

The interaction of forces is, in a way, similar to what happens in a star. In a star, gravitational force tends to pull the star together. The internal pressure generated by heat and light tends to make the star expand. The balance between these two forces determines the size of the star. Many forces are involved in shaping the surface of the earth. Conditions in the interior are slowly but steadily changing. As a result, the equilibrium between mountain building and mountain erosion is never quite reached. Over millions of years, the earth's surface changes.

In what ways, if any, has erosion been beneficial to man? What are some methods man has used to control erosion?

DO IT YOURSELF

Study maps showing the mouths of large rivers

Obtain detailed maps of those areas of the world where large rivers, such as the Mississippi, the Amazon, the Nile, and the Ganges, empty into the ocean. How would you explain the fact that a large city is located near the mouth of each of these rivers? Which rivers form deltas? Look up the term *distributary*. Find examples of distributaries on the maps you are studying.

3. Glaciers

The nature of glaciers. Some portions of the earth are covered with snow all through the year. This is true of almost all of Antarctica. It is also true of the very northern edges of both the Eurasian and American continents. In the temperate zones, high mountains often have year-round snowcaps. Many valleys high in the mountains are always filled with snow.

Imagine what happens as the snow on these high mountains builds up year after year, never completely melting away between one winter and the next. The layer of accumulated snow will become quite deep. The snow at the bottom of this layer will be compressed by the weight of the snow above it. Eventually, when enough snow has accumulated, the lower portion will be compressed into ice. As the mass of the snow and ice increases, the force of gravity on the snow and ice increases. Finally, the force of gravity will cause the mass of snow and ice to slide slowly down the mountainside. The mass of snow and ice is now a glacier.

As the glacier moves down the side of the mountain, repeated snowfalls higher up on the mountain continue to build up more and more packed snow and ice to "feed" the glacier. In many ways, this arrangement is like a lake with a river flowing out of it. Water from the surrounding land collects in the lake until it is deep enough to run over some low spot on the shore of the lake and down through a valley.

Figure 16-15. A glacier is sometimes called a "river of ice." A glacier is like a river in that it moves through a valley and it erodes the valley through which it moves. Of course, a glacier moves much more slowly than a river, because the glacier is made up of ice and snow, whereas the river is water.

HOLZGRAF FROM MONKMEYER

Basically, a glacier follows the same pattern. Of course, the glacier is a solid mass, whereas the river is a liquid.

Naturally, glaciers move much more slowly than rivers. Some glaciers flow only a tiny fraction of an inch in a day. Others—in Antarctica—move many tens of feet in a single day. As they move, glaciers wear away the rocks of the valleys which contain the glaciers.

What factors, do you think, affect the rate of movement of a glacier?

FIND OUT BY TRYING

Materials you will need: aluminum foil, hammer, 2 blocks of wood, 1-kg weight

Ice is usually considered to be a brittle solid. In a glacier, however, ice flows. What factors determine whether ice is brittle or able to flow? To find out, freeze two bars of ice $18 \times 2 \times 2$ inches. Use aluminum foil to make a tray of the correct size. After you have frozen two bars of ice, support one bar of ice by placing a block of wood under each end of the bar. Strike the center of the bar with a hammer. What happens to the bar? Then support the other bar of ice in the same manner. Place the weight in the middle of the bar, and keep the bar at a low enough temperature so the bar does not melt. HINT: Make sure the weight is very cold when placed on the ice. Observe what happens to the bar of ice after one or two days.

Conduct the experiment under various conditions—that is, change the weight, or the temperature, or any other factor which you think might be important. From the results of your experiment, how would you explain the fact that crevasses, or cracks, in a glacier seldom extend all the way through the glacier?

Figure 16-16. The valley shown above has the characteristic shape of a glaciated valley. The sides of the valley form a U. Also, although the valley curves, it does not have sharp curves or bends.

Figure 16-17. This valley exhibits the characteristic shape of a young river valley. The valley's sides are steep, forming a V. Also, sharp curves and bends occur as the valley follows the river's winding course.

Features of glaciated valleys. A glaciated valley has a very distinctive shape. One such valley is shown in *Figure 16-16*. This valley is in Glacier Park, Montana. The mountains and valleys of the Swiss Alps have also been sculptured by the action of glaciers. Most glaciers do not excavate valleys themselves. They remodel valleys that already exist.

The cross section of a glaciated valley is U-shaped. In contrast, many valleys formed by rivers have a more V-shaped cross section, such as the one shown in *Figure 16-17*. The Grand Canyon is also an example of a V-shaped river valley, but on a much larger scale than that shown in *Figure 16-17*.

Glaciated valleys do not have sharp curves. The ice in a moving glacier resists bending. Thus, the glacier tends to cut as straight a valley as possible and to wear away any sharp irregularities in the sides. A river valley, on the other hand, may wind back and forth in a very tortuous manner.

If a glacier has moved into a valley that was once occupied by a river, it leaves telltale signs of its invasion. One such sign is the hanging tributary. Picture a river valley with small tributary streams coming into the side, as shown in *A* of *Figure 16-18*. Now imagine that a glacier enters this valley and deepens it considerably. The tributary streams are probably frozen but are not really a part of the glacier. Therefore, the valleys of the small tributary streams are not deepened, although the glacier deepens the main valley as the ice scrapes out rock and debris. (*B* of *Figure 16-18*.) After thousands—or millions—of years have gone by, the glacier disappears. It leaves behind it the deepened valley in the center with the tributary valleys ending high up on the sides. (*C* of *Figure 16-18*.) Quite often beautiful waterfalls result as the streams in these hanging tributary valleys discharge their water into the main valley.

The ice ages. Glaciers that no longer exist have left many signs of their presence. As a matter of fact, through a study of these signs, scientists know that much of the land area in the Northern Hemisphere was covered with snow and ice at various times in the past. Glaciers were common as far south as the

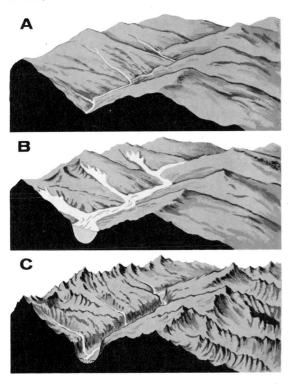

Figure 16-18. A glacier shapes a valley in several ways. Hanging tributaries are formed, and the valley is deepened, widened, and somewhat straightened.

A

B

C

Ohio River. In more level regions, the area was simply covered by a huge ice sheet, such as that which occupies the central portion of Greenland today. Where mountain ranges existed, glaciers formed and moved, sculpturing the mountain peaks and cutting the deep valleys that we see today. The map in *Figure 16-19* shows the extent of the ice sheet that covered North America in the last ice age.

There is evidence that vast sheets of ice have covered large portions of both the Northern Hemisphere and the Southern Hemisphere on a number of different occasions during the last million years. So far, the cause of these ice ages is not known. Judging simply from past history, however, there is every reason to believe that there will be additional ice ages in the future.

What types of evidence could be left by glaciers to indicate that large portions of both the Northern Hemisphere and Southern Hemisphere have been covered by glaciers at several different times?

Figure 16-19. As indicated on the map at the right, Canada and large areas of the United States were covered by ice during the most recent ice age, about 10,000 years ago. Do you think those parts of the United States not actually covered by the ice sheets and glaciers were affected by them in any way?

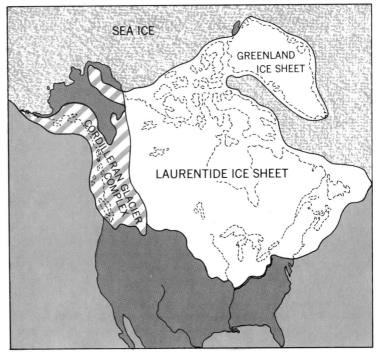

4. Plains

The leveling of mountains. In a region where mountain building has stopped, the action of the rivers controls further change. The rivers will eventually wash away the mountains and leave only a flat, or nearly flat, expanse of land. Such a tract of land is called a *plain*. Suppose we follow the steps in this process of mountain leveling.

In *A* of *Figure 16-20,* there are three ranges of mountains. Rivers have formed on the sides of the mountains and have already started to cut small canyons. Small lakes are forming in the valleys. As time goes on, the rivers cut more deeply into the mountainsides, as shown in *B.* Some material washed down from the mountains begins to accumulate in the valleys. Some is carried away to the sea.

Figure 16-20. Mountains are leveled by erosion. As you study this process, keep in mind that the process requires a very long time.

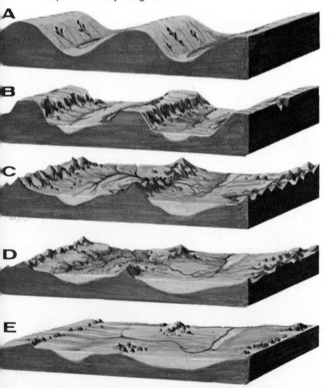

Eventually, the tops of the mountains are completely worn away, as in *C.* The river system in the higher valley to the left has cut through the range of mountains in the center, carrying water and soil to the lower valley on the right. In *D,* the mountains are almost gone. The material that once filled the higher valley on the left is now being carried away to the lower valley on the right. Some of the material is being carried to the sea. In *E,* nothing is left of the old mountains but a few small peaks. These peaks are composed of very hard rock that was able to withstand the wearing action of the streams. The valleys are almost level, and the only evidences of the original mountain ranges are the small peaks and a series of low, rolling hills. In time, even these will be leveled.

Much of the central area of the United States and Canada exists as a plain today. Long ago, this region may have been mountainous. There are several other places in the world where such broad, fairly flat plains stretch for hundreds of miles. Two well-known areas of this type are Siberia in the northern portion of Asia and the Amazon jungle in northern Brazil. Flat plains also exist in northern India, in central Australia, and in northern Africa.

What agents, other than running water, might be factors in mountain leveling? As the mountains are reduced in height, will the climate of the region be affected? If so, how?

The presence of sediment. Often when geologists investigate extensive plains, they see no evidence that mountains once existed where these plains are now. Perhaps there is no evidence of them because the mountains once there were worn away by the action of rivers. But perhaps there is no evidence because no mountains ever existed there.

Many of these broad plains are covered to great depths with soil and debris. Presumably, the material washed down from mountains around the edges of the plain. Thus, the central plains of the United States are covered with debris washed down from mountains in the west and the east. This debris is called sediment. In some places it is several miles deep. Furthermore, many of the sediments have become cemented together to form sedimentary rock.

The rock beneath the uncemented sediment does not form a level floor. Instead, it is a rolling floor, like a series of ranges of underground hills. *(Figure 16-21.)* In some places, the layers of rock which normally are below the surface have become exposed on the surface of the plain. Geologists have investigated this rock and found that it contains many different types of minerals and that its structure is quite complicated. Beneath the sedimentary rock are formations of very old igneous and metamorphic rock.

The continental shields. Mountains contain rock of all types, including great amounts of igneous rock, such as granite. Compared to the igneous and metamorphic rock of the mountains, the igneous and metamorphic rock under the plains is much older. Geologists have given a special name to these extensive formations of very old rock under the plains of the various continents. They are called *continental shields.*

Geologists have discovered one important characteristic of the continental shields. They are in areas quite separate from those regions where mountains have formed. We can see this on a map such as the one in *Figure 16-22.* On this map, the continental shields are indicated by the shaded areas. The locations of active volcanoes are also indicated. These

Figure 16-21. Plains are usually covered with sediment, the top layer of which is soil. Rock may be exposed in some places, as shown in this diagram.

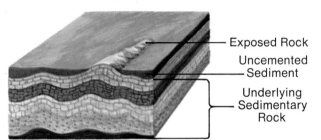

Exposed Rock

Uncemented Sediment

Underlying Sedimentary Rock

Figure 16-22. The continental shields, shown in brown, are very old formations of igneous and metamorphic rock that lie under the plains in many areas of the world. In some regions these shields are exposed on the surface, but the exposed areas are very small compared with the total areas of the shields. More research is needed to determine the true extent of the shields. New evidence may reveal that the shields are even more extensive than indicated here.

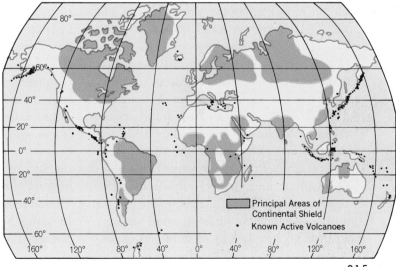

Principal Areas of Continental Shield
• Known Active Volcanoes

315

active volcanoes are in the regions where mountain building is going on at the present time. As you can see, active volcanoes are very rare in the continental shields. The regions of the earth where volcanoes are found seem to be quite distinct from the continental shields.

Many geologists feel that the continental shields form the nuclei of the continents. Mountains have been built up around the edges of the shields, extending the continents out on the sides of the shields. But the shields themselves have always been fairly level plains, much as we see them today. Keep in mind that, so far, this idea about mountains and continental shields is only a theory. In later chapters we shall learn more about this theory and the evidence that supports it.

Very few fossils have been found in the rock of the continental shields. What explanations can you give for this fact?

5. Sediments

Materials carried by running water. Running water is one agent which carries material from the mountains and across the plains. As a mountain stream rushes down a slope, it can easily carry with it sand and pebbles. The steeper the slope is, the faster the water moves. The faster the water moves, the larger are the rock particles that can be carried by the water. In fact, mountain streams can move boulders several feet across and weighing many tons. However, the streams soon gather into a river, and the river winds its way out of the mountains into the more level region of the foothills. Then, the movement of the water becomes less rapid. The heavier material begins to settle to the bottom of the river. As the water moves out across a plain on its way toward the ocean, still more material settles from it. Finally, only the fine particles of mud and sand are left to continue on their way toward the ocean. Eventually, in one place or another, all of the solid material settles out of the water. This settled material is called sediment.

Sediment occurs in many forms. In the delta of the Mississippi River, the sediment is mud and clay. A great number of small streams wind through this deposit of sediment. Thus, the delta of the Mississippi contains a great network of small streams and swamps called *bayous* (bī′üz). Another form of sediment is found in deserts where, ordinarily, no rivers are to be seen. However, when a heavy rainfall hits the surrounding mountains, the water forms a temporary river as it rushes down gullies and canyons through the mountains. Of course, the river eventually empties out onto a dry valley. The rapidly running water spreads out across the valley as a flash flood. The rushing water carries with it tons of loose sand and rock. This loose sand and rock is spread out in a fan-shaped pattern across the floor of the valley near the mouth of the mountain canyon through which the temporary river flows. *(Figure 16-23.)* Such deposits of sediment are called *alluvial* (ə lü′vi əl) *fans.*

A third form of sediment can be found on some of the great plains of the world. These plains, which are now dry land, were once the floors of shallow seas or swamps. Rivers from the surrounding hills and mountains carried material into these ancient bodies of water. There the material was deposited as sediment. In some places, the depth of sediment deposited is as great as 30,000 feet.

DWIGHT WARREN FROM WESTERN WAYS

How could deposits of sediment accumulate to a thickness of 30,000 feet in a shallow sea?

Sediments produced by living organisms. Some sediments are the remains of living organisms. There are many sea creatures which absorb calcium carbonate from sea water. The calcium carbonate is used in the formation of the shells of these animals. Most of these creatures live in shallow portions of the ocean or swim near the surface of the ocean. Eventually they die, and their shells sink to the bottom. Some of these shells are microscopic. Other shells, such as those of conches or giant clams, are rather large. A thick layer of such shells, deposited over millions of years, is usually compressed into solid limestone. Often, limestone contains identifiable pieces of the shells from which it was made.

Another source of sediment is the *diatom* (dī′ə tom), a microscopic plant that lives inside of its own glassy shell. Billions of diatoms live near the surface of the sea in all parts of the world. After diatoms complete their life cycle, their glassy shells sink slowly to the floor of the ocean. At great depths, where the diatom itself could never live, there is a constant "snowfall" of these tiny particles of silica which steadily accumulates on the floor of the ocean.

Sediments produced by chemical action. In some regions of the ocean, chemical reactions within the bodies of living organisms are not required to produce sediment. For example, just off the southeast coast of Florida is a shallow region of the sea, some 7,000 square miles in area. This area is called the Bahama Banks. The average depth of the water is 20 feet. Here, the sea water contains a high percentage of calcium carbonate. Slight changes in temperature or a loss of dissolved carbon dioxide from the water in this region will cause some of the calcium carbonate to crystallize out of the sea water. The calcium carbonate forms tiny crystals that fall to the sea floor to form a limestone sediment. These particles of calcium carbonate stick together by chemical action, forming solid limestone.

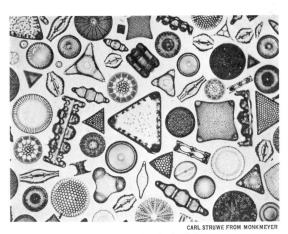

CARL STRUWE FROM MONKMEYER

Figure 16-24. Over a long period of time, an accumulation of diatom shells, such as those shown, may become cemented together to form diatomite—a porous, lightweight, sedimentary rock.

Obtain samples of various sedimentary and igneous rocks. Using a strong magnifying glass, study the rocks. What properties, if any, can you find which are common to the sedimentary rocks you are studying? To the igneous rocks?

Pulverize a small sample of each rock. Examine the fine particles obtained from each sample. Are the particles of each rock the same? If not, how do they differ? Do the differences, if any, provide clues to the origin of the rocks?

Forming sedimentary rock from sediments. The sediment carried to the sea by rivers consists of silt, sand, and gravel. As such sediments accumulate, particles near the bottom of the deposit are squeezed together by tremendous pressure. If the pressure is great enough, it can cause the particles to be welded together, forming solid rock. This is how sandstone is formed.

What rock layers reveal. Deposits of sedimentary rock are easy to recognize. They form in flat layers. Each layer represents a different stage of sediment deposit. In many cases, millions of years have passed between the formation of one sediment layer and the one either above it or below it. It is easy for geologists to find examples where, at one time, a thick layer of limestone was deposited, perhaps on the floor of a shallow sea. Then, millions of years later, perhaps after the formation of new mountain ranges and a change in the weather patterns of the world, sand was washed down on top of the limestone. This sand eventually turned into a layer of sandstone. Above that there might be a layer of shale, a compacted form of clay.

The Grand Canyon provides a beautiful display of such a series of layers. *Figure 16-25* shows a photograph of the south wall of the Grand Canyon. Various layers of rock are identified on the side. The lowest layer, marked T, is a combination of shale mixed with sand and sandstone. Above it is a 500-foot layer of reddish limestone, marked R. This material is rather hard compared to the sandstone and so has been able to maintain itself in fairly rugged cliffs, whereas the sandstone below has washed away into gentler slopes. Above the layer marked R is another thick layer of shale and sandstone marked S. On the layer of shale and sandstone is a layer consisting entirely of shale, marked H. This layer of shale is very soft compared to the sandstone and the limestone. Thus, the layer of shale has been worn into a gentler slope. Above this shale is a harder layer of pure sandstone, marked C. This sandstone is a particular form of white sandstone which was formed in an ancient desert. The top layer, marked K, is limestone. This same layer of limestone is also the rock which lies across the top of the whole plateau in northern Arizona through which the Grand Canyon runs.

By examining this structure of layers, geologists can tell that at one time the region of the Grand Canyon was the floor of a valley. The valley was covered with sand and gravel washed down from the surrounding mountains which have long since disappeared. At another time, the region of the Grand Canyon was the floor of a shallow sea, with limestone being laid down as sea creatures died and as calcium

Figure 16-25. The Grand Canyon is an outstanding example of how layers of sedimentary rock may be exposed by erosion. By examining these exposed layers, geologists can reconstruct a rather complete record of geologic events that occurred in this region of the earth's surface.

KAIBAB LIMESTONE

COCONINO SANDSTONE

HERMIT SHALE

SUPAI FORMATION

REDWALL LIMESTONE

TONTO GROUP

carbonate was precipitated from the sea water. At still another time, the region of the Grand Canyon was a vast desert covered with wind-swept sand. Eventually, the desert sank (or the level of the ocean rose), and another shallow sea covered the area, leaving behind another deposit of limestone. Then, the whole plateau was pushed upward again, far above sea level. The Colorado River, relentlessly making its way toward the ocean, has cut the mile-deep gorge through these many layers of ancient sediment.

Was the Colorado river, at one time, as wide as the Grand Canyon? If not, how do you account for the width of the canyon, which is more than 15 miles from rim to rim in some places?

The rock cycle. As we have seen, the principal features of the continents are mountains, rivers, and plains. The action of rivers and glaciers is to constantly move material from high areas to low areas. The plains of the earth are almost completely covered with thick layers of sedimentary rock made of material which has washed down off mountains. Many of the ancient mountains which contributed this material have now disappeared. Mountains which are now in the process of being raised are being worn down and washed away almost as fast as they are raised. As sediments pile upon each other, great pressure, together with chemical action, causes solid rock to form out of what was once a layer of loose particles. Thus, one form of rock is worn away only to become another form in a different location.

319

Checking Your Knowledge

IMPORTANT IDEAS

1. Mountains usually exist in groups called mountain ranges.

2. Mountains are formed by volcanism, by plateau erosion, and by crustal movement.

3. River systems carry millions of tons of silt and sediment to the ocean each year.

4. Rivers usually run parallel to mountain ranges. Occasionally they cut across a range.

5. The processes of mountain building and erosion work in opposition to each other in shaping the earth's surface.

6. Continental shields are extensive formations of very old igneous and metamorphic rock. They may be the nuclei of continents.

7. Most sedimentary rock forms from accumulated deposits of the shells of sea animals and plants or of materials eroded from various land forms.

8. Millions of years were required to form thick layers of sedimentary rock.

USING NEW WORDS

Study the terms listed below. On your paper write the numerals *1-6*. After each numeral, write the correct terms to answer the question having the corresponding numeral.

range	deposition	plateau erosion
diatom	volcanism	crustal movement
erosion	tributary	sediments
	continental shield	

1. Which terms refer to mountain building?

2. Which term names a layer of ancient rock?

3. Which term refers to a group of mountains that have a common origin?

4. Which term is the name of a plant?

5. Which terms are related to the formation of sedimentary rock?

6. Which term is related to a river system?

TEST YOURSELF

Study the test below. On your paper write the numerals *1-10*. Beside each numeral write the correct response to that part of the test having the corresponding numeral.

1. A group of mountains which are related in terms of structure and origin form what is known as a mountain _____.

2. The highest mountains in the world were produced by shifts in the position of portions of the earth's crust. This process of mountain building is called _____.

3. One form of sediment is produced when the compound _____ crystallizes out of sea water as a result of a change in temperature or in carbon dioxide content of the sea water.

4. Erosion is the wearing away of land forms by moving air, water, or ice. The process by which the transported material is placed in a new location is known as _____.

5. There is a layer of old igneous and metamorphic rock which underlies the sedimentary rock in certain large areas of a continent. Such a layer is called a _____.

6. A river system consists of the main stream and all the _____ which empty into the main stream.

7. A deposit of sediment formed where a river meets the sea is known as a _____.

8. As the shells of many sea creatures settle to the bottom of the sea and become cemented together, layers of *(shale, limestone, sandstone)* are formed.

9. The *(Himalayas, Andes, Alps, Catskills)* are mountains that have been formed by the process of plateau erosion.

10. In general, active volcanoes are *(located in the center of, located around the edges of, randomly distributed throughout)* the areas covered by the continental shields.

Extending Your Knowledge

QUESTIONS TO EXPLORE

1. If man continues to check erosion (as he continually tries to do), is there any danger that the continents will be built up too high? Justify your answer.

2. What would you consider to be some important features of a continent for our present civilization? Why are these features important? Would you have picked the same features if you had lived 500 years ago? If not, what features would you have selected?

3. What types of rock are being formed today? Where is this formation occurring?

4. What factors affect the amount of material a moving stream of water can carry? Why are some slow-moving rivers muddy, while fast-moving mountain streams are often clear?

5. What factors determine whether or not a delta forms at the mouth of a river?

SOME THINGS TO DO

1. Construct a stream table to use in conducting experiments concerning factors which affect rate of erosion, delta formation, and so on. A good basic design is given on pages 334-336 of the American Geological Institute's *Geology and Earth Sciences Sourcebook*. However, you may wish to modify this design by making your stream table larger. Or, you may wish to include features which you need for specific experiments.

2. Make a study of glaciers. Find out how a valley glacier differs from a continental glacier. Prepare a chart in which you compare valley glaciers with continental glaciers. Include such information as the area covered by each type, thickness of each type, the distance traveled by each type, and how each type affects the surface of the land over which it

moves. Find out what theories have been proposed to explain the recurrent ice ages.

3. Study a river or stream near your home. On a map, trace the course of this stream. Is it a tributary of any larger stream? Does it eventually empty into the sea, or does it empty into a lake? Determine what types of sediment are transported by this stream. Are any sediments deposited in your locality?

CHALLENGES IN SCIENCE

1. Ice is much softer than rock, yet one form of evidence which indicates that glaciers have been present in an area is the scratches which glaciers leave on rocks. Explain how such scratches are produced.

2. Look at a map of the United States and examine the coastline along the Gulf of Mexico. Count the rivers which empty into the Gulf. Count the deltas you find. How would you explain why there are so many more rivers than there are deltas?

3. Describe what is meant by the term *yazoo stream*. On a map showing the valley of a large river system, identify the yazoo streams. How did the term yazoo stream originate?

4. Do you think it is possible for a portion of a fresh-water lake to be below sea level, although the lake drains into the ocean? Explain your answer.

5. In Asia Minor there are many hills called *tells*. Some of these tells are more than 100 feet high. When archaeologists dig into these tells, they find the ruins of ancient civilizations. Are these tells examples of uplift of the earth's crust? If ancient cities were built on top of hills, how did the cities get covered with soil? Why hasn't the soil eroded to expose the ruins?

The ocean represents a relatively unexplored aspect of the earth's surface.

ZENTRALE FARBBILD AGENTUR

CHAPTER 17

The Oceans

Space, although it is a great challenge to today's scientists, is not the only frontier remaining for man to explore. The earth, too, has some aspects which are relatively unexplored. For instance, it is difficult to realize that man knows more about the surface of the moon than he does about the floor of the earth's oceans. Yet, such is the case.

Much of the information scientists have about the oceans has been obtained in the last decade. The scientists doing the research have often been surprised by what they have found. For example, they have found huge mountains and deep valleys on the floor of the oceans. In the oceans, they have detected great currents which carry more water than our greatest rivers. They have also found that certain streams of muddy water in the oceans move more solid material in a few hours than a large river on the continents moves in several years.

In the past, the oceans have been used only as a route of transportation and as a source of a relatively small amount of food. In the future, it is believed the oceans will rival the land as a source of man's food and other essential materials.

What are some of the things scientists have discovered about the oceans? In Chapter 17 you will find out. Also, you will have the opportunity to try, just as scientists do, to use this information in suggesting ways in which the features of the ocean floor might have been formed.

1. The Nature of the Oceans

What are the oceans? The oceans consist of the whole body of salt water that covers much of the surface of the earth. In fact, of the total surface of the earth, 70.8 per cent is covered by the salt water of the oceans. Thus, the oceans are the earth's most extensive surface feature, with an area more than twice that of the continents and islands combined.

Interactions between oceans and atmosphere. The oceans play a vital role in the lives of all of us, for the earth's weather is primarily the result of the interactions between the oceans and the atmosphere. In what ways do these interactions occur?

Consider the vast expanse of water in the oceans at the earth's surface. This water acts as a reservoir of heat. When the atmosphere above the oceans is colder than the water of the oceans, heat flows from the water into the air. When the air is warmer than the water in the oceans, heat flows in the opposite direction.

The oceans, in addition to being a reservoir of heat, serve as a great reservoir of water. As water evaporates from the vast surface of the oceans, the content of water vapor in the air increases. As the air moves, this water vapor is carried to other parts of the earth. If the water vapor is carried to colder regions, the vapor condenses and falls to earth as rain or snow. Some of the water which falls to the earth is evaporated again, returning as vapor to the atmosphere. Some of the fallen water flows back to the oceans through the streams and rivers of the continents. Thus, the water lost to the atmosphere and to the land surfaces is, eventually, returned to the great reservoir of the oceans.

Interactions with the solid earth. One aspect of the geologic importance of the oceans is their role in shaping the solid portions of the earth. As you have already studied, falling rain and flowing water act to wear away mountains and thus change the earth's surface. Since the source of the water in rain and rivers is water which evaporated from the surface of the oceans, the oceans are an important link in a continuing chain of events.

Glaciers, too, act to shape the land. As glaciers slowly advance, not only is a great mass of frozen water being moved, but tons of rock and soil are also moved. Glaciers and ice sheets covering thousands of square miles of the northern continents and of Antarctica owe their existence, primarily, to the oceans. The snow which fell to make these great masses of ice was, at one time, water in the oceans. Thus, indirectly, through the action of flowing rivers and moving glaciers, the oceans shape the continents.

In addition, the oceans act directly to shape the continents. Ocean waves are constantly eating away at the shoreline, eroding both beaches and cliffs. Moreover, ocean currents shape the floor of the oceans by carrying particles of solid materials from one part of the ocean floor to another.

Figure 17-1. The "sandfall" pictured below is about thirty feet high. It represents one example of how ocean currents are continually shaping the ocean floor by moving material from one place to another.

Which, do you think, produces greater changes in the continents—the action of ocean waves against the shoreline, or glaciation? Justify your answer.

The geologic importance of the oceans goes beyond anything we have mentioned. The oceans hide vast areas of the earth's solid surface from our view. In a study of the earth, we would expect that a square mile of ocean floor would be as important as a square mile of any continent. However, until now, the ocean floor has not been studied in detail. Thus, geologists have had to formulate their theories about the nature of the earth almost completely from observations made on dry land—less than 30 per cent of the earth's surface.

Of course, scientists have observed the ocean floor to some extent, but the data they have gathered are far from complete. However, through the use of new methods and new equipment, scientists are slowly adding to their knowledge of the ocean floor.

Observing the floor of the oceans. Compared to observing the surface of the continents, observing the floor of the oceans is an extremely difficult task. Two kinds of observations are of primary importance.

Depth measurement is a very important type of observation. By using many depth measurements, man has been able to construct a map of the ocean floor showing hills and valleys, and mountains and canyons. For hundreds of years, *soundings*—that is, depth measurements—were made by lowering a weight on the end of a calibrated line. This is called "taking a sounding." Sailors have used this method throughout recorded history to make sure the water they were in was deep enough to carry their ships safely. Until about a hundred years ago, rope lines were used for taking soundings. The deepest parts of the ocean had never been sounded, since long ropes strong enough to use in taking such soundings were simply not available. Then, when steel wires and cables became available and were used for taking soundings, geologists discovered that in most areas, the ocean is thousands of feet deep.

In 1920 the first echo-sounding system was used. Echo sounding is often called *sonar,* for *s*ound *n*avigation *a*nd *r*anging. See *Figure 17-2.* In using the echo sounder, a sharp ping of sound is sent out from the ship being used in taking the sounding. The time it takes the sound to travel to the ocean bottom and back to the ship is measured. To determine the

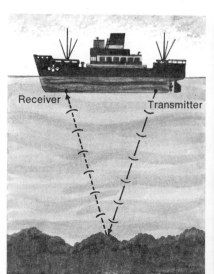

RAYTHEON COMPANY

Figure 17-2. The fathometer shown in the center picture is a device which detects reflected sounds, measures the time of their travel, and computes the ocean's depth. This information is automatically recorded on a chart, such as the one below, revealing a profile of the ocean floor.

RAYTHEON COMPANY

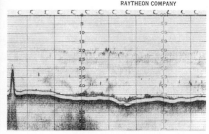

depth of the water beneath the ship, the measure of the time elapsed is divided by two. Then that quotient is multiplied by the measure of the speed of sound in water. The resulting product is the measure of the depth of the water.

Determining the ocean's depth is accomplished more rapidly when sonar is used than when soundings are taken by using a weighted line. However, even this process of sounding the ocean floor is still time-consuming, and only a few regions of the ocean floor have been carefully mapped.

The second important type of observation for learning about the ocean floor is the gathering of samples. A century ago this was done in a very simple manner. Sailors used the same weight with which they took soundings. The bottom of the weight was hollowed out and a piece of soap pushed into it. When the weight was pulled up from the ocean bottom, the sailors would examine any materials that had stuck to the wet soap. As you can imagine, this procedure does not provide a very accurate picture of the ocean floor.

Suppose you were to take a bar of wet soap out to the school yard and push it down onto the surface of the ground. What do you suppose you would find? Then suppose you walked a hundred feet in a random direction and tried it again, and again in another hundred feet, and so on. As you can imagine, you could get more information by simply looking around than you could get by using the "wet-soap method."

Sampling the ocean floor. Certainly, geologists need to know much more about the floor of the ocean than they can find out by simply examining the material sticking to a piece of soap that has touched the floor of the ocean. To sample the sea floor, geologists now use *coring devices.* Basically, a coring device is a long pipe with a weight on top of it. It is

Figure 17-3. The men in the top picture are preparing to lower a coring device to sample the material on the ocean's floor. Parts of the coring device and the core obtained are shown in the bottom picture.

lowered from a ship to a few hundred feet above the floor of the ocean. Then the cable to which the coring device is attached is allowed to run free so that the corer sinks to the ocean floor as fast as possible. Quite often there are fins on the top end of the device to guide it so that the hollow pipe strikes squarely into the ocean bottom. As the pipe plunges into the ocean floor, the material of the floor is pushed up inside the hollow pipe. The coring device is then pulled back up to the ship. A plunger is used to push the captured material, called a *core,* out onto the deck where geologists can study it.

Figure 17-4. The oceanographer shown is preparing to lower a Nansen reversing bottle into the ocean. This device is used to record the temperature and to collect samples of ocean water at various depths.

Continuing studies of the oceans. Scientists who study the oceans are called oceanographers. Oceanographers use many instruments other than echo sounders and coring devices. For example, a dredge is often towed behind a research ship to scrape samples of material off the ocean bottom. It is also important to measure the temperature of the oceans at various depths, and to take samples of the water to determine what chemicals it contains.

Photographs are an important means of obtaining information about the deep ocean floor. Special cameras and lighting equipment have been developed for use in the deep oceans. Special equipment, such as the bathyscaphs *Trieste* and *Trieste II,* enable scientists to descend to the bottom of the oceans for firsthand observations of the conditions there. *(Figure 1-3.)* Research submarines,

Figure 17-5. The conditions which exist under the sea make it necessary for man to devise special equipment and apparatus to study the ocean. Most of this equipment is complex and highly specialized. Even with this equipment, however, man has barely begun to obtain all the information he desires about the ocean.

TEMPERATURE OF SURFACE WATER			
North Latitude	Temperature	South Latitude	Temperature
70°-60°	5.60°C	70°-60°	−1.30°C
60°-50°	8.66°C	60°-50°	1.76°C
50°-40°	13.16°C	50°-40°	8.68°C
40°-30°	20.40°C	40°-30°	16.90°C
30°-20°	24.16°C	30°-20°	21.20°C
20°-10°	25.81°C	20°-10°	23.16°C
10°-0°	26.66°C	10°-0°	25.18°C

SALINITY OF THE OCEAN'S SURFACE WATER	
Location	Salinity (per 1,000 g of H_2O)
All Oceans (average)	34.6 g
Red Sea	40.0 g
30° North Latitude and 30° South Latitude	35.5 g
Near Equator	34.8 g
Near South Pole	34.0 g

TEMPERATURE OF WATER IN MONTEREY BAY, CALIFORNIA			
Depth (meters)	Temperature in January	Temperature in May	Temperature in September
0	11.5°C	11.5°C	14.5°C
10	11.5°C	11.0°C	13.5°C
25	11.0°C	9.0°C	11.0°C
50	10.5°C	8.5°C	9.0°C
100	9.8°C	7.5°C	8.0°C

OXYGEN CONTENT OF OCEAN WATER (ml/l)			
Location	2,000 Meters Deep	3,000 Meters Deep	4,000 Meters Deep
Northwest Atlantic	6.30	6.17	6.34
Northcentral Atlantic	5.07	5.27	5.42
Southcentral Atlantic	4.68	4.89	5.14
North Pacific	1.64	2.58	—
Central Pacific	2.56	3.15	3.27
South Pacific	4.32	4.49	—

Figure 17-6. The tables represent a small sample of data concerning the water of the ocean. Such data enable oceanographers to make inferences about the nature of ocean water.

such as *Star III* and *Aluminaut,* are used to perform various tasks under the sea. For shallow water research, self-contained underwater breathing apparatus—*scuba,* for short—is often used. Some aspects of the oceanographer's work are shown in *Figure 17-5.*

Oceanographers are particularly interested in the temperature of the ocean's water. In addition, they wish to know the amounts of salt and oxygen that are dissolved in the water. The salt content, or salinity, of the water varies from place to place. Fresh water is brought into some parts of the ocean from nearby rivers, thus lowering the salt content in these parts of the ocean. In other parts of the ocean, evaporation removes pure water, leaving the remaining water with a greater concentration of salt.

The oxygen content of ocean water, like its salt content, varies from place to place. Oxygen from the atmosphere dissolves in the ocean. Marine organisms use this dissolved oxygen in carrying on basic life processes. Certain ocean currents move surface water, which is comparatively rich in oxygen, down to deeper portions of the ocean. If currents did not continually carry oxygen-rich water to the deeper portions of the ocean, the supply of oxygen there would soon be used up by marine organisms. In parts of the ocean where currents of this type do not occur, the deep water contains much less oxygen than the water near the surface.

Where did the salt and other dissolved minerals in sea water come from?

2. The Continental Shelves

Interesting features of continental shelves. The great number of depth measurements made possible by the echo sounder has led to some surprising discoveries. One of the first of these was the discovery that the ocean water is comparatively shallow for many kilometers out from the coast of many continents. Such a gently sloping—almost flat—area of the ocean bottom, lying just off the coast of a continent, is called a *continental shelf*. The continental shelf off the east coast of the United States slopes downward gently until it reaches a depth of about 160 to 200 meters. At that point the slope of the bottom becomes much steeper, dropping more than a thousand meters in only a few kilometers.

Some of the characteristics of the continental shelf off the east coast of the United States can be observed in the map of the ocean floor shown in *Figure 17-7*. As you can observe, this gently sloping shelf seems to be an extension of the continent itself.

Continental shelves which have been found to exist have an average width of 67 km. Oceanographers have calculated that these shelves account for more than 5 per cent of the surface area of the earth. You may be able to understand how gentle the slope of a continental shelf is if the slope is described in the following way. For every thousand meters (or one kilometer) further out from shore, the water gets only two meters deeper.

At the outer edge of the continental shelves, the steepness of the ocean floor increases. Here, in the region called the *continental slope,* for every kilometer further from shore, the water gets more than 70 meters deeper. Of course, these values are averages. Continental shelves and the continental slopes beyond them vary from place to place.

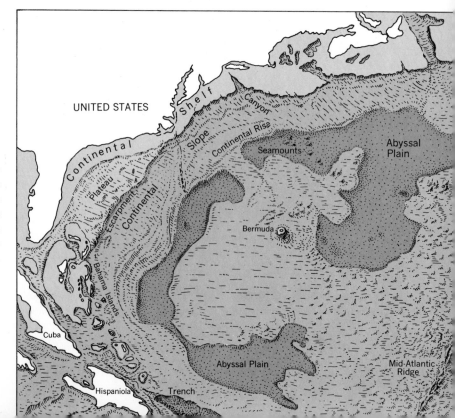

Figure 17-7. Naturally, no two regions of the ocean floor are identical. However, the ocean floor in the region just off the east coast of the United States contains many of the ocean's common, subsurface features.

In some places there are no continental shelves at all. For example, there is no such shelf off the west coast of South America. Along this coast, the water gets deep quite rapidly. The depth increases at about the same rate as it does along a typical continental slope. That is, starting right from the shoreline the water gets steadily deeper at the rate of about 70 meters for every kilometer further out from shore.

How would you explain the fact that the width of a continental shelf is much greater at some places than at others?

FIND OUT BY TRYING

Materials you will need: carpenter's level, several sheets of paper

Determine whether a table top or a desk top is as level as a typical continental shelf. Place the level on the table top that is to be examined. Is the table top level? If so, the table top is obviously more nearly level than a continental shelf. If not, how many sheets of paper must be inserted under the low end of the level in order to center the bubble in the level? How thick is a sheet of the paper you used? Hint: You can find out by measuring the thickness of a stack of 50 sheets of paper, and dividing the measure by 50. Which has the greater slope, a typical continental shelf or the table top?

Materials in the continental shelves. After the discovery of continental shelves, scientists speculated about the proper interpretation of these shelves. Their speculations followed this pattern. Suppose continental shelves are extensions of a continent and are not a portion of what originally formed as the ocean floor. Then, the material to be found in these shelves should be similar to the material of the continents which they border.

To find out what materials make up the continental shelves, coring devices were used to obtain samples of material. These core samples revealed that, in general, the material of the shelves is loose sediment, much like the material in river deltas. Also revealed was the fact that the continental shelves extend farthest from the shoreline near the mouths of large rivers, such as the Yellow River of China, the Mississippi, and the Amazon.

The longest cores obtained in the investigations of the shelves were 18 meters long. In other words, scientists have only been able to sample the materials 18 meters down from the surface of the ocean floor. But, at least to these depths, they have found that the material of the continental shelves is sediment—silt, sand, and loose gravel.

In their investigations, scientists have also noted the characteristics of regions where no continental shelves have formed. These regions include the west coasts of South America, Central America, and some of North America. In these regions there are no large rivers emptying into the oceans. From the evidence they have gathered, scientists have concluded that the continental shelves are composed of the sediments washed down off the continents and deposited onto the ocean floor. Evidently the rock which originally formed the ocean floor lies beneath the continental shelves. The boundary, then, between the edge of the continents and the beginning of the oceans, is under a blanket of sediment.

The boundary between oceans and continents. In Chapter 14 the types of rock on the continents and on the ocean floor were described. In describing these rock types, we were referring to what is called the *basement complex*—an underlying deposit of igneous and metamorphic rock. Usually the basement complex, or basement rock, is covered with layers of sediment or sedimentary rock. In some places on the continents, however, the basement rock is exposed for us to see. In some portions of the deep ocean floor, too, the basement rock is exposed and can be sampled with coring devices or underwater drills. In other places on the floor of the oceans, the basement rock is covered by a layer of sediment or sedimentary rock just as it is on the continents.

In your study of Chapter 14, you learned that the floor of the oceans—that is, the basement rock of the ocean floor—is primarily basalt, a comparatively heavy rock. You will recall that the basement rock of the continents is primarily granite, a comparatively light rock. You learned, too, that the basalt rock on the floor of the ocean also runs as a thin layer under the continents. *(Figure 14-10.)*

If we forget about sediments and sedimentary rock for the moment, then we can visualize the granitic basement rock of the continents "floating" on the layer of basaltic rock which forms the floor of the oceans. Thus, the continents do not necessarily end at the shoreline. The edges of the continents are those places where the granitic basement rock of the continents ends. See *Figure 14-10,* and imagine how it would look if the sediments were removed. In some portions of the world the continents' edges are quite near the shoreline. In other places—that is, wherever a continental shelf exists—the continents' edges seem to lie out some distance from the shoreline under the water of the oceans.

Do you suppose the boundary between the continents and the oceans coincided with the shoreline of the continents at one time? If so, how would you explain the fact that they no longer coincide?

Locating the boundary between oceans and continents. Wherever a continental shelf exists, the boundary between the continents' basement rock and the basement rock beneath the oceans is covered by sediment. How then can its location be discovered? How can scientists discover the nature of rocks buried under a layer of sediment?

In Chapters 13 and 14 you found that scientists have learned about the interior of the earth thousands of kilometers below the surface by using seismology. This same approach can be used to learn about layers of rock at the edges of continents and even about layers of rock under the waters of the oceans. An explosive charge is lowered to the ocean floor, and then set off. Vibrations are reflected from the various boundaries in the underlying materials. Seismologists measure the time between the explosion and the return of the reflected waves. By analyzing these measurements, scientists determine the depths of the boundaries between different kinds of rock. Other characteristics of the reflected waves are analyzed in order to obtain information about the rocks themselves.

In *A* of *Figure 17-8* the data obtained from one such series of measurements are shown. The various lines show the depth at which reflections were returned from various boundaries beneath the ocean floor. The numbers show the speed at which the vibrations traveled through the intervening rock. Different speeds indicate different types of rock. A theoretical picture of the interior structure of the earth in this region was made on the basis of these measurements. This picture is shown in *B.*

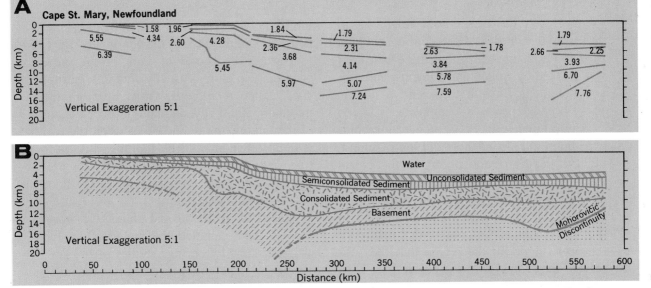

Figure 17-8. One way to study the material of the ocean floor is to analyze the vibrations reflected from various layers of rock when an explosion is set off on the ocean floor. From data obtained in this manner (A), a cross section of the earth's crust may be inferred (B).

In both drawings—*A* and *B*—the vertical distances were enlarged five times compared to the horizontal distances. Without this change of scale, all of the details would be squeezed into such a shallow space it would be impossible to read them. The term "unconsolidated sediment" means loose sand and gravel. "Semiconsolidated sediment" means the same sort of material but packed rather hard, like a mud bank, but not as hard as rock. "Consolidated sediment" means material as hard as sedimentary rock, such as sandstone.

3. The Deep Ocean Floor

A changing concept. Many years ago, soundings of the deep regions of the ocean were few and far between. At that time, many people believed the deep ocean floor was a vast, fairly smooth plain spreading several thousand meters below the surface of the sea.

What reasons would you give in explaining why man's first mental picture of the ocean floor was that of a vast, fairly smooth plain?

Gradually, as more and more information began to accumulate, there was evidence of many elevations on the sea floor that were similar to the mountains on land. In addition, deep canyons were discovered near the outer edges of the continental shelves. These canyons cut through the shelves and back toward shore. Furthermore, soundings taken near the center of the Atlantic Ocean indicated the presence of a long range of submarine mountains extending along the ocean floor in a north-south direction.

As a result of the accumulation of such data, oceanographers began to change their mental picture of the ocean floor. They began

331

to think that the ocean floor might be as varied as the surface of the continents. That is, they began to realize that the ocean floor was marked by valleys and canyons, and hills and mountains. But still, the scientists' picture of the ocean floor was not complete.

Abyssal plains. In 1947, an oceanographic expedition did a very thorough job of sounding the depths of the ocean in the North Atlantic. The scientists of this expedition discovered a vast, very flat plain. Surprisingly enough, this plain seemed to correspond to the ideas held earlier about the nature of the ocean floor. In the region that they observed, they found that the ocean floor is so level that for every thousand meters of horizontal distance there is only a one-meter change in depth. Since 1947, similar flat plains have been discovered in the Indian and Pacific oceans as well as in the Caribbean Sea and the Gulf of Mexico.

These large, flat plains have been given the name *abyssal* (ə bis′əl) *plains.* Their characteristics have been carefully studied. Near the edge of continental shelves, there is a very gradual change in slope of such plains. In these regions, the floor of the ocean very gradually gets more and more steep,

until finally it becomes the continental slope, rising to join the edge of the continental shelf.

Toward the center of each of the large oceans, the picture is usually different. Abrupt rises, called *seamounts,* thrust up from the flat plain. If the abyssal plain borders a chain of mountains, the boundary between the two is quite often marked by foothills, just as is true on the continents. *Figure 17-9* represents two different cross sections of the floor of the Atlantic Ocean.

Materials on the abyssal plains. Oceanographers have sampled the materials on the abyssal plains by coring. Studies of the core samples obtained have revealed that the abyssal plains are covered with sediment.

The fact that the abyssal plains are covered with sediment is to be expected. After all, shells and bones of sea creatures have been sinking to the bottom of the sea for billions of years. Obviously, in this length of time, a thick layer of calcium carbonate would build up. The weight of the material on top would gradually compress the material underneath, resulting in the formation of limestone.

However, a surprising discovery was made. The floors of the abyssal plains are not covered by limestone. Instead, they are covered

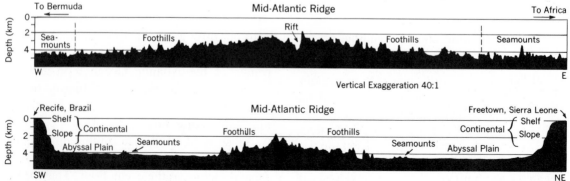

Figure 17-9. These two profiles of the floor of the Atlantic Ocean reveal two somewhat different sets of features of the ocean floor. The profiles are based upon soundings continuously recorded by echo-sounding equipment on the research vessel *Atlantis.*

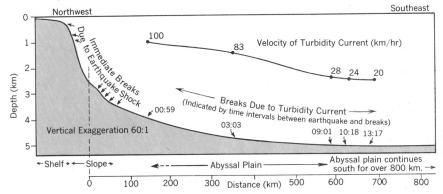

Figure 17-10. A profile of the sea floor in the Grand Banks region of the North Atlantic is shown here. The broken line, if extended downward, would pass through the center of the 1929 earthquake. Cable breaks are indicated, along with the time of each break. Note the exaggeration of the vertical scale.

by sand and gravel and a wide variety of other sediments. Where have these sediments come from? They could not have simply fallen out of the waters of the oceans above. These are sediments typical of those carried into the oceans by rivers. And yet, the abyssal plains are hundreds of miles from the mouths of rivers. The plains extend over hundreds of thousands of square miles. How could sand and gravel have been deposited across such a large area? Consider the abyssal plain in the North Atlantic, for example. It is about 6,000 meters below the ocean's surface. And yet, cores from this section of the ocean floor revealed fragments of plants which grow only in shallow water. How could such things be?

Turbidity currents. The mystery about how the sediments on the abyssal plains were deposited was finally solved in a very unusual manner. Scientists used evidence from the records of international telephone companies. In 1929 an earthquake occurred in the Grand Banks region of the North Atlantic Ocean. This portion of the North Atlantic is crossed by many submarine cables carrying telephone and telegraph signals between Europe and America. As a result of this earthquake, many of the cables were broken. But it was not until 1952, twenty-three years after the earthquake, that two scientists looked over the detailed records of the telegraph companies and understood the significance of what they were studying.

The earthquake that was recorded occurred on November 18, 1929, at 3:32 P.M., Eastern Standard Time. Cables lying on the ocean floor directly above the center of the earthquake were broken immediately. Following that immediate event, other cables farther south were broken. The farther south each cable was from the center of the earthquake, the greater was the time interval between the occurrence of the earthquake and the breaking of the cable. In fact, thirteen hours and seventeen minutes after the earthquake occurred, a cable 680 kilometers away from the center of the earthquake was broken. Scientists noted that not only did breaks occur in cables located progressively farther south but that each of the breaks was at a successively greater depth. The first cables to be broken were high up on the edge of the continental shelf. Next to be broken were those further down the continental slope, and finally those out on the floor of the abyssal plain were broken. (*Figure 17-10.*)

From these records, the scientists reasoned that a vast current of mud and rock must have started out from the region of the earthquake and flowed down the continental slope toward the abyssal plain. The current of mud and rock broke the cables as it went. By carefully noting the time at which each break occurred and the position of each of the cables, scientists were able to determine the manner in which this current moved. They discovered that soon after it started, this current must have been moving with the speed of 100 kilometers per hour. The current slowed gradually as it flowed down the sides of the sloping ocean floor. The current was moving across the abyssal plain at 20 kilometers per hour when it broke the last cable.

The name *turbidity current* has been given to such a flowing stream of mud and rock. The discovery of turbidity currents was the first evidence of the vast currents that flow like rivers across the sea floor. Many of them are caused by earthquakes. Others seem to be related to large rivers. The effect of such currents is to move sediment from the continental shelves down to the deepest parts of the ocean floor. It is in this way that the abyssal plain has been covered with sediment that was at one time part of the continents.

What effects might turbidity currents have on the slopes down which they travel?

4. Submarine Canyons and Mountains

The origin of submarine canyons. In some places, the continental shelf is cut by deep canyons, rather like the Grand Canyon which cuts through the plains of northern Arizona. Many of these submarine canyons are related to rivers. Off the east coast of the United States, for example, a canyon cuts through the continental shelf near the mouth of the Hudson River. Other submarine canyons seem to have been cut by glaciers during the ice ages. Many of the steep-sided, rugged bays called *fiords* (fyôrds) which occur along the coast of Norway have submarine canyons extending out from them to the edge of the continental shelf. These canyons seem to have been cut by glaciers.

But there are many submarine canyons which are not related to rivers and which are not in places where glaciers are known to have existed. How can we account for these submarine canyons? What forces eroded away huge channels in the floor of the sea and cut through the continental shelf? Many scientists believe that they were cut by turbidity currents which originated from earthquakes, much like the turbidity current that was first discovered in the North Atlantic.

In addition to the canyons in the continental shelves and continental slopes, submarine canyons have also been discovered in the deep ocean floor. Scientists are not certain whether they form a continuous system like the valley of a river, or whether they are simply depressions scattered here and there without any connection to each other. The reason for the uncertainty is that not enough soundings are available to make a complete map of the ocean floor.

DO IT YOURSELF

Make a comparison

The submarine canyon in the continental shelf just off the mouth of the Hudson River has been studied extensively by oceanographers. Using various reference books and periodicals, find the depth, length, and width of this submarine canyon. Make a chart on which you compare this submarine canyon with the Grand Canyon in Arizona.

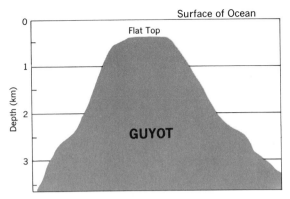

Figure 17-11. This diagram represents a cross section of a typical guyot. The flat top may be from about 500 meters to more than 1,000 meters beneath the ocean's surface. It may be several kilometers across.

The origin of submarine mountains. Numerous mountains rise from the deep ocean floor. Many of these are volcanoes. Some are quite isolated from any other mountains in the ocean. A few of these mountains are high enough so that their peaks are above sea level. Bermuda is the top of one group of ancient submarine volcanoes. See *Figure 17-7.*

There are other mountains which rise thousands of feet from the floor of the oceans but do not quite come up to the surface of the oceans. Surprisingly, many of these have flat tops. Such a flat-topped seamount is called a *guyot* (gī′ət). Guyots appear as if their tops were washed away by waves on the surface of the oceans. Such wave erosion has taken place on many islands in the South Pacific, tending to level the surface of islands that were once very rugged. And yet, the tops of these submarine mountains are several hundred meters below the ocean surface. *(Figure 17-11.)* At this depth, wave action would have little effect.

One theory concerning guyots is that these flat-topped mountains in the Pacific were once at the surface of the sea. The reason that the tops are now below sea level is not known. Possibly, the level of the sea rose following the melting of the ice after the last great ice age. Or perhaps the floor of the ocean has gradually sunk since the time when these mountains were originally raised. Another theory is that the weight of the mountains themselves has caused the ocean floor about them to sink slowly. This would mean that the base of such mountains has gradually pushed its way down toward the earth's mantle, making a depression in the crust. No one can be sure which of these theories is correct. It may well be that some combination of theories is the proper explanation. As with so many other aspects of oceanography, there is much that remains to be investigated about the origin and history of submarine mountains.

Mid-ocean ridges. One of the important features of the ocean basins are the *mid-ocean ridges.* These ridges are long chains of submarine mountains. Such chains of mountains cross the floors of several large oceans. The map in *Figure 17-12* shows these ridges as black lines in the oceans between the continents. The continents are also shown on this map, along with the shallow portions of the ocean, most of which are continental shelves.

The Mid-Atlantic Ridge is the best known of the mid-ocean ridges, and it has been the most carefully studied. On either side of this range of submarine mountains, the ocean is about 5,000 meters deep. The ridge itself is about 1,000 kilometers wide. Like ranges of mountains on land, the Mid-Atlantic Ridge consists of a series of peaks with valleys between them. Many of these peaks rise 3,000 to 4,000 meters above the surrounding ocean floor. In other words, the peaks come within 1,000 to 2,000 meters of the surface of the sea. Some peaks of the Mid-Atlantic Ridge extend above the surface. The Azores and Ascension Island are such peaks.

The mid-ocean ridge in the Pacific is not mapped as well as the Mid-Atlantic Ridge is.

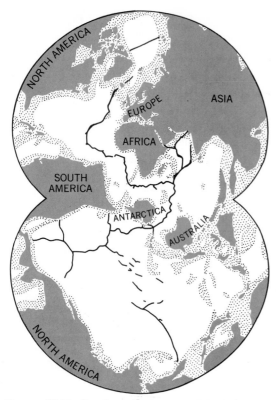

Figure 17-12. On the above map, the dark areas represent land. The dotted areas represent the continental shelves. The black lines represent the mid-ocean ridges. Mid-ocean ridges are long chains of submarine mountains. As indicated on the map, these submarine mountains form a continuous ridge which extends for nearly 64,000 kilometers.

As the map in *Figure 17-12* shows, the mid-ocean ridge in the Pacific seems to be broken up near its southern end into a series of smaller ridges. The Hawaiian Islands lie along the mid-ocean ridge in the Pacific. Many coral islands in the South Pacific may also be a part of this ridge. But as yet, this has not been definitely established.

Along most of their length, the mid-ocean ridges are far from the edges of continents. But near the ends of the ridges, the ridges actually contact the continental regions of the earth's surface. The Mid-Atlantic Ridge goes

through Iceland, and connects to a region of the sea floor that seems to be a continental shelf stretching between Europe and Greenland. The Mid-Indian Ridge is connected to the continents near the base of the Arabian Peninsula and the Red Sea. Portions of the Pacific Ridge appear to be connected to South America and to Central America.

You will notice that in some of these descriptions we have used such words as "appears to be," or "seems to be." The fact that we must use these words of uncertainty is just another example of the incomplete nature of the knowledge which scientists now have about the ocean floor.

Do you believe the time and money spent in learning about the ocean floor is of any benefit to man? If so, how will man benefit? If not, why do you suppose these expenditures are made?

Earthquakes and mid-ocean ridges. Although there is much to be learned about the mid-ocean ridges, one thing is clear. Many regions of the mid-ocean ridges are also regions where shallow earthquakes occur frequently. Shallow earthquakes are earthquakes which occur within 70 kilometers of the earth's surface. See *Figure 13-2*. Scientists reason that the earthquakes must somehow be related to the mid-ocean ridges. Many theories have been suggested to explain this relationship. However, scientists readily admit that their knowledge of the ocean floor is very incomplete. Thus, they are not able to reach any firm conclusions about the nature and causes of the mid-ocean ridges. Nor are they sure of the relationship between the ridges and the earthquakes which frequently occur beneath the ridges. In later chapters, we will describe some theories which have been developed to explain the relationship between earthquakes and mid-ocean ridges.

5. Ocean Currents

Surface currents in the North Atlantic. The portion of the oceans with which we are most familiar is the surface of the water. Winds create waves on this surface. Gravitational interaction between the earth and the moon causes tides to move across the surface of the oceans. Waves and tides are effects which we can observe simply by standing on the shore and watching the ocean water. But there are other phenomena on the surface which we can discover only by sailing away from the shore. Vast systems of ocean currents are such phenomena.

Most of us have heard of the Gulf Stream which flows northward along the eastern edge of the United States. The Gulf Stream is like a river of water moving within the ocean itself. It was discovered many years ago during the early explorations of the Atlantic Ocean.

The Gulf Stream is only a part of a larger pattern of currents. *Figure 17-13* shows the

Figure 17-13. Although surface currents in various parts of the North Atlantic Ocean have been given different names, the overall pattern of these currents is that of a large, clockwise-moving whirlpool.

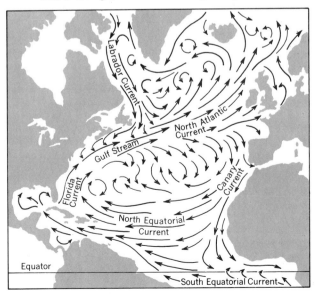

pattern of currents in the Atlantic Ocean. As you can see, this pattern consists of a number of huge, interlocking whirlpools. In the North Atlantic, the Gulf Stream system consists of three segments—the Florida Current, the Gulf Stream proper, and the North Atlantic Current. A part of the North Atlantic Current turns southward near the coast of Europe. Farther south, it is called the Canary Current. The Canary Current, in turn, flows into the North Equatorial Current.

The North Equatorial Current splits into two branches as it approaches the West Indies. One branch flows northward past the Bahama Islands, the other continues westward into the Caribbean Sea, then up into the Gulf of Mexico. The current turns to the east and flows through the Florida Straits. In this region the current is called the Florida Current.

We have traced the path of the water in a complete cycle around the largest whirlpool in the North Atlantic. Early sailors and mapmakers who gave each segment of this whirlpool a different name did not realize that the whole pattern was a single current system.

Other surface currents. In *Figure 17-14* the current patterns in all of the oceans of the world are represented. As you can see, there is a great regularity in the pattern of ocean currents. One large whirlpool occupies the North Atlantic Ocean. It rotates in a clockwise direction. Another whirlpool occupies the South Atlantic Ocean. This whirlpool rotates in a counterclockwise direction.

In the Pacific Ocean, a similar pair of whirlpools exists. In the North Pacific the motion is clockwise, and in the South Pacific, counterclockwise. Even the Indian Ocean has a pair of such large whirlpools, although the subcontinent of India causes some irregularity in the pattern.

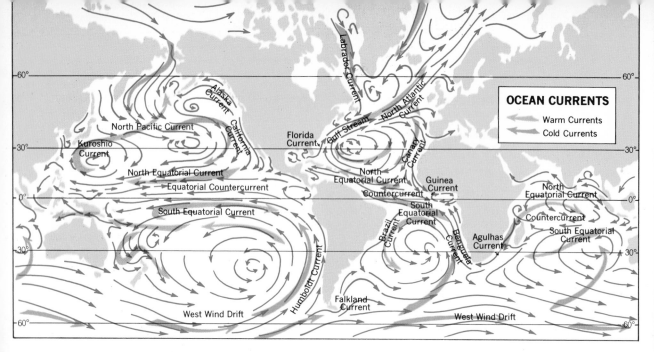

Figure 17-14. This diagram represents the general, world-wide pattern of the motion of the ocean's surface waters. Note the general direction in which currents flow in each hemisphere. Note, too, the general pattern of flow for warm and cold currents.

The patterns in the Pacific Ocean are the most regular and easiest to study. Observe the currents in the Pacific Ocean represented in *Figure 17-14*. Notice that the two large whirlpools—one in the northern region and one in the southern region of the ocean—come closest to each other near the equator. Strangely enough, the currents do not merge together, although the water in each of these current systems is flowing from east to west. Between the two currents there is another current, called the Equatorial Countercurrent, flowing in the opposite direction. Notice, also, that each of the current systems has smaller whirlpools joining it. In the North Pacific, the Alaska Current breaks away from the main whirlpool and rotates in a counterclockwise direction along the coast of Alaska. In the South Pacific, between Australia and New Zealand, another smaller whirlpool is connected to the main current of the South Pacific current system.

How would you explain why the direction of rotation of ocean currents in the Northern Hemisphere is different from that of currents in the Southern Hemisphere?

The interaction of wind and water. How can we account for surface currents? How can the large regular pattern of currents be explained? How do we explain the smaller currents—that is, the small details of the current pattern? To answer these questions we must observe not only the ocean but also the atmosphere above the ocean.

Sailors were probably the first to understand the reason for ocean currents, since they were most familiar with the two aspects of nature which interact to form the currents —the wind and the sea.

A wind blowing over the ocean surface does more than create waves. In fact, waves are usually the result of storm winds which blow only for a few days. Currents are the result of the steady winds that blow almost constantly in some regions of the world. The most famous of these steady winds are the trade winds which blow from east to west near the equator. These steady trade winds, as they blow across the surface of the sea, cause the surface water to move in the same direction in which the wind blows. Thus, the trade winds are responsible for the east-to-west movement of the surface water near the equator.

There are other zones of prevailing winds that help to complete the current pattern. These are the zones of westerly winds in the Northern Hemisphere and in the Southern Hemisphere. The trade winds blow steadily from east to west near the equator. The westerlies blow steadily from west to east in the temperate zones north and south of the equator. See *Figure 18-11.* This combination of winds encourages the development of the large whirlpool patterns in the surface currents of the oceans.

Small currents, such as the Labrador Current and the Alaska Current, result from the interaction of the large currents with the shorelines of the continents and with the ocean floor. If the ocean basins were exactly circular, or perhaps if they had some other very regular shape, the very simple, large whirlpools might be the only currents. But continental shelves and islands cause the currents to break up, forming the smaller whirlpools.

Do you think the surface currents in the ocean have always moved as they move now? If not, what factors might have produced changes?

Deep ocean currents. The surface currents are wind-driven and extend only a few hundred meters below the surface of the water. Are there other currents at greater depths? You have already read about turbidity currents which move across the ocean floor at depths of several thousand meters. However, these currents are irregular. They are often caused by earthquakes. Most of them disappear quickly, within a few hours of their origin. What about regular current patterns in the deep ocean? We would expect such currents to exist. Water which cools in the far north and south polar regions becomes more dense. It would tend to sink and move toward the equator where the water is being warmed by the sun.

In discussing deep ocean currents, we are considering another subject about which much remains to be discovered. However, there is good evidence that there are steady current patterns deep in the ocean. The deep currents interact with the currents on the surface. For example, the Gulf Stream—a surface current—carries warm water from the equatorial region, along the coast of North America, and then on to the northern coast of Europe. At the same time, there is a deep current flowing in the opposite direction, almost directly under the Gulf Stream. This deep current carries cold water from the Arctic region, down toward the equatorial regions. Although other deep currents are known, few of these deep currents have been traced, since following their movement is an extremely difficult task.

It seems that these deep currents are directly related to the surface currents, but the relationship is not yet well understood. It is clear that surface currents are related to the wind systems of the atmosphere. So it would seem that all of the major currents in the ocean are connected to the major winds of the atmosphere. As we said earlier, the exchange of heat and water between the ocean and the atmosphere is directly related to weather patterns all over the earth. Thus, the study of the ocean is directly related to the study of the atmosphere.

Checking Your Knowledge

IMPORTANT IDEAS

1. Detailed study of the earth's most extensive surface feature—the oceans—is difficult because of the great area and depth of the oceans.

2. The ocean floor has such features as continental slopes, submarine canyons, abyssal plains, and mid-ocean ridges.

3. The continental shelves are covered with sediment that appears to have been eroded from the continents.

4. The sediment which covers the abyssal plains appears to have been carried to these areas (probably by turbidity currents) from shallow regions of the oceans.

5. Some submarine canyons are related to rivers, some to glaciers, and some to turbidity currents. Others are of unknown origin.

6. The mid-ocean ridges form an interconnected system of submarine mountains. Some of their peaks are above sea level.

7. The chief factor in producing currents in the ocean appears to be the pattern of winds in the atmosphere.

USING NEW WORDS

Study the terms below. Write the letters *a* through *l* on your paper. Beside each letter describe the corresponding term from the list. Then, prepare a sketch (or a series of sketches) of imaginary portions of the sea. In the sketch (or sketches) use every term from the list, either as a label or in a description of some feature of the sketches.

a. abyssal plain
b. seamount
c. sonar
d. guyot
e. coring device
f. mid-ocean ridge
g. continental shelf
h. basement complex
i. turbidity current
j. continental slope
k. submarine canyon
l. sounding

TEST YOURSELF

Study the test below. On your paper write the numerals *1-10*. After each numeral write the correct response to that part of the test with the corresponding numeral.

1. Measuring the depth of the oceans by lowering a weight tied to a calibrated line is called "taking a _____."

2. The gently sloping floor of those shallow regions of the oceans which border on a continent is called a _____.

3. A sample of material from the ocean floor obtained by forcing a hollow pipe into the ocean floor is called a _____.

4. Undersea earthquakes can cause _____, which are underwater currents capable of moving enormous amounts of sediment along the ocean floor in a short time.

5. Using the technique of echo sounding, scientists have discovered an important feature of the deep ocean floor. Long chains of submarine mountains, called _____, stretch across the floor of almost every large ocean.

6. The floor of the Atlantic Ocean is crossed by a long chain of submarine mountains called the _____.

7. The basement rock of the ocean floor is (*basalt, granite, sedimentary rock*).

8. Large, flat areas of the deep ocean floor are known as (*continental shelves, guyots, abyssal plains*).

9. The largest surface currents in the oceans of the Northern Hemisphere circulate in a (*clockwise, counterclockwise, completely unpredictable*) direction.

10. The most important factor in the formation of surface currents in the water of the oceans appears to be the effect of (*the tides, earthquakes, winds that always blow in the same general direction*).

Extending Your Knowledge

QUESTIONS TO EXPLORE

1. Is there any evidence of volcanic activity on the ocean floor at the present time? If so, give details.

2. Some evidence indicates that the salinity (salt content) of ocean water is increasing with time. How would you explain this?

3. Why, do you suppose, does the salinity of ocean water vary from place to place and from time to time?

4. What sort of educational background do you think is necessary to become an oceanographer? Do you think an oceanographer needs some knowledge of chemistry? Of physics? Of biology? Of mathematics?

5. What is the speed with which sound travels in water? Suppose you are in a ship at a location where the ocean is 10 km deep. How long would it take for sound to travel from your ship to the ocean floor and back to your ship? At this same location, how long do you suppose it would take to measure the depth of the water by lowering a weight attached to a calibrated line?

SOME THINGS TO DO

1. Use a large, flat pan to represent the ocean and a fan to represent the prevailing winds. Show how surface currents are formed. Some sawdust or chalkdust sprinkled on the surface of the water will aid in detecting any current flow.

2. Make a study of how ocean waves shape a shoreline. Use modeling clay or plaster of Paris to make models of various types of shorelines and of some features of shorelines which are formed by the action of waves.

3. Make a model of a sloping ocean floor. Place an empty aquarium on the table. Raise one end of the aquarium by placing a book or a block of wood under it. Add tap water to the aquarium until the bottom is covered.

Demonstrate that differences in salinity can cause currents. Make a concentrated solution of salt water. Add a few drops of ink or food coloring to color the solution. Slowly pour the salt solution into the shallow end of the aquarium. Observe and describe its flow. Does the salt solution gradually become diffused throughout the "ocean"?

Demonstrate sedimentation. Pour a well-mixed sludge of water, fine sand, and clay onto the sloping bottom to simulate a muddy river flowing into the ocean. Observe and describe the resulting sedimentation.

Devise and conduct demonstrations in which you demonstrate turbidity currents and sediment shifts.

CHALLENGES IN SCIENCE

1. Predict the relationship between the rate of sedimentation and the salinity of water. Devise and conduct experiments to see if you can verify your prediction.

2. Make a detailed study of the Mediterranean Sea. Find answers to the following questions. How does its salinity compare to that of the Atlantic Ocean? What causes the currents flowing between the Mediterranean Sea and the Atlantic Ocean? Is the amount of water flowing into the Mediterranean Sea equal to the amount flowing out? Explain.

3. Calculate the area covered by oceans. Assume the diameter of the earth to be 12,750 km and that the oceans cover 70.8 per cent of its surface. After you have calculated the area, estimate the average depth of the oceans. Use your calculation and your estimate to calculate the volume of water in the oceans. What is the mass of this volume of water?

CHAPTER 18

Clouds often indicate conditions of the atmosphere.

The Atmosphere

You know, of course, that a great ocean of water covers more than 70 per cent of the earth's surface. You are about to begin a study of another great ocean— the atmosphere. The atmosphere is sometimes referred to as the ocean of air that completely envelops the earth. To man, who lives at the bottom of this ocean, the atmosphere is vitally important. During the day the atmosphere shields us from much of the radiation emitted by the sun. At night the atmosphere acts as a blanket, holding in some of the heat that the earth absorbed from the sun during the day. On an earth without an atmosphere, the change in temperature from day to night would be unbearable.

What is the atmosphere made of? Is it the same everywhere about the earth? Why does the atmosphere move as it does? As you study Chapter 18, you will discover the answers to these questions. You will also discover that many factors interact to produce the weather on our earth's surface. The weather, of course, is nothing more than the condition of the earth's atmosphere at a particular place and at a particular time.

Naturally, you will not become an expert meteorologist through your experiences in studying this one chapter. Hopefully, however, you will discover some of the fundamental processes that produce the winds and other atmospheric conditions. Perhaps you may decide to continue your study of the atmosphere and work toward a career in some aspect of meteorology.

1. The Composition of the Atmosphere

What makes up the atmosphere? The atmosphere, as you know, is the layer of gas that surrounds the earth. This gas is, in reality, a mixture of gases and is usually called air. To be more precise, however, the atmosphere consists of more than just air. Water vapor and dust particles are also present in amounts that vary from place to place and from time to time.

Up to an altitude of about 50 km, the composition of clean, dry air—that is, the atmosphere without water and dust—is the same all over the world. As you can see in *Figure 18-1,* the most abundant constituent of dry air is nitrogen. Next in abundance is oxygen. Oxygen is one element that is essential for life, and this essential element makes up about 21 per cent of atmosphere. Examine *Figure 18-1* to see what other gases are present and what percentage of the total volume of dry air is represented by each gas.

Air and water vapor are in the gaseous state—that is, the individual particles of these substances are molecules. The dust consists of solid particles made up of many molecules. These particles are much larger than molecules, although they are small enough to be suspended in the atmosphere and to stay suspended for long periods of time. Clouds, which are considered as part of the atmos-phere, are composed of tiny water droplets or ice crystals. Like each dust particle, each droplet or ice crystal contains many molecules. However, the size of each droplet or crystal is small enough that it stays suspended. Unlike the dust, the droplets and ice crystals often become larger and fall to earth when the atmospheric conditions change.

The density of the atmosphere. The atmosphere is most dense near the surface of the earth. If you were to start at the earth's surface and climb an imaginary stairway into the atmosphere, you would find that the atmosphere would be more rarefied as you traveled farther and farther from the surface of the earth. Since the density gradually becomes less and less, it is impossible to say precisely where the atmosphere stops and space begins.

Under normal conditions at sea level, a cubic centimeter of air contains 2.7×10^{19} molecules of gas. The density, in terms of molecules per cubic centimeter, becomes steadily less with increasing altitude. For example, at an altitude of 100 km, there are 2×10^{12} molecules per cubic centimeter. At an altitude of 200 km, a cubic centimeter of air contains 5×10^9 molecules. At 300 kilometers, the atmosphere contains only 4×10^8 molecules per cubic centimeter. At distances

Figure 18-1. The composition of dry air is represented in this diagram. Although air is a mixture of many gases, two gases account for 99 per cent of the volume of dry air.

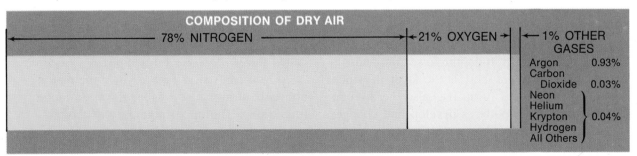

of several million kilometers from the earth —that is, out in space between the planets— there are approximately 1×10^3 molecules of gas in every cubic centimeter. Even between the galaxies, space is not completely empty. Scientists think that intergalactic space con- tains, on the average, about 1 molecule per cubic centimeter.

In what ways have scientists obtained all the information they have about the upper layers of the earth's atmosphere?

DO IT YOURSELF

Draw a graph

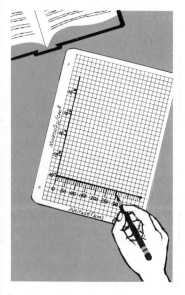

On a piece of graph paper, plot the number of molecules per cubic centimeter of air against altitude above the earth's surface. On the vertical scale, indicate the number of molecules by writing powers of ten from 10^0 at the bottom to 10^{20} near the top. Along the horizontal axis, mark altitudes from 0 (sea level) on the left to 300 km near the right. Use the information in this book to plot points on the graph. If possible, connect the points with a smooth curve.

Using the curve you drew, tell how many molecules there would be in a cubic centimeter of the atmosphere at an altitude of 10 km. At an altitude of 50 km. Is your curve useful in predicting the number of molecules per cubic centimeter that would be present at an altitude of 10 km below sea level? 700 km above sea level? How is this curve related to the one in *Figure 12-6* on page 226?

The layers of the atmosphere. As you will recall, the interior of the earth seems to be divided into separate layers by changes in the physical properties of the earth's material. In a similar manner, the atmosphere seems divided into separate layers by changes in properties of the air. See *Figure 18-2*.

Temperature is one property scientists use as a basis for describing the layers of the atmosphere. In a naming system based on temperature measurements, the lowest layer, extending from sea level up to an altitude of about 10 to 15 km, is called the *troposphere* (trop'ə sfir). Measurements made of the temperatures in the troposphere reveal that the higher the altitude, the lower the temperature. The troposphere is the layer in which almost all clouds form. It is also the layer in which weather patterns develop and change.

Between the troposphere and the region above it is a boundary called the *tropopause* (trop'ə pôz). The tropopause, however, is not a fixed boundary at a constant altitude. For instance, over the poles the altitude of the tropopause is about 10 km. Over the equator, however, the tropopause is about 15 km above the earth's surface.

The region directly above the tropopause is called the *stratosphere* (strat'ə sfir). In this layer of the atmosphere, the temperature is almost constant and changes only a very small amount with altitude. The stratosphere continues up to an altitude of about 30 km. The upper boundary of the stratosphere is called the *stratopause* (strat'ə pôz).

As you can see in *Figure 18-2*, the region above the stratopause is called the *mesosphere* (mes'ə sfir). The upper boundary of the mesosphere—called the *mesopause* (mes′ə pôz) —is about 80 km above the earth's surface. In the mesosphere the temperature fluctuates. From an altitude of 30 km to one of 50 km, the temperature increases. Then there is a reversal of this trend at 50 km, and the temperature drops as the altitude increases.

Figure 18-2. The diagram below indicates the relative positions of some layers of the atmosphere. The white line, used with the temperature scale across the bottom, indicates the temperature at various altitudes.

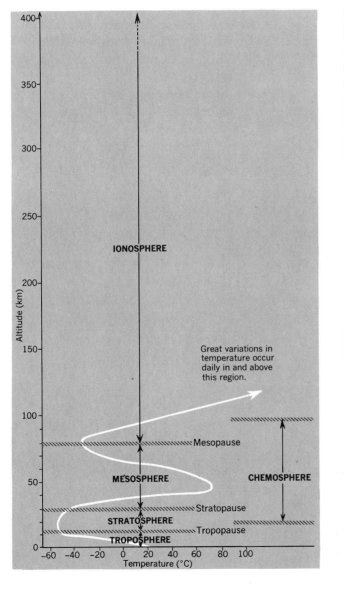

Above the mesosphere and extending out to an altitude of 400 to 500 km is a region called the *ionosphere* (ī on′ə sfir). The ionosphere is so named because of its special properties. These properties are not related to temperature conditions. In the ionosphere the molecules and atoms are broken down electrically. That is, atoms are broken apart due to the action of radiation from the sun. In the process, electrons and ions are produced. Hence, the name ionosphere.

The freely floating ions and electrons in the ionosphere form a slightly conducting layer of gas. This layer reflects low frequency radio waves. For this reason, it is possible to send certain radio signals great distances over the earth. See *Figure 18-3*. The signal sent out from the transmitter travels to the ionosphere. The ionosphere reflects the signal to the earth. When the signal strikes the earth, it is reflected back to the ionosphere. Under

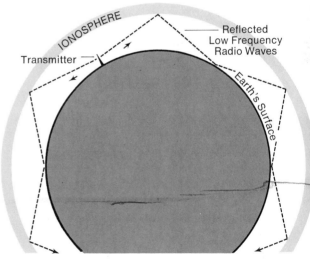

Figure 18-3. Through a series of reflections, radio signals may be transmitted great distances—perhaps around the earth. The ionosphere's thickness and altitude are exaggerated in this diagram. The pattern of reflections depends on atmospheric conditions. Thus, the pattern varies from time to time.

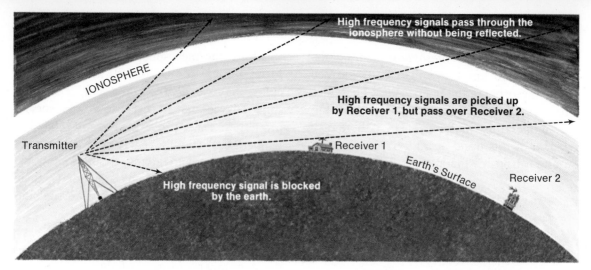

High frequency signals pass through the ionosphere without being reflected.

IONOSPHERE

High frequency signals are picked up by Receiver 1, but pass over Receiver 2.

Transmitter

Receiver 1

Earth's Surface

Receiver 2

High frequency signal is blocked by the earth.

Figure 18-4. Television signals are sent out in all directions from a transmitting tower. As the dashed lines indicate, the signals picked up by receiving antennas are signals that travel in a straight line from the transmitter to the receiver.

certain conditions the signal could be reflected several times, traveling a great distance. Perhaps the signal could travel all the way around the earth and back to the station that first sent it out.

Very high frequency signals penetrate through the ionosphere. They are not reflected. Television signals have a very high frequency, and that is why it is very difficult to receive good television signals unless you are in a direct line with the transmitting antenna. Television signals are electromagnetic waves, just as light waves are. They travel in straight lines, just as light waves do. Only those signals which travel directly from the transmitter to the receiver are picked up. Signals directed lower are blocked by the earth. Those directed higher pass through the ionosphere without being reflected. Thus, the ionosphere does not "bounce" television signals around the curvature of the earth as it does radio signals. (*Figure 18-4.*)

How do communications satellites, such as Echo *and* Telstar, *function? Why are such satellites necessary?*

The *chemosphere* (kem′ə sfir) is another layer of the atmosphere to be considered. This layer includes the mesosphere and portions of both the ionosphere and the stratosphere. (*Figure 18-2.*) The boundaries of the chemosphere are not determined by temperature measurements. Instead, the chemosphere is so named because many chemical reactions take place, changing the molecules of gas in this region. In some reactions, molecules break down into atoms. For example, a molecule of water vapor breaks down into two hydrogen atoms and an oxygen atom. A molecule of oxygen, which consists of two atoms of oxygen linked together, breaks down into separate oxygen atoms that are no longer connected.

In other reactions, atoms combine to form molecules. Several types of reactions combining oxygen atoms and nitrogen atoms take place in the chemosphere. For example, molecules containing one atom each of nitrogen and oxygen are formed. Molecules which contain an atom of nitrogen and two atoms of oxygen are also formed. Ozone—a molecular form of oxygen in which each molecule contains three atoms of oxygen (O_3)—is also formed in reactions occurring in this region. Ozone molecules are rare near the surface of the earth because ozone is not formed in any great quantities here. Furthermore, those ozone molecules that are formed near the earth's surface soon break apart. The oxygen atoms then combine, either with other elements to form oxides, or with each other to form ordinary molecular oxygen (O_2).

The layers which determine the weather. There are many aspects of the atmosphere which would make interesting subjects of study. In this chapter, we will concentrate on the lower portion of the atmosphere—namely, the troposphere and the stratosphere. It is in these layers, and particularly in the troposphere, that most of the interactions take place which affect the weather. In fact, meteorologists often refer to the troposphere as the primary "heat engine" that exchanges energy between the earth's surface and the atmosphere. In the remaining portions of this chapter, you will find out some of the fundamental processes in the operation of this heat engine.

2. Wind

What makes the wind blow? This is a question that almost every child asks before he is five years old. It seems to be a very simple question and one that should have a very simple answer. Basically, the answer is simple. That is, scientists can explain, in general, why winds blow. But, when we look at the details of any specific wind pattern, the answer is much more complicated.

The motion of the air—in other words, the wind—and all of the results of this motion are the subject of meteorology, the science of the weather. Meteorologists study weather conditions over the earth. This study has a special problem which does not affect the geologist or the astronomer. Weather conditions change rapidly. In fact, in most cases the meteorologist cannot even collect his data before the weather has changed. Even if data could be collected quickly, carrying out the calculations needed to analyze the data requires some time. Therefore, a new situation could arise before the old situation is analyzed. So, when you hear the weather forecaster predicting the next day's weather,

you must realize that he is really presenting a rough approximation. If only he could stop the clock, take two or three weeks to collect data, and spend two or three months more to analyze it, he could tell you more precisely what tomorrow's weather will be like. Unfortunately, nature will not wait.

Figure 18-5. Making accurate weather predictions requires considerable training and the availability of data from a widespread network of weather stations.

There are many difficulties in understanding and predicting the details of weather. However, meteorologists have gained a broad understanding of the basic forces that cause the motion of the air. This understanding has, in turn, led to an understanding of many phenomena which are associated with the motion of the air. For example, as we mentioned earlier, there is a simple answer to the question of why winds blow. Winds blow because different portions of the atmosphere are at different temperatures. When air is heated, it expands. Thus, warm air is less dense than cold air. Portions of the atmosphere that are comparatively warm tend to rise to a higher altitude. In regions where the atmosphere is comparatively cold, the air is comparatively dense. Thus, the cold air tends to descend to lower altitudes.

As warm air rises, it leaves a partial vacuum—or an area of low pressure—in the region from which it rises. Air moves in to replace the air that has ascended. Thus, wind is created. In contrast, cool air descends. An area of high pressure is formed beneath the descending air. Wind is created as air is pushed away from beneath the descending air. Thus, a difference in the temperatures of air masses is the fundamental cause of wind.

What advances in technology have taken place in recent years that enable meteorologists to obtain and process weather data more rapidly?

FIND OUT BY TRYING

Materials you will need: electric fan, punk or incense

Position the electric fan so that when the fan operates it will provide a current of air which moves straight up. CAUTION: Make certain the fan is adequately screened. With the fan in position, use the smoke from lighted punk or incense to investigate the direction of air currents in the room. What is the overall pattern of circulation in the room? What are some factors which affect or interfere with the pattern of circulation?

If possible, devise a way to support the fan near the ceiling so that it produces a downward-flowing current of air. What changes can you detect in the overall pattern of currents?

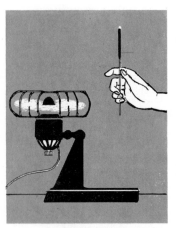

Heating the atmosphere. How does a body of air become warmer than the air around it? Of course, the sun is the ultimate source of the energy which warms the atmosphere. However, the atmosphere is not heated to any great extent by the direct rays of the sun. Of the total amount of the sun's radiation reaching the earth, only about one sixth is absorbed by the atmosphere. One third is reflected into space from the clouds and from the earth's surface. The remaining one half is absorbed by the water, rock, and soil at the earth's surface. In absorbing this energy, the earth's surface is warmed, and some heat is transferred directly to that portion of the atmosphere in contact with the earth's surface. In addition, the warmed surface radiates energy away in the form of infrared radiation which is absorbed by the atmosphere. Thus, air is warmed more by energy coming from the earth than by energy coming directly from the sun.

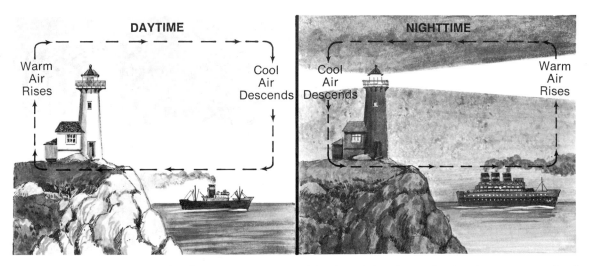

Warm
Air
Rises

Cool
Air
Descends

Cool
Air
Descends

Warm
Air
Rises

Figure 18-6. In coastal areas, unequal heating of the air over land and water causes local winds which change direction from day to night. Which diagram, would you say, represents a sea breeze? Which represents a land breeze?

You can see, then, that if a particular area of the earth's surface is slightly warmer than surrounding areas, the air above the warm area also tends to be warmer than the surrounding air. A common example of this phenomenon occurs along the seacoast. In the daytime, the radiant energy of sunlight causes the land to warm up more rapidly than the water. This unequal heating results because the solid surface of the earth is affected differently by incoming radiation than water is. If land areas and water areas are exposed to the same sunlight, the surface of the land will become warmer than the water.

As the land becomes warmer than the water offshore, the air above the land becomes warmer than the air above the water. The warm air expands, and its density decreases. Soon, the air above the land begins to rise. The air above the ocean moves toward the land to fill the space left by the rising air. At the same time, cooler air above the ocean —being more dense than warm air—descends toward the surface. The cycle is completed when the warm air which rose from the land to a high altitude moves out over the ocean,

cools, and begins to fall back toward the surface, as shown in *Figure 18-6*.

After sunset, the land cools more quickly than the ocean. After the sun has been down for an hour or two, the land is cooler than the water offshore. The air above the land becomes cooler than the air above the ocean. The daytime pattern of circulation is now reversed. The cool air descends over the land, moves out toward the ocean, and rises above the ocean, as shown in *Figure 18-6*.

The planetary winds. The effect of unequal heating and cooling of land and water occurs over the entire surface of the earth. The surface of the earth is warmer at the equator than it is near the poles. We would expect, therefore, that warm air would rise near the equator and cold air would descend toward the poles. If this were to happen, a global circulation pattern would be set up. As a matter of fact, this does happen. The result is a large, general, wind pattern over the whole earth. The winds that make up this pattern are called the *planetary winds*.

If the only factor involved in producing this pattern were the unequal heating between

349

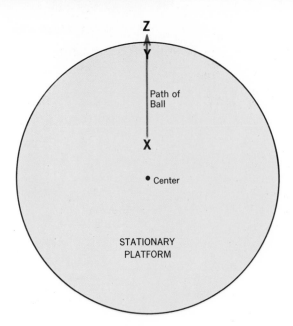

Figure 18-7. A ball rolled from X toward Z follows a straight path, passing over Y.

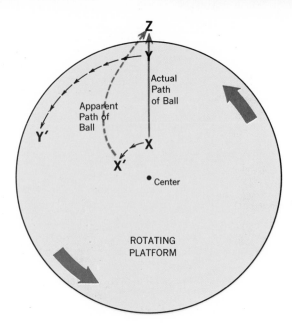

Figure 18-8. Viewed from a rotating platform, a ball appears to follow a curved path in going from X to Z.

the poles and the equator, the pattern would be very simple. However, there are three complications that cause the overall pattern of winds to be somewhat irregular. One is that the earth has seasons. Thus, the portion of the earth that is receiving the direct rays of the sun and is being warmed to the greatest extent is not always the portion of the earth nearest the equator. When it is summer in the Northern Hemisphere, a region north of the equator is receiving the most heat from the sun. When it is winter in the Northern Hemisphere, it is a region south of the equator which is warmest. Thus, the pattern of winds has a regular variation, moving north and south as the seasons change.

A second complication is that the earth is separated into oceans and continents. As you know, the land on the continents reacts to sunlight differently than does the water in the oceans. Therefore, the air above the continents is heated at a different rate than is the air above the oceans. This difference in heating rates affects the planetary winds.

A third complication is the rotation of the earth. The rotation of the earth causes an effect called the *Coriolis* (kôr′i ō′lis) *effect*. The Coriolis effect must be considered in any phenomenon that involves motion over the earth's surface.

Explaining the Coriolis effect. To understand how the rotation of the earth affects the movement of air, or anything else, imagine that you are standing on a platform, such as a stationary merry-go-round. See *Figure 18-7*. From your position—marked X— suppose you roll a ball across the platform, over Y, and directly toward the position marked Z.

Now suppose the platform is rotating, as in *Figure 18-8*. From the position marked X, you again roll the ball over Y toward Z. Again the ball will follow a straight line as it moves from X to Z. However, in the time it takes the ball to get from X to Z, the platform will have rotated so that X is at X′ and Y is at Y′. From your vantage point on the rotating merry-go-round, the ball would appear to

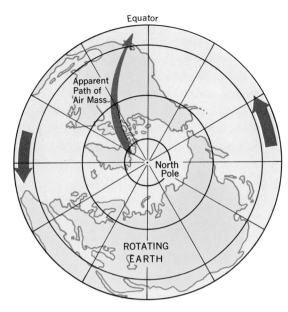

Figure 18-9. In the Northern Hemisphere, moving air is deflected in a clockwise manner.

have followed a curved path, apparently curving to the right of Y and to the left of Z.

Next, imagine the rotating merry-go-round is the earth as viewed from a position directly above the North Pole. Imagine the ball to be a mass of air moving from near the North Pole toward the equator. It is as if the air were moving across the surface of a spherical merry-go-round. From the point of view of one of us, riding this spherical merry-go-round, the moving air would be deflected in a clockwise manner, as shown in *Figure 18-9*. If we were in the Southern Hemisphere, the effect would result in the air mass being deflected in a counterclockwise manner.

Another way to think of the Coriolis effect is this. The earth rotates on its axis once a day. The circumference of the earth at the equator is about 25 thousand miles. Therefore, a point on the surface of the earth at the equator is moving through space in an easterly direction at about 1,000 miles per hour. The atmosphere rotates with the earth, so the air above any point on the earth's

surface tends to move with the same rate of speed as the earth below it. At either the North Pole or the South Pole, however, the speed of a point on the surface is zero, since, with respect to the spinning earth, the poles do not move. Halfway between the poles and the equator, at latitude 45°, a point on the surface of the earth (and the air above that point) is moving to the east with a speed of about 700 miles per hour.

Now suppose that you plan to take off in a rocket ship from a point at latitude 45° N, say a little bit to the north of Bangor, Maine. Suppose your rocket ship is aimed so that, after being launched, the rocket will head south toward the equator. Although you cannot detect your eastward motion, you are moving eastward at 700 miles per hour before you are launched. Now, your rocket is launched and heads toward the equator. How will the surface of the earth look when you arrive at the equator? When you left your launching pad at latitude 45° N, both you and the surface of the earth on which you rested had an eastward component of velocity of 700 miles per hour. As you come down over the equator, you will still be moving eastward at the rate of 700 miles per hour. However, the surface of the earth at the equator is moving eastward at more than 1,000 miles per hour. As you look down, the surface appears to you to be heading to the east at a rate of 300 miles per hour. However, from the point of view of the people standing on the surface watching you descend, you appear to be moving toward the west with a speed of 300 miles per hour. The apparent westward component of your motion is a result of the Coriolis effect.

Just as the imaginary rocket was affected by the Coriolis effect, a moving mass of air would be affected. Thus, winds are strongly influenced by the Coriolis effect. Scientists have found that any mass of air moving in any direction and at any place on the surface of the earth (except directly over the equator) will be subject to the Coriolis effect. In the Northern Hemisphere, winds will always be turned toward the right of the direction in which they are moving. In the Southern Hemisphere, the effect is reversed. The winds will be turned toward the left.

The global pattern of winds. The overall pattern of winds is complicated by the Coriolis effect, the earth's seasons, and the separation of the earth's surface into oceans and continents. Suppose we consider each of the complications in turn. We start with a hypothetical situation. Imagine that the earth is not spinning. There is no night-to-day variation of temperature. Nor is there any temperature difference between oceans and continents. Imagine, also, that most of the heat coming to the earth comes in near the equator and that no heat comes in at either of the poles. In this situation, air would rise near the equator, where the surface of the earth is warmest, and would sink near the poles, where the earth is coldest. In order for this motion to continue, the air which rises

over the equator must move to the polar regions. Also, the air descending near the poles must move to the equator. Thus, in this imaginary situation, air moves along the earth's surface from the poles toward the equator, and from the equator to the poles at high altitude. There would be one continuous loop of moving air in each hemisphere, as shown in *A* of *Figure 18-10*.

Now suppose we add a complication. We know the earth to be spinning on its axis once a day. This rotation causes the Coriolis effect. A detailed explanation of the resulting complex pattern of circulation is too involved to be given here. However, the pattern produced is represented in *B* of *Figure 18-10*. As you can see, the simple pattern of one big loop of air rising at the equator and descending at the poles is changed into three "cells" of circulation.

At the equator, the air tends to rise, creating an area of low pressure. In this region, winds seldom blow across the earth's surface. This is a region of calms called the *doldrums,* made famous in many sea stories and poems. At latitudes 30° N and 30° S, descending air produces a region of generally high pressure.

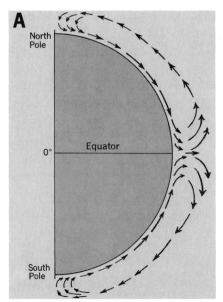 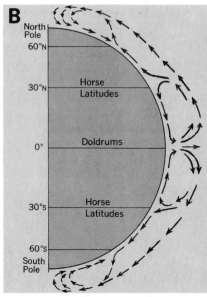

Figure 18-10. If the earth were not rotating, and if temperature differences resulted only from differences in latitude, the circulation of air could be represented by arrows such as those in A. But the earth does rotate, and there are temperature differences. In B, the arrows represent a more accurate cross-sectional view of the pattern of air circulation about the earth.

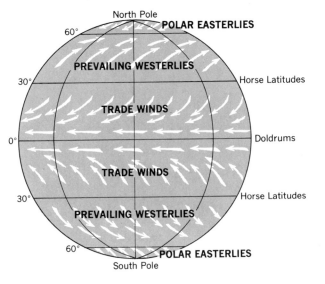

Figure 18-11. The arrows indicate the usual direction of winds over the earth's surface. Note that winds are deflected clockwise in the Northern Hemisphere and counterclockwise in the Southern Hemisphere.

This is another area of calms, called the *horse latitudes*. At latitudes 60° N and 60° S, there is another area of ascending air (low pressure), and at the poles there is descending air (high pressure).

Now let us consider the motion of air along the earth's surface—that is, the actual winds that blow in various regions. Keep in mind that the Coriolis effect deflects winds in the Northern Hemisphere to the right and winds in the Southern Hemisphere to the left. See

Figure 18-11. Air moving along the earth's surface from the horse latitudes toward the equator is deflected to the west. These are the *trade winds*. Winds blowing from the horse latitudes toward the poles are deflected to the east, producing winds that are known as the *prevailing westerlies*. (The direction assigned to a wind is the direction the wind comes from. Thus, as you face into the wind, the direction you are facing is the direction you assign to the wind.) Of course, the air descending at the poles can move only one way—that is, toward the equator. In both hemispheres, the Coriolis effect deflects this air movement toward the west, causing east winds called the *polar easterlies*.

The wind patterns over the earth do not always exist in the neat, orderly manner we have just described. Remember, there are factors other than the Coriolis effect which must be considered. The fact that the earth's axis is tilted in relation to the plane of its orbit about the sun results in seasonal changes in the wind patterns. In *Figure 18-12* a comparison is made between the wind patterns over the Atlantic Ocean in the winter and the summer. You can see that as the seasons change, the general, overall pattern of winds stays the same. However, the whole pattern moves north or south.

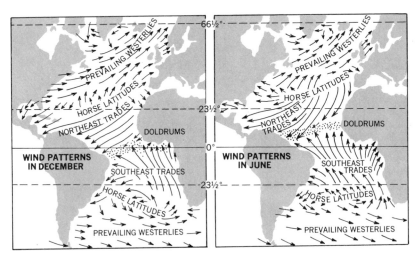

Figure 18-12. The overall pattern of winds does not change as the seasons change. However, the pattern does shift slightly to the north in the summer and to the south in the winter. This shift is especially noticeable in the change in the position of the doldrums, represented by the dotted area.

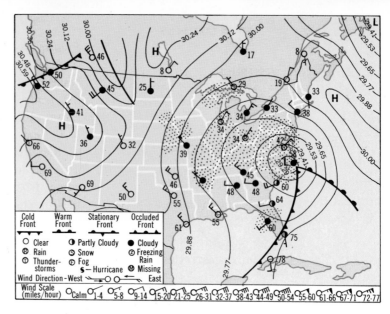

Figure 18-13. Weather maps contain much information. The legend of the map shown indicates the meanings of the various symbols. Note the curved lines, called isobars, which indicate atmospheric pressure. Isobars connect points reporting equal atmospheric pressure. Notice that the wind velocity (speed and direction) varies greatly from one place to another, creating local wind patterns. Note, too, that local wind patterns differ from the general, global pattern illustrated in *Figure 18-11.*

As you already know, land heats up and cools off more easily than water. In the winter, land masses are colder than the neighboring ocean water. The air above the continents tends to descend and blow out toward the sea. Of course, in the summer this trend is reversed. However, local features, such as mountains and large lakes, influence the flow of air. For this reason, wind patterns are usually more complicated over the land than they are over the sea. The prevailing air currents that were just described are often broken up over the continents. Smaller wind patterns develop, as shown in *Figure 18-13.*

From your own experience, can you give examples of local air disturbances that have occurred in your vicinity?

DO IT YOURSELF

Make a report on monsoons

From various earth science and meteorology books, gather as much information as you can about monsoons. What are monsoons? What causes them? What country is famous for its monsoons? Is it the only country where monsoons occur? If not, where else do they occur? Organize your information into a report that you can present to the class. Use maps and diagrams in presenting your report.

3. Storms

Changes in prevailing winds. So far, we have discussed only the prevailing wind patterns over the surface of the earth. What does the term "prevailing" mean? You can think of it this way. Suppose at a particular spot on the earth's surface we measure and record the velocity of the wind at regular intervals, say twice a day, over a long period of time. (Velocity—as you may already know—includes both speed and direction.) The average of the velocities you observe represents the most common wind speed and direction for that locality. Such an average, obtained from measurements taken over many years, is the prevailing wind.

You know from experience that the velocity of the wind frequently differs from the average. Unusual disturbances in the atmosphere are called *storms*. Sometimes when a storm develops, the condition of the atmosphere—especially of the wind—can change spectacularly. The change may be in speed, in direction, or both. In the tropics, for example, the prevailing winds are the trade winds. The usual wind speed is 10 to 20 miles per hour. But in a hurricane, wind speeds are often well over 100 miles per hour. Other examples can be observed in other parts of our country. Over most of the United States, the prevailing winds are the westerlies. But, during a thunderstorm, the winds can come from any direction. Furthermore, the speed of these winds can vary greatly.

The problem of observing weather. In a sense, the problem of understanding the weather is directly opposite to the problem of understanding the earth's interior. Geophysicists studying the earth's interior have an extremely difficult time getting data. They can never observe the objects of their investigation directly. Nevertheless, they have some reason to believe that the earth's interior changes very, very slowly. They can be pretty certain that things will be pretty much the same tomorrow as they were yesterday.

In contrast, the meteorologist can observe and measure all of the factors that interest him. Of course, he may have difficulty collecting information from distant places. But, if he wishes to go to enough trouble, he can make whatever observations and measurements he requires. Usually, however, the subject of his investigation changes very rapidly. Before he can gather enough data to describe the weather, the weather has changed. Nevertheless, through their studies of the weather, meteorologists have gained some knowledge of the nature of storms.

Who, do you think, would be able to make predictions in their own field of study that are more reliable—geophysicists or meteorologists? Justify your answer.

How do storms develop? Fundamentally, the reason for storm winds is the same as the reason for any other kind of wind. That is, one portion of the atmosphere is warmer than a neighboring portion. The warmer portion tends to rise, and the cooler portion tends to sink. At the earth's surface, of course, the cooler air cannot sink. Instead, it moves over to take the place of the rising warm air. At high altitudes, the warm air moves over to take the place of the descending cool air. This common circulation pattern is the fundamental basis for all wind. Keep in mind that the atmosphere is three-dimensional. When air moves over to replace other air it can move in any direction, just as when you pour too much milk into a glass, the milk flows out over the rim in all directions.

To see how temperature differences affect the motion of air in the troposphere, suppose we imagine that we have a very special kind of balloon. The balloon is made of material that is weightless. The balloon will stretch easily, offering no resistance when the air inside of it expands. The balloon will collapse when the air inside contracts. Thus, we have an imaginary, ideal, weightless, perfectly elastic balloon. Now suppose that we place one cubic meter of air in this elastic balloon. Suppose, too, that the air we use is from near the surface of the ground outside your school. The pressure and temperature of the air inside the balloon are the same as those of the air outside.

After filling the balloon at ground level, imagine that we carry the balloon up to the second floor, 3 meters higher than the point at which we filled it. What will happen to the air in the balloon?

As you probably know, an increase in altitude results in a decrease in pressure. Since we have increased our altitude by 3 meters, the atmospheric pressure on the balloon is somewhat less, and the balloon will expand to equalize the pressure of the air inside and outside of the balloon. In the lower portion of the troposphere, an increase of 3 meters in altitude causes a 0.04 per cent decrease in pressure. Thus, when we increase the altitude of the balloon, the gas in the balloon will expand very slightly. As it expands, the gas will cool very slightly. As a matter of fact, the expansion that results from a 3-meter increase in altitude will cause the gas to become 0.03°C cooler.

We know that our balloon adjusts immediately to compensate for pressure differences —no matter how small—between the air inside the balloon and the air outside the balloon. Thus, we know that the pressure inside the balloon will exactly match the pressure outside it. But the temperature inside the balloon could be different from the temperature outside it, since the balloon prevents the outside air from mixing with the air inside. Thus, it is possible that the air inside our balloon is slightly warmer than the air outside. If so, the density of the air inside the balloon is less than the density of the air outside, since a warm gas is less dense than the same cool gas at the same pressure. According

to Archimedes' principle, there will be a buoyant force acting on the balloon, tending to make it rise still farther. Of course, the force is extremely small, since we are talking about very small differences in temperature. Nevertheless, the force is not zero, and the warmer air in the balloon would tend to rise still higher.

Suppose the balloon rises another 3 meters. Once more the pressure in the balloon drops by 0.04 per cent because the atmospheric pressure at this slightly higher altitude is decreased by 0.04 per cent. The decrease in pressure causes further expansion of the air in the balloon. This, in turn, causes the gas in the balloon to become cooler by 0.03°C. But, if the air outside the balloon is colder than that inside, the outside air will still be more dense than the air inside. There will still be a buoyant force tending to make the balloon rise. As long as such a temperature difference exists, the balloon filled with air will continue to rise.

Now let us return once more to the ground. Set aside the balloon for the moment and just think about a mass of air. Suppose something starts this mass of air moving upward. What will happen to this rising mass of air? The rising mass of air will behave exactly the same as the mass of air inside our imaginary balloon did. As the air rises, it will expand and cool. But if the air around it is colder still, the upward-moving air will continue rising at an ever-increasing rate. In fact, all the air in the vicinity of this rising mass will also begin to rise. There will be a strong column of rising air, a powerful updraft. As air rises from the earth's surface, air from the surrounding regions will move in to take its place. Air will be moving from all directions toward the base of the rising column of air.

But now we must remember that air does not move across the ground in a straight line. As air moves across the ground toward the

Figure 18-14. In this photograph, taken from a very high altitude, the clouds associated with a hurricane illustrate the swirling motion around the rising column of air at the hurricane's center.

base of the rising column, the Coriolis effect will cause its path to be deflected. This will happen to all of the air moving across the ground, regardless of the direction in which it is moving. The result of this deflection will be a whirlpool effect near the ground, and about the center of the rising air column. Some of the air circling the base will finally move into the center of the rising column. Once in the center, this air will also begin to rise, swirling as it goes. Under these conditions—that is, when the temperature of the air surrounding a mass of rising air stays lower than that of the rising air itself—the atmosphere is said to be *unstable*.

Some types of storms. By now, you probably have in mind the phenomenon we are describing. This phenomenon comes in many different sizes. The smallest one, and one which you see quite often, is the dust devil. A dust devil is a small, swirling column of rising air that picks up grains of dust and other light objects from the earth's surface. Some dust devils rise hundreds of meters into the air. A much more violent air disturbance of this type is the tornado. The winds of a tornado are so violent they can pick up houses

and automobiles and carry them great distances. A very big disturbance of this type—one covering many square kilometers—is a hurricane.

Each of these disturbances has the same basic type of motion. At the center of each of these disturbances is a rising column of air. The upward motion of this air is maintained by temperature differences between itself and the outside atmosphere. Surrounding the base of the column is a swirling mass of air, working its way in toward the base of the rising column. See *Figure 18-14.*

Would the air swirling about a rising column of air be swirling clockwise or counterclockwise? How would you explain your answer?

A stable atmosphere. Now suppose we return to our example of the imaginary balloon containing a fixed amount of air. Again, we will start near the surface of the ground, and carry the balloon up to the second floor, a distance of 3 meters. As before, the pressure will be less by 0.04 per cent, and the cooling effect of the expansion will amount to 0.03°C. But this time, suppose the air outside the balloon is slightly warmer than the air in the balloon. What will be the effect?

If the air inside the balloon is colder than the air outside, it will also be denser. Consequently, the balloon will tend to fall back down toward the surface of the earth. Once more, suppose we set aside our imaginary balloon and just think about a mass of air near the surface of the earth. If this mass of air were to move upward under these conditions, it would, as before, expand slightly and cool. But now—assuming the air around it were not cooler—it would have a greater density than the air around it. Thus, the air which started to rise would fall back to the earth's surface. There would be no tendency to maintain a rising column of air. In fact, there would be no tendency to create or maintain any sort of air motion. Such a situation —in which the rising air becomes cooler than the surrounding atmosphere—is called a *stable atmosphere.*

You know that atmospheric pressure decreases with altitude. Therefore, as a mass of air rises, the atmospheric pressure on the rising air mass decreases. The mass of rising air expands. However, expansion requires energy. If energy is not added from outside the sample of gas, the energy for expansion must come from the molecules within the sample. As these molecules lose energy, the temperature of the sample of gas becomes lower. Such cooling—in which no energy is transferred between the gas and its surroundings—is called *adiabatic* (ad′i ə bat′ik) *cooling.* This is the type of cooling we have been discussing.

Certain physical laws relate the amount of this cooling to the amount of expansion which takes place. In general, as a column of gas rises through 100 meters of the troposphere, the temperature of the rising gas changes 1°C as a result of adiabatic cooling.

Suppose, at a certain place and time, the temperature of the atmosphere drops more than 1°C for each 100 meters of altitude. Then, the air around a column of rising air will be cooler than the rising air. Since the surrounding air is cooler than the column, the surrounding air will also be more dense. The rising air will be pushed higher and higher. Thus, if measurements indicate that the temperature of the atmosphere decreases more than 1°C per 100 meters of altitude, meteorologists know the atmosphere is unstable.

On the other hand, suppose the atmospheric temperature decreases less than 1°C per 100 meters of altitude. Then, adiabatic cooling of a rising air mass would result in the rising air becoming cooler than its surroundings. The rising air, being cooler, would also be more dense than the surrounding air. Naturally, it would soon stop rising and come back toward the earth's surface. Under these conditions the atmosphere is stable.

Measurements have shown that over some regions of the earth, particularly over forests and grasslands, the atmosphere is generally stable. In contrast, the atmosphere over deserts is often unstable.

Water vapor and atmospheric stability. The relationship between temperature and altitude —that is, the stability of the atmosphere— is greatly affected by water vapor. A mixture of air and water vapor is slightly lighter —that is, less dense—than dry air at the same temperature and pressure. Thus, moist air has a natural tendency to rise when it is surrounded by dry air. As moist air rises and becomes steadily cooler, a point is reached where the water molecules begin to condense, forming water droplets. If such a mass of moist air continues to rise, a cloud is produced. If the air rises still further, condensation affects the temperature of the whole mass of moist air.

As you probably know, when water evaporates, it absorbs heat. Your body, for instance, is cooled by the evaporation of perspiration. Condensation produces the opposite effect— that is, during condensation, the condensing liquid releases heat. The surrounding air is made slightly warmer. Thus, if water droplets condense out of a rising column of moist air, the air will not cool off as rapidly as it would if the air were dry. Thus, condensation prevents the complete cooling that would take place as a dry gas expands. In fact, if condensation is rapid in moist and expanding air, the air might even warm up.

How important is this effect? As you have read, when dry air rises 100 meters, it cools

Figure 18-15. The layered structure of a hailstone is an indication of how the hailstone formed. How many layers make up this hailstone?

1°C. If moist air in which condensation is taking place rises 100 meters, it cools only 0.6°C. In order to be stable, the atmosphere in those regions in which water is condensing must cool less than 0.6°C per 100 meters of altitude. The cooling rate of the atmosphere is greater than this over most of the earth's surface. The atmosphere, then, is generally unstable with respect to upward-moving masses of moist air.

Thunderstorms and hailstorms. You are observing the effects of an unstable atmosphere when you watch thunderheads form on the tops of clouds. Thunderheads are the rounded, swelling masses which often form on the tops of clouds. The large raindrops and hailstones that can accompany thunderstorms are also results of an unstable atmosphere.

In a thunderstorm, the violent upward motion of moist air creates great updrafts high in the troposphere. Droplets of water are carried to high altitudes where they freeze into small particles of ice. Then, a swirling downdraft catches them. The ice particles are carried downward. As the ice particles fall, water droplets collect on them. Frequently, the ice particles—now covered with water—are again caught in an updraft inside the cloud. Once more they rise high into the troposphere, or even into the stratosphere, where the water freezes. At very high altitudes, the updraft loses strength. The ice particles drop toward the earth. But, they may be caught by another updraft and carried upward again. Sometimes, these cycles are repeated dozens of times. When the ice particles finally fall to the earth, they may have grown to the size of baseballs.

Ice particles, or hailstones, the size of baseballs are rare, but hailstones about one-half inch in diameter are not uncommon. If you ever get a chance, collect some hailstones. If you break or cut a hailstone in two, you will probably detect a layered structure. (*Figure 18-15.*) The layers are evidence of the number of times the hailstone was carried up through the thunderstorm. Each time the hailstone started downward, it picked up a layer of water. As the hailstone was again carried upward, the water froze. Naturally,

Figure 18-16. Although no two thunderstorms are identical in all respects, thunderstorms do follow a general pattern as they develop. Three stages in this pattern of thunderstorm development are shown in the diagram at right.

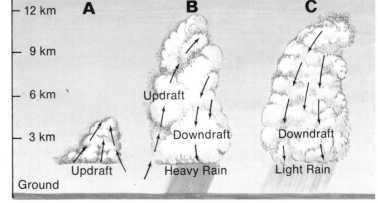

with each cycle, the hailstone became larger, until it was too large to be carried by the updrafts in the cloud. Then it fell to the earth.

Apparently, thunderstorms go through three stages. At first, a column of moist air rises, forming a cloud. (*A* of *Figure 18-16.*) Later, as the cloud gets larger, water vapor begins to condense. Rain, and sometimes hail, falls. At this stage—as shown in *B*—there are strong updrafts and downdrafts in the cloud. In its last stage, *C*, downdrafts are predominant in the thunderstorm, but they gradually weaken as the cloud loses its moisture.

What would happen to a rising column of air as it reached the tropopause? Would it continue into the stratosphere? Explain your answers.

Figure 18-17. Two effects—the Coriolis effect and the effect of low pressure—cause the counterclockwise flow of air about a low-pressure area.

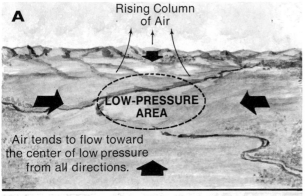

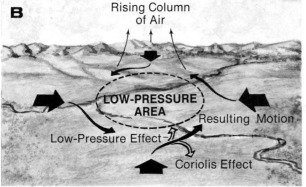

Winds about low-pressure areas. So far, we have given most of our attention to rising columns of air. But we have also pointed out that, as a column of air rises, other air moves in from the sides to take its place. The general region where the air rises is a region of low pressure, compared to the average atmosphere. The rising column of air has produced this low-pressure area. The difference in the atmospheric pressure beneath the rising column of air and the surrounding area is very small. However, the difference is enough to draw air from the surrounding area in toward the center of the area beneath the rising column. Sometimes these low-pressure areas can be quite extensive, covering several thousand square kilometers.

Suppose we follow the motion of air as it is affected by such a low-pressure area. We will assume that the situation we are describing is in the Northern Hemisphere. The low-pressure area acts like a weak, but very large, vacuum cleaner. Air moves toward the low-pressure area from all directions. (*A* of *Figure 18-17.*) As air moves toward the center of the low-pressure area, it is deflected to the right by the Coriolis effect. The air is no longer moving directly toward the low-pressure area. Instead, it is heading off to one side. But two effects are influencing the motion of the air. In addition to the Coriolis effect, the effect of the low-pressure area is that the air continues to be forced to the left, toward the center of low pressure. These effects balance each other, as shown in *B* of *Figure 18-17.* The mass of air will move in a counterclockwise direction about the low-pressure area.

Cyclones. The name given to the counterclockwise flow of air about a low-pressure area over land is *cyclone*. Near the outer edge of the cyclone, the winds are not very strong. Near the center of the cyclone, however, the wind's velocity often reaches forty to fifty miles per hour.

Over the ocean, cyclones can become much stronger. Here they are called hurricanes. Near the center of a hurricane, wind speeds of more than 100 miles per hour are common. By now you can understand why storms over the ocean tend to be much more violent than storms over the land. Because of the behavior of moist air compared with that of dry air, the moist atmosphere over the ocean is generally less stable than the atmosphere over the land. Thus, the resulting air motions are often more violent.

Meteorologists still do not know all the reasons behind the development of cyclones. One thing is certain. Such air movements are related to differences in temperature and are strongly dependent on the amount of water vapor in various parts of the atmosphere.

The jet stream. In addition to differences in temperature and differences in water vapor content, air movement near the surface of the earth seems to be related to air movement at extremely high altitudes. Little was known about the movement of air at high altitudes until the late stages of World War II. Then, a new bomber—the B-29 "Superfortress"—came into use. Such planes, flying at altitudes greater than 25,000 feet, often encountered a very strong wind. Sometimes, when headed into this wind, the planes were able to make very little headway.

This high-velocity, high-altitude wind is called the *jet stream*. The jet stream is an almost constant air current and is actually part of the atmosphere's overall pattern of circulation. In the jet stream, air often moves at more than 200 miles per hour. The direction of motion is from west to east. In the Northern Hemisphere the jet stream is usually found as a narrow band somewhere between latitudes 30° N and 40° N. See *Fig-*

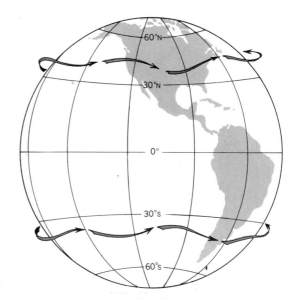

Figure 18-18. The jet streams seem to be related to weather conditions at the earth's surface. Meteorologists hope to discover the nature of this relationship.

ure 18-18. In the Southern Hemisphere there is a similar jet stream between latitudes 30° S and 40° S. By comparing *Figure 18-18* with *B* of *Figure 18-10*, you can imagine how the jet stream fits into the overall circulation pattern of the earth's atmosphere.

Meteorologists have long been observing storm winds as variations upon the steady background of the prevailing planetary winds near the surface of the earth. Perhaps when more is learned about the behavior of the upper atmosphere, we will see that here, too, there are storm patterns acting as variations upon steady winds such as the jet stream. Hopefully, we will eventually recognize the relationship between the motions in the upper atmosphere and the weather conditions which affect our daily lives here on the earth's surface.

In what ways might man be able to use the jet stream to his advantage? In what ways might the jet stream be a disadvantage?

Checking Your Knowledge

IMPORTANT IDEAS

1. The atmosphere consists of all the air, water vapor, and suspended dust particles that surround the earth.

2. The density of the atmosphere—that is, the number of molecules per cubic centimeter —varies inversely with altitude. The outer limit of the atmosphere is not defined.

3. Winds result when a mass of air becomes warmer than its surroundings. Warm air rises and cool air moves in to replace it.

4. The overall wind pattern of the earth is complicated by the Coriolis effect, the seasons, and the continents and oceans.

5. In general, storms develop when unequal heating causes moisture-laden air to rise through an unstable atmosphere.

6. Winds blow counterclockwise about the low-pressure areas created by rising air.

7. Strong winds, called jet streams, have been discovered at very high altitudes.

USING NEW WORDS

Study the terms listed below. On your paper write the numerals *1-3*. After each numeral write terms or statements to satisfy the instructions having the corresponding numeral.

storm	tropopause	stratosphere
cyclone	chemosphere	adiabatic cooling
ionosphere	trade winds	Coriolis effect
doldrums	jet stream	horse latitudes
westerlies	troposphere	polar easterlies

1. List the terms related to winds. Describe the relationships.

2. List the terms which name layers or boundaries in the atmosphere. Describe each term.

3. List the terms which name factors in the development of winds. Explain each term.

TEST YOURSELF

Study the test below. On your paper write the numerals *1-10*. After each numeral write the correct response to that part of the test having the corresponding numeral.

1. Which of the following layers of the earth's atmosphere is farthest from the surface of the earth? (a) chemosphere, (b) stratosphere, (c) troposphere, (d) ionosphere.

2. In which of the following layers of the earth's atmosphere do most of the changes in our weather occur? (a) chemosphere, (b) stratosphere, (c) troposphere.

3. Which one of the following elements makes up about 21 per cent of the total volume of the earth's atmosphere? (a) nitrogen, (b) oxygen, (c) argon, (d) hydrogen.

4. With an increase in altitude, the density of the atmosphere *(remains the same, increases, decreases)*.

5. As a mass of air is warmed, it expands. Thus, its density *(remains the same, increases, decreases)*.

6. In the Northern Hemisphere, the Coriolis effect causes winds to *(be deflected to the right, deflected to the left, move along straight lines)*.

7. If the temperature of the atmosphere decreases only 0.5°C per 100 meters of altitude, the atmosphere is *(stable, unstable)*.

8. As water droplets condense out of moist air, the temperature of this air *(remains unchanged, decreases, increases)*.

9. Although no heat is removed from a gas, the temperature of the gas will become lower when the gas expands. Such cooling is called _____ cooling.

10. The high-velocity wind found at extremely high altitudes between latitudes 30° and 60° is called the _____.

Extending Your Knowledge

QUESTIONS TO EXPLORE

1. The earth's axis is tilted with respect to the plane of the earth's orbit. How does this fact affect the global pattern of winds over the earth?

2. Why do storms usually move across the United States from west to east? In what regions of the world would storms move from east to west?

3. How would you explain why local winds blow from water to land during the day and from land to water during the night?

4. How does the topography of the region in which you live affect the weather and the prevailing winds of your locality?

5. Why, do you suppose, do aviators avoid flying through a thunderstorm?

6. What is the most important factor in producing winds in an atmosphere?

7. What would be the pattern of circulation of the atmosphere if the earth did not rotate on its axis?

SOME THINGS TO DO

1. Find the explanation of why moist air—that is, air with water vapor in it—is less dense than dry air. When you are sure you understand the explanation, report the detailed explanation to the class.

2. On a bright, sunny day, place a large container of water near a plot of freshly spaded soil. Place one thermometer in the water and one about 3 inches below the surface of the soil. Suspend a third thermometer just above the surface of the soil, but keep this thermometer shaded. At regular intervals, observe and record the readings of each of these thermometers. Continue taking readings after sunset. Try to explain any differences in temperature which you detect.

3. Find out the following statistics for your state. What is the record high temperature? The record low temperature? What is the greatest amount of rainfall ever recorded in one 24-hour period? In one month? In one year? What is the least amount of rainfall in one year? Do these statistics give an accurate picture of the general weather conditions in your state? What name is given to the average weather conditions for a particular region on the earth's surface?

CHALLENGES IN SCIENCE

1. Put a teaspoonful of denatured alcohol mixed with a teaspoonful of water into a gallon jug. Stopper the jug tightly. Somehow, raise the pressure inside the jug for a minute or two. Then, release the pressure rapidly. What do you observe? Explain what you observe.

2. In many parts of the country, thunderstorms do not occur as frequently in the winter as they do in the summer. Make a study of thunderstorms. See if you can discover why they occur more frequently in the summer than they do in the winter.

3. Make a comparison between the energy released in a thunderstorm and the energy released in the detonation of a hydrogen bomb. Which releases more energy? Which is more destructive? Explain your findings.

4. Collect weather maps from a local newspaper for 5 consecutive days. Study the maps to determine what each of the symbols represents. From your observations, try to predict the weather for the next 2 days. Check your predictions. How does your record of accuracy compare with that of the United States Weather Bureau? (They claim to be right about 80% of the time.)

CHAPTER 19

The deeply cut path of the San Juan River provides spectacular evidence of change.

Geologic Records

Finding evidence of change on the surface of the earth is not very difficult. Think of the changes you can observe. You can see rivers and streams carving and shaping the land through which they flow. You have seen pictures of changes made by earthquakes and volcanoes. These changes happen in a relatively short time. Some changes, however, go unnoticed in one lifetime because they are so very slow. But even slow changes, in time, alter the earth's surface to a great extent.

Geologists, of course, want to do more than just observe changes. Most geologists reason that any forces which ever acted to shape the earth are also acting today. Furthermore, these forces are probably no more active, nor any less active, today than at any time in the past. On the basis of this reasoning, geologists search for evidence of change so they can reconstruct the history of the earth and perhaps uncover some clues as to the origin of the earth.

In Chapter 19, you will discover some ways in which geologists use their observations of the earth today to reconstruct the earth's past. You will find out how the order of events in the earth's past has been determined. Furthermore, the geologic time scale and some methods of determining the age of the earth are described. You may be surprised at how much information scientists **have obtained** from the earth's geologic record.

1. Evidences of Past Changes

Observing and using evidence. In describing the earth's surface, we have frequently spoken of changes that have taken place in the distant past. We have described how rivers cut valleys in mountain ranges and plains. We have referred to the deposition of sediment throughout millions of years. We have described the slow but powerful erosive force of a glacier and the characteristic shape of the valley that is left behind after the glacier has melted.

All of these activities take place over extremely long periods of time compared to the lifetime of a human being. In fact, in discussing geologic changes that take place over hundreds of millions of years, we are going far beyond the limits of human history. How can geologists be certain that these changes have actually occurred? What evidence do we have to show that the earth was not always the way we see it now? In a very real sense, the geologist must play the role of a detective who has arrived on the scene long after the events have taken place. He must piece together the story from the clues which the participants left behind.

But where does the geologist look in his search for clues that will reveal the earth's past? He might find such clues in the rocks and other material that he examines. He might find clues in the shape of the earth's surface. A particularly good source of clues to the earth's past is the relationship of one portion of the surface to that of another. An example of such a relationship is the relationship between a river valley and a mountain range. As you can imagine, the geologist must use every detail which he can observe and measure to reconstruct the record of the earth's geologic history.

Examples of evidence. Suppose we look at some typical examples of evidence showing past changes. You may recall that in a previous chapter we referred to the ice ages. We stated that, at various times in the past, much of North America was covered with ice and glaciers. Scientists say that the last of these ice ages ended about 10,000 years ago. But 10,000 years is a very long time. On what type of evidence do scientists base their statements about the extent of the area covered by ice during the ice ages?

One type of evidence which geologists use to determine the extent of the area covered by ice during a glacial period is shown in *Figure 19-2*. In this picture you can see a large

B. P. SINGER FEATURES

Figure 19-1. Geologists examine many types of material in their search for clues to the earth's history. These geologists are examining a core of sand and gravel obtained from beneath the Greenland Ice Sheet. This sample had been covered by ice for more than 10,000 years. At the present time, the ice sheet is more than 1.5 km thick.

Figure 19-2. This boulder was probably moved to its present location by a glacier. When the ice melted, the boulder remained, far from the place of its origin.

boulder of sandstone resting on an outcrop of limestone. The nearest deposit of sandstone is many miles away. Furthermore, investigations have revealed that the sandstone was formed earlier than the limestone under it. How could the boulder have gotten to this particular location? The boulder is obviously much too heavy to have been carried there by any animals. There is no evidence of river action. However, the boulder could have been moved there by a glacier.

In observing glaciers that are active today, geologists see boulders of this size being carried along on top of the glacier or being pushed along in front of it. Some glaciers have melted back substantially during the lifetimes of people living nearby. As the glacier melts, these large boulders, called *glacial erratics* (glā′shəl ə rat′iks), are left strewn about. Such cases offer proof that a glacier can transport large boulders and leave them behind as the glacier melts. With such evidence, geologists can conclude that the boulder of sandstone was left on top of the limestone outcrop by a glacier. Geologists reach this conclusion even though there are no glaciers anywhere near that vicinity at the present time.

Is there a way in which geologists could use present-day observations of glaciers to determine when the sandstone boulder was left on the limestone outcrop? If so, how? If not, why not?

The canyons and valleys through which streams and rivers move seem to offer their own proof of erosion and the ability of streams to change the shape of the land. But we can actually see the process of erosion occurring in many places. In *Figure 19-3* is shown the side of a typical, small stream bed. If we observe such a stream bed for a comparatively short time, we can see erosion as it occurs. Seeing the process of erosion makes it easier to understand the process which created the Grand Canyon, even though we must realize it took a very long time.

The changing of rock into soil is another evidence of change that you may be able to observe. Near your home, there may be a

Figure 19-3. In terms of geologic time, erosion often occurs relatively rapidly. What evidence of rather rapid change can you observe in the picture below?

ZENTRALE FARBBILD AGENTUR

Figure 19-4. As rock changes into soil, it goes through several stages, as revealed on this hillside. The solid rock (bottom) crumbles into clay containing rock fragments (center). This becomes a layer of soil (top) that is darkened with decaying plant material.

U. S. NAVY PHOTOGRAPH

Figure 19-5. In terms of geologic time, volcanoes can form mountains or islands very quickly. Volcanism resulted in the formation of this small island in less than one decade. What further changes would you expect the island to undergo?

place where a hill has been cut through to make a level roadway. If so, look at the side of the hill exposed by the cut. You will probably find that the lower portion is primarily rocky, perhaps even solid rock, whereas the top is soil, with trees and other plants growing in it. If you look carefully, you will notice that there is no distinct boundary between the soil and the rock. (See *Figure 19-4.*) Instead, the solid rock seems to become less solid near its top edge. Above the rock is a region of clay mixed with rock fragments. On the surface is soil, usually made dark by the presence of humus. If you were to keep observing this area for several years, or perhaps even for just several months, you would see that the rock is gradually breaking down into fine particles. Soil forms from these particles of rock.

Perhaps the most spectacular evidence of change is the volcano. In many places in the

world, people have watched mountains being formed by volcanism. In *Figure 19-5* the island shown is being created by volcanic action in the ocean south of Tokyo, Japan. It is easy for scientists to compare the lava and cinders from this present volcanic action with lava and cinders found in other areas of the world, far from any volcanoes which are now active. The geologist uses the results of such a comparison as evidence of changes in the pattern of volcanic action on the earth.

Thus, the geologic activities of the earth leave their bits of evidence behind. It is often quite simple to piece the evidence together and determine what happened. Sometimes, however, it is a very difficult task to determine when a particular geological event took place. The determination of when an event took place usually requires a very detailed examination of the evidence.

367

Study and observe the area near where you live. What evidence of changes can you find? Are you able to find any of the examples of geologic change given in this book? If so, which ones? If not, what evidence of changes on the earth might be found in your area? Find pictures in newspapers or magazines that give evidence of changes on the earth's surface, either in your locality or elsewhere.

2. The Record of Sedimentary Rock

Information obtained from sedimentary rock. One of the most important sources of geologic information is sedimentary rock. As he studies the layers of sedimentary rock formations, the geologist finds three important types of information.

1. He finds a record of the sequence in which certain events have happened. Obviously, an upper layer of rock has been deposited after a lower layer. So, the sequence of layers in a rock formation is a record of the sequence of deposition of sedimentary material.

2. Sedimentary rock gives evidence of movement in the earth's crust. In many places, layers of sedimentary rock are tipped up at a steep angle. Certainly, these layers must have been deposited originally in horizontal layers. The fact that they are now tipped is evidence of motions of the crust of the earth underneath the sedimentary layer.

3. The thickness of a particular sedimentary rock layer makes it possible to estimate the time required to deposit that layer of sedimentary rock. Adding the times required to deposit all of the known layers of such rock enables scientists to make a rough estimate of the age of the crust of the earth.

Correlating layers of rock. Geologists have discovered layers of sedimentary rock which extend many hundreds of kilometers across the earth. For example, a particular type of sandstone found in the northeastern part of the United States is also found in southeastern United States. After examining this sandstone, geologists concluded that the areas in which this sandstone occurs were once covered by the same shallow ocean or lake. Furthermore, they concluded that all of this sandstone was formed during the same period of time.

Layers of sedimentary rock, laid down at successively later times, also spread over many kilometers. The thickness of a particular layer may vary from one place to another. However, whether it is thick or thin, each layer can be recognized wherever it is exposed.

An example of how various layers of rock, or *strata* (strā′tə), are related is shown in *Figure 19-6*. The locations represented in the diagram are about 150 km apart in the Grand Canyon. Matching up the layers of rock in two separate areas is called *correlation* (kôr′ə lā′shən). The same strata represented in this diagram can also be found in other regions of southwestern United States.

Index fossils. It is possible to correlate layers of sedimentary rock over widely separated portions of the surface of the earth.

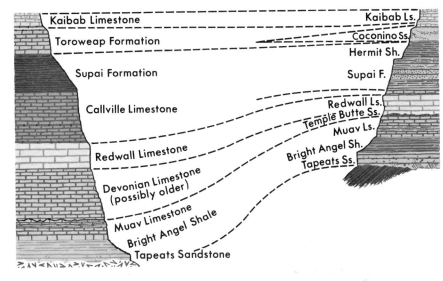

Figure 19-6. The exposed rock formations represented here are about 150 km apart in the Grand Canyon, and yet, with a few exceptions, layers of the same type of rock appear in each formation. Upon what information do scientists base their conclusion that the layers in one formation are the same as those in another formation?

This correlation is made possible through the study of fossils. Fossils, as you will recall, are the remains or evidences of ancient plants or animals. Most typically, fossils are the remains of shells of sea creatures. Sometimes the shells themselves are preserved, as are those shown in *Figure 19-7*. In other cases, the imprint of the shell remains in rock, although the material of the shell itself has been dissolved away.

Suppose a particular species of animal existed only during a particular period of geologic time. The material of any sedimentary rock which bears a fossil of this animal must have been deposited during the period of geologic time in which the animal was alive. Many such animals were transported by ocean currents and spread rapidly throughout the earth. The fossils of such species are found all over the world. Fossils of a species of plant or animal that lived in all parts of the world, but only during a certain geologic age, are called *index fossils*.

Index fossils found in a particular sample of rock in Asia might also be found in a sample of rock in America. Geologists conclude that these two samples of rock were deposited as sediment within the same period of time. By using such index fossils, then, it is

Figure 19-7. One type of sedimentary rock, called coquina, is composed almost entirely of shells and pieces of shells of various sea creatures.

FIELD MUSEUM OF NATURAL HISTORY

possible to correlate layers of sedimentary rock all over the world. In this way, the sequence of geologic events in one portion of the world can be related to the sequence of events in another portion.

Do you think dinosaur remains are good index fossils? Do you think fossils of human beings will be considered good index fossils by geologists millions of years from now? Explain your answers.

369

Demonstrate one way in which fossils are formed

Place a layer of clay in the bottom of a shallow box. Press a clam shell into the clay. Then, carefully remove the shell so that a clear imprint remains in the clay. Mix some plaster of Paris and pour a layer of it over the clay. When the plaster has set, separate the layer of plaster from the layer of clay and examine each layer. Which layer, would you say, contains the "fossil"?

In your demonstration, what could be compared to the soft mud of ancient times? What could be compared to the body parts of an animal of ancient times? What could be compared to the formation of a sedimentary rock?

Crustal movement. If layers of sedimentary rock are tipped from the horizontal position in which they were formed, the crust of the earth in that area has moved. Sometimes layers of rock are bent as well as tipped. In fact, the layers are sometimes folded back upon themselves. In some areas, the deformed sedimentary rocks are overlain by horizontal layers of rock. Photographs such as those in *Figure 19-8* give ample evidence that portions of the crust of the earth have been deformed in a violent manner.

What sequence of events could result in tilted and folded layers of rock being overlain by horizontal layers of rock?

In some places, layers of rock appear to have been broken and displaced with respect to their previous position. *(Figure 19-9.)* Such a break in the crust of the earth is called a *fault* (fôlt).

A fault is the result of an earthquake or a series of earthquakes. The evidence left behind by earthquakes is often quite impressive.

Figure 19-8. The material that forms sedimentary rock is deposited in horizontal, or nearly horizontal, layers. However, after the rock is formed, forces within the earth may disturb and distort the layers.

370

Figure 19-9. The displacement of the material on one side of a fault, relative to that on the other, may be vertical, horizontal, or a combination of horizontal and vertical displacement.

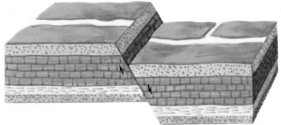

Vertical Displacement

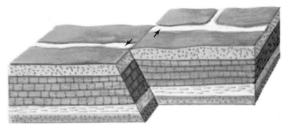

Horizontal Displacement

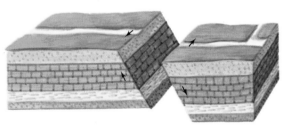

Vertical and Horizontal Displacement

SPENCE AIR PHOTOS

Figure 19-10. The nearly straight boundary that is clearly visible just to the left of the center of the picture above marks the San Andreas fault.

Figure 19-11. The main movement along the San Andreas fault has been horizontal, as indicated by the displaced stream beds shown below.

U. S. DEPARTMENT OF THE INTERIOR, GEOLOGICAL SURVEY

It shows up not only in sedimentary rock layers, but in many other features of the earth's surface. The San Andreas fault in California shows clear evidence of the motion which occurred along it, as shown in *Figure 19-10*.

Along some faults, the earth's crust has moved up and down. Along others, such as the San Andreas fault, the earth's crust has moved from side to side. Sometimes, the crust on opposite sides of the fault has moved both vertically and horizontally. In each case, the motion of the crust can be determined by carefully examining the relative positions of the features on either side of the fault. Observe *Figure 19-11*.

371

3. A Geologic Time Scale

Determining time intervals. Close examination of geologic formations can often tell us the sequence of geologic events. But how can we determine how many years elapsed between one event and the next? How can we tell how long it took to build up a particular layer of sedimentary rock? The task of establishing a time scale is much more difficult than figuring out the relative order of events.

Suppose we think about a single layer of sedimentary rock. How could we determine the time it took to build this particular sedimentary layer? Geologists use a number of methods. First, they look for places around the earth where a similar kind of sedimentary rock is in the process of formation today. Suppose the layer is sandstone. Geologists would look for river deltas where sand is being deposited. By observing the delta for many years, it is possible to determine how rapidly the sand is being deposited.

How many ways can you suggest for making observations or measurements of the deposition of sand in a river delta? Suppose the average of all of the measurements showed that five millimeters of sand were deposited in ten years. At that rate, how long would it take to build up a layer ten meters thick?

A geologist would go through a process such as observing a river delta to estimate the time period represented by a thick layer of sandstone rock. Of course, he would have to realize a possible error in his conclusion. After all, he can only measure the rate at which sand is being deposited today. The rock which he is investigating was actually deposited a long time ago. If the rate of deposition of rock was different then than it is now, his calculation would be in error.

There is another factor which he must take into account. As a layer of sand turns into a layer of sandstone, it is compressed slightly. Thus, the thickness of the sandstone will be slightly less than the thickness of the original layer of sand.

Some sedimentary rock shows a fine pattern of alternate layers of light and dark material. Such a banded rock is shown in *Figure 19-12*. Geologists have suggested a reason to account for this layering. It might be due to some naturally occurring cycle, such as the ebb and flow of the tide or the recurrence of summer and winter. There are some observations of lake-bottom deposits now forming which seem to show a similar pattern—regular cycles from light material to dark material corresponding to the change in seasons from summer to winter each year. If this is the correct explanation for such banded rock, and there is no way of proving that this is true, then it permits geologists to simply count the years required for any such rock layer to be formed.

Using methods such as these, geologists have estimated the time required to form specific layers of sedimentary rock. For example, geologists have estimated the time required to form each of the layers that are

Figure 19-12. The light and dark bands in some sedimentary rock may be clues to the origin of the rock and to the time required to form the rock.

exposed in the Grand Canyon. These times can be added together. The sum represents the time required to lay down all the layers from the bottom of the canyon to the canyon's rim.

The use of index fossils. Although the Grand Canyon presents us with a beautiful example of sedimentary rock formations, it also presents us with a problem. It shows us that rivers can wear away sedimentary rock. How can we be sure that some of these layers of rock were not worn away before the next layer was deposited? Perhaps one particular layer was originally ten times as thick as it is now, and another layer five times as thick. Perhaps a whole group of layers is now completely missing.

The use of index fossils helps to solve this problem. With the help of index fossils, geologists have been able to correlate layers of sedimentary rock all over the world. Look at the diagram of *Figure 19-13.* In *1* a formation of three sedimentary layers—labeled A, B, and C—is shown. Each layer has its particular index fossil. In *2,* A is the same thickness as in *1.* However, B is much thinner, and C is much thicker. In *3,* A and B are thicker than in the other cases, and C is missing. Suppose these were the only three examples a geologist could find of these types of sedimentary rock. How would he use these three cases to help establish a geologic time scale?

First he would say that only the thickest examples of each type of rock were important. The thickest examples represent the maximum time that he can assume was spent in building up that particular rock layer. Thus, he would be interested in the thickness of layer C from the second case and the thicknesses of layers A and B from the third case.

After measuring the thickness of each of these layers, he would then try to determine the age each thickness represents. He would

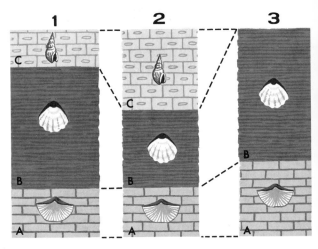

Figure 19-13. By studying separate rock formations, such as the ones labeled 1, 2, and 3, geologists can learn about the history of various parts of the earth.

use either of the methods we have already described. Suppose he determined that layer C represents 20 million years and that layer A and layer B represent 10 million years each.

Now, the geologist has a piece of the earth's history as follows. The total period represented by the three types of rock is 40 million years. This is the period from the time that the animals whose fossils are in layer A first appeared on earth until the time that the animals with the fossils in layer C became extinct. This also includes the period in which the animals whose fossils are in layer B existed.

The next task is to try to find some place on the earth where rock of layer A lies on top of a still older rock, and some other place where rock of layer C lies underneath a younger one. If such older and younger rocks can be discovered, then this particular 40-million-year slice of the earth's history can be fitted into its proper place in time.

What factors can you suggest that could introduce errors into a geologist's estimate of the time required to deposit a given layer of sedimentary rock?

Periods in geologic history. In the 200 years that geologists have been working on a geologic time scale, they have succeeded in making a record stretching back 600 million years into the past. This record was constructed in the way we have outlined. That is, layer by layer and case by case, geologists using index fossils have been able to fit together 600 million years of the earth's history.

As you know, history is usually divided into various periods. Quite often, for convenience, each such period is given a name. In American history, for example, there were periods of colonization, westward expansion, industrialization, and so on. The division between one period and the next is not always sharp. Nevertheless, each period has its own distinguishing features. Different kinds of events were going on in each period. Thus, activities in America were quite different in the days of colonization than they were in the time of the westward movement.

In a similar way, geologic history is divided into long intervals of time called *eras*. Each era is divided into *periods*. During each one of these periods, a different type of geologic activity was taking place. In *Figure 19-14* these eras and periods are listed. Also listed are the time intervals that geologists now associate with each period.

You will notice that the periods in this geologic time scale go back only 600 million years. Yet in other places in this book we have

ERA	PERIOD	TIME FROM BEGINNING OF PERIOD TO PRESENT (Millions of Years)
Cenozoic	Quaternary	1
	Tertiary	70 ± 2
Mesozoic	Cretaceous	135 ± 5
	Jurassic	180 ± 5
	Triassic	225 ± 5
Paleozoic	Permian	270 ± 5
	Pennsylvanian	305 ± 5
	Mississippian	350 ± 10
	Devonian	400 ± 10
	Silurian	430 ± 10
	Ordovician	500 ± 15
	Cambrian	600 ± 20
Precambrian		4,500 ± ?

Figure 19-14. This geologic time scale indicates the accepted names of the various eras and periods into which geologic history has been divided. The interval of time covered by each period is also shown.

talked about the age of the earth as 4.5 billion years. The difficulty is this. The oldest known fossils are found in rocks which appear to be about 600 million years old. Furthermore, most of the rocks which lie beneath the layers of these oldest fossil-bearing rocks seem to be metamorphic. That is, their form has been changed, and it is hard to tell whether or not these metamorphic rocks were ever sedimentary. It is impossible to tell anything about their ages by the methods we have been describing. Obviously, we cannot use index fossils to extend the time scale back beyond the age of the oldest known fossils.

DO IT YOURSELF

Make a report

Select one of the periods in the geologic time scale and make a special study of it. Find out what geologic events occurred during that period. What were the distinctive features of the plant and animal life of that period? Why was that period given its special name? What research is now being done to learn more about that period? Organize your findings into a report to be given to the class.

4. Radioactive Dating

Understanding radioactivity. In the final years of the 19th century, radioactivity was discovered. Soon after the discovery of radioactivity, a scientist named Boltwood suggested that radioactivity could be used in determining the age of rock.

To understand the way in which radioactivity can be used in determining the age of rock, we must first understand something about radioactivity itself. Uranium is a well-known radioactive element, so we will use it as an example. The nucleus of a uranium atom will spontaneously throw off an *alpha particle.* An alpha particle consists of two protons and two neutrons. The remaining nucleus is no longer that of a uranium atom. It is now the nucleus of a thorium atom. Thorium is also a radioactive element, and it, too, changes to another element. This step-by-step process proceeds through a long series of changes involving radioactive elements until, finally, a lead atom remains in place of the original uranium atom. The lead is not radioactive, and the process stops there.

The concept of half-life. Understanding why some elements are radioactive and exactly how the process of nuclear disintegration proceeds are two major problems of modern physics. We need not study these problems here. The important thing for the geologist to know is how long it takes for the various steps in the radioactive process to occur. In particular, the geologist wants to know how long it takes for uranium to change into lead.

As a matter of fact, there is no fixed time for any particular uranium nucleus to throw off an alpha particle and start the series of steps. Instead, scientists measure the average time for a large number of such nuclei to make a change. The time required for such a change is described by the term *half-life.* Let us see

what half-life means by describing a hypothetical situation.

Suppose you have some red blocks, and you wish to paint them blue. But, you are going to go about this job in a very special way. Each hour you are going to paint half the total number of red blocks blue. This does not mean that you will have painted all the blocks blue in two hours. Instead, it works like this. Suppose you start with 128 red blocks. In the first hour you will paint 64 of them blue. Now, 64 blocks remain red. In the second hour, you will paint half of these, or 32 blocks, blue. Now, 32 remain red. In the third hour, you will paint half of these, or 16 blocks, blue. In the fourth hour, you will paint 8 blocks. In the fifth hour, you will paint 4 blocks, and so on. (When you get down to one block, you will have a problem. But this is only a hypothetical situation, and, in nature, this particular problem is automatically taken care of.)

Now suppose at some time during your painting process, a friend of yours had come along and counted 96 blue blocks and 32 red ones. If he knew the rules by which you had been working, he would know immediately that you had been at your job for two hours. If at a later time he came back and noticed 120 blue blocks and only 8 reds, then he would know that you had spent 4 hours on the job. As you may have guessed, for this particular block-painting process the half-life is one hour.

Of course, if you scattered the blocks around or threw some away after you were done painting them, your friend could never get an accurate measure of the time you had been painting. But, suppose you kept them all in one group and just changed their color from red to blue. Then, anyone who knew the half-life of the painting process could tell how long the painting process had been going on by simply counting how many blocks of each color there were.

The set of rules we used for painting the blocks seems to be a terribly artificial set of rules for making changes. Does anything in nature really happen this way? Actually, any natural phenomena in which something in one condition is changed into a different condition *purely by chance* follows exactly the set of rules we have just described. That is, the number that changes in any particular time period depends only on the number remaining unchanged at the beginning of the period. It has nothing to do with the number that have already made the switch.

Now we can understand the meaning of the term half-life. Half-life is the length of time it takes for half of the nuclei of a given radioactive element to change into another element. The half-life of uranium is 4.5×10^9 years. Suppose we had a sample containing the nuclei of one million uranium atoms and suppose we were able to keep a record of them over 4.5 billion years. At the end of 4.5 billion years, we would find that only 500,000 of the uranium nuclei were left. In the intervening half-life, the other 500,000 have decayed —that is, they have started the series of radioactive steps which ends in lead. After the first step, the other steps in the series take place in a relatively short time—about 300,000 years. Thus, for our purposes, we can assume that once an atom of uranium decays it has become an atom of lead.

What would be the ratio (approximately) of the number of uranium atoms to the number of lead atoms in a meteorite that is 4.5 billion years old? Assume the meteorite contained no lead to begin with.

The geologist can use radioactive elements to determine the age of minerals by following a procedure like that which we described in our example with the painted blocks. First, he must find a small portion of his sample in which uranium and lead are mixed together. He then analyzes this sample to determine the ratio of uranium to lead.

You will remember that, in our example, we counted the red and blue blocks only at intervals which were whole-number multiples of the half-life of the process. If we had made our count after only 25 minutes had gone by, our problem would have been more difficult. We would have had to use a special formula. Of course, the age of the sample a geologist analyzes is not a whole-number multiple of the half-life of uranium. Thus the geologist must also use a special formula.

There are a number of difficulties and possible pitfalls in arriving at such determinations of the ages of rocks. First of all, geologists must find rocks with uranium and lead present in them. Actually, not very many rocks contain measurable quantities of these elements. Second, he must be careful to select a very small sample to be sure that the lead he is analyzing is very close to the uranium. This is important, because only then is it likely that the lead was formed by the radioactive decay of the uranium. Third, he must have some way to tell that small fractions of either the lead or the uranium were not removed by some sort of chemical action over the years. After all, uranium and lead are different elements, and each will react in a different way to such things as seawater and various chemicals which may have come in contact with the rock.

In spite of all of these difficulties, a number of reliable age determinations have been made. The oldest rocks found on the earth are about 3.5 billion years old. The oldest rocks found in meteorites are about 4.5 billion years old. Geologists reason that the oldest rocks found on the earth must have formed after the earth itself formed. Probably, the age of the meteorites represents the best estimate for the age of the earth as well as for the rest of the solar system. Thus, 4.5 billion years is the age which most geologists now accept as the age of the earth and of the solar system.

How would you explain the one-billion-year difference between the age of the oldest meteorites and the oldest rocks found in the earth's crust?

Dating sedimentary rock. A particular difficulty arises in determining the age of sedimentary rock. Very few sedimentary rocks have enough uranium in them to make an age determination possible. In many cases, geologists have approached the problem of sedimentary rock in a different way. They have used *intrusions* (in trü′zhənz)—the masses of igneous rock which rise up through cracks in sedimentary rock—to estimate the age of the sedimentary rock. In *Figure 19-15* an intrusion into a formation of sedimentary rock is shown. Above the intrusion, other layers of sedimentary rock have been formed on top of it. Thus, the igneous rock is younger than the layers it passes through but older than the layers which are on top of it. If this igneous rock contains uranium and lead, it can be used to determine an age somewhere between the formation of these two layers of sedimentary rock. In this way, the age estimates which we described earlier for sedimentary rock have been somewhat improved with the use of radioactive dating.

Uncertainty in geologic time estimates. The uncertainty involved in estimating geologic time is an important consideration. Geologists readily admit that most specific age determinations are in error by as much as 10 or 20 per cent. Some of them are in error by as much as 50 per cent. Thus, no single age determination can be used as a reliable measure. In-

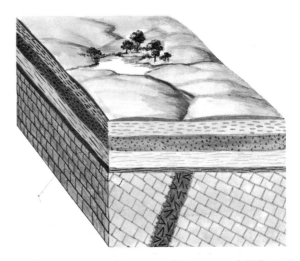

Figure 19-15. The igneous intrusion shown is older than the overlying sedimentary rock, but younger than the rock through which the intrusion passes.

stead, geologists take the average of several hundred determinations. In this way, the errors in one determination tend to cancel out those in another, and the average of many is believed to be fairly reliable. Geologists, however, are still not satisfied with the results they have obtained. There is still a considerable amount of discussion and continuing research to determine the age of the earth, as well as of the various formations that are found within it.

Thus, we see that evidences of change in the earth's crust are visible all around us. Change can be observed in everything from the shape of the continents to such minute details as the relative abundance of the uranium and lead atoms in a small sample of rock. By carefully examining such evidence, geologists can determine not only what changes have taken place on the earth's surface, but also the order in which the changes occurred. In many cases, the actual time of certain important geologic events can be determined. To the trained eye of the geologist, the earth itself is a clock, revealing its own age.

Checking Your Knowledge

IMPORTANT IDEAS

1. Geologic activities produce changes on the earth, leaving behind bits of evidence of the nature and sequence of the activities.

2. In sedimentary rock strata, a geologist may find a record of the sequence of geologic events, some evidence of crustal movement, and an indication of the earth's age.

3. Determining what has happened in the earth's past is easier than determining when it happened.

4. Index fossils are useful in correlating rock strata in one portion of the world to rock strata in another portion.

5. A geologic time scale, with the earth's past divided into eras and periods, has been developed by geologists.

6. An understanding of radioactivity and half-life aids scientists in determining the age of certain rocks on the earth's surface.

USING NEW WORDS

Study the words listed below. On your paper write the numerals *1-7*. After each numeral write words or statements to answer the question having the corresponding numeral.

index fossil	strata	intrusion
alpha particle	half-life	Mesozoic
Quaternary	Cenozoic	fault
correlation	Cambrian	Paleozoic

1. Which words name eras in the geologic time scale?

2. Which era is most recent?

3. Which words name periods in the geologic time scale?

4. In which period do we live?

5. Which words relate to radioactivity?

6. Which words relate to rock formations?

7. How are the words you listed for *6* related to rock formations?

TEST YOURSELF

Study the test below. On your paper write the numerals *1-10*. After each numeral write the correct response to that part of the test having the corresponding numeral.

1. Strata of sedimentary rock reveal the sequence of events in the earth's past, since in any formation of strata, each layer is (*younger than, older than, the same age as*) the layer laid down directly beneath it.

2. Tilted or folded strata are evidence of (*volcanism, crustal movement, erosion*).

3. The half-life of a radioactive element is (*the time required for half its atoms to change, half the time required for all its atoms to change, not related to the time required for the changing of its atoms*).

4. Soil is formed as ____ breaks down into tiny particles.

5. Fossils of species of plants and animals that lived all over the earth, but only during a certain geologic period, are called ____ because of their usefulness in identifying rock layers.

6. As used in geology, the term ____ means to match up the layers of rock in two separate areas of the earth's surface.

7. Movement of the earth's crust may break rock formations and cause a displacement of the materials on either side of the break. Such a break is called a ____.

8. Masses of igneous rock which rise up through the layers of sedimentary rock formations are known as ____.

9. One way to estimate the rate at which beds of sedimentary rock were deposited is by observing and measuring the rate at which a ____ forms at the mouth of a river.

10. The age of the oldest rock discovered on the earth is about ____ years.

Extending Your Knowledge

QUESTIONS TO EXPLORE

1. Eroded rock is a basic ingredient in soil. What other ingredients are there? How did the other ingredients get into the soil?

2. What radioactive elements, other than uranium, have been used for determining the ages of materials of the earth's surface? What are the advantages of having more than one way to make age determinations?

3. What reasons can you give to explain the fact that although fossil dating is useful only for periods of less than 1 billion years, some rocks in the earth's crust are believed to be more than 3 billion years old?

4. The federal government is building many dams to aid in flood control. What is the interaction between such projects and the natural process of erosion?

5. What evidence is there that the earth's surface has undergone some changes in your locality? How recent were these changes? Are any changes occurring at the present time?

6. How would you describe a fault? What are some of the motions that are associated with rock formations along a fault?

7. How would you explain the statement, "The only constant feature of the earth is change"?

SOME THINGS TO DO

1. Fill a test tube about one-fourth full of dry, powdered clay. Press the clay into the tube. Measure and record the depth of the clay and then remove the clay from the tube. Fill the tube about one-half full of water, and pour the same clay into the water. Cover the tube and shake it well. Allow the clay to settle. Then, remove most of the water with a pipette. Measure and record the depth of the settled clay at periodic intervals as the remainder of the water evaporates. Explain any differences in the depths recorded. Do the same experiment with sand and water. Compare the results of the two experiments.

2. Obtain information about the volcanoes at Surtsey and Paricutin. Find out when they first became active. How fast did they develop? What is their present state of activity? What effect did these volcanoes have on organisms living nearby?

3. Fasten a 45-inch piece of adding machine tape on a door in your room. The length of this tape represents the lifetime of the earth. How many years does each inch represent? Starting with the most recent period at the top, mark the tape into segments representing the periods and eras shown in the geologic time scale on page 374. Label each segment. Which segment of the tape is longest?

CHALLENGES IN SCIENCE

1. Distinguish between a facies fossil and an index fossil. What present-day animals and plants do you know of that would make good facies fossils? What plants and animals would make good index fossils?

2. The Grand Canyon is an example of a deep, comparatively narrow gorge that has been formed by erosion. What is an example of a broad expanse of rock which has been worn by erosion?

3. Use the data below to determine which of the rock samples is oldest and which is youngest. Explain your reasoning.

Sample	Amount of U^{238}	Amount of Pb^{206}
A	1.0 gram	0.5 gram
B	0.5 gram	1.0 gram
C	4.0 grams	26.0 grams

Man still has much to learn about mountains.

CHAPTER 20

The Development of Mountains

In one way or another, mountains have always presented a challenge to man. To some, the challenge is just to know what is on the other side. To others, the challenge is to get to the top of the mountain. To a geologist, the challenge is to learn as much as possible about the mountain itself and about its development.

Until the 18th century, man's contact with mountains was, in general, as infrequent as he could make it. Travel through mountainous terrain was very difficult and was undertaken only if absolutely necessary. To climb a mountain to study it or just for the sake of climbing it was considered just short of insane.

Gradually, however, a change in attitude took place. Geologists began to realize that mountains are particularly good subjects of study in that they offer a great variety of visible rocks and minerals, spectacular evidence of erosion, obvious examples of crustal movement, and so on. Through their studies, geologists have learned much about mountains. But they are still far from understanding the processes which operate within the earth to raise mountains to their imposing heights.

In Chapter 20, you will discover some of the observed features of the earth—both surface and subsurface—that are associated with mountains. Two theories of mountain development are discussed. Each theory explains certain of these observed features, but neither theory is completely acceptable. Someday, various aspects of these two theories may be combined into one theory. Or, perhaps a totally new and completely different theory will be found acceptable.

1. Features of the Earth's Surface Related to Mountains

Studying dry-land mountains. We begin our study of mountain development just as geologists do—by collecting information about mountains. We will limit our study to those mountains which occur on dry land. It may be that submarine mountains, such as those that comprise the mid-ocean ridges, are similar to continental mountains. As yet, we have very little evidence about these submarine formations. There is some reason, however, to believe they are quite different from the mountains on continents.

About 30 years ago, the American geologist R. A. Daly listed eight characteristic features of the earth's surface which have to do with mountains. The reasons for these features must be explained by any theory that is suggested to account for the origin and growth of mountains.

Ranges and geosynclines. One characteristic feature of the earth's surface that has to do with mountains was described in Chapter 16. That is, mountains usually occur in long, narrow belts. In these belts separate ranges may be parallel to each other, or ranges may merge with one another at their ends. However, each belt of mountains occupies a very small part of the total surface of the earth. The smallness of this pattern indicates that the forces which build mountains affect only a very small portion of the earth's surface at any one time.

A second characteristic feature of the earth's surface closely associated with typical mountain ranges is called a *geosyncline* (jē′ō sin′klīn). A geosyncline is a long, narrow portion of the earth's surface—lying between mountain ranges. The long dimension of a geosyncline runs parallel to the ranges of mountains between which it lies. Across its short dimension, a geosyncline has been bent downward, like a huge, rocky valley below the surface of the earth. Quite often there is evidence that such geosynclines were submerged beneath the sea at some time in the past. Usually, a geosyncline is filled with sediment and sedimentary rock. See *Figure 20-1*.

Compression, folding, and erosion. The sedimentary rock which was originally deposited in level layers in a geosyncline has since been compressed and folded. This compression and folding is the third characteristic feature of the earth's surface that Daly has associated with mountains. The sedimentary rock looks as if it has been squeezed from both

Figure 20-1. Some stages in the development of a geosyncline are shown below. Compression and folding of the rock layers form a range of mountains.

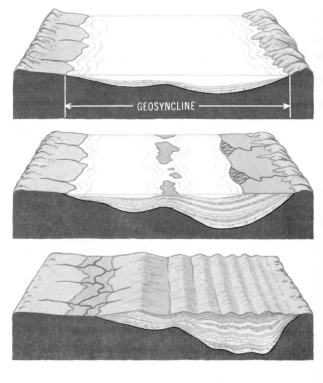

sides by the growing ranges of mountains which border the geosyncline.

Would you say that the force required to bend or break the crust of the earth is great or small? What could be the origin of this force?

The fourth characteristic feature of the earth's surface associated with mountains has to do with the direction of folding and compression in the sedimentary material in a geosyncline. The compression is always across a geosyncline, producing folds that are parallel to the length of the geosyncline. See *Figure 20-1*. Since a geosyncline is a very large feature, the observed folding probably could not result from a single event, such as a large earthquake. But rather, the folding and compression must have resulted from a whole series of events.

The folding and compression of the rock in a geosyncline has forced comparatively light-weight sedimentary rock down into the earth's crust in some places. In other places, such rock is high above sea level. The unusual positioning of this rock is the fifth characteristic feature of the earth's surface which is often associated with mountains.

The sixth characteristic feature has to do with erosion. Over the millions of years in which mountain ranges were growing, the tops were continually being eroded away. The rock now at the tops of such mountains was deep in the interior of the crust at some time in the past, when the mountains were in an earlier stage of formation.

Batholiths. In many mountain ranges, a huge mass of igneous rock is located in the center of the mountain range. This mass of igneous rock is called a *batholith* (bath′ə lith). It is the seventh feature listed by Daly. The chemical nature of the rock in such a batholith is similar to that of the sedimentary rock around its edges. Geologists have examined the region around the edges of batholiths, where folded sedimentary rock lies beside the batholiths and over them. In all such cases, it seems that the batholiths have simply replaced rock that was originally there, without disturbing the nearby rock. That is, a typical batholith has eaten its way into the formation, rather than having pushed its way in as an intrusion. See *Figure 20-2*.

Ages and positions of mountain ranges. The eighth and last general observation concerns the ages and positions of mountains. Using the techniques we have described for determining the ages of rock formations, geologists can determine which mountain ranges are young and which are old. The youngest mountain ranges are those which are, in general, the highest and most rugged. They consist of two large groups, as shown in *Figure 16-3*. One group surrounds the Pacific Ocean, and the other group stretches from Indonesia westward, across Asia, and into southern

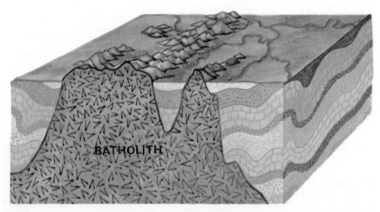

BATHOLITH

Figure 20-2. Although the layers of sedimentary rock in the diagram show folding, they are not deformed as they would be if the batholith had been forced into its present location. Describe a process by which a batholith could replace the original rock of a formation without distorting the layers of the formation.

Europe. All of these mountains seem to have been formed in the last 70 million years.

In the previous 100 million years, other groups of mountains were formed. The eroded remains of these mountains are found in Siberia, China, Malaya, and Borneo, generally north of the young mountains in Asia. Another group of these older mountains is found in South Africa, with no apparent connection to the younger mountains. Other groups of mountains have been identified which are more than 200 million years old. These are the Appalachians in North America, the Urals in Russia, a group of separate ranges along the Atlantic Coast of Europe, and some mountains in eastern Australia.

DO IT YOURSELF

Write a description

Describe a region of old mountains (older than 200 million years). Make sure you include such features as peneplains and monadnocks in your description. Also, explain how these features were formed.

An additional observation. About 15 years after Daly's list of eight characteristics of the earth's surface associated with mountains was first published, another geologist, J. T. Wilson, added an additional item. This additional characteristic feature is based on a detailed observation of the shapes of mountain ranges. Wilson pointed out that ranges of young, folded mountains—as well as island groups formed by young, folded mountains—form a series of arcs. These arcs are joined at their ends to make the overall pattern of mountain belts. This pattern is shown by the heavy lines in *Figure 20-3*. He also found fractures, or faults, extending back from the ends of some of these arcs, particularly in North America. Other features of the earth's surface and of young, folded mountains are also shown in *Figure 20-3*. Wilson felt that these features were also associated with the main pattern of mountain arcs and island arcs.

Why, do you think, is it important that the observed features associated with mountains be listed before we study theories of mountain development?

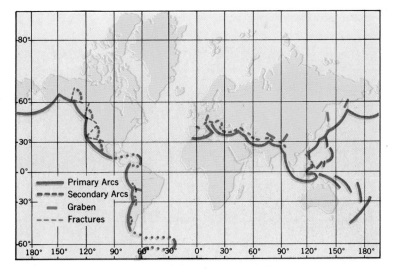

Figure 20-3. The pattern of mountain ranges about the earth seems to consist of a series of arcs, as shown on the map at the right. Also indicated on the map are other features of the earth's surface that seem to be associated with the development of mountains.

2. Features of the Earth's Interior Related to Mountains

Earthquakes. It seems logical to believe that the development of mountains is related to processes taking place in the interior of the earth. As you have learned, scientists can obtain information about such processes through seismology. Seismologists have discovered what appears to be an important relationship between earthquakes and mountain building. As we pointed out in Chapter 13, many earthquakes occur quite close to the belts of young mountains.

The point within the earth at which an earthquake takes place is called the *focus* of the earthquake. Geologists have made detailed studies of earthquake foci near mountain belts. They have found that these foci are arranged in what appears to be a regular pattern. For example, *Figure 20-4* shows a section of the earth's interior that lies beneath the northernmost island of Japan and northwest into Asia. As you can see from this figure, earthquakes nearest the surface occur southeast of the island, under the floor of the ocean. Deeper earthquakes occur farther west. In fact, on a diagram such as this, it would appear that the

earthquakes generally occur along a line. The line extends down into the earth, making an angle of about 30° with the earth's surface.

Does this situation happen in other places? Apparently it does, but in many places the line is not a single one but a broken one. *Figure 20-5* shows a cross section of the earth under the coast of Chile. The earthquake foci are marked with circles. Here, the circles form a pattern that is sloping eastward—that is, down underneath the continent of South America. Close to the surface, the pattern has a slope of 23° from the horizontal. Circles representing deeper earthquakes seem to form a different pattern, sloping down at an angle of 58°.

Volcanoes. The fact that volcanoes usually occur near chains of young mountains must be considered in formulating theories of mountain development. Of course, a volcano is a surface phenomenon. However, a volcano is also evidence of subsurface activity. *Figure 20-6* shows a map of the region around the *Kuril* (kü′rēl) *Islands* north of Japan. This map reveals the close relationship between

Figure 20-4. The depths of the foci of earthquakes occurring along AB are shown below. Notice that the depths increase from the ocean in toward the land.

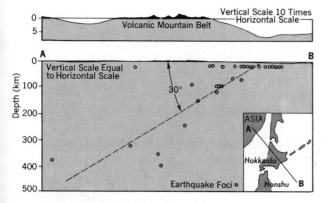

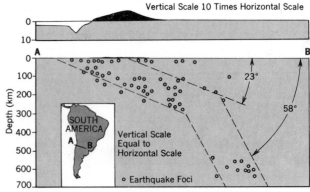

Figure 20-5. In South America, earthquakes along AB also occurred at various depths. Notice the two distinct patterns formed by lines through the foci.

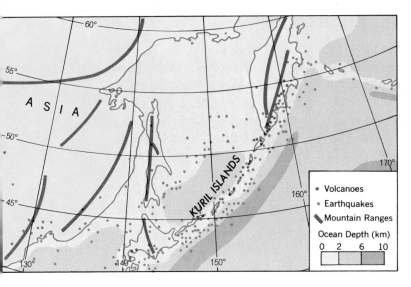

volcanoes, earthquakes, and mountain ranges in this region of the earth's surface.

There are only a few active volcanoes in North America, but there are many inactive ones that can easily be identified. A large number of these occur along the arc of mountains which includes the young Sierra Nevada and Cascade ranges in the western part of the United States. In South America, a line of volcanoes follows the Andes range almost exactly. The locations of these volcanoes offer further confirmation that there is a relationship between volcanoes and mountains.

What are some ways in which volcanoes affect the shape of the earth's surface?

Trenches. There is another observation which you might think of as either a surface or a subsurface characteristic. It is this. Along the borders of many of the young mountain ranges—most of which are along the edges of

Figure 20-7. When a mountain range occurs very close to a coastline, quite often a deep trench lies just offshore. The inset illustrates the profile of such an area as that shown in the photograph.

C. W. HERBERT FROM WESTERN WAYS

continents—there are deep ocean trenches. These trenches occur off the west coasts of both North America and South America. A trench also exists south of the Aleutian Islands, along the coast of Japan, and on down beside the mountainous islands south of Japan. Another trench is just east of the Philippine Islands.

But there is an important exception to the general rule that ocean trenches are associated with young mountains. The exception is the region of southern Asia. There is no ocean trench associated with the Himalaya Mountains. This mountain range is part of the general pattern of young mountains. Yet, where we would expect to find an ocean trench, there is, instead, the subcontinent of India. Just as the deep ocean trenches must be explained where they occur, so the absence of a trench in this region of India must also be explained.

3. The Contraction Theory

The history of the contraction theory. One of the oldest theories about mountain development is still very important today. This old theory has as its starting point the idea that the earth has been gradually cooling and contracting since its formation. According to this theory, as the earth shrinks in volume, the area of its surface must also shrink. However, the surface is covered with a shell of solid rock. This rock must wrinkle to compensate for the shrinking. The wrinkling of the crust, of course, resulted in the development of mountains on the earth's surface.

Many years ago, the contraction theory was the most important and generally accepted theory of mountain building. Geologists believed that the earth had been formed out of a hot, molten mass of rock and had been cooling steadily ever since its formation. However, this simple picture was destroyed by the discovery of radioactivity. It was found that many rocks contain radioactive elements. Geologists realized that the earth might well have been becoming hotter throughout much of its history, rather than becoming cooler. If this were true, then the earth would be expanding, and the crust would be steadily pulled apart. In this case, the earth might be expected to have the appearance of a dried mudflat. That is, it might be covered with a pattern of cracks instead of a pattern of mountain ranges.

What features of the earth's surface might be explained by comparing them to large cracks which might be opened up by the expansion of the earth?

For a while, it seemed that the contraction theory was doomed, but there were two ideas which saved it. First, geologists pointed out that we can only sample the materials near the earth's surface. Thus, we really do not know how much radioactivity is buried deep in the earth's interior. Materials near the surface may contain an unusually high proportion of radioactive elements. After all, radioactive elements would tend to heat the rock around them. This rock would be melted and would tend to expand. Thus, the rock containing the radioactive elements would rise up through cracks in the surface, form volcanoes, and spread out over the crust. The rock left behind in the interior of the earth might contain only small amounts of radioactive elements. In this case, the rate at which the earth is cooling by radiation out into space might be faster than

Figure 20-8. A key factor in any theory of mountain development is the temperature of the earth's interior. This temperature depends, in part, upon the radioactivity of the materials in the interior. Thus, many scientists, including this nuclear chemist, are engaged in research projects devoted to determining the radioactivity of various materials found in the earth.

the rate of heating caused by radioactive elements in its interior. If so, the earth might still be slowly but steadily contracting.

The second idea that helped save the contraction theory is this. Scientists do not know what kinds of minerals might form under very high pressure. During the eons of time since the earth formed, it may be that the rocks in the interior of the earth have been gradually readjusting themselves into new mineral forms. Such an adjustment occurs when graphite is converted to diamond at extremely high pressures and temperatures.

The same adjustment may also occur in other minerals. It is possible that the new mineral forms are more compact than the original forms. If so, the result would be a steadily shrinking earth.

As you can imagine, there is no way of proving whether these ideas are right or wrong. Therefore, geologists cannot reject the contraction theory on the basis of physical impossibility. Instead, they must consider this theory just as they would any theory. That is, they must test the contraction theory against the evidence which can be observed.

FIND OUT BY TRYING

Materials you will need: apple, tape measure, balance

Measure and record the size and weight of an apple. Note the apple's appearance. Then keep the apple at room temperature for a period of several weeks. Measure and record the apple's size and weight at intervals of 3 days. Does the apple change in any way? If so, how can you account for the changes observed? How are your observations of the apple related to the theory that mountains are the result of the contraction of the earth?

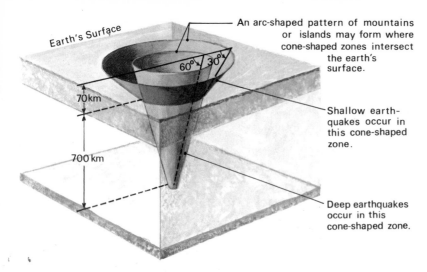

An arc-shaped pattern of mountains or islands may form where cone-shaped zones intersect the earth's surface.

Earth's Surface

70km

700 km

60° 30°

Shallow earth-quakes occur in this cone-shaped zone.

Deep earthquakes occur in this cone-shaped zone.

Figure 20-9. If the contraction theory is correct, earthquakes do not occur at random points. Instead, their foci seem to lie on the surfaces of cone-shaped zones within the earth's interior. The intersection of such a surface with the earth's surface is an arc. Thus, this theory explains the arc-shaped patterns of mountain ranges and island arcs.

The contraction theory today. Earlier in this chapter, we pointed out that mountain systems are arranged in a pattern of arcs. Later, we pointed out that earthquake foci beneath mountain ranges are also arranged in a pattern. Earthquake foci seem to occur on a line sloping down into the interior of the earth. According to the contraction theory, earthquakes beneath island and mountain arcs tend to occur in two cone-shaped zones. The cone-shaped zone of shallow earthquakes—those within 70 km of the earth's surface—has sides that slope downward at an angle about 30° below the horizon. Deep earthquakes —those below 70 km—occur in a cone-shaped zone with sides that slant down about 60° below the horizon. One edge of the cone-shaped zone of shallow earthquakes intersects the surface of the earth in a curved line. This curved line is the arc which is the basis for the arc-shaped pattern of mountains and islands. See *Figure 20-9.* But, what is responsible for the two cone-shaped zones?

A cross section of the interior of the earth as it is described by the contraction theory is shown in *Figure 20-10.* The core of the earth and the lower part of the mantle are still hot and not contracting. The portion of the mantle from a depth of 700 km up to 70 km is cooling

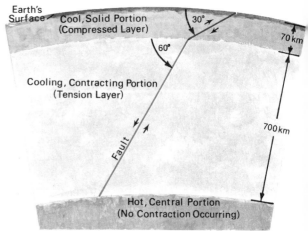

Figure 20-10. Faults could occur as shown, provided conditions within the earth resemble those described in the diagram. How can scientists be certain as to what conditions exist deep in the earth's interior?

and contracting. The upper portion of the earth, from a depth of 70 km up to the surface, is cool and solid. This includes the top portion of the mantle and all of the crust.

If this description of the earth's interior were correct, what would be the result? The layer of cooling material would tend to shrink. However, the interior beneath it is not shrinking. Thus, the cooling, shrinking layer of rock would be constantly tending to pull itself apart. It would be like a thick rubber balloon, stretched tight and trying to shrink, but not able to do so. In this layer, there would be a tendency for cracks to develop. Suppose such a crack were on an angle, as shown in *Figure 20-10*. Such a crack in the earth is called a fault. Movement along the fault would allow this layer to shrink a little bit.

Of course, if this happened, it would disturb the cool and rigid rocky material above it. This upper layer of material cannot shrink any more. As the layer below contracts, the layer above will be compressed, or squeezed together, like the shriveling skin on a drying apple. Here, again, a fault through the material can relieve the situation and allow movement to take place. It would be natural for the fault in the outer layer to form immediately

above the fault in the lower layer, as shown in *Figure 20-10*, since this would have marked a weak place in both layers.

Scientists have carried out theoretical studies of such a situation. Of course, they have had to use rather simple, idealized models of the rocky material of the earth. Thus, the results of their studies represent what might happen in an idealized situation. These results are as follows.

1. The fault through the upper, compressed layer would be at an angle of 30° to the horizontal.
2. The fault in the lower, tension layer would be at an angle of about 60° to the horizontal.
3. Both faults would have a conical shape.

FIND OUT BY TRYING

Materials you will need: hammer, nail, can, plasterboard

Remove the cardboard from the back of a small piece of plasterboard. Place the plasterboard over the open end of a can. Then place a nail with the head down on the center of the plasterboard. Drive the nail through the plasterboard by striking the point of the nail sharply with a hammer. Observe the hole made by the nail. Then turn the plasterboard over and observe the hole from the other side. What is the shape of the hole made as the nail went through the plasterboard? How might this experiment be related to the contraction theory of mountain building? How do the forces exerted in this experiment differ from those exerted as the earth contracts? How is plasterboard like the materials of the earth? How is it different?

Strong points of the contraction theory. If earth materials were the same everywhere, a few, large conical faults would develop on the earth's surface. However, the earth is a complicated body, with many variations from place to place. As a result, according to the contraction theory, a long series of such conical faults has developed. Each fault joins onto another to make the overall pattern of mountains around the earth.

So far, explanations based on the contraction theory seem to agree very well with observations of the locations of earthquakes. This version of the contraction theory also accounts for the arc-shaped ranges of mountains on the earth's surface. The contraction theory also explains other details, such as how a deep fault encourages the growth of volcanoes immediately above the fault. A cross section of a portion of the earth is shown in

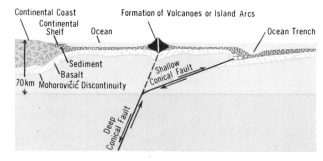

Figure 20-11. Not all the observed features of the earth's surface that are associated with mountains can be satisfactorily explained by the contraction theory. However, as you can see, it accounts for features such as volcanic arcs and ocean trenches.

Figure 20-11. This diagram represents a typical island arc, such as the islands which comprise the country of Japan. On the earth's surface, the pattern of volcanoes will follow the arc pattern of the deep conical fault. This diagram also shows why a deep portion of the ocean will be found outside of the island arc.

The contraction theory also offers an explanation for the mountain ranges—the secondary arcs in *Figure 20-3*—that are found on the inland side of the volcanic arc. Within the boundaries of each separate volcanic—or primary—arc, the material at the surface is gradually pushing outward toward the edge of the arc. Where the two primary arcs join, there will be a place of violent adjustment to these different directions of motion. This will cause the crust of the earth to buckle and fold, creating another large range of mountains. The Rocky Mountains of North America comprise such a range.

Shortcomings of the contraction theory. Although the contraction theory seems to offer some very good explanations for mountain building, not all geologists accept it. These geologists point out that the amount of contraction required to develop the mountains as they are today is very large. For example, in order to explain the folding and wrinkling in the Himalaya Mountains, we would have to assume that the earth had shrunk by more than 7 per cent in the last 100 million years. Many geologists feel that this is an unreasonably great amount of shrinkage. Another problem is the fact that faults seem to have occurred only in very limited regions. As you will recall, we pointed out earlier that mountain belts occupy only a small fraction of the surface of the earth. If wrinkling was caused by uniform contraction all over the earth, why has it not formed mountains scattered more generally over the whole surface of the earth?

H. ARMSTRONG ROBERTS

Figure 20-12. According to the contraction theory, the Rocky Mountains represent a secondary mountain arc. That is, they formed as a result of crustal movement in a place where two primary arcs joined.

4. The Convection Theory

Convection in the mantle. In Chapter 15, we discussed a theory in which we assumed that currents of molten iron and nickel exist in the core of the earth. According to this theory, these currents are responsible for the earth's magnetic field. These currents are generated by differences in temperature, that is, they are convection currents.

If such convection currents exist in the core, then they would form a very efficient mechanism for transferring heat from deeper parts of the core to the core-mantle boundary. But then what happens to the heat? Does it travel to the surface of the earth? What happens to the additional heat that is generated by the radioactive material in the rocks of the mantle? In order to answer these questions, one theory suggests that convection currents also occur in the mantle of the earth.

It may be difficult to understand how the mantle could have convection currents. After all, when earthquake waves move through the mantle, it behaves just as a solid substance would. However, there are materials that have a dual nature. That is, they seem to be solids when subjected to rapid vibrations or sudden forces. These same materials can be deformed slowly into new shapes by forces applied steadily over a long period of time. A common example is a candle. On a warm summer day, you can easily see how the force of gravity changes the shape of a candle. And yet, the candle is not melted. In fact, if you were to drop the candle on the floor, it would probably break. If you were to tap it lightly on one end, you could feel the vibrations transmitted to the other end.

According to the convection theory, the mantle of the earth has these same properties. Although it will transmit earthquake waves just as a solid would, the mantle can move slowly just as a waxy substance does. All that is required to cause such motion is a steady force lasting for hundreds of millions of years. Of course, we know how such a force might arise—from differences in density caused by differences in temperature. Thus, there might be convection currents in the mantle, causing the material there to move very slowly, and to carry heat from deeper layers toward the surface of the earth.

How fast would such convection currents move? Since we know very little about the nature of the material in the mantle, we cannot be certain. However, some properties of the materials in the mantle have been determined by seismologists. The laws of physics describe how materials with these properties would behave. Based on this approach, one calculation gives a speed of four millimeters per year for currents in the mantle.

How long would it take a mass of rock to move from the core-mantle boundary to the Mohorovičić discontinuity, assuming the mass traveled straight up all the time?

Surface effects of convection currents. Suppose convection currents do exist in the mantle. What evidence would they leave on the surface? Geologists have attempted to set up laboratory experiments which would demonstrate the effects of convection in the interior of the earth. The materials used in these experiments are difficult to choose. In a laboratory, scientists wish to carry out their experiments in a few hours. In contrast, the phenomena they are trying to demonstrate take hundreds of millions of years in the earth itself. Thus, choosing materials that will react in a reasonable length of time the way the earth's materials react over very long periods of time becomes something of a problem.

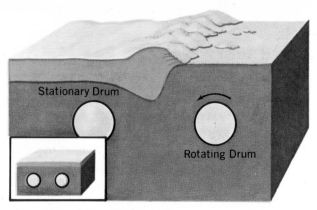

Figure 20-13. The slow rotation of the drum causes the material near the drum to move, simulating a convection current in the mantle.

However, some experiments have been set up to demonstrate the effect of convection currents in the mantle. *Figure 20-13* shows a diagram of one such experiment.

The rotating drum in this experiment was intended to be like a convection current in the mantle. The result was very much as geologists had predicted. The light material on top, corresponding to the crust of the earth, was pushed to one side. Thus, this experiment seems to confirm the ideas of many geologists. A convection current in the mantle could account for the separation between ocean basins and continents. Furthermore, such a convection current could account for the fact that mountain ranges are formed near the edges of continents.

Shortcomings of the convection theory. Not all observations are explained by the convection theory. First of all, the convection theory would suggest that near the edge of the current there would be a large, downward warp of crustal material, as indicated in the diagram of *Figure 20-13*. However, studies by seismologists near the edge of mountainous regions show that no such deep layer of crustal material exists.

Geologists who favor the convection theory have offered an explanation for the absence of a deep layer of crustal material near the edge of a mountainous region. This explanation also explains the occurrence of batholiths. Geologists point out that crustal material contains radioactive elements. Suppose a large amount of crustal material was pulled down into a lump below the surface. Then the heat generated by radioactive material would not be able to escape easily. Instead, it would melt the surrounding rocks, creating a batholith. Since batholiths are characteristic of folded mountain ranges, this explanation appears to fit the facts.

There are other observations which the convection theory has not been able to explain. One of the most important of these is that mountain ranges and particularly volcanic ranges appear to occur in arc-shaped patterns. There seems to be no reason why convection currents should cause such patterns.

There is another phenomenon which the convection current theory has not been able to explain. As was pointed out earlier, earthquakes with foci several hundred kilometers below the surface of the earth are observed. Presumably, an earthquake occurs when a buildup of force or stress in solid rock finally reaches the point where the rock gives way and moves along a fault. If the deep rock is fluid enough to contain a slowly moving convection current, how can strong stresses build up within it? It would seem that the slow movement would relieve these stresses before any earthquake occurred.

Contraction theory or convection theory? Suppose we consider the observed characteristics of the earth's surface that are associated with mountains. These characteristics were outlined in the first part of this chapter. If we compare these characteristics with the two major theories about mountain building, we will notice that some observations are best explained by one theory, some by the other, and some observations are not adequately accounted for by either theory.

For example, the contraction theory offers a good explanation for the arclike formation of mountain chains. But this theory cannot give a very good explanation for the existence of batholiths, or for the fact that high ranges, with geosynclines in between them, are raised far above sea level. Thus, this theory explains very well the formations characteristic of the islands in the region of Japan. However, it does not offer a good explanation for the features of the Sierra Nevada and Cascade ranges in western America. These ranges are far above sea level, and their volcanoes are now almost completely extinct.

The geologists who favor the contraction theory readily admit that, as yet, they cannot fully explain all of the observed features of mountains. Nevertheless, these geologists feel that their basic idea is correct. They believe that further work with the contraction theory, perhaps involving a few changes in details, will eventually enable them to explain all the observations that have been made about mountains.

At the same time, geologists who favor the convection theory concentrate their efforts on explaining the folded character of mountains and the existence of geosynclines and batholiths. As we have pointed out, the convection theory does not give a satisfactory explanation of the arclike shape of mountain ranges. Proponents of the convection theory disagree with their colleagues who favor the contraction theory, even though they realize that the convection theory does not explain all the details of mountain formation. They also feel that, with sufficient information and a few minor changes in their theory, they will be able to explain observations about mountains on the basis of the convection currents they believe to exist in the mantle.

Perhaps geologists will find evidence to advance one or the other of the theories toward a complete explanation of all observations. Or, perhaps a new and different theory, more acceptable than any yet proposed, will be formulated in the future. As is the case with almost every other major problem we have discussed so far, a complete explanation of mountain building remains to be found.

What are some other aspects of natural science which are not completely understood? What are some aspects which are completely understood?

Figure 20-14. Mountains, like all features of the earth, are continually being observed by scientists. Perhaps these observations will contribute to an acceptable theory of mountain development.

MONKMEYER

Checking Your Knowledge

IMPORTANT IDEAS

1. There are many observed features—in and below the earth's surface—associated with mountains. Any theory of mountain development must explain these features.

2. One theory of mountain development assumes that the earth is contracting, causing wrinkles (or mountains) on its surface.

3. Another theory of mountain development assumes that convection currents in the earth's mantle are responsible for the development of mountains on the earth's surface.

4. No theory explains all of the features characteristic of mountainous regions.

5. Scientists are continually making observations of mountains and seeking new ways to use their observations in explaining mountain development.

USING NEW WORDS

Study the terms listed below. On your paper write the numerals *1-8*. After each numeral write the term most closely related to the statement having the corresponding numeral.

geosyncline	convection theory
contraction theory	trench
old mountains	batholith
arc	young mountains

1. High, rugged mountains
2. A great mass of igneous rock
3. General shape of ranges of young, folded mountains
4. Gently rolling, eroded mountains
5. Elongated depression in the earth's crust between mountain ranges
6. Deep, narrow region of the ocean floor
7. Movement of material in the earth's mantle causes mountains on the surface.
8. Mountains form as a result of the shrinking of the earth.

TEST YOURSELF

A satisfactory theory of mountain development must explain all the observations made by scientists. Each observation fits into one of these categories.

a. Favors the contraction theory
b. Favors the convection theory
c. Can be explained by either theory
d. Cannot be explained by either theory

Listed below are 10 statements concerning the earth. Each statement fits into one of the categories listed above. On your paper write the numerals *1-10*. Beside each numeral tell the category to which the statement having the corresponding numeral belongs. (Use the letter to designate the category instead of writing the complete statement.)

1. Young mountains and volcanoes seem to occur in arcs along the edges of continents.
2. The earth may have been molten at one time, and the continents may have formed as the earth cooled.
3. The foci of shallow earthquakes are not directly under mountain arcs, but seem to be along a line which slopes away from the base of the mountains.
4. Radioactive elements may be present in the core and the mantle of the earth.
5. The crust of the earth is less dense, but about 25 km thicker, in the areas of the continents than it is under the oceans.
6. There are deep trenches in the ocean floor just offshore from many young mountain ranges.
7. In many mountain ranges there are huge batholiths.
8. Mountains occur in long, narrow belts.
9. Volcanoes are still being formed.
10. The earth's magnetic field changes.

Extending Your Knowledge

QUESTIONS TO EXPLORE

1. Where does the sediment which collects in a geosyncline come from? Are there any geosynclines in the United States today? If so, where? How can they be identified?

2. Of what type rock are batholiths composed? Are any batholiths located in the United States? If so, where?

3. What is the difference between the process by which batholiths form and the forcing of molten material into cracks in rock or between layers of rock?

4. Are there any characteristic features of mountains that are not explained by the contraction theory? By the convection theory? By either theory?

5. What types of rocks are generally associated with mountain ranges?

6. Do you think that the study of mountain development is important? How would you justify your answer?

SOME THINGS TO DO

1. On a map of the earth, indicate the position of the major mountain ranges, the heights of some peaks in each range, and an approximate age for each range. What are the relative positions of the older mountains and the younger mountains? Is there any relationship between the heights of the mountains and their age?

2. Conduct some experiments with paraffin. Obtain a pound of paraffin from the grocery store. It usually comes in four, flat, rectangular, pieces. Clamp one end of a piece of paraffin to the edge of the table so that the unclamped end extends beyond the table top. Hang a weight on the unsupported end. Observe what happens over a long period of time. Place another piece of paraffin so that the ends of the paraffin are supported by blocks of wood, but the center is unsupported. Apply downward pressure to the center. What happens? Repeat these experiments with pieces of paraffin that have been warmed, but are not melted. Does paraffin in this condition behave differently than it did when it was cool? How does this experiment relate to the behavior of the earth's crust and mantle?

3. Make a scale drawing of a cross section of a typical geosyncline. A typical geosyncline might be 600 km across and about 12,000 meters deep. Usually a geosyncline is filled with thick deposits of sedimentary rock that were laid down in relatively shallow water. Explain how sediments 12,000 meters thick could be deposited in water that was always relatively shallow.

CHALLENGES IN SCIENCE

1. Obtain pictures and topographic maps of mountainous regions. In the pictures and maps, try to identify the characteristic features of the earth's surface that are associated with mountains.

2. Investigate theories which explain the formation of the various surface features of the moon and of the moon itself. How will controversies between the proponents of the various theories ever be solved? How might exploration of the moon assist man in his attempts to explain the processes of mountain formation here on the earth?

3. Find out what you can about the geology of the area in which you live. Is your area mountainous? If so, when and how were the mountains formed? If not, is there evidence to suggest that your area was ever mountainous? Are there any reasons to believe that mountains will someday form in your area?

G. R. ROBERTS

CHAPTER 21

A continent's outline changes with time.

The History of a Continent

In order to consider the problem of how the continents came into existence, it is necessary to go back to the beginning of the earth. Over the years, man has made countless observations of his planet. He has acquired a considerable fund of knowledge of the earth's structure, of geologic processes, and of the laws of nature. As we take our trip into the past in describing the history of a continent, we must try to combine these observations and this knowledge.

But how, you might ask, can we be certain that our descriptions of events that happened billions of years ago are correct? As a matter of fact, we cannot say that the descriptions in Chapter 21 are absolutely correct. But, based on the available evidence, we can say that these descriptions are reasonable.

As you study Chapter 21, you will find that scientists do not agree about some aspects of the development of the continents. For example, how did continents form? Did each continent form in its present location? Or, did one huge mass form and later split apart with the individual pieces drifting to their present locations? With the data available, a clear-cut case cannot be made for either theory. In Chapter 21, then, you will find out how some of the current theories explain the development of a continent. You will also discover how the continent of North America developed from a small nucleus of lightweight rock to its present form and size. As a sort of by-product, you will get some idea of how far man still has to go in his search for complete knowledge and understanding of the earth.

1. The First Billion Years

When did the earth form? Earlier in this book, you studied theories concerning a very important event—the origin of the earth. Geologists believe that the earth condensed from a cloud of gas and dust about 4.5 billion years ago. So far, geologists have not found any rock from the surface of the earth which is this old. Thus, there is no direct evidence to support their belief about the earth's age. However, as you have read, some meteorites have been found that are 4.5 billion years old, but none older than this have been found. On this indirect evidence, geologists have tentatively assigned an age of 4.5 billion years to the earth.

Convection currents. What happened immediately after the earth condensed at the center of the protoearth? What developments led to the formation of the crust? In particular, what happened to lead to the formation of the continents? We have already described one possible method of differentiation which can account for the iron core and the rocky mantle of the earth. Presumably, further differentiation resulted in the formation of the crust. But, in going back to the beginnings of the continents, we must explain why the lightweight

rock of the crust—the rock which forms the continents—appeared in only a few specific places. Why was this rock not spread generally over the whole surface of the earth?

The principal theory to account for the special location of the lightweight rock of the continents is the convection theory. We described this theory in Chapter 20 when we talked about mountain building. Now we are taking the convection theory back to a much earlier stage in the earth's history.

The stage we are talking about is the first billion years, from 4.5 billion years ago to 3.5 billion years ago. It is possible that at this time the earth was somewhat warmer than it is now. Perhaps the material in the mantle was in a more fluid state, and convection currents could move more rapidly in the mantle than they can now. A complicated pattern of convection currents, but one that seems to correspond closely with the present positions of the continents, may be represented by a *tetrahedron* (tet′rə he′drən) placed inside a sphere. (*A* in *Figure 21-1.*) The relationship between this tetrahedron and convection currents in the earth is as follows. The points and edges of the tetrahedron correspond to rising

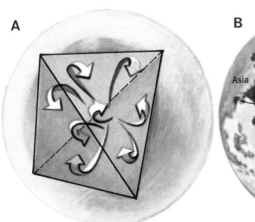

A

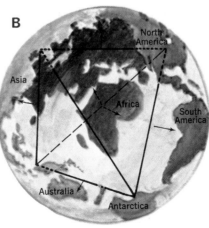

B

Figure 21-1. One version of the convection theory states that the pattern formed by convection currents in the earth may have been similar to that shown in A. Convection currents operating in such a pattern could account for the present locations of certain land masses, as seen in B.

portions of the convection currents. The faces of the tetrahedron correspond to descending portions of the currents.

Now, consider that the sphere in which the tetrahedron is placed represents the earth. (*B* in *Figure 21-1*.) As the labels indicate, the points and edges of the tetrahedron correspond to the positions of the main continental masses, including Antarctica. Thus, a pattern of currents, such as the one shown in *A* of *Figure 21-1*, might account for the fact that lightweight material from the mantle was brought to the surface in specific locations. This lightweight material was probably the beginning of the continents.

Would convection currents in the mantle move more rapidly or more slowly than they now do if the material in the mantle were hotter than it now is?

Checking the convection theory. Scientists have found no rock on the surface of the earth older than 3.5 billion years. Thus, it is very difficult to check the convection theory. However, the very fact that no such rock has been discovered lends support to the theory. Some geologists reason this way. If no rock older than 3.5 billion years exists, and if the earth is 4.5 billion years old, then it must be that in the intervening billion years the surface of the earth was essentially molten. If the surface of the earth was molten, then the mantle was probably molten too. There undoubtedly would have been convection currents in the molten material, because convection currents are likely to form in any liquid which has temperature differences within it. Such convection currents could easily account for the origin of the continents.

There is another effect that would result from the earth being completely molten at this time. There would have been no liquid water on the surface. In fact, even the atmosphere of the earth would have been so hot that most of the gases would have escaped into space. Thus, according to this theory, all of the water that might have been present on or near the surface of the protoearth during its formation would have been lost in the first billion years. The water that now exists on the earth's surface would have appeared on the surface more recently.

In particular, this water is believed to have come from the interior of the earth. Such water was trapped in small pockets so deep in the earth that it was unable to escape in the early, molten phase of the earth's existence. Gradually, however, it has worked its way up to the crust. Today, scientists find that water vapor, along with other gases, is thrown out by volcanoes. Many geologists believe that the oceans of today were formed by the condensation of water vapor from volcanoes. Thus, almost all the water in the original condensing cloud from which the earth formed has long since been lost. Only a tiny fraction is still here, and this water was originally deep in the earth's interior.

Major occurrences in the first billion years. The events listed below were of great importance in the history of continents during the first billion years of the earth's existence.

1. The materials of the planet earth condensed at the center of the protoearth about 4.5 billion years ago.

2. During the condensation, and for a few hundred million years thereafter, the first differentiation took place. Iron and nickel collected at the center of the earth. Various types of silicate rock and iron sulfide minerals collected in the outer portion of the earth.

3. After condensing from the protoearth as a hot, molten ball, the earth became even hotter, due to the action of radioactive minerals within the earth.

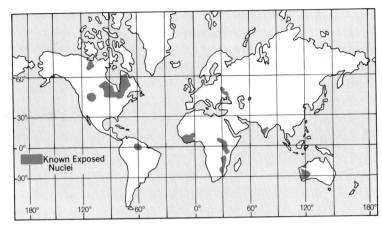

Figure 21-2. The areas where continental nuclei have been observed and are known to exist are shown on the map. In each of these areas, the crust of the earth is known to be at least 2 billion years old.

Known Exposed Nuclei

4. As the earth became hotter, the material in the mantle became more fluid. Convection currents were set up. These currents not only carried heat from the interior of the earth to the surface but also caused lightweight rock to be carried from the interior to the surface.

5. By the end of its first billion years, the earth had cooled enough for the crust to become a solid shell. The oldest rock of the earth's crust solidified at this time. Water vapor, put into the atmosphere by volcanoes, condensed, forming the first rivers and oceans.

What difficulties do scientists encounter in reconstructing the first billion years of the earth's history?

Continental nuclei. As the first billion years of the earth's history ended, what did the earth's surface look like? It may be that the oceans were not yet fully formed. Thus, much of the layer of basalt that now lies under the oceans may have been exposed. But, in addition, in various areas of the earth's surface lightweight rock had been forced up through the layer of basalt, had solidified, and was exposed on the surface. These areas of lightweight rock probably were the beginnings of the continents.

Today, geologists call the areas of continents which formed first the *continental nuclei.* Rock from these areas is the oldest rock yet found. Geologists have identified a number of such nuclei in the various continents. They are shown as shaded areas in *Figure 21-2.* There may be other continental nuclei which have not yet been discovered. Many such nuclei may be covered up by rock which was deposited at a later stage in geologic history. At present, however, the extent of direct geologic evidence about this early period of the earth's history is represented by these few areas of exposed, ancient rock.

2. The Second Billion Years

Enlarging the continental nuclei and the oceans. The second billion-year period of the earth's history covers the time from about 3.5 billion years ago to 2.5 billion years ago. There is little direct evidence to indicate what geologic processes were taking place during that interval of time. However, geologists have been able to piece together at least a rough picture of the earth's surface features during that time.

399

The continental nuclei had already formed. There is some evidence that during the earth's second billion years, a range of volcanic mountains appeared in an almost circular pattern around each of the continental nuclei. The volcanoes poured out great amounts of lava. Thus, the continental nuclei were enlarged. Eventually, the first ring of volcanoes became extinct and a second ring of volcanoes formed farther from the center of each of the continental nuclei. As this process was repeated several times, lava was deposited in an ever-widening circle. Much of the lava that poured from these volcanoes was more dense than the lava that pours out of volcanoes that form on continents today. It was a type of rock more dense than granite, but less dense than the basalt of the ocean floors.

The oceans grew larger as more water vapor was carried into the atmosphere to condense as rain. Eventually, the oceans surrounded the continental nuclei and the young volcanoes around the edges of the nuclei. A water cycle had already been established. Rain was falling on the slopes of the young volcanic mountains and eroding the loose material, just as it does today. Sediments were deposited in the valleys between the mountains. These sediments eventually became sedimentary rock. This early sedimentary rock can still be found in areas about the continental nuclei.

Suppose we use one of the nuclei in North America as a specific example of the develop-

Figure 21-3. The exposed, igneous rock formation is part of a continental nucleus. The rock of this formation is more than 2 billion years old and is one of the oldest portions of North America.

ment of a continent. The area in east-central Canada, generally south of Hudson Bay, has been studied in considerable detail. Much of this region is covered today by alternate bands of igneous and sedimentary rock. The igneous rock represents the worn-down stumps of ancient volcanoes. The sedimentary rock seems to have been deposited in valleys between the volcanoes. All such rock is very old, dating back more than two billion years.

Along the southern portion of this area are the Great Lakes. Evidence indicates that much of the sedimentary rock in this region formed in a shallow sea that surrounded the first, small beginning of the continent. Some of this sedimentary rock formed from volcanic ash which fell into the sea or along the seashore and finally compacted into solid rock. As far as is known, this nucleus in Canada is typical of all continental nuclei.

DO IT YOURSELF
Draw a map

Collect information about the geology of the east-central region of Canada. On an outline map of the continent of North America as it appears today, draw a map of what the continent may have looked like 2.5 billion years ago. Were any features of today's continent evident 2.5 billion years ago? If so, which ones? Were the Great Lakes, Hudson Bay, or the Rocky Mountains in existence then?

Events in the earth's second billion years. In the second billion years of the earth's history, then, these were the important events in the history of a continent.

1. Volcanoes in the continental nuclei poured lava out over the surrounding surface, and the nuclei increased in size.
2. Additional volcanoes grew up around the edges of the nuclei, extending the lava field still farther.
3. Rainfall wore away the early volcanoes, and layers of sedimentary rock formed in the valleys between the ranges of volcanic mountains.
4. The oceans increased in size until they completely surrounded the early continents. Sediments washed down from the volcanoes into the surrounding, shallow sea. These sediments, together with volcanic ash, were formed into layers of sedimentary rock.

Apparently, the process of mountain building in this early period was different from that which is going on today. Thus, the original process of development and growth of the nuclei seems to have been a different sort of process from the later stages in the growth of the continents.

Do you think it is likely that the rate of erosion was different at this stage in the continents' development than it is today? If so, do you think it was more rapid or less rapid? Explain your answer.

3. The Third Billion Years

Mountain building. In the third billion years of the earth's history—from about 2.5 billion years ago to 1.5 billion years ago—a new process of mountain building seems to have begun. There is evidence of arc-shaped ranges of mountains forming around the edges of the lava flows from the earlier volcanic mountains. There is also evidence that faults occurred around the edges of the continental nuclei at about this time. Suppose we again use North America as a specific example of how a continent develops. The oldest region in the ancient continental nucleus in Canada has been given the name *Keewatin* (kē wä′tin). To the southeast is another region with the name *Grenville* (gren′vil). Age determinations of the rock from this region indicate that the Grenville region is younger than the continental nucleus. Between these two regions is a zone of ancient faults. (*Figure 21-4.*)

After piecing together the bits of evidence found there, some geologists have concluded that the Grenville region originally contained arc-shaped mountain ranges. If this is so, when

Figure 21-4. The oldest part of North America is the portion of the continental nucleus known as Keewatin. On this map you can see where this region lies in relation to the present-day outline of North America.

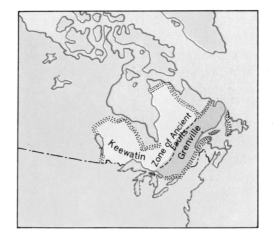

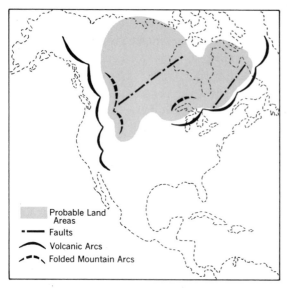

Figure 21-5. One and a half billion years ago, North America may have had the shape and surface features shown above. Naturally, we are not certain that such descriptions are correct in every detail. The broken line indicates the continent's present shape.

these mountains were forming, they would have looked much like young mountain ranges do today. The arcs in the pattern of the remaining traces of old mountains and valleys, together with the evidence of ancient faults, lend support to this idea.

Other geologists feel that there is insufficient evidence to support so detailed a picture. They feel that more must be learned about this region. Until more information is available, we cannot say for certain that arc-shaped ranges existed in the Grenville region or in other portions of North America during this period of the earth's history.

There are two possible descriptions of the situation during the third billion years of the earth's history. One description is of patterns of arc-shaped mountain ranges with secondary arc patterns behind them—that is, toward the nucleus. For example, the pattern in North America might have looked something like that of *Figure 21-5*.

The second description assumes a continuing spread of volcanoes in a circular pattern about the continental nucleus. However, the lava from these volcanoes was somewhat less dense than that from the volcanoes of the continental nucleus. Thus, the lava from volcanoes of this period—the third billion years —was gradually becoming more and more similar to the lava from the volcanoes which are active on the continents today.

Whichever description is correct, one thing is certain. The continent was continuing to grow out away from its nucleus. More and more lightweight rock was rising up from the interior of the earth. As the rock reached the surface, it was formed into mountains. Some of these mountains were undoubtedly volcanoes. Others may have been huge folds of the earth's crust, formed in a manner similar to that in which folds are being created today. Around the shores of the growing continent and in valleys between the mountains, layers of sedimentary rock were forming.

Changes in the oceans. Presumably, other nuclei around the world were also spreading at this time. Gradually, the newly formed ocean was being pushed back as the young continents increased in size. Changes probably were also taking place on the floors of the young oceans. As yet, however, geologists have almost no information which would tell them what sort of changes these might have been.

It is very likely that primitive forms of life had developed in the oceans. However, they were not the sort of organisms which would leave recognizable shells or skeletons behind. These organisms decomposed completely. Thus, there is no fossil record of their existence. Biochemists have found traces of certain chemicals in ancient sedimentary rock. These chemicals are characteristic of compounds produced by living organisms. Such traces of chemicals indicate that living organisms may have existed at this early date. But, since neither shells nor any other positive evidence of its existence remains, this early life is of principal interest to the biologist rather than the geologist.

4. The Fourth Billion Years

The further development of the continents. During the earth's first three billion years, the continents had grown considerably about their nuclei. By the end of the first three billion years, three nuclei in the northernmost portion of North America had joined. The boundary between them is marked by a distinct fault zone. It may be that, as the nuclei grew, they shifted their positions relative to each other. This shift in position may be the cause of the ancient faults that are still evident today.

In the next few hundred million years, this pattern of continental growth continued. More mountains were formed by volcanoes and uplifts. For example, rock found in South Dakota, Wyoming, Colorado, Arizona, and New Mexico indicates that these regions were originally part of a continent dating back about 1.35 billion years. Rock about one billion years old has been found in parts of Texas and Oklahoma.

Thus, at this time, the continent of North America was still changing. Each continental nucleus had now been worn down by erosion. Ranges of mountains had formed around each nucleus and had also been worn down. Younger mountains formed around the outer edges of the enlarged nuclei. These younger mountains formed a broadening pattern of interlocking arcs. As the nuclei became larger, they came in contact with other nuclei, uniting to form a single continent.

Suppose we review this mountain-building process. On the ocean side of a continent, an arc of volcanoes begins to grow. This is the primary island arc. Behind it, toward the center of the continent, a second arc of mountains grows. This arc—called the secondary arc—curves in the opposite direction, as shown in *Figure 21-5*. The material in this mountain range is a mixture of the igneous, metamorphic, and sedimentary rock of the continent. Forces in the interior of the earth compress, fold, and lift this material to form the secondary mountain arc.

As the primary arc of volcanic mountains and the secondary arc of folded mountains continue to grow, erosion wears them away. More and more sediment is washed into the region between the primary and secondary arcs. Long valleys, called geosynclines, between the mountain ranges become filled with such sediment. The sediment becomes cemented together to form sedimentary rock. The forces of mountain building fold and raise the layers of sedimentary rock that formed in the geosyncline.

Eventually, the process of mountain building slows down and stops. For reasons which are still not understood, the process of mountain building moves farther away from the continental center and toward the ocean basin. Other arcs of volcanic islands—a new set of primary arcs—are formed. Other arcs of folded mountains—new secondary arcs—begin to grow. Behind them, on the continent, the old primary and secondary arcs are gradually worn away. These processes apparently have been going on for about two billion years.

Is there any place in North America where this type of mountain-arc formation is still in progress? If so, where?

Fossils. Near the end of the first four billion years of the earth's history, a new event took place—not on the continents but in the oceans. Scientists are not certain about the circumstances which led to this event. Perhaps the ocean water had gradually become richer in calcium. Perhaps the event was simply a stage in the evolution of life. But, whatever the reason, about 600 million years ago (give or take 100 million years) a new kind of animal developed. These animals were special. When they died, their remains were preserved as fossils. These animals, through their fossils, have left a detailed record of the most recent portion of the earth's history. Thus, the emergence of this type of animal was an important event from a geologic standpoint.

The geologic record of events which occurred before the time when the first fossils formed is very fragmentary. Of the geologic formations that do not contain fossils, only a few contain evidence of the time of their formation. As a matter of fact, the exact date of the formation of the first clearly recognizable fossils is not known. However, it must have been somewhere between 750 million years ago and 500 million years ago. But, considering the amount of uncertainty in the time of the events we have described so far, a few hundred million years one way or another is not very important. At least, it is not very important for our present discussion.

5. The Most Recent 600 Million Years

The Paleozoic Era. The table in *Figure 19-14* shows the various periods in the earth's history. As you can see, all of the time we have discussed up until now is identified as the *Precambrian* (prē kam'bri ən) *Era.* The end of the Precambrian Era is the time of the first clearly recognizable fossils. The next era—the *Paleozoic* (pā'li ə zō'ik) *Era*—extends from about 600 million years ago to about 225 million years ago. During the Paleozoic Era, the process of mountain building was apparently going on as it had been for the previous one or two billion years.

At the beginning of the Paleozoic Era, a broad coastal plain covered what is now the St. Lawrence River Valley and the northeastern portion of the United States. Other coastal plains bordered other regions of what was then the continent of North America. Offshore, in the area where the New England States are today, was a deep ocean. In this ocean, a series of volcanic island arcs formed. Over the next 200 million years, they grew and were eroded. By the middle of the Paleozoic Era, about 400 million years ago, the ocean that had once been in this region was filled by sediment and lava.

During the next 100 million years, the volcanoes in this region became extinct. However, the earth's crust continued to crack and shift along faults in this region. The sediment behind the arc of extinct volcanoes began to be squeezed and folded. Both this basin of sedimentary rock and the extinct volcanoes were gradually lifted above their original level.

The inner portion of the sedimentary deposit and the remains of older mountains inland from the volcanic arc formed a secondary mountain arc. As these mountains rose, they were eroded. Some eroded material was washed toward the continental nucleus. Some was washed toward the sea.

Figure 21-6. By the end of the Paleozoic Era, ever-widening rings of volcanic arcs had practically surrounded the continent as we know it today. Folded mountains formed in the east and south. The sea moved in to cover the western part of the United States.

Then another brief period of volcanism occurred as a few new volcanoes became active in the region where the White Mountains of New Hampshire now stand. Finally, all such activity subsided, and the whole range began to erode. Thus, another broad coastal plain was forming over the region that is now New England and the continental shelf beyond it.

Rings of mountains had probably formed around all of North America and around South America. However, there is no evidence that North America and South America were connected at this time. The mountain building which resulted in the creation of Central America had not yet taken place. At the close of the Paleozoic Era, the continent of North America probably had a ring of mountains around it similar to that shown in *Figure 21-6*.

Continental drift. From 225 million years ago until today, the continents continued to change, gradually assuming their present positions and outlines. However, this may have come about in a rather surprising manner. One theory states that the continents have not always been located as they are today. Instead, according to this theory, they were once bunched very closely together. Then, about 200 million years ago, the continents split apart and have since been drifting into their present locations. As this drifting process goes on, the mountains and continents continue to grow and develop.

How could such an occurrence have taken place? To start with, *Figure 21-7* shows how the continents which are now North America, South America, Africa, and Europe might have fit together at some time in the past. On

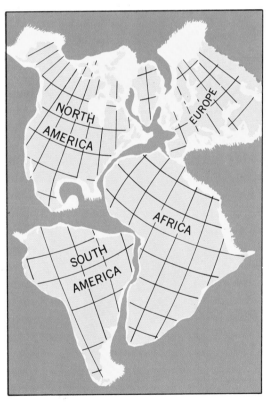

Figure 21-7. The theory of continental drift was originally proposed because the continents' shapes fit together like pieces of a huge puzzle. Of course, other evidence has also been found to support this theory.

this map, the continental shelves are included as parts of the continents. As you can see, there are regions in which the continents fit together surprisingly well. As a matter of fact, this jigsawlike fitting was one of the reasons why this theory was originally proposed.

Allowing that the outlines of the continents fit together surprisingly well (at least in some regions) we still have a number of questions to answer. For example, what sort of forces would have caused such a continental mass to break up into smaller fragments? The rock of the continents is less dense than that of the mantle. Thus, in a sense, the continents float upon the mantle. If the material in the mantle is sufficiently mobile, the floating mass of continental rock might be able to drift about, just as blocks of wood float in a pan of water.

However, seismic evidence indicates that the rock of the mantle is actually rather stiff. It would take a considerable force to push the continents around in this stiff material. So far, no one has offered any good suggestions concerning the origin of the required force.

FIND OUT BY TRYING

Materials you will need: large globe, tracing paper, scissors

Trace the outlines of the continents from a globe onto sheets of tracing paper. You will need to wrinkle the paper somewhat to make it fit the curved surface. Cut out the continents and try to fit them together into one huge continent. In what regions do the continents seem to fit together naturally? In what regions is the fit very poor? Would the continents fit better if you made two large continents? What evidence, other than fitting together, would you look for in order to substantiate the theory of continental drift?

More recent changes. Some geologists disagree with the theory of continental drift. These geologists believe the continents are changing and growing, but they also believe that the continental nuclei have always been located pretty much where they are today. These geologists believe that mountains have grown up around the continents, causing the continents to spread out in a manner similar to that which we have already described. Gradually, the continents have spread to the size and shape that we see today.

Of course, no one knows for sure which theories of continental development are correct. No matter what theory we favor, however, the evidence indicates that the continents are changing today, just as they must have been during the distant past. In fact, it seems as if most of the changes have taken place in rather recent geologic time.

The forces within the earth that participate in this continual change are still unknown. Convection currents in the mantle may cause the material of the crust to be squeezed and folded. Uneven heating in the earth's interior may cause pressure and tension in different parts of the earth's crust. Still another effect, as yet unthought of, may be responsible for the changes. But one thing is certain. The continents are a growing and changing characteristic of the earth's surface.

What reasons can you suggest to explain why it seems as if most geologic changes have taken place in recent geologic time? Is there a danger of observational bias?

Checking Your Knowledge

IMPORTANT IDEAS

1. In each continent there is at least one area of very old, lightweight rock which is believed to be the original nucleus of that continent.

2. Continental nuclei may have formed as convection currents brought lightweight rock from the interior of the molten earth to the earth's surface, where the rock cooled and solidified.

3. One theory states that the continental nuclei were always located in the same places they are today. The continents grew as a succession of volcanic arcs poured lightweight rock over the earth's surface.

4. The theory of continental drift states that the continents formed as one huge mass. The mass broke apart and the pieces (the continents) have been drifting on the semifluid mantle to their present locations.

5. The earliest, clearly recognizable fossils date back only about 600 million years. However, other forms of life may have appeared two or three billion years ago.

USING NEW WORDS

Study the terms listed below. Some of the terms are not new terms, but each of them is related to a discussion of the history of a continent. Write the letters *a* through *j* on a sheet of paper. Beside each letter write a statement or statements explaining the meaning of the term having the corresponding letter. Then tell how the term is related to the history of a continent.

a. volcanic arc
b. fossil
c. Keewatin
d. convection
e. Precambrian
f. continental nuclei
g. Grenville
h. Paleozoic
i. mountain arc
j. continental drift

TEST YOURSELF

Study the test below. On your paper write the numerals *1-10*. Beside each numeral write the correct response to that part of the test having the corresponding numeral.

1. The lightweight rock found in the continents was probably brought to the earth's surface by (*the sun's gravitational attraction, convection currents, the earth's rotation*).

2. The name given to that portion of the earth's history before the first recognizable fossils formed is the (*Precambrian Era, Paleozoic Era, Age of Continental Drift*).

3. The density of the lava from the first volcanoes to form (*was greater than, was less than, was the same as*) the density of the lava from volcanoes on the continents today.

4. Most of the water molecules that were in the gases of the protoearth (*are in the oceans today, have escaped into space, are trapped in the earth's interior*).

5. The first areas of the continents to form were the (*continental nuclei, folded mountains, geosynclines*).

6. The earth's first mountains were (*volcanic, folded, complex*).

7. Which of these events occurred first? (a) the first clearly recognizable fossils formed, (b) the oceans formed, (c) the first volcanoes formed.

8. Which of these events occurred most recently? (a) the first clearly recognizable fossils formed, (b) the oceans formed, (c) the first volcanoes formed.

9. Which of the following formed first? (a) the protoearth, (b) the first sedimentary rock, (c) the continental nuclei.

10. Which of the following formed most recently? (a) the protoearth, (b) the first sedimentary rock, (c) the continental nuclei.

Extending Your Knowledge

QUESTIONS TO EXPLORE

1. Have the rates of erosion and deposition been constant throughout geologic time? If not, what factors would affect rates of erosion and deposition in any given period?

2. Why is the presence of life during the Precambrian Era so difficult to establish?

3. What has been the role of volcanism in the formation of continents?

4. What are some of the unknowns concerning the earth's mantle that make it difficult to develop theories of continent development?

5. The exposed areas of the Canadian shield contain some of the oldest rock known. What are some possible reasons why such ancient rock is not more commonly found at or near the earth's surface?

6. What kinds of evidence would a scientist seek in order to determine whether an area was above or below sea level during a certain period of time?

7. What are some of the types of evidence which indicate that North America may have developed from a smaller continent?

SOME THINGS TO DO

1. Make a series of posters. On each poster show how the area in which you live may have appeared at different times in the geologic history of that area. Make a poster for each of these times—4 billion years ago, 1 billion years ago, 150 million years ago, and 20,000 years ago.

2. Consult your State Geological Survey or the Geology Department of your state university. Learn from geologists where outcrops of geologically important rock are located in your state. If possible, visit these areas. Try to find answers to these questions. Is the rock igneous, metamorphic, or sedimentary? How old is the rock? Does the rock contain fossils? If so, what kinds of fossils? Are the fossils all one kind, or a mixture of many kinds?

3. Consider the following statement. "In the distant past, the subcontinent of India was located farther south than it is now. Somehow, the forces which operate within the earth pushed India northward into the continent of Asia." Study a map of the region of southern Asia. What evidence can you find which supports this statement? What evidence is there to disprove this statement?

CHALLENGES IN SCIENCE

1. Think of ways which might be developed for using volcanism for the benefit of man. What would be some of the advantages of such a project? What dangers can you think of which might be associated with such a project? Are there any places where volcanism is now being used effectively?

2. Trace the evolution of various forms of life from the Cambrian period to the present day. When were dinosaurs common? When did mammals appear? Assume the age of the earth to be 4.5×10^9 years. What percentage of this time has man been on the earth? Try to relate changes in the nature of the earth to the changes in the forms of life which prevailed. What changes in the earth, do you think, may have been brought about by the presence of living organisms? What changes, if any, may be attributed to man?

3. Suggest an explanation as to why the growth of a continent should consist of stages in which the regions around the continent become unstable, are subjected to volcanism and mountain building, and later become part of the stable continental area.

BREAKTHROUGHS IN SCIENCE

In 1896, a discovery was made which has been affecting man's life on earth ever since. The phenomenon discovered—radioactivity—is usually associated with nuclear physics, but applications and uses of radioactivity are common in all areas of science. Even today, more than 70 years after its discovery, new uses for radioactivity are still being suggested.

The discovery of radioactivity may be considered accidental. Certainly, the French physicist *Becquerel* (bek rel′), who made the discovery, did not set out to discover radioactivity. He was studying the phenomenon by which certain substances glow when exposed to ultraviolet radiation. For his studies he had obtained samples of various minerals. These minerals, along with several unopened packages of photographic plates, were in his desk. When he wanted to use the plates, Becquerel found them badly fogged, as if they had been exposed to light. But light could not have penetrated the materials in which the plates were wrapped. Investigation revealed that a mineral labeled "Pitchblende from Bohemia" was emitting radiation that fogged the plates, even through their protective wrappers.

It was known that certain radiation could penetrate materials that are opaque to visible light, since *Roentgen* (rent′gən) had discovered X rays the year before. But the production of X rays required special equipment, whereas the radiation emitted by the pitchblende (uranium ore) flowed steadily, without using power from any outside source. This natural emission of radiation was called radioactivity.

Further study convinced Becquerel and other early investigators that radioactivity is related to the structure of the atom. Thus, through radioactivity, new ways to study the structure of the atom were devised, and man was able to make important progress toward the goal of understanding the nature of matter.

Consider the circumstances surrounding the discovery of radioactivity. Then consider the following question. Was the discovery accidental? It is true that Becquerel did not purposely set out to discover radioactivity. But, under the same circumstances, how many of us would have made the same discovery? Perhaps we would have just bought new photographic plates and ignored the fogged ones, blaming the manufacturer. Becquerel could have done the same thing. In fact, there were many courses Becquerel could have followed. But he chose the course which led to an important discovery. Was he just lucky? It has been said, "Chance favors the prepared mind." In other words, it isn't just luck that determines who will make important contributions and discoveries. Part of the "luck" is in noticing details and following up observations in a meaningful way.

Whether or not the discovery of radioactivity was accidental is of little importance. But there is no doubt of the importance of the discovery itself. Any discovery with such significant and diverse applications as diagnosis and treatment in medicine, age determination of materials in geology and archaeology, and nuclear energy for war or peace must be regarded as a breakthrough in science.

REVIEWING UNIT FIVE

SUMMARY

1. The earth's surface features result from geologic processes which have shaped the earth from its beginnings and are still shaping the earth today.

2. The study of the oceans is a challenge to man's ingenuity. The ocean floor and the deep ocean currents are subjects of intensive study by oceanographers today.

3. The atmosphere becomes less dense with increasing altitude. Winds result from differences in temperature, and wind patterns are affected by the Coriolis effect, the seasons, and the continents and oceans.

4. Geologic processes leave behind bits of evidence concerning the nature and sequence of past events.

5. Radioactive dating is used by geologists to determine the age of very old rock.

6. The rock of the continents is less dense than that of the ocean floor. Possibly, convection currents carried the less dense rock to a level near the earth's surface, and continents developed as volcanoes poured the lightweight rock over the earth's surface.

7. Continents may have formed in their present locations, or they may have drifted there after one huge continent split apart.

QUESTIONS TO DISCUSS

1. How do density differences provide the driving force for the supposed convection currents in the earth's interior?

2. What is half-life? Do all radioactive elements have the same half-life?

3. What are the factors that combine to produce our weather?

4. How is weather different from climate?

5. How would you explain the formation of a canyon? An island arc? A geosyncline?

UNIT TEST

Study the test below. On your paper write the numerals *1-10*. Beside each numeral write the correct response to that part of the test having the corresponding numeral.

1. The three processes of mountain formation are volcanism, plateau erosion, and _____.

2. A stream of running water which empties into a larger stream is called a _____ of the larger stream.

3. Surface currents in the ocean appear to be caused by the _____ winds in the atmosphere's global pattern of circulation.

4. Fossils of organisms that lived in many areas of the earth, but only for a relatively short period of time, are used to correlate the rock layers in which the fossils are found. Such fossils are called _____.

5. The _____ theory explains why mountains form in arc-shaped ranges.

6. The heat energy required to produce convection currents in the earth's mantle may be provided by _____ elements included within the protoearth as it condensed from a cloud of gas and dust.

7. Each continent contains at least one small area of very old rock, called the continental _____, around which the continent is believed to have formed.

8. In the Northern Hemisphere, a balance of forces between the Coriolis effect and pressure causes the air flowing around a low-pressure area to move in a *(clockwise, counterclockwise)* direction.

9. A batholith is a huge mass of *(igneous, sedimentary, metamorphic)* rock.

10. Moist air has *(a greater density than, a lesser density than, the same density as)* dry air under the same conditions of temperature and pressure.

ENRICHING YOUR SCIENCE EXPERIENCES

INVESTIGATIONS TO CARRY OUT

1. Observe and keep a record of the following weather conditions every day for an extended period of time: atmospheric pressure, temperature, wind direction, wind speed, number and types of clouds present, and precipitation. According to your observations, are any of the conditions related to each other? If so, how? Do your observations help you forecast the weather? What other observations might be helpful in predicting the weather?

If your observations of weather conditions meet their standards, you may be able to contribute your data to the United States Weather Bureau. For more information and an application, write to: Environmental Science Services Administration, Weather Bureau, Silver Springs, Maryland 20910.

2. Investigate the effects of the prolonged application of forces to various materials. For example, one possible experiment is to measure the rate and amount of bending in a long, narrow strip of metal supported at only one end. Using C-clamps, clamp one of the narrow ends of the metal strip to a table top. Leave the other end unsupported. Measure and record the distance between the bottom of the strip and the floor once each week for a period of several weeks. A similar experiment involves placing the ends of a long, narrow strip of plasterboard on supports. Observe what happens to the plasterboard when a weight is placed on the unsupported center of the strip and allowed to remain there for several weeks.

ADDITIONAL READING IN SCIENCE

Battan, Louis J., *Radar Observes the Weather*. Garden City, New York, Doubleday & Company, Inc., 1962. 158 pp.

Battan, Louis J., *The Nature of Violent Storms*. Garden City, New York, Doubleday & Company, Inc., 1961. 158 pp.

Carrington, Richard, *A Guide to Earth History*. New York, New American Library, Inc., 1961. 284 pp.

Ericson, Davis B., and Wollin, Goesta, *The Ever-Changing Sea*. New York, Alfred A. Knopf, Inc., 1967. 354 pp.

Gamow, George, *A Planet Called Earth*. New York, Viking Press, 1963. 257 pp.

Gaskell, T. F., *World Beneath the Oceans*. Garden City, New York, The Natural History Press, 1964. 154 pp.

Leet, L. Don, and Judson, Sheldon, *Physical Geology*. 3rd ed. New York, Prentice-Hall, Inc., 1965. 406 pp.

Loebsack, Theo, *Our Atmosphere*. New York, New American Library, Inc., 1961. 190 pp.

Sanders, Howard J., "Chemistry and the Solid Earth." *Chemical and Engineering News* (October 2, 1967), pp. 1A–48A.

Viorst, Judith, *The Changing Earth*. New York, Bantam Books, 1967. 244 pp.

UNIT 6

ROCKS, FOSSILS, AND MINERALS

The rocks and minerals near the surface of the earth are very important to man. These rocks and minerals are essential for the production of food that makes life possible. They are also essential for the production of the clothing and fuels that make it possible for man to live in many different climates on the earth. Rocks and minerals provide the raw materials for many of the manufacturing processes of modern civilization. In short, rocks and minerals, together with the energy of the sun, provide many of the resources upon which man depends for maintaining life and developing his civilization.

Since man's future depends to some extent on his ability to use the resources provided by rocks and minerals, it makes sense to learn as much as we can about them. In addition to being an important factor in man's future, rocks—and the fossils in them—reveal a fascinating story about the earth's past. This story tells of changes in the seas and land forms, of the development of living things, and even of conditions on the earth before life was possible.

In UNIT 6 you will study the variety of rocks and minerals which comprise the crust of the earth. You will discover something of the role played by each type of rock and mineral in the history of this space platform on which we live. You will find out how fossils form and what can be learned from them. In this unit you will learn of the value of certain minerals. You will also study the history of a specific rock formation. Perhaps, after learning about the value and importance of our natural mineral resources, you will have a better understanding of why conservation practices are important.

◄ Knowledge and proper use of the earth's crustal materials is vital to man's civilization.

Knowledge of rocks requires laboratory work as well as field study.

CHAPTER 22

Types of Rock

"Go my Sons, buy stout shoes, climb mountains, search the valleys, the deserts, the sea shores and deep recesses of the earth. Look for the various kinds of minerals, note their characters and mark their origin. Lastly . . . observe and experiment without ceasing, for in this way and in no other will you arrive at a knowledge of the nature and properties of things."

Follow this advice from a book written in 1778 and you will make countless discoveries. Of course, your findings will depend, in part, upon where you live. In southern Indiana, you might observe great deposits of limestone. In Vermont, marble is a common rock. In many places you may find rock that has been folded and squeezed by enormous forces. Or, you may find beautiful crystals embedded in layers of otherwise uninteresting rock. You will probably want to know more about rocks and minerals than you can learn by studying the rocks in your locality. A field study of rocks can be combined with laboratory studies and with a study of the things that are known about rocks and minerals not found in your locality.

In Chapter 22 you will make a more detailed study of rocks and minerals than you had previously made. You will discover some factors that are important in crystal formation. The complex process that begins with the solidification of igneous rock and results in the formation of many types of rock is discussed. After studying Chapter 22, you should have a better idea than you now have of the processes that combine to produce the environment in which you live.

1. Minerals

What is a mineral? Some pieces of the earth's crustal material consist of only one substance. Gold nuggets, for example, contain only one substance—the element gold. However, such examples of crustal material composed of only one substance are rare. Most rock, including the granite and basalt which we have mentioned frequently in previous chapters, consists of various combinations of many different substances called minerals.

Why are some substances called minerals while others are not? Several characteristics are considered in defining a mineral. One is that a mineral is a naturally occurring substance. Metallic ores found in the earth, such as taconite and bauxite, are minerals. However, man-made materials, such as stainless steel, are not minerals.

Another characteristic of minerals is that they are inorganic—that is, they are not parts of living creatures nor have they ever been. In this aspect of the definition of a mineral—that is, whether or not a mineral must be inorganic—we must be a little flexible. Most geologists would classify the calcium carbonate found in limestone as a mineral, although it may have been part of the shell of a sea creature. Coal and oil are sometimes classified as minerals, although they are very probably the remains of partially decayed plants and animals. However, another characteristic of minerals tends to rule out coal and oil as minerals. This characteristic has to do with the chemical composition of a mineral.

In general, each mineral has a definite chemical composition. For example, pure quartz—a mineral with the chemical formula SiO_2—is composed of only two elements, silicon (Si) and oxygen (O). Furthermore, of the total number of atoms in any mass of pure quartz, one third are silicon atoms and two thirds are oxygen atoms. Pure quartz found anywhere in the world has exactly this chemical composition. In contrast, coal and oil have a wide variety of chemical compositions. Therefore, according to the statement that each mineral has a definite chemical composition, coal and oil are not minerals.

In most minerals, the particles—ions, atoms, or molecules—are arranged in a very precise pattern. This arrangement of particles, called the *crystal lattice,* permits the formation of crystals. One mineral with which we are all familiar is common table salt. Salt consists of equal amounts of two different chemical elements, sodium and chlorine. In a salt crystal, ions of chlorine and sodium are arranged alternately on a cubic lattice. See *Figure 22-1*. As a result, the crystal of salt has

Figure 22-1. The arrangement of ions of sodium and chlorine in a crystal of sodium chloride is shown in the diagram below. The positions of the nuclei of the ions are shown as well as the relative sizes of the ions. Below the diagram is a picture of a large crystal of sodium chloride. Observe its form.

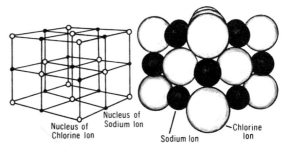

Nucleus of Chlorine Ion   Nucleus of Sodium Ion   Sodium Ion   Chlorine Ion

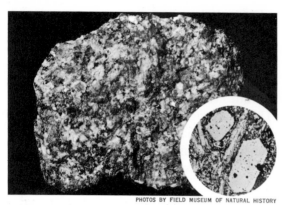

Figure 22-2. The grainy texture of granite can be seen when a piece of it is broken. The grains—shown in the inset—are crystals and fragments of crystals.

Figure 22-3. Large crystals of any mineral are relatively rare in nature. The large crystals of quartz in this picture undoubtedly formed very slowly.

a cubic shape. Naturally occurring salt is called *halite* (hal′īt).

Crystals and crystal formation. Although most minerals form beautiful crystals under ideal conditions, we seldom find large crystals in nature. In fact, a large crystal is a rare and beautiful discovery. Instead, most minerals occur in rock as fine grains. Sometimes these grains are difficult to see, especially if the surface of a rock has been worn smooth. If the rock is broken open, however, the grains become more easily seen. They can easily be observed through an ordinary hand lens. The grains are very seldom large crystals. Nevertheless, the basic atomic arrangement is still present. If these grains are examined with a microscope, tiny crystals or fragments of crystals can usually be seen, as in *Figure 22-2*.

What factors determine whether a mineral will form into a large crystal or into a small grain with only microscopic crystals? Basically, two processes are involved. These processes are cooling and mixing. Suppose we imagine a situation in which the elements which form a crystal are dispersed in a liquid. Perhaps the liquid is water, such as the salt water of Great Salt Lake. From this water, halite crystals might form. For most mineral

crystals, however, the liquid is not water, but molten rock material.

When rock material is in a molten state, the minerals in it are usually well mixed. As a mass of molten material cools, here and there within the mass tiny portions will suddenly become solid. Each portion will be composed of a pure mineral, perhaps just a few atoms of silicon and oxygen combining to form a tiny speck of quartz. This tiny speck of quartz will be surrounded by other minerals still in a molten state. The liquid material is not yet cool enough for other minerals to solidify. That is, the still-liquid minerals have a lower freezing point (melting point) than that of quartz. But, after one tiny speck of quartz has changed from a liquid to a solid, it rapidly attracts other molecules of silica (SiO_2) which are nearby in the molten mass. The crystallized speck of quartz becomes the nucleus of a growing crystal.

The process of crystal growth is not completely understood. It appears that the arrangement of molecules (or atoms) in a particular crystal makes it easy for other molecules (or atoms) of the same material to attach themselves. As an example, let us consider the same speck of crystallizing quartz which we talked about in the preceding paragraph. The silica molecules in the immediate vicinity of the speck of crystallizing quartz are used up very quickly. However, if the molten rock material is cooling very, very slowly, then it is possible for continued mixing to take place. The original, small crystal of quartz will slowly swirl through the molten rock. In the process, the crystal will come into contact with other molecules of silica. The molecules will become part of the crystal and the crystal will increase in size. If this process continues long enough, the crystal of quartz can become quite large.

But what happens if the cooling process is faster? Then, minerals other than quartz also begin to form crystals throughout the liquid. Of course, other quartz crystals will also be forming throughout the cooling liquid. But now, with so many various kinds of crystals forming, it is impossible for large crystals of any one kind to form. Instead, when the molten material solidifies, the rock formed is made up of a mass of small grains of various materials, all mixed together.

A similar process takes place when a mineral crystallizes from a water solution. If the process happens very slowly, then large crystals can be built up. If the process happens rapidly, the crystals formed will be small and irregular. Even when there is only one mineral involved, such as salt in water, it is still necessary to have the formation proceed slowly in order to form large, perfect crystals.

As yet, scientists are not certain as to why the crystallization process must proceed slowly in order to form large crystals. Apparently, when an ion of sodium or chlorine becomes attached to a growing salt crystal, the ion must slide across the surface until it fits into the right position in the crystal lattice. Suppose the process is happening too quickly. For example, if the water is evaporating rapidly, the salt must leave the solution quickly and become a solid. Then the ions do not have a chance to move across the crystal face and into the right location. Thus, a mass of small crystals—rather than one, large, perfect crystal—is formed.

Although the process of crystal formation is not completely understood, these things are known. The formation of large crystals requires a long time. If crystals of two or more substances are forming within the same solution or within the same molten material at the same time, they tend to interfere with one another. Then the crystals of all the substances involved are usually much smaller and more irregularly shaped than if only one type of crystal were forming.

FIND OUT BY TRYING

Materials you will need: ordinary table salt, kosher salt, 2 evaporating dishes, distilled water, graduated cylinder, hand lens

Place 50 milliliters of distilled water in each of the evaporating dishes. Dissolve one-half teaspoon of ordinary table salt in one dish and one-half teaspoon of kosher salt (which can be obtained at most large grocery stores) in the other. Allow the water to evaporate. When the water has evaporated, examine the residue with a hand lens. What differences, if any, can you observe? How do you account for any differences? HINT: Read the labels on the salt packages.

The silicon-oxygen tetrahedron. We have already described quartz. Quartz has its own characteristic crystalline structure. That is, the atoms in a quartz crystal are arranged in a special way. The arrangement in quartz is called the *silicon-oxygen tetrahedron*. The arrangement of these tetrahedrons in quartz results in a specific shape for quartz crystals, as shown in *Figure 22-3*.

The silicon-oxygen tetrahedron is a very important structural pattern. As you know, silicon and oxygen are the most abundant elements in the rock of the earth's crust. Minerals which contain silicon and oxygen are, therefore, the most abundant minerals. Quartz is one such mineral, and there are many others. Minerals containing silicon and oxygen are called the *silicate minerals*. Almost all of them have the silicon-oxygen tetrahedron as a unit of their crystal structure. In fact, about 90 per cent of the minerals in the crust of the earth have the silicon tetrahedron as part of their internal structure. Some of the most common silicate minerals are shown in *Figure 22-5*.

Variations in chemical composition. Most minerals have exact chemical formulas. However, as was mentioned earlier, there may be some slight variations in certain minerals. The typical silicate rocks are examples of minerals that may have slight variations in their chemical composition. In the chemical formula of hornblende, for example, there is the expression *(Mg, Fe)₄*. This expression in the chemical formula means that either magnesium (Mg) atoms or iron (Fe) atoms can fit into the molecule of the mineral hornblende. In fact, most hornblende has a mixture of molecules, some with magnesium and some with

Figure 22-4. The arrangement of the ions of silicon and oxygen in the silicon-oxygen tetrahedron is shown in these diagrams. The relative sizes of these ions are shown in the diagram on the right.

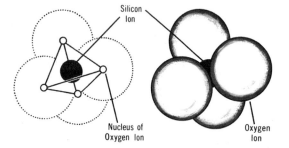

Silicon Ion

Nucleus of Oxygen Ion

Oxygen Ion

Figure 22-5. The crystal shown in the vertical picture is orthoclase feldspar, a mineral having the chemical formula $KAlSi_3O_8$. Shown in the top horizontal picture is hornblende, $Ca_2(Mg, Fe)_4Al(OH)_2AlSi_3O_{10}$. Mica, shown in the bottom horizontal picture, has the formula $K(Mg, Fe)_3(OH, F)_2AlSi_3O_{10}$. Notice that each of these minerals are silicates—that is, they contain a combination of silicon and oxygen.

418

iron. The difference in composition results in a slight variation in the color of hornblende, depending upon the proportion of these two types of molecules. Within the crystal structure of hornblende, an atom of magnesium occupies a certain specific position. However, an atom of iron can fit into this same position without changing the crystal's structure. That is why this particular substance is called a single mineral, regardless of whether iron or magnesium is present. The basic crystal structure is unchanged, and the basic chemical formula has only a minor change.

What is the effect of crystalline structure on the properties of a mineral?

2. Igneous Rock

Magma and lava. You will recall that igneous rock is that rock which has solidified from a molten state. Geologists believe that all of the rocks and minerals that are now on the surface of the earth were once molten. Molten rock material beneath the surface of the earth is called *magma*. When magma reaches the surface of the earth, as in a volcanic eruption, it is called *lava*. In many cases, magma pushes up toward the surface of the earth but solidifies before breaking through the surface.

As you have learned, many things can happen to rock after it solidifies. It can be broken down into fine particles and the fine particles can be carried away by water or by the wind. Such particles are then deposited in another location and formed into sedimentary rock. Both sedimentary and igneous rock can be changed by pressure and temperature, without melting, into a new form called metamorphic rock. But each of these changes starts with rock which solidified from a molten state. Thus, igneous rock is considered to be the primary rock of the earth's surface.

How would you explain how sandstone can come from igneous rock? How limestone can?

Formations of igneous rock. Igneous rock contains a wide variety of different minerals in different proportions. Consequently, there are many different kinds of igneous rock. One way of classifying igneous rock is on the basis of where it solidified. On this basis, igneous rock can be classified into two groups: *intrusive* (in trü′siv) and *extrusive* (ek strü′ siv). Intrusive igneous rock is rock formed when magma solidified beneath the surface of the earth. Extrusive igneous rock is rock which solidified from lava—that is, it solidified at or above the earth's surface.

A batholith is a large mass of intrusive rock. Batholiths were described briefly in Chapter 20. Batholiths generally consist of granitic rock. They are the largest masses of rock in the crust of the earth. For example, most of the Sierra Nevada range of mountains in California is a huge batholith, approximately 110 km across and 650 km long.

When batholiths form, they tend to replace the older layers of solid rock above them, as shown in *Figure 20-2*. Much of the older rock is melted by the heat of the batholith and so contributes to the magma. In some cases, solid blocks of rock from overlying layers break off and slowly sink into the molten rock of the batholith. Sometimes, the temperature of the magma is below the melting point of these blocks of rock. Then these blocks remain as solid chunks, called *xenoliths* (zen′ə liths).

After the batholith has cooled and solidified, the overlying crust of rock may be worn away by erosion. Then the batholith itself is revealed on the surface.

There are other forms of intrusive rock which are smaller than batholiths. Two such common formations are *dikes* and *sills*. A dike is formed as magma pushes up through a crack in layers of rock and then solidifies. A sill is formed as magma forces its way between two layers of sedimentary rock and solidifies there. See *Figure 22-6*.

In some cases, when magma is forced between layers of sedimentary rock, the overlying layers are pushed upward. The magma then cools into a domelike mass of rock, as shown on the right in *Figure 14-7*. A formation formed in this manner is called a *laccolith* (lak′ə lith). Laccoliths are typically about one or two kilometers across.

The most common type of intrusive rock is granite. The composition of granite depends upon the composition of the magma which solidified to form the granite. The kinds and proportions of minerals present vary from one mass of magma to another. Thus, granite occurs in many different forms. However, the freshly broken surface of any granitic rock is coarse, showing that the mineral grains are comparatively large. Another type of igneous rock is basalt. Basalt is typically much darker than granite. Also, the surface of a freshly broken piece of basalt shows much finer grains than those of granite.

Figure 22-6. Both the dike (left) and the sill (right) are intrusive rock formations. They differ in that dikes form in nearly vertical cracks through layers of rock, whereas sills form between layers of rock.

JEROME WYCKOFF   HAROLD R. WANLESS

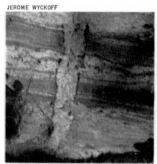

DO IT YOURSELF

Compare the grains in granite and basalt

Use a hand lens to examine a freshly broken piece of granite. Are the grains easy to see? If so, how many different minerals can you observe? How many minerals can you identify?

Make a similar examination of a piece of basalt. Compare the grains in the basalt with those in the granite. Are the grains in basalt the same size as those in granite? Are they composed of the same material as those in the granite?

Extrusive rock. Extrusive igneous rock forms as lava cools. Lava cools comparatively quickly, since it is exposed on the earth's surface. In fact, some materials thrown out by volcanoes cool so rapidly that they are solid before they hit the ground. The solid particles produced in this way are usually quite small, taking the form of ashes or cinders. Sometimes, however, the solid particles emitted by volcanoes are rather large. The largest ones are called *volcanic bombs*.

Volcanoes that produce ashes and cinders usually assume a characteristic shape, and are called *cinder cones*. Paricutin, a recently

420

Figure 22-7. Paricutin, the cinder cone shown above, became active in 1943. It is one of the more recent volcanoes on the earth.

formed volcano in Mexico, is a good example of a cinder cone. *(Figure 22-7.)* Not all the ash from such a volcano stays in the immediate vicinity to form the cinder cone. The larger particles accumulate near the volcano to form the cone. The finer particles of ash are carried in the wind and may fall to earth many kilometers away. Thus, layers of volcanic ash may accumulate over a wide area.

In many cases, gas bubbles are trapped within the lava, making the lava foamy. When such lava solidifies, the rock is very porous and appears to be frothy. *Pumice* (pum′is) and *scoria* (skôr′i ə) are two such frothy appearing types of rock. Another typical volcanic rock is obsidian, a natural glass. Obsidian, like other glasses, is not crystallized at all. A mixture of different minerals within it gives it a dark color, usually black or dark brown. These types of rock are shown in *Figure 14-8.*

Do you think that all the differences between extrusive rock and intrusive rock are related to the rate at which each type of rock cools? If not, what other factors do you think might be important?

3. Sedimentary Rock

Weathering and erosion. We have spoken of sedimentary rock many times in previous chapters. You know that sedimentary rock is formed from particles which were at one time loose and separate. Somehow, these particles have become compacted and cemented together to form a solid mass of rock. But where did the particles come from?

The material in many types of sedimentary rock was, at one time, part of other rock. This earlier rock broke down into finer and finer particles through the process called *weathering*. There are many forms of weathering. Sand carried by the winds in a desert will wear away the surface of the rock across which the wind blows. Also, temperature changes between summer and winter and

Figure 22-8. Formations of rock are gradually broken down into smaller and smaller fragments of rock by the processes of weathering. Even in the desert, weathering is an important geologic process. Wind-blown sand is one agent of weathering that is effective in producing a form such as the one shown below.

between day and night cause rock to expand and contract. The expansion and contraction are not uniform throughout the rock. As a consequence, pieces of rock flake off. In some cases, pieces of rock bumping and rubbing together in a stream bed are gradually worn down into fine particles.

As weathering causes rocks and minerals to break into smaller fragments, erosion removes the fragments. In most cases, the fine particles produced by weathering are carried to a lake or to the ocean by rivers. Here they settle. As layers of this material accumulate and become cemented together, sedimentary rock is formed. In some cases, the weathered material is not carried away to a lake or to the ocean. It stays where it is, forming an ever-deepening layer of sediment. Eventually, this sediment may solidify to form a type of sedimentary rock.

Can you think of a process in which man has used the weathering action of wind-blown sand? If so, describe the process.

DO IT YOURSELF

Find examples of weathering

Observe examples of weathering in your community. Make a list of the examples of weathering you observe. What types of rock that you observed are most affected by weathering? How does weathering differ from erosion? Select one type of weathering and study it in detail.

Limestone. Not all sedimentary rock is composed of particles produced by the weathering of rock. For example, the materials which become cemented together to form limestone are not necessarily products of the weathering of other rock. As you may recall, limestone is composed mainly of the mineral calcium carbonate. One way for deposits of calcium carbonate to originate is by the accumulation of the shells and skeletons of sea creatures on the ocean floor. Another way is the direct precipitation of calcium carbonate from ocean water. Whenever deposits of calcium carbonate become cemented together, no matter what the origin of the calcium carbonate, limestone is formed.

Other types of sedimentary rock. Most forms of sedimentary rock are mixtures of many different types of particles and different chemicals. However, the most common types of sedimentary rock belong to one of three classes. These classes are sandstone, composed of sand particles; limestone, composed of calcium carbonate in one form or another; and shale, which is consolidated clay. Examples of these classes of sedimentary rock are shown in *Figure 14-8.* Very few sedimentary rocks are pure forms of any one of these classes. Most are mixtures. For example, most limestone has a little bit of sand and a little bit of clay mixed with it.

Some sedimentary rock does not fit into any of these three classes. One type which does not fit these classes is *conglomerate* (kən glom′ər it). Conglomerate is a consolidated mixture of gravel, sand, and mud. In some cases, the large, rocky particles in conglomerate can be the size of boulders—that is, more than ten inches in diameter. *Flint* is another sedimentary rock which does not fit neatly into any class. Flint is composed primarily of the same mineral as sand—that is, silica (SiO_2). However, flint does not have the grainy texture of sandstone.

Figure 22-9. Although conglomerate (left) and flint (right) are forms of sedimentary rock, they differ greatly from each other—especially in texture.

Certain types of sedimentary rock are important natural resources. Some forms of sedimentary rock contain enough iron ore to make them good commercial sources of iron. Another type of sedimentary rock is made up of the glassy, microscopic shells of diatoms. Diatoms are small plants that live by the millions in the ocean near the surface. See *Figure 16-24.* As diatoms die, their shells slowly sink to the ocean bottom, accumulating to form thick layers. The tiny shells become compacted to form a light, chalky rock. In addition, each diatom contains a drop of oil. Some geologists believe that the major oil supplies of the world originated from diatoms.

What other types of sediment or sedimentary rock can you think of that are important natural resources?

Stratification and fossils. One of the most striking features of sedimentary rock and an indication of the way it formed is *stratification* (strat′ə fə kā′shən), or the presence of layers. Sometimes, layers form because different types of sediment are washed into a lake or into the ocean at different times of the year or in different geologic periods. In some sedimentary rock, the difference between one layer and another is simply the result of different colors of the material.

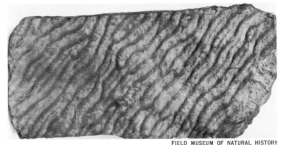

Figure 22-10. Ripple marks such as these are found only in sedimentary rock.

Some layers of sedimentary rock show ripple marks on the surface. *(Figure 22-10.)* These ripple marks are clues to the environment in which the rock formed. Can you imagine how these marks were formed?

As you already know, many formations of sedimentary rock contain fossils. *Coquina* (kō kē′nə) is composed almost completely of fossils. *(Figure 19-7.)* Other sedimentary rock may contain only a few traces of bones or shells. In some fossils, the organism or part of the organism is preserved, but in many cases only an imprint remains. The chemicals which originally formed the organism were dissolved during the history of the rock. Other chemicals took their place. But, in the slow interchange, the form of the original organism was retained. This form can still be seen when the rock containing the fossil is cracked open, as shown in *Figure 22-11.*

Figure 22-11. The pieces of broken rock contain the forms of ancient shells. However, the materials that composed the original shells have been replaced.

4. Metamorphic Rock

Factors in metamorphism. Rock buried several thousand feet beneath the surface of the earth is subjected to an enormous amount of pressure. In most cases, this pressure is much greater than the pressure which was present when the rock was originally formed. In addition, the temperature deep beneath the surface of the earth is greater than the temperature at the earth's surface. Thus, deeply buried rock is subjected to a greater temperature and a higher pressure than is the rock near the earth's surface. As a result, deeply buried rock may undergo important changes in its internal structure. Such a change is called *metamorphism* (met'ə môr'fiz əm). As a result of this change, it is usually impossible to identify the original rock. Both sedimentary rock and igneous rock could have been changed into the same type of metamorphic rock, provided they had the same chemical composition.

The temperature required for metamorphism is just below the temperature needed for melting of the rock undergoing the change. If the temperature becomes high enough, the rock will melt. Then, when it solidifies, the new rock will be an igneous rock, not a metamorphic rock. In some masses of rock, it appears that portions of the rock may have melted, whereas other portions remained solid. In such a case as this, it is almost impossible to classify the resulting rock as igneous or metamorphic. But, in general, metamorphic rock is rock which has changed without melting.

During metamorphism, one change that takes place is the formation of new crystals. The chemical composition of the new crystals is usually the same as that of the original crystals. In some cases, chemical elements are added in the process of the change, but the important change is to new crystal forms.

Fluids trapped within the rock are extremely important in metamorphic changes. Water is one fluid which is often trapped in rock. As the temperature and pressure increase, water within the rock will flow from one place to another, carrying dissolved chemicals with it. This water assists in the breakdown of old crystals and the formation of new crystals.

Processes in metamorphism. There are four principal processes that may take place when a rock is undergoing metamorphism. One of these processes is *rock flowage*. Most materials, when placed under high pressure for a long period of time, will move or flow. In Chapter 20 we described the convection theory of mountain building. We talked about the idea that material in the mantle of the earth is constantly circulating in huge convection currents. Rock in the crust of the earth can also flow if the pressures are great enough. When the rock is at a very high temperature, it will flow more readily. Under the right conditions, most rock will flow slowly, without cracking or breaking. *(Figure 22-12.)*

Figure 22-12. The rock shown below must have been subjected to great forces and must have flowed as a viscous fluid to attain the contours shown.

HAROLD R. WANLESS

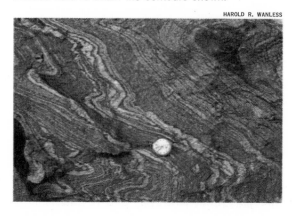

Figure 22-13. Because extremely great pressure and temperature occur during metamorphism, new mineral forms are sometimes produced. One result, as shown above, may be the formation of crystals of garnet.

A second process associated with metamorphism is *granulation* (gran′yə lā′shən). Under high pressure, large crystals and large mineral grains will break down. The process of granulation is most likely to take place when the minerals involved are brittle and resist flowage. The result is. a fine powder rather than a coarse mixture of large grains.

Recrystallization and *recombination* are also processes which may occur during metamorphism. When a rock is subjected to high temperature and great pressure for a long time, the various elements in the rock may form new crystals. These processes are more apt to happen if water is present. Sometimes the same mineral forms will be present, but the crystal sizes will change. In other cases new mineral forms will emerge as the elements are rearranged in a different crystal structure. Which of these processes occurs depends upon the nature of the minerals.

In general, the minerals favored are those in which the atoms can be fitted together in a way which occupies the least volume. A mineral in which the atoms are loosely packed will tend to break down under high pressure. Thus, if atoms pack together into a smaller space in a particular crystal structure, this structure will be favored under high pressure. One crystal which often forms under high pressure in metamorphic rock is *garnet* (gär′ nit), shown in *Figure 22-13*.

Types of metamorphic rock. Metamorphic rock is generally classified into two groups— *foliated* (fō′li ā′tid) and *unfoliated*. The term foliated means having a layered structure. One type of foliated metamorphic rock is slate. Common blackboard slates have been split from large blocks of foliated metamorphic rock. The layers in such a rock favor fractures in one plane only. The plane along which such a fracture occurs is called a *cleavage* (klē′vij) *plane*.

A typical unfoliated metamorphic rock is marble. Marble can occur in many forms. Some forms of marble have rather large grains, but very few forms have simple cleavage planes. If marble contains large amounts of

Figure 22-14. Marble is useful as a building material and for statuary. Thus, marble has great commercial value. Marble quarries, such as the one shown below, are valuable assets.

an impurity such as mica, the marble will have a tendency to be foliated. However, this form of marble is not common. Because of its unfoliated structure, its comparative softness, and its regular grain structure, marble is favored by sculptors for carving.

What rocks or minerals do you know of that have well-defined cleavage planes which determine where the rocks or minerals will break?

The most common type of metamorphic rock is called *gneiss* (nīs). Gneiss is a foliated rock. In some cases, the bands are quite pronounced, as is shown in *Figure 22-15*. In most cases the bands in gneiss show an irregular, folded pattern, as if the rock had been subjected to strong bending and twisting forces after the banded pattern had formed.

Figure 22-15. The rock shown appears to have layers, just as some types of sedimentary rock do. However, an examination of the rock would reveal that it is not sedimentary, but metamorphic. The formation of the dark bands—usually a dark form of mica or hornblende—is not completely understood at the present time.

FIELD MUSEUM OF NATURAL HISTORY

DO IT YOURSELF

Compare types of metamorphic rock

Make a list of metamorphic rock types. If possible, classify the types of metamorphic rock into a few main groups. What form of rock was changed to produce each particular metamorphic rock on your list? Is there any metamorphic rock of unknown origin? Examine samples of metamorphic rock. Try to determine what these rocks were before they underwent metamorphism. What happens to the fossils in a sedimentary rock that undergoes metamorphism?

Laboratory studies of metamorphic rock. Geochemists have managed to learn quite a bit about rocks and minerals by studying metamorphic rock. They have managed to produce certain metamorphic rock forms in a laboratory. Using special equipment, scientists can produce extremely great pressures, equivalent to those which exist 80 km beneath the surface of the earth. Other conditions, such as the temperature and the amount of water present, can also be controlled. By experimenting, geologists can determine what particular mineral forms are stable under a specific set of conditions. Another sample, with exactly the same chemical nature, might be subjected to different conditions of temperature and pressure. Thus, geologists might discover that a slightly different mineral form results when conditions are changed.

Through such experiments, geologists determine what mineral forms would be created in a metamorphic rock at a specific temperature and pressure. Then, by comparing the laboratory findings with observations of metamorphic rock found in the field, the geochemist can learn about the history of the rock which he finds in the field.

On the basis of such studies, geologists have concluded that much of the metamorphic rock which is now on the surface of the earth was formed about 15 km beneath the earth's surface. Somehow this rock was brought up near the surface, and the overlying layers of rock were eroded away. Thus, examination of such metamorphic rock tells us something about the history of the earth's surface in that particular region. Examination of metamorphic rock also reveals something about the conditions in the interior of the earth's crust.

How would you explain the fact that rock formed deep in the earth can now be found near the earth's surface?

Summarizing our study of rock. We have learned that each rock on the earth's surface can be classified. We can say that it is either igneous, sedimentary, or metamorphic. We can also specify the mineral content of each rock. In addition, we can describe its structure, such as, for example, whether or not it is foliated. Thus, each rock can be fitted into its proper place in a general scheme of rock classification.

In spite of the fact that rock can be described in detail and classified, each rock is unique. Each one has its own special history, and each one is the result of a long and complicated series of chemical and physical processes. The processes which have shaped the surface of the earth have left a record of their occurrence in the many forms of rock on the earth's surface.

Figure 22-16. Studying various rock formations in the field is not the only way by which geologists obtain information about the processes and conditions which produced the rock. However, such field studies are important in determining the history of a particular region of the earth's surface.

Checking Your Knowledge

1. Most minerals occur naturally, have a definite chemical composition, and occur in crystalline form.

2. Most of the earth's crust is composed of crystalline materials. However, the crystals are usually small and mixed with other types of crystals.

3. Silicon and oxygen are the most common elements in the earth's crust. They may occur together as sand or quartz, or combined with other elements in silicate rocks.

4. Scientists believe that all the rocks and minerals that now form the crust of the earth were once molten.

5. The sedimentary rock which covers a large portion of the earth is composed chiefly of materials that were derived from the breakdown, or weathering, of earlier rock.

6. Metamorphic rock was formed from igneous or sedimentary rock that changed as a result of being subjected to extremely high temperature and great pressure.

7. Scientists have learned much about the mineral forms in rock by studying minerals under laboratory conditions of great pressure and high temperature.

USING NEW WORDS

Study the pairs of words listed below. On your paper write the letters *a* through *f*. Beside each letter, write two brief statements about the pair of words having the corresponding letter. In one statement tell how the words of the pair are related. In the other, tell the differences in the meanings of the words in that pair.

a. rock—mineral   d. batholith—laccolith
b. magma—lava   e. intrusive—extrusive
c. dike—sill   f. silica—silicate

TEST YOURSELF

Study the test below. Write the numerals *1-10* on your paper. Beside each numeral, write the correct response to that part of the test having the corresponding numeral.

1. The two most common elements in the earth's crust are _____ and silicon.

2. Rock formed by the deposition and consolidation of clay has the name _____.

3. A _____ is a vertical, or nearly vertical, slab of intrusive rock formed as magma solidified after being forced into a crack in layers of sedimentary rock.

4. Of the following rocks, fossils would most likely be found in (*granite, marble, shale, scoria*).

5. A rock that might float on water is (*granite, marble, shale, scoria*).

6. Scientists believe that when the crust of the earth was originally formed, it was composed of (*sedimentary, igneous, metamorphic*) rock.

7. As the original rock of the earth's crust weathered and eroded, and as the particles deposited in different locations became cemented, (*sedimentary, igneous, metamorphic*) rock formed.

8. When rock is subjected to conditions of extremely high temperature and great pressure, the structure of the rock is usually altered, producing (*sedimentary, igneous, metamorphic*) rock.

9. In order for large crystals to form in a cooling mass of magma, the rate of cooling (*must be very rapid, must be very slow, is not a factor*).

10. The presence of several different substances in a mass of cooling magma usually (*helps, hinders, does not affect*) the formation of large crystals.

Extending Your Knowledge

1. What is the probability that crystals are now forming in the earth's crust? Under what conditions would this process occur?

2. Could you grow crystals of quartz in your school laboratory? If so, how? If not, why not?

3. Do you think there would be any relationship between the size of an intrusive rock formation and the size of the crystals that formed within the formation? If so, why? If not, why not?

4. Assuming that granite and basalt were both formed from magma, how would you account for differences in their chemical compositions and in other properties, such as grain size and hardness?

5. If slate and shale were formed from clay, what was the clay formed from?

6. Would you consider marble a good building material? Give reasons for your answer.

7. If the entire crust of the earth is composed of the rocks and minerals from which many of our manufactured products are being made, why is there any need for concern about the conservation of mineral resources?

SOME THINGS TO DO

1. Demonstrate rapid crystal growth. Obtain a pound of sodium thiosulfate (ordinary photographer's hypo) from a photo supply store. Be sure to get pure hypo, not hypo with acid already added. Fill a very clean, Pyrex flask about three-fourths full of hypo crystals. Add enough distilled water to come about one fifth of the way to the top of the level of the crystals. Heat the flask slowly until all the crystals have dissolved. Place the flask in a refrigerator to cool. When it has cooled, add one crystal of hypo to the contents. What happens? The demonstration may be repeated if the flask is reheated and then cooled. Drop a crystal of sodium chloride into the solution. What happens? Try shaking the flask. What happens?

2. Grow some crystals. Suggestions as to what chemicals to use and what procedures to follow may be found in the book *Crystals and Crystal Growing,* by Alan Holden and Phylis Singer.

3. Make a chart of all the types of metamorphic rock you know of. Opposite the name of each type of metamorphic rock, write the name of the sedimentary and/or igneous rock which was changed in the formation of that particular type of metamorphic rock.

CHALLENGES IN SCIENCE

1. In separate beakers, place small samples of granite, limestone, and marble. Add dilute hydrochloric acid to each beaker. CAUTION: Use care in handling hydrochloric acid.

Observe what happens in the beakers. Does a chemical reaction take place in all of the beakers? Does a chemical reaction take place in any of the beakers? What can you infer about the chemical compositions of these types of rock? After sufficient time has elapsed to allow any chemical reactions to be completed, carefully remove the rocks, or what remains of them, from the acid. Rinse off the acid and examine the rocks or the residue. Try to explain what you have observed.

2. Using various reference materials, find the relative sizes of a silicon atom and an oxygen atom. Using Styrofoam balls of the same relative sizes as the sizes of silicon and oxygen atoms, construct a model of a silicon-oxygen tetrahedron.

CHAPTER 23

To many people, the most fascinating of all fossils are dinosaur remains.

DE WYS, INC.

Fossils and Their Stories

Not all traces of organisms living on the earth long ago were lost when these organisms died. Bones, shells, imprints, and other evidences of the existence of these organisms are preserved in ancient rock for man's study. As you know, these evidences of earlier forms of life are called fossils. Even in the very early recorded history of man, there are references to the finding of fossils.

Of course, fossils have not always been regarded as evidences of earlier forms of life on the earth. Earlier, some people labeled them as "sports of nature." Others called them "works of the devil placed on earth to deceive man." In the early part of the 18th century, fossils were widely regarded as the remnants of familiar plants and animals that perished in the Biblical flood.

Scientists consider fossils to be remnants or traces of forms of life that existed on the earth long ago. However, the evidence indicates that not all these forms were the familiar plants and animals that live on the earth today. Of course, some forms —certain shellfish, for example—are related to present-day life. But others, such as the dinosaurs, have long since ceased to exist.

How have these evidences survived through the ages? How do fossils form? How do scientists use fossils to obtain information about the earth's past? How do scientists determine the age of a fossil? These are some of the questions explored in Chapter 23. The study of fossils is very interesting and rewarding for some people. Perhaps it will be for you.

1. Kinds of Fossils

What is a fossil? A fossil is any evidence of a form of life that lived sometime in the past. There are many forms of fossils. Some fossils are so small that they can only be examined through a microscope. Diatoms are examples of such small fossils. Other forms of fossils are the preserved footprints or tracks left by animals. Occasionally, frozen carcasses of now-extinct animals are found. These, too, are called fossils. A much more common fossil form is represented by the remains of ancient sea creatures, such as shellfish and crinoids. Evidences of early plant life, such as ferns, are also relatively common fossils.

Most fossils are found in layers of sedimentary rock. By studying these layers and the fossils they contain, geologists have been able to construct a record of geologic history covering the past several hundred million years. Such studies have also enabled scientists to describe the history of life as it has developed in that time.

How do fossils form? As you can imagine, many fossils are the remains or evidence of the hard parts—that is, the skeletons or shells—of animals. Bones and most shells contain calcium carbonate, the mineral that also makes up limestone. Another substance that forms the hard parts of some animals is called *chitin* (kī′tin). Chitin is a horny substance similar to that which makes up your fingernails. Chitin forms the protective covering of many animals, such as insects, shrimps, and crabs. One very common type of fossil, that of the *trilobite* (trī′lə bīt), formed because the trilobite had a hard, protective covering of chitin.

Shells of animals that lived in shallow ocean water are often preserved by burial. After the animal dies, its shell remains on the floor of the sea. There, if the water is quiet, fine particles of silt and clay bury the shell. The shell is not affected by the seawater immediately, but the soft parts of the animal decompose. The products of decomposition escape or are dissolved in the seawater. Thus, remains or traces of animals which have no shells or other hard parts are seldom preserved. Traces of ancient jellyfish have been found in rock, and in some cases the trails left by worms still remain. But in general, animals without some sort of hard structure have left little evidence of their existence.

Bones of animals that lived on land may also be buried under layers of clay and silt. Usually, such bones are found separately— that is, not as a complete skeleton. There are several factors which may cause the bones to become separated. After an animal dies, the tissues which connect the bones decay. Forces such as running water in a stream or waves on a beach might disturb the skeleton and separate the bones from one another. In many cases, other animals have torn the body apart and scattered the bones. Finally, the bones are

Figure 23-1. Trilobites (left) were very numerous during the Cambrian and Ordovician periods but became extinct by the end of the Paleozoic Era. Fossils of crinoids (right) have been found in Ordovician rock, but some species of crinoids still exist today.

431

buried. Perhaps they are covered by sand in the bottom of a stream or by silt on the bottom of a lake.

Occasionally, the complete skeleton of an animal is discovered, but this is unusual. Only if burial takes place very quickly after the animal has died will the bones stay together as a complete skeleton. This might happen, for example, if the animal were caught in an avalanche or in a mud slide.

There are some places in which the bones of many different animals are found quite close together. Geologists guess that these regions may once have been areas of quicksand in which many animals were trapped over the years.

What other explanations can you think of which might account for the fact that the bones of many different animals are often found quite close to one another?

Bones and skeletons are not the only kinds of fossils to be preserved by burial. Footprints may also be preserved by burial, and thus become fossils. The footprints of many animals may be imprinted in the mudflats along the coast of a shallow sea. Even trails of worms are left in such mudflats. If waves do not wash the footprints and trails away, they may eventually become filled and covered by layers of mud and clay.

Fossils which are formed by burial are usually found when the sedimentary rock containing them is split open. Sedimentary rock containing such fossils often splits in such a way as to reveal the fossil inside. The plane along which the rock breaks easily is the same plane that contains the fossil. You can understand this if you think about the formation of the fossil footprints. For a long time, the muddy shore was the exposed surface. Later, this muddy shore is covered with other material, marking the beginning of a new layer of sediment. When the sediment becomes cemented together, the rock is relatively weak along the boundary between two separate layers. Thus, it tends to break easily along this boundary.

Unusual forms of burial. One unusual form of burial is that of being encased in *amber*. Amber is the hardened remains of resin—the sticky, yellow fluid that oozes from pine trees. Small organisms, such as insects or spiders, have become stuck in this resin and have been preserved in it when the resin hardened.

Another unusual form of burial is in tar pits. The skeletons of many animals have been recovered from the famous Rancho La Brea tar pits near Los Angeles. The pits contain a natural asphaltlike material. Animals become trapped in this material as they attempt to cross the pit or as they prey on other animals already caught. The remains of these animals gradually sink into the tar. The soft parts decay, but the bones are preserved in the tar.

Petrifaction. Some buried fossils have the same chemical composition as that of the organism from which the fossil formed. However, if the rock in which they are found is

Figure 23-2. The internal organs of the spider below decayed long ago. However, the form of its outer skeleton is perfectly preserved in amber which hardened millions of years ago.

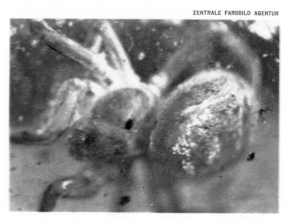

ZENTRALE FARBBILD AGENTUR

porous and water has slowly filtered through it, then changes will have taken place. Over a long period of time, water moving through a layer of sedimentary rock may dissolve the original material. Quite often, minerals will be deposited in the space originally occupied by the organic material of the organism. In such a case, the exact form of the organism will be reproduced in all its detail. This process of replacing the original material of an organism with minerals is called *petrifaction* (pet'rə fak'shən).

Petrified wood is an example of the results of petrifaction. The cellulose, of which the tree was originally composed, has gradually been dissolved. In the process, minerals in the water that filtered through the wood replaced the dissolved cellulose. In some cases, this process seems to have gone on very slowly and delicately. The original structure of the tree is preserved in rock, even on a microscopic scale. The form of the original cells of the tree can be observed, along with the growth rings, as shown in the bottom picture of *Figure 23-3*.

Carbonization. Another way in which fossils form is called *carbonization* (kär'bə nə zā'shən). Carbon fossils are extremely important in tracing the history of life on the earth. This form of fossil is usually of a leaf or other part of an ancient plant, but carbon fossils of insects have also been

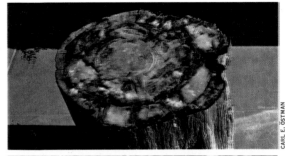
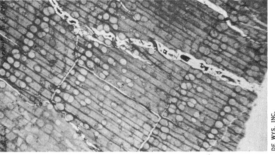

Figure 23-3. Petrified wood results when the original material of the wood is replaced by minerals. In the photomicrograph at the bottom, cells and growth rings of the original tree are still recognizable.

found. After an organism is buried, it decays. The hydrogen and oxygen that were part of its chemical composition escape during the decay process. However, particles of pure carbon often remain. If the buried remains of the organism are undisturbed, these remaining carbon particles leave a clear pattern which indicates the structure of the original organism.

DO IT YOURSELF

Collect and examine fossils

Contact geologists at your State Geological Survey and at the Geology Department of your state university. Find out where fossils have been found in your state. If possible, visit these areas and search for fossils yourself. Also, visit a natural history museum in your locality and examine the fossil collection there. Make a list of the various types of evidence of past life (bones, shells, footprints, and so on) which have been discovered in your state. Collect examples of as many of these types as you can.

2. Ordered Layers

Development of an important concept. Fossils have been observed since ancient times. However, it was not until about 150 years ago that scientists began to understand the significance of fossils. One of the first to recognize the geologic significance of fossils was an English engineer and scientist, William Smith. At the time the Revolutionary War was being fought in America, William Smith reached his eighteenth birthday and became a surveyor's assistant in England. As he tramped across the fields of England in making surveys, he carried on what had been a childhood hobby. He collected fossils. He carefully classified all the fossils he found. Soon he began to realize that certain varieties of fossils were to be found only in certain layers of rock. These varieties of fossils were never found together in the same layer. Although two separate layers of sandstone might at first appear to be the same, he could distinguish between them because one layer contained different varieties of fossils than did the other layer.

When he was twenty-five, Smith became an engineer and surveyor for a company building a canal. For six years as he worked on this project, he examined the layers of rock through which the canal was being cut. He identified some layers by the particular type of fossils of sea urchins they contained. Other layers contained fossils of a different type of sea urchin. Still other layers could be identified because they contained fossils of a particular type of clam. One particular layer of rock always contained a variety of petrified nuts. He also noticed that the layers occurred in an ordered succession. That is, if a layer of rock containing one type of fossil occurred on top of a layer containing a different type of fossil in one locality, then these layers occurred in this relative order wherever they were found together.

Smith realized that this regular order of different strata was connected to geologic history. He understood that the lower layers of rock were formed first and the upper layers at a later time. This understanding was one of the greatest discoveries in geology, for it permitted the construction of a geologic history of the earth in which events were placed in their proper order.

Because of his interest in rock layers and the fossils in them, William Smith acquired the nickname "Strata" Smith. Even today geologists refer to him by that name. In 1815, he described his work in this way.

> I have, with immense labour and expense, collected specimens of each stratum, and of the peculiar fossils, organic remains and vegetable impressions, and compared them with others from very distant parts of the island, with reference to the exact habitation of each, and have arranged them in the same order as they lay in the earth; which arrangement must convince every scientific or discerning person, that the earth is formed as well as governed, like the other works of its great Creator, according to regular and immutable laws, and which form a legitimate and most important object of science.

Why, do you think, had no one discovered the regularity of the formation of rock strata before 1815—that is, before the time of William Smith?

Interpreting the fossil record. In later years another geologist, while working in France, used "Strata" Smith's ideas in his study of the countryside around Paris. He was able to identify the same kinds of fossils in the strata which he examined in France that Smith had studied in England. Thus, he was able to connect the geologic history of the European continent with that of England. This geologist was *Sir Charles Lyell* (lī′əl). In his book, *Principles of Geology*, written in 1883, he set down some rules for the interpretation of the fossil record. These rules, summarized as follows, are now considered fundamental to the study of fossils.

1. Changes in plants and animals occur gradually.

2. Certain species continued to flourish for a much longer time than others. Some species disappeared when environmental conditions—particularly temperature—changed. Other species were able to adapt to the new conditions.

3. Some species migrate freely in order to find favorable climatic conditions. They may disappear from one area, but they will be found in others.

4. By comparing collections of fossils to animals living today, scientists determine the climatic conditions in which the ancient species lived.

5. Certain fossils can be used to correlate layers of rock between one continent and another. Thus, rock formations of the same age may be identified, even though they are found in widely separated parts of the earth.

What other English scientist probably influenced Lyell in formulating his rules for interpreting fossils?

Index fossils. The importance of index fossils cannot be overestimated. As the second of Lyell's rules states, some species of organisms flourish for extended periods of time. Their fossils are found in the strata of many different periods. Thus, they are not very useful in correlating strata from two widely separated places. But consider a species which existed for only a relatively short period of time. Fossils of such a species would enable scientists to obtain a more precise determination of the ages of the strata in which they are contained. Thus, one important requirement a species must meet in order to form index fossils is that the species did not exist for an extremely long period of time.

A second important requirement for index fossils is that they be widespread. If a particular species of animal lived and died in one particular landlocked sea or lake, fossils of this species are of little use in identifying strata in different parts of the world. However, if the species was widespread, its fossils became very useful. Thus, fossils of any species which was both widespread and existed for only a short time could be useful as index fossils. But, can fossils of such species be found?

Fortunately, there are a number of such fossils. Most of these index fossils are fossils of free-swimming marine creatures, and many are microscopic. Any two rock layers which contain the same index fossil are considered to have formed in the same geologic time period, regardless of where they are located on the earth.

3. History in Rocks

A fundamental law. In using fossils to interpret the history of the earth, geologists examine various formations of rock. A formation may consist of various layers of sedimentary rock. They know that the material in the bottom layer of a rock formation was

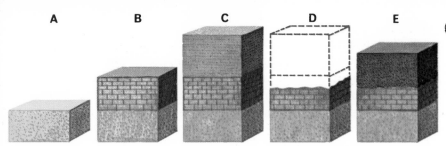

A B C D E

Figure 23-4. Illustrated in the diagram at the left are stages in a sequence of events which resulted in a particular rock formation.

deposited first, and material in the layer at the top was deposited last. Anywhere within the series of layers, an upper layer is more recent than a layer below it. You know enough about the formation of sedimentary rock to realize that this relationship is very obvious. And yet it is a very important relationship. One of the fundamental laws of geology, the *law of superposition*, is based on this relationship.

Geologists must be careful when applying this law to their observations. The law of superposition states only that the layers of sedimentary rock were deposited in order. It does not say that all the layers we see are as thick today as they were when they were deposited. Rock can be eroded as well as be deposited. Thus, some layers in a series of sedimentary strata might have been worn down and might now be much thinner than they were originally. In fact, some layers might be missing completely.

How would a geologist determine if the boundary between two layers of sedimentary rock is an ancient erosion surface or if the upper layer was deposited immediately after the lower layer?

Applying the law of superposition. Suppose a series of sedimentary rock layers were built up as shown in *Figure 23-4*. The bottom layer of sandstone, shown in *A*, may have been the bed of an ancient lake. Later, this portion of the earth's crust sank, or perhaps the ocean rose. At any rate, this region became the bottom of a shallow sea. A layer of limestone was

deposited as in *B*. Next, a river brought mud from the nearby land to this sea and deposited the mud over this particular region. The mud became a layer of shale, and the formation at this stage consisted of three layers, as shown in *C*. After that, this area of the earth's surface rose high above sea level. Rivers formed on the exposed surface of the shale. Eventually, the layer of shale was completely washed away, as was part of the layer of limestone underneath. (*D* in *Figure 23-4*) Still later, the region again sank beneath the surface of the sea, and a layer of sandstone was deposited on top of the remaining layers. See *E* in *Figure 23-4*. Still later, the land rose once more, and a glacier cut through this region, exposing these layers of rock for geologists to examine. But now, the layer of shale and part of the layer of limestone are missing. There is no record of the eroded layers in the other rock and no way to tell that they were ever there. As you can imagine, making a mistake in interpreting the history of the rock formation would be easy. To avoid making such a mistake, geologists use index fossils.

How would index fossils be useful? Suppose the lowest layer of sandstone contains traces of a particular type of algae that is rather rare and is associated only with rock formations found in this area. Examining such traces, geologists might infer that this layer of sandstone was deposited on the bottom of a lake. They might conclude that the lake was comparatively small and cut off from the ocean. This would explain why only a special type of unusual fossil was found there.

Suppose, too, that the next layer (of lime-stone) contains many trilobite fossils, including some recognized index fossils. Geologists would know the period during which these fossils were deposited, and that this limestone was once the bottom of a shallow sea, or perhaps was a continental shelf. They could relate this layer to other layers found in different parts of the world.

We might also suppose that the uppermost of the exposed layers contains fossils of a particular type of turtle shell. Geologists would recognize these turtle shells as characteristic of a particular period in the earth's history. But geologists know that the interval between the time of the trilobites and that of the turtles represents a long span of time. Layers of sedimentary rock in other parts of the world would contain fossils of many different species that lived during this span of time. Because of the absence of the fossils of many species, geologists would realize that a long portion of geologic history was missing from this particular sequence of sedimentary layers.

Geologists must examine fossils from many different formations of sedimentary rock before they can fully understand any single formation. The diagram in *Figure 23-5* is an example of how information concerning fossils may be arranged. It is necessary to build up a catalog of fossils with the fossils arranged

Figure 23-5. In the diagram, each type of organism is associated with a vertical black line indicating the time interval during which these organisms lived. Heavy lines indicate that many fossils of that type have been found in rocks of that period. Light lines indicate times for which only a few fossils have been found. Numerals in parentheses in the PERIOD column indicate the duration of that geologic period in millions of years.

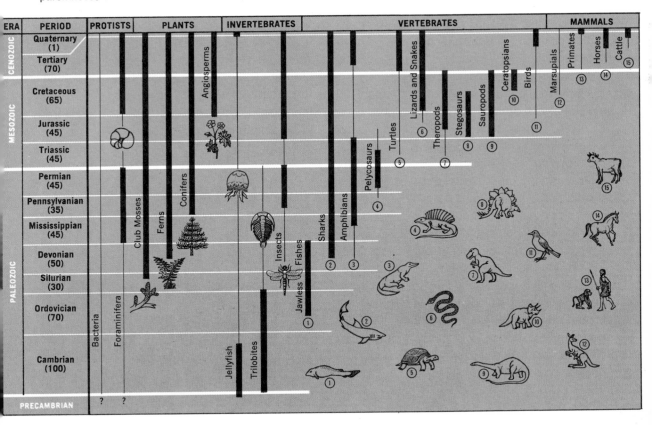

Figure 23-6. Several species of Foraminifera are shown above. Certain species of Foraminifera are useful as index fossils. What characteristics make a species useful as index fossils?

in order, just as "Strata" Smith did 150 years ago. By now a great number of fossils have been put into such ordered catalogs.

One-celled organisms that are neither plants nor animals are called *protists* (prō′ tists). Bacteria, for example, are protists. Fossils of bacteria are important because they are some of the most ancient fossils yet discovered. Fossils of *Foraminifera* (fə ram′ə nif′ ər ə), another type of protist, are also important. They are important because certain species of *Foraminifera* serve as index fossils for various geologic periods.

Club mosses and ferns are among the earliest types of land plants that have been identified in the fossil record. Conifers, such as pine trees and fir trees, came later. The *angiosperms* (an′ji ə spėrmz), or flowering plants, are the most recent types of plants to evolve.

The invertebrate animals, as you probably know, are the animals without backbones. Invertebrates, including the well-known trilobites, are the earliest animal forms. Impressions of jellyfish, a type of invertebrate, have been discovered in some Precambrian rock formations. Insects are invertebrates that are very common today. The fossil record indicates that insects also lived on the earth 350 million years ago.

The vertebrates are animals with backbones. In locating these animals on the diagram, we must connect the numeral near each drawing with the line having the same numeral, since there is not room to put each drawing directly on or under the line it represents. The earliest types of vertebrates were the fishes. One type of fish that existed in ancient times and is still plentiful today is the shark. We usually think of reptiles in terms of lizards and snakes. However, there were earlier reptile forms, including *pelycosaurs* (pel′ə kō sôrz) and turtles. In fact, lizards and snakes are fairly recent arrivals.

As the diagram indicates, the dinosaurs and the birds preceded the mammals. Strangely enough, all of the dinosaurs died off in what was, geologically speaking, a very short time. From the time of their greatest number until they became extinct may have been a period of no more than one or two million years. Few other large groups of animals seem to have died off so abruptly. It is also interesting to note that the mammals began to spread at very nearly the same time that the dinosaurs died off. Many scientists believe that this is not accidental, but that the end of the dinosaurs is directly related to the beginning of the mammals.

Figure 23-7. A skeleton and an "in-the-flesh" restoration of a stegosaur are shown below. During what geologic periods might this type dinosaur have lived?

4. Carbon 14, Potassium 40, and Radioactive Dating

Another method needed. The uranium-lead method of radioactive dating that was described in Chapter 19 is extremely useful in determining the age of certain rock samples. However, as we mentioned then, this method has certain limitations. First of all, uranium is not a mineral that is commonly found in sedimentary rock. Therefore, the uranium-lead method of age determination cannot be used too successfully with either sedimentary rock or the fossils contained in sedimentary rock.

A second difficulty is related to the long half-life of uranium. The half-life is about 4.5 billion years. Thus, the uranium-lead method is very good for measuring ages of a few hundred million years or a few billion years. This method can even be used for ages of about 10 million years, although the precision is not very good for such ages. The uranium-lead method, however, is not precise enough to measure ages or age differences of, say, a hundred thousand or even a million years. The uranium-lead method may be compared to a very good clock having only an hour hand. Such a clock could be used to tell the time of day, but it would be completely useless for measuring short time intervals, such as timing a runner in a 100-yard dash.

Many fossils are of fairly recent origin—that is, they are only a few hundred thousand or a few million years old. In particular, fossils of animals similar to man appear to be only a few million years old. Of course, biologists as well as geologists want to establish accurate ages for such fossils.

Radioactive dating with carbon 14. What is needed for age determinations of relatively recent fossils is a radioactive element that has a shorter half-life than uranium, and one that is likely to be found in sedimentary rock. If possible, it would be very useful if the element also occurred in bones and shells. Such a substance has been discovered. It is a radioactive form of carbon called carbon 14. A carbon 14 nucleus contains six protons and eight neutrons, whereas the nucleus of the commonest form of carbon contains six protons and only six neutrons. Professor Willard Libby of the University of California at Los Angeles received a Nobel prize for working out the method by which scientists use carbon 14 for age determinations.

The half-life of carbon 14 is 5,770 years. Thus, carbon 14 satisfies one requirement. It is a substance with a short half-life. In fact, it is too short for determining the ages of some materials. If a sample of material is more

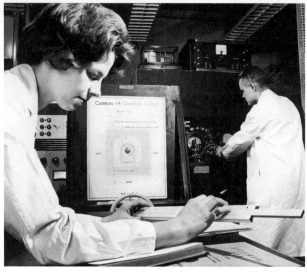

Figure 23-8. Detecting radiation from old materials containing carbon 14 requires sensitive, complex equipment. The sample must be heavily shielded since the experimenter contains more carbon 14 than the sample.

than 35,000 years old, almost all of its original carbon 14 atoms have decayed. An accurate age determination of such material is difficult to make.

Carbon 14 also satisfies a second requirement—namely, it is found in sedimentary rock and in fossils. Calcium carbonate is a common ingredient of limestone, seashells, and bones.

In radioactive dating, it is necessary to measure the ratio between the number of atoms of the radioactive element and the number of atoms of its decay product. Lead is the decay product of the radioactive element uranium. The decay product of carbon 14 is nitrogen 14, or ordinary nitrogen. But, nitrogen 14 is a very common element. The lead which results from the decay of uranium can be easily identified. However, the nitrogen that results from the decay of carbon 14 is very common and not distinctive. In fact, it makes up about 80 per cent of the atmosphere. How, then, can carbon 14 be used in determining the ages of fossils?

Before we find out how carbon 14 is used, suppose we ask this question. Why is there any carbon 14 to be found on our earth at all? With such a short half-life, any carbon 14 present when the earth formed would have decayed in the 4.5 billion years that the earth has been in existence. The answer to the question about the occurrence of carbon 14 leads us on our way to learn how carbon 14 is used.

The production of carbon 14. Carbon 14 is constantly being produced in the atmosphere. Cosmic rays cause the nitrogen of the atmosphere to change into carbon 14. As a cosmic ray penetrates the earth's atmosphere, it eventually collides with the nucleus of an atom, causing a nuclear reaction to take place. One particle that often results from such a nuclear reaction is the neutron.

When a neutron strikes the nucleus of a nitrogen atom, there is a nuclear reaction. The neutron is absorbed into the nucleus and a proton is given off. As a result, the number of neutrons in the nucleus is increased from 7 to 8, and the number of protons is decreased from 7 to 6. The result, then, is carbon 14.

The nucleus of carbon 14 is not stable. Eventually, one of the eight neutrons within the carbon 14 nucleus will change to a proton. Then the nucleus will again be a nitrogen 14 nucleus. In the meantime, however, many more nuclei of carbon 14 are produced by the steady rain of cosmic rays upon the earth. Thus, two natural phenomena balance each other. On the one hand, there is the continuing production of carbon 14. On the other hand, there is the steady decay of carbon 14 into nitrogen 14. The result is an equilibrium. It is like a leaky bucket into which water is steadily being poured, and out of which water is steadily leaking. There is a particular level of water in the bucket which will be maintained so long as both the rate of filling and the rate of leaking stay constant.

What happens to an atom of carbon 14 after it has been formed? Most of these atoms combine very quickly with oxygen in the atmosphere to make carbon dioxide. The carbon 14 is, of course, still radioactive in this molecule. The fact that it is combined with other atoms in a molecule makes no difference in its radioactive characteristics. This radioactive molecule of carbon dioxide takes its place in the atmosphere with all of the ordinary molecules of carbon dioxide.

Determining the age of a fossil. To understand how carbon 14 can be used for age determinations, consider a living plant. When a plant is alive, it is constantly exchanging chemicals with its environment. Therefore, the ratio of the number of carbon 14 atoms to the number of carbon 12 atoms in the living plant is the same as that in the atmosphere.

But what happens when the plant dies? After death, the plant no longer interchanges chemicals with its environment. The carbon that was in the plant at the time of its death stays in the remains of the plant. The fraction which is carbon 14 gradually decays to form nitrogen. In fact, after 5,770 years, half of the carbon 14 will have decayed, changing into nitrogen 14. No carbon 14 will have replaced the decayed carbon 14.

Now suppose a scientist takes a sample of a plant that has been dead for 5,770 years and analyzes the carbon which it contains. He will discover that the material from the dead plant contains only half as much carbon 14 as the material from a living plant. Nothing will have happened to the carbon 12, but half the carbon 14 will have decayed. If the plant has been dead 11,000 years, about one fourth of the carbon 14 would be left, and so on.

The decay of carbon 14 can be used to date fossils of plants, but what about its use in dating fossils of animals? Although some animals eat other animals, we can always trace the food chain back to plants, since plants are the primary food producers on the earth. Thus, living animals are also constantly interchanging carbon with their environment. In the body of an animal, each molecule that contains carbon (and almost all of them do) will have the same ratio of carbon 14 to carbon 12 as does the atmosphere around them. But again, when the animal dies, this chemical interchange stops. From then on, the situation is just as it was for the dead plant. A geologist finding a buried shell or bone can analyze its carbon content, find the ratio of carbon 14 to carbon 12, and so determine the age of the shell or bone.

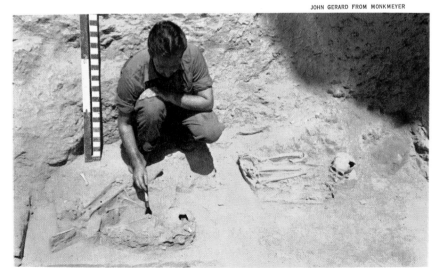

Figure 23-9. Carbon 14 is best used in dating recent fossils, such as these skeletons of Indians. The age of these fossils was determined to be 3,600 years. They are the oldest Indian skeletons yet discovered in the United States east of the Mississippi River.

Figure 23-10. In using radioactive dating, scientists must count nuclear disintegrations. Special equipment, such as that being operated by the physicist in this picture, is needed to detect and count these nuclear reactions.

E. F. PATTERSON FROM U. S. GEOLOGICAL SURVEY

How does the per cent of carbon 14 in a scientist's body compare with the per cent of carbon 14 in an ancient fossil that he is examining? How about the carbon in his instruments? How can he be certain his instruments are detecting only the radioactivity of the fossil?

Radioactive dating with potassium 40. The carbon 14 method of radioactive dating works very well for the remains of plants and animals of recent origin. In particular, it has been used by archaeologists in dating early man in North America, and so on. But the carbon 14 and uranium-lead methods leave a gap in man's record of the past—the interval from about 10 million years ago to about 35,000 years ago. Fortunately, scientists have learned to use other radioactive elements for dating purposes. One of the most useful of these radioactive elements is a radioactive form of potassium known as potassium 40. Potassium is a relatively common element in the earth's crust. Furthermore, one atom out of every 8,400 atoms of potassium is an atom of potassium

40. The remainder of the potassium atoms consists primarily of potassium ⌒ and potassium 41, neither of which is radoactive.

The half-life of potassium 40 is 1.31 billion years. However, potassium 40 can decay into two different elements. About 10 per cent of the potassium 40 decays to form calcium 40. The other 90 per cent decays to form argon 40. Scientists cannot be absolutely certain that the calcium and argon they find in a sample of rock are the products of the decay of potassium 40. Nevertheless, the ratio of the number of atoms of potassium 40 to the number of atoms of argon 40 is used as a method of age determination.

Argon is a gas. It will, therefore, escape from most rock, if given enough time. However, there are some mineral forms, such as a type of mica, from which argon escapes very, very slowly. Thus, by selecting such a mineral form for analysis, scientists can use the potassium 40 method of dating, exactly as they use the uranium-lead method. The important advantage in using potassium 40 is that potassium 40 has a shorter half-life than uranium.

Through the use of the potassium-argon method of radioactive dating, geologists have filled in some of the gap in the historical record from 10 million years ago to about 35,000 years ago. The potassium-argon method also works quite well for determining ages as great as several billion years. Thus, it can be used to check the results obtained by using the uranium-lead method.

Unfortunately, the potassium-argon method has one of the same limitations that the uranium-lead method has. Both work almost exclusively for igneous rock. Since most fossils occur in sedimentary rock, neither method can be used directly to determine the ages of these fossils. Instead, the ages of fossils are estimated by determining the age of the igneous rock found near fossils, such as the igneous rock of an intrusion into fossil-bearing strata.

Information from fossils. In this chapter we have concentrated on the geologic story which fossils can tell. But fossils also have given us an enormous amount of information about the history of life. The fossil record contains much of the story of evolution—the gradual change from primitive life forms into those forms which exist today. Fossils tell us about the sort of climate that existed on the earth in ancient times. They tell us not only about the location of oceans. They even tell about the temperature of the water and the depth of the water at various places. Some fossils provide us with a record of our early ancestors, allowing us to trace the history of man far beyond the written records left by some of the earliest civilizations known.

It was 150 years ago that "Strata" Smith described the true importance of fossils for science. But even now, the picture is far from complete. Each year scientists add still more information to the story of the earth as it is revealed by fossils.

How can the environmental conditions—such as climate, depth of the oceans, and temperature of ocean water—be determined for ancient times from a study of fossils?

Figure 23-11. Much varied information can be obtained from a study of fossils. Carbonized fossils, casts and molds, and footprints are only three of the many ways in which traces of earlier forms of life have been preserved. More and more fossils will undoubtedly be discovered, thus adding to our knowledge of the past.

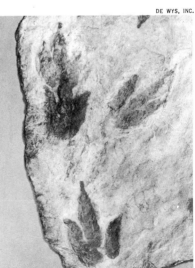

Checking Your Knowledge

IMPORTANT IDEAS

1. Our knowledge of early forms of life has been obtained through studies of fossils.

2. Fossils are the remains or traces of organisms. Most fossils are of organisms that had hard parts that were not easily destroyed.

3. The chemical composition of a fossil is usually different from that of the material in a living organism. Changes in chemical composition, such as petrifaction and carbonization, occur very slowly.

4. By comparing collections of fossils with organisms living today, the climate a region had in ancient times can be inferred.

5. Sedimentary rock formed in an ordered sequence of layers. However, erosion removed some layers or portions of layers, leaving gaps in the sequence in some localities.

6. The uranium-lead method is not very useful in dating most fossils. However, radioactive dating based on carbon 14 can be very useful in determining the age of recent fossils. The potassium-argon method is used to date igneous rock found near fossils.

USING NEW WORDS

Study the list below. On your paper write the letters *a* through *f*. Beside each letter write two brief statements. In one statement, tell how the work of the individuals or the meanings of the terms in the pair are related. In the other statement, tell how the work of the individuals or the meanings of the terms in the pair differ.

a. William Smith — Sir Charles Lyell
b. chitin — amber
c. trilobite — dinosaur
d. *Foraminifera* — protist
e. carbon 14 — nitrogen 14
f. potassium 40 — argon 40

TEST YOURSELF

Study the test below. Write the numerals *1-10* on your paper. Beside each numeral write the correct response to that part of the test having the corresponding numeral.

1. One of the first men to recognize the geologic significance of fossils was the English engineer and scientist named _____.

2. Most fossils are found in (*sedimentary, igneous, metamorphic*) rock.

3. When the original material of an organism is replaced by minerals to form a fossil, the process is called _____.

4. The protective covering of insects, shrimps, and crabs is formed from a substance called _____.

5. By comparing collections of fossils to animals living today, scientists determine the _____ conditions in which the ancient species lived.

6. The law of superposition is based on the fact that sediment which became cemented together to form the bottom layer of a rock formation was deposited (*at the same time as, before, after*) the material which composes the top layer.

7. In some rock formations, layers of rock appear to be missing. Apparently, these layers were removed by (*erosion, earthquakes, volcanic activity*).

8. Index fossils are fossils of species of plants or animals that lived only during certain geologic periods and lived in (*isolated sections of the world, many regions about the earth's surface*).

9. Carbon 14 is useful in dating recent fossils because it is an element found in many fossils, and because the half-life (*varies greatly, is relatively short, is very long*).

10. The decay product of carbon 14 is _____.

Extending Your Knowledge

1. Scientists have sometimes found piles of bones thrown away by early man after he had eaten the meat. What could be learned by studying such evidence?

2. What characteristics of an animal might be determined from its footprints? Where might fossil footprints of man be found?

3. Why is it much simpler to understand the work of William Smith and Sir Charles Lyell now than it was for them to figure out their principles in the first place?

4. Why are fossils of land animals so different on different continents, while fossils of marine creatures from different oceans are quite similar?

5. What animals can adapt to a wide range of environmental conditions? What evidence can you give to support your answer?

6. Why is radioactive dating with carbon 14 more useful than other methods in dating earth materials?

SOME THINGS TO DO

1. Demonstrate how the form of a fossil may be retained, although its original material is replaced. Suspend a clam shell or an oyster shell in melted paraffin. Allow the paraffin to harden. Make several tiny holes through the paraffin to the shell. Place the paraffin containing the shell in dilute hydrochloric acid. CAUTION: Hydrochloric acid is caustic. Do not allow it to contact your skin.

After chemical action has removed the shell and the acid has been thoroughly rinsed away, pour very thin plaster of Paris into the cavity left by the shell. Let the plaster harden. Then, heat the specimen at a low temperature. The paraffin will melt, leaving a plaster cast of the original shell.

2. Make a "carbonized fossil." Lightly coat a piece of wrapping paper with petroleum jelly. Then, coat the greased side of this paper with soot (carbon) by passing the paper back and forth above a lighted candle. Place the paper—black side up—on a flat surface and drop a leaf onto the black surface. Cover the leaf with newspaper and apply pressure to the leaf by rubbing the newspaper with your hand. Remove the newspaper, pick up the leaf with a forceps, and place the leaf—black side down —on a piece of white paper. Again cover the leaf with newspaper and rub the newspaper. Then, when the newspaper and the leaf are removed, the white paper will bear an imprint of the leaf. In this experiment you placed a coating of carbon on the leaf to leave an imprint. In forming a carbonized fossil, the leaf itself carbonizes to leave an imprint on the rock above and below it.

3. Study radioactive dating. Are there methods of radioactive dating other than those listed in this text? What are the limitations of each method? Where and how can each method be used best?

CHALLENGES IN SCIENCE

1. Conduct a library research project concerning the Berezovka mammoth. Devise an explanation of how this animal could have died. Have there been any other discoveries of fossils of this type? What method of radioactive dating would be most accurate in determining the age of a fossil of this type? Explain.

2. Imagine you are a geologist, living fifty thousand years in the future. Prepare a list of the types of evidence which might be found at that time that would give clues as to the forms of life and the type of society that we have on the earth right now.

THREE LIONS, INC.

CHAPTER 24

Obtaining metals from the earth's crust is vital to man's civilization.

Buried Wealth

The highly mechanized society in which we live would not be possible without the buried wealth in the crust of the earth. Metals refined from ores present in the earth's crust are essential materials in machines, buildings, and other man-made structures. From the coal, petroleum, and natural gas obtained from the crust is released much of the energy to operate the machinery of today's civilization. Precious and semi-precious stones—valued as jewels and ornaments—are also in demand for many scientific and industrial uses. Man, as you know, searches the crust of the earth for these essential materials. Fortunately, this search has yielded more than the sought-after minerals and gems. A great deal of knowledge about the nature of the earth has been gained as a result of man's search for buried wealth.

As you study Chapter 24, you will find answers to various questions about the materials buried in the earth's crust. However, one very important question is not answered in this chapter. It is this. How can we conserve the buried wealth in the crust so that mankind will not be faced with serious shortages in the future? This question must be carefully considered, for, if our civilization is to survive, we must find the answer to this question.

1. Metals and Ores

Man's use of metals. A modern, industrial society requires large amounts of various metals. Think of all the metal products that are in your home. One product that contains a large amount of metal and that is owned by many individuals in America is the automobile. But there are many other products, such as railroads, bridges, and buildings with steel girders, which we use even though we do not own them. Thus, all of us are consumers of metal products, whether we own them or not.

How can we estimate the amount of a particular metal used by each individual in our country? Suppose you know the number of pounds of iron and steel produced each year in the United States. Then, suppose you divide this number by the total number of people who live in the United States. The result would be the average amount of iron and steel produced per citizen in America each year. How much iron and steel do you think that would be? The answer is about 2,200 pounds. Thus, in the United States, the production of iron and steel amounts to more than one ton per person each year.

On this same average basis, about 14 pounds of copper per person and 27 pounds of aluminum per person are produced in the United States. In addition, considerable quantities of other metals are produced.

DO IT YOURSELF

Make a list

List as many items as you can that are made of iron and steel. In compiling your list, include items other than those in your own home. Prepare similar lists of items made of aluminum and copper. What items on your lists are also made from other materials, such as plastic or fiberglass? What items from your list, do you think, will be made from other materials in the future?

Figure 24-1. Iron and copper are two very important metals. The photo at the left shows molten iron being poured into a furnace where it will be converted into steel. The other photo shows an open-pit copper mine. More copper has been obtained from this mine than from any other mine on the earth.

Where does man obtain metals? Practically all the metals used by man are obtained from minerals found in the crust of the earth. For example, the mineral *hematite* (hem′ə tīt) is a chemical combination of iron and oxygen. Hematite is the mineral from which most iron is obtained.

As you have learned, minerals are rarely found in a pure form. They are usually mixed with other minerals. A mixture of minerals is called an *ore* if the production of a pure metal from this mixture is possible and is economically profitable.

There are certain places in the crust of the earth where minerals containing some particular metal are especially concentrated. These regions are called *ore deposits*. Some ore deposits are shown in *Figure 15-4*. Whether or not a particular mineral deposit is called an ore deposit depends on three things: (1) the concentration of the metal in the deposit, (2) the process that is available for purifying the metal from the mineral, and (3) the value of the metal in its pure form.

Figure 24-2. Most of the high-grade ore has been taken from the Mesabi Range. However, new smelting processes make it profitable to mine a lower grade of ore (taconite) that is still plentiful in this region.

GRANT HEILMAN

A deposit of iron oxide is considered an ore deposit only if the material in it is at least 25 per cent iron (by weight). On the other hand, a deposit of platinum-bearing minerals is considered an ore deposit if it contains only 0.00005 per cent platinum.

Some ore deposits are very large. The deposit of iron ore in northern Minnesota called the *Mesabi* (mə säb′ē) *Range* has sometimes been called a mountain of iron. The pit from which iron ore is now being dug covers more than 1,250 acres and extends as deep as 435 feet. In contrast, a deposit of gold ore can be valuable, although it is quite small. Gold is often found mixed with quartz in a dike or a sill intruding into some other rock. Such gold-bearing intrusions may be only a few inches thick, and they may extend down into the rock only a few feet.

Where will man obtain iron when the iron-rich ore deposits such as the Mesabi Range become depleted? What will man do when all iron ore deposits are depleted?

The formation of ore deposits. If you were a prospector, you would be primarily interested in locating ore deposits. As a geologist or a geochemist, however, you would be primarily interested in understanding how ore deposits form. Of course, the knowledge gained by the geologist and the geochemist can be of great help to the prospector.

The attempt to understand the formation of ore deposits is basically an attempt to answer the following question. How did a particular mineral become so concentrated in one particular region? Consider iron ore deposits. Some of these deposits contain more than 60 per cent iron. Yet, as you learned in Chapter 12, the average amount of iron in the crust of the earth is only about 5 per cent. Thus, in such ore deposits, iron is more than twelve times as concentrated as it is in the average rock of the earth's crust. What processes were responsible for such a concentration?

In order to answer this question, think about the natural processes that take place in the formation of the minerals and rock within the crust of the earth. One process is the melting of rock. Another is the combination of weathering and erosion of surface rock which breaks rock down and carries material from one place to another. A third process is the deposition of sediments which eventually results in the formation of sedimentary rock. Still another process is the changing of both sedimentary and igneous rock by heat and pressure to produce metamorphic rock.

Concentrations from molten rock. When rock is in a molten state, is there any way by which specific minerals could become concentrated in a certain region? As a matter of fact, there are several ways. One way has to do with the melting point and the density of a mineral. Imagine what happens as molten rock, or magma, begins to cool. The mineral with the highest freezing point (melting point) would solidify first. If this mineral is less dense than the remaining molten rock, it would rise through the molten rock. If the solidified mineral is more dense, it would sink. If the first mineral to solidify contains a particular metal, then this metal would tend to become concentrated at either the top or the bottom of the cooling pool of magma.

Concentrations of minerals could result from molten material in another way. Some magmas are hot enough to vaporize certain minerals. If such a pool of very hot magma is trapped beneath the earth's surface, the vaporized minerals would force their way up through cracks in the crust above the magma. As the vapors move farther and farther from the hot magma, they would cool, condense, and finally solidify. If these condensing vapors are the vapors of metal-bearing minerals, then

deposits of these minerals would be along the cracks through which the vapors moved.

The mineral zinc chloride ($ZnCl_2$), for example, boils at 732°C. This is below the melting point of quartz. Thus, if zinc chloride and quartz were mixed together and heated, the zinc chloride would boil even before the quartz melted. As soon as the quartz melted, bubbles of zinc chloride would rise through it. If this occurred in a pool of magma under the surface of the earth, the zinc chloride would be concentrated near the top of the magma. If there were any cracks in the rock above the magma, the zinc chloride vapors would rise up through them.

Of course, the example just given—that of the zinc chloride—has been stated very simply. This example is merely an illustration of how a concentration of a mineral might develop from molten rock material. Whether or not any particular mineral would vaporize and become concentrated above a magma would depend on several factors, including pressure and the presence of other minerals.

Concentrations resulting from solution and evaporation. The processes of solution and evaporation may also be factors in the formation of mineral deposits. As water moves around rock formations and through cracks between pieces of rock, it dissolves some chemicals more easily than others. An illustration of this is the fact that the ocean is very salty. Salt from the surface materials of the earth has been dissolved in the moving water and carried to the ocean, where it accumulates. In some places the shoreline of the ocean has gradually retreated. If the shoreline retreats very slowly, the shallow water near the shore evaporates, leaving solid salt behind. Such a salt deposit can be a source of the salt we use at our tables.

Not every mineral is as easily dissolved as salt is. However, the processes of solution, evaporation, and deposition can also take place with other minerals. A typical example is iron oxide. Some very large deposits of iron ore seem to have been formed by the evaporation of an inland sea.

Concentrations of uncertain origin. In a few cases, geologists are fairly certain as to how an ore deposit was formed. But in most cases the origin of an ore deposit is uncertain. A particular deposit might have been formed from a slowly cooling magma, either by gases or lightweight liquids rising to the top of the magma, or by other processes. Some iron ore deposits may have been formed by evaporation of an inland sea or by a slight change in the chemical composition and temperature of a particular portion of the ocean. In fact, geologists believe that some iron deposits were formed by the combined action of bacteria and other plant life.

Although the origin of many ore deposits is not certain, geologists are fairly certain that ore deposits do not originate as a result of metamorphism. If a rock formation was rich in a particular mineral before metamorphism occurred, then the resulting metamorphic rock would also be rich in that mineral. However, there is no evidence that concentration of minerals ever takes place during the metamorphic process.

2. Coal

Uses of coal. One very valuable material which man takes from the earth is coal. Notice we use the term material, rather than mineral. Many geologists do not consider coal a true mineral. In fact, many do not even classify it as rock.

Regardless of its classification, however, coal has for centuries been a major source of heat in homes and in industrial plants. It is used to smelt iron ore—that is, to convert iron ore into iron—and then to convert iron into steel. Generators that are run by steam produced in coal-fired boilers are the major source of electrical power in the world. Chemicals derived from coal are contained in many plastics, medicines, and other organic materials. In the United States, about 500 million tons of coal are used each year. This amount of coal represents about 2.5 tons per person per year.

When was coal formed? There is much geologic evidence to show that coal was formed from plants which grew millions of years ago. Fossil remains of a wide variety of plant forms

PALMER FROM MONKMEYER

Figure 24-3. A fern imprint found in shale overlying a deposit of coal lends support to the theory that coal was formed from plants that grew during the Pennsylvanian and Mississippian periods.

are found in coal and in the rock next to coal deposits.

Almost all the coal being mined and used today was formed during the *Mississippian* (mis′ə sip′i ən) and *Pennsylvanian* (pen′səl vā′ni ən) geologic periods—that is, between

Figure 24-4. Scientists believe that the vegetation from which coal formed grew in swampy areas such as the one shown at the right. This picture shows a model constructed on the basis of fossil evidence.

AUTHENTICATED NEWS INTERNATIONAL

350 and 270 million years ago. Geologists believe that during this interval, many regions of the earth were, from time to time, covered by vast, low-lying swamps. The climate of these swamps was nearly tropical, and lush vegetation grew year-round. A reconstruction of such a swamp is shown in *Figure 24-4*. As these plants died and fell onto the swampy ground, the process which resulted in the formation of coal began.

On what evidence do scientists base their inferences about the climate and the amount of vegetation during the Mississippian and Pennsylvanian periods?

Processes in the formation of coal. There is no way to be certain as to the nature of the process by which the remains of plants were converted into coal. However, geologic and chemical evidence indicates that two steps were involved. The first step was bacterial action. Cellulose and lignin—complex chemicals common in plants—were broken down by bacteria and changed into simpler chemical compounds. Some chemical compounds created in this process were poisonous to the bacteria. These poisons eventually killed the bacteria, thus stopping the bacterial action.

The next step in the formation of coal could take place only if the surface of the earth in the region of the swamp gradually sank lower and lower. If the swamp did not sink, the accumulation of dead plants would gradually fill the swamp. Then, the region would not be able to support the same kind of vegetation it did when it was swampy. However, if the swamp gradually sank, two things would happen. First, the accumulation of dead plant material would become deeper and deeper as more plants grew and then died. Second, if the sinking process continued long enough, the sea would eventually cover the whole area, and the growth of vegetation would stop. Then a process you have already studied would take place—that is, the deposition of sediment and the eventual formation of sedimentary rock. This rock would lie above the layer of decayed plant matter.

As the layer of sedimentary rock became thicker, the layer of decayed plant matter would be subjected to great pressure. The deeper the layer of plant matter sank into the earth, the higher the temperature would be. These two effects, great pressure and high temperature, would combine to complete the conversion of the plant material into coal.

Varieties of coal. Naturally, each deposit of coal formed by the processes just described would not be exactly like every other deposit. In fact, there are many different varieties of

HAROLD R. WANLESS

Figure 24-5. Lignite is not as valuable as coal is, but mining lignite can be profitable. How would you explain why most lignite is mined in the manner shown?

coal. Each variety has its own unique composition. However, all coal has one principal ingredient—carbon. Coal is graded according to the percentage of carbon it contains. The higher the percentage of carbon is, the more valuable the coal is.

The most common kind of coal is called *bituminous* (bə tü′mə nəs) *coal*. A higher grade of coal—that is, a coal richer in carbon —is also mined. It is called *anthracite* (an′thrə sīt). Apparently, a third step has to take place to convert bituminous coal to anthracite. This conversion is similar to the formation of metamorphic rock. That is, it involves heat and pressure and is associated with the motion and folding of the material

in the earth's crust. Anthracite is always found in folded strata.

Coal-like materials. Other materials, similar to coal, are found in the earth. Apparently, these coal-like materials have not gone through the entire second step in the process of coal formation. *Peat* is such a material. It is decayed plant matter, and it will burn. However, peat is a very low-grade fuel. *Lignite* (lig′nīt), another coal-like product, is a better fuel than peat is, but lignite is not as high in carbon or as useful a fuel as coal is. The regions where coal and lignite are found in the United States are indicated on the map in *Figure 24-6*.

Figure 24-6. In the United States, bituminous coal and lignite are more plentiful than anthracite is.

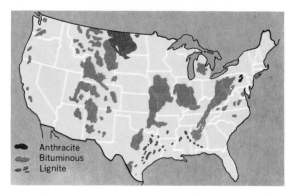

Anthracite
Bituminous
Lignite

FIND OUT BY TRYING

Materials you will need: anthracite, bituminous coal, peat, lignite, asbestos pad, ring stand, burner

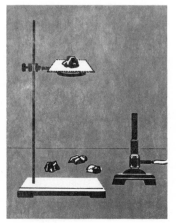

Examine each of the coal-like materials. In what aspects are they similar? How do these materials differ? In a fume hood, or in some other safe place, attempt to burn a small sample of each coal-like material. Which material is easiest to ignite? Are any of these coal-like materials impossible to ignite? Which appears to produce the most heat? Which gives off the least smoke and soot? What are some characteristic properties of a good fuel? On the basis of your observations, rate these coal-like materials in the order of their value as a fuel. How can anthracite be used as a fuel?

3. Petroleum and Natural Gas

Fossil fuels. Coal, *petroleum* (pə trō′li əm), and natural gas are called *fossil fuels* because, apparently, they are all derived from ancient plants and animals. Throughout the world, coal is the most widely used fossil fuel. However, petroleum and natural gas have become increasingly important in recent years, because they are more convenient to use than coal is. Petroleum and natural gas can be piped in, and they leave less residue than coal does. In 1940, the primary source of energy in the United States was coal. But now we obtain about three times as much energy from petroleum and natural gas as we do from the burning of coal.

Observations concerning petroleum and natural gas. Many observations have been made about petroleum and natural gas. For example, they always are found in sedimentary rock formations. Furthermore, the rock formations which contain petroleum and natural gas were formed during various geologic periods, ranging from the *Ordovician* (ôr′də vish′ən) through the *Tertiary* (tėr′shi er′i). These periods cover the time from about 500 million years ago to about one million years ago. Very few petroleum and natural gas deposits have been found in either Cambrian or Precambrian formations. Chemically, petroleum and natural gas consist of a wide variety of *hydrocarbons* (hī′drō kär′bənz)—that is, compounds containing only hydrogen and carbon.

The formation of petroleum. Based on the observations that have been made concerning petroleum, most geologists are of the opinion that petroleum is derived from the remains of plants and animals. However, geologists are not as certain of the origin of petroleum as they are of the origin of coal.

Why, do you suppose, are geologists less certain about the origin of petroleum than they are about the origin of coal?

Two questions about the origin of petroleum are unanswered. Exactly how did the formation take place? Which plants or animals were involved? Most geologists believe that petroleum was formed from marine plants and animals which probably lived in shallow seas. The bodies of these animals sank to the bottom of the sea when the animals died. The bodies were only partially decayed before they

Figure 24-7. Petroleum and natural gas deposits are reached by drilling deep wells. Whether the wells are on land or offshore, derricks are required for the drilling operation. The bottom picture is a close view of a drill bit used in drilling a deep well.

453

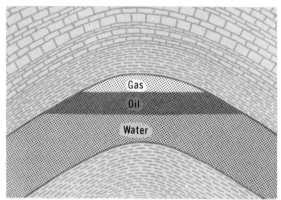

Figure 24-8. Petroleum, natural gas, and water have different densities. Thus, they separate into layers if trapped below a layer of impermeable rock.

were covered with silt. Eventually, the high temperature and pressure within the earth converted this trapped organic matter into petroleum in a way not at all understood.

The petroleum formed in this way then seeped through pores and cracks in the overlying rock, rising until it was trapped by a layer of *impermeable* (im pėr'mi ə bəl) *rock*. Impermeable rock is rock, such as shale, through which liquids and gases cannot pass. Gradually, a large amount of petroleum would accumulate beneath such an impermeable rock barrier. The trapped petroleum would form an oil pool, such as shown in the diagram of *Figure 24-8*. Notice that in this diagram a deposit of natural gas is also shown. Natural gas is often found together with petroleum, and for this reason, it is believed that natural gas is derived from the petroleum.

If such an oil pool is in a sandstone layer, then droplets of oil and microscopic bubbles of gas fill all of the pores between the separate grains of sand which make up the layer of sandstone. If a hole is drilled into the layer filled with petroleum, then the petroleum filters through the pores and escapes into the hole. The petroleum is then pumped to the surface. In some cases, the pressure of the natural gas above the petroleum is great enough to force the petroleum to the surface without the need of pumping.

What, do you suppose, would happen if a hole were drilled into the layer of porous rock which contained only natural gas and no petroleum?

Locating petroleum deposits. Searching for petroleum deposits has become a highly specialized application of geology. A great deal of geologic knowledge has been brought to bear on the problem of finding petroleum. In return, a great deal of geologic knowledge has been gained in the process of searching for petroleum deposits.

Commercially useful deposits of petroleum have been found all the way down to 7,000 meters below the surface of the earth. However, most pools of petroleum which have been tapped so far are between 700 and 5,000 meters deep.

Figure 24-9. Man-made seismic waves are often useful in locating petroleum deposits. The men shown below are setting a charge to produce such seismic waves.

DO IT YOURSELF

Find out how petroleum geologists search for oil

Use reference books or obtain information from oil companies to discover various ways in which petroleum deposits are located. What rock formations do petroleum geologists look for? What equipment do they use? How can they be sure there is petroleum in a certain deposit? Are all petroleum deposits located under the dry-land portions of the earth's surface?

4. Jewels

Types of jewels. Almost all mineral crystals are beautiful. However, certain ones, because of their rarity and special qualities, are especially valuable. These valuable crystals are called gemstones or precious stones because they can be cut and polished to make jewels. The most valuable precious stones are *diamond, emerald, ruby,* and *sapphire.* Although we usually think of precious stones in terms of jewels, there are also industrial and scientific uses for these materials.

Diamond. The best known and the most valuable of all precious stones is diamond. Diamond is pure carbon. Thus, chemically, diamond is identical with *graphite* (graf'īt). However, the crystal structure of the two materials is different, as shown in *Figure 24-10.* The result of the difference in crystal structure is not only a difference in appearance but also a difference in other properties. Diamond is denser than graphite. Furthermore, diamond is the hardest mineral known, whereas graphite is comparatively soft.

Apparently, diamond forms in slowly cooling lava. Pure carbon crystallized in the cooling lava, perhaps in the form of graphite. As the material around the graphite crystals continued to cool and solidify, it also contracted. Within the contracting material, the crystals of graphite were subjected to tremendous

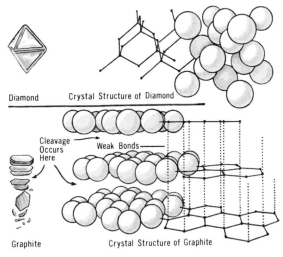

Figure 24-10. The crystal structures of graphite and diamond are shown above. What properties of diamond and graphite are determined by crystal structure?

Figure 24-11. Rough diamond, such as shown below, is often found embedded in a rocky material known as blue ground or kimberlite.

THREE LIONS, INC.

455

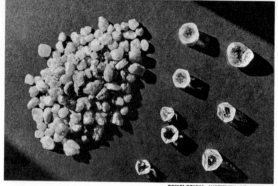

Figure 24-12. None of the diamond crystals shown above has been cut or polished. However, the material in which each was embedded has been removed.

GEMOLOGICAL INSTITUTE OF AMERICA

Figure 24-13. The necklace (top left) contains the 44.5-carat Hope diamond, believed to be part of a larger diamond that was stolen and never recovered. The Cullinan I (top right) is in the crown jewels of England. This 530.2-carat diamond was cut from a rough diamond weighing 3,106 carats, the largest diamond ever found. The Sancy diamond (lower left) has had many famous owners. The Eureka diamond (lower right) has a weight of 10.73 carats.

AUTHENTICATED NEWS INTERNATIONAL   GEMOLOGICAL INSTITUTE OF AMERICA

GEMOLOGICAL INSTITUTE OF AMERICA   AUTHENTICATED NEWS INTERNATIONAL

pressure. The extremely great pressure might have converted the graphite to the more dense crystal form of diamond. Although carbon is a common material on the earth, diamond is a rare mineral form. Therefore, the formation of diamond must not have been a very commonplace process in the earth's history.

Before it is cut and polished, a diamond crystal looks rather like a broken piece of glass. *(Figure 24-12.)* Such raw diamonds are cut into somewhat smaller pieces and into a variety of special shapes. Then the pieces of diamond are polished. Some famous diamonds are shown in *Figure 24-13*.

DO IT YOURSELF

Study uses of diamond

The weight of diamond used for industrial purposes far exceeds that used for jewels. What are the industrial uses of diamond? Is the diamond used for industrial purposes different in any way from that used as gems? What properties of diamond make it useful? Can man make artificial diamond? If so, how?

Emerald. Emerald is a silicate mineral that also contains the elements *beryllium* (bə ril′ i əm) and aluminum. In crystals of emerald, there is a small amount of the element *chromium* (krō′mi əm), which is actually an impurity in these crystals. This impurity gives emerald its color and its special value. Without it, the mineral is called *beryl* (ber′əl). Beryl is also a valuable material for jewelry, but not as valuable as emerald.

Ruby and sapphire. Ruby and sapphire are each, basically, crystals of aluminum oxide. In its pure form, aluminum oxide is called *corundum* (kə run'dəm). If a small amount of chromium oxide is present as an impurity in a sample of corundum, the result is ruby. If small amounts of iron oxide and *titanium* (tī tā'ni əm) *oxide* are present in a sample of corundum, the result is sapphire. Although natural ruby is very valuable as a gemstone, ruby can also be made artificially. In fact, ruby is now quite commonly made for use in one of the newest pieces of technical equipment, the *laser* (lā'zər).

What are some advantages you can think of in using man-made ruby rather than natural ruby in scientific equipment?

Other jewels. There are many other valuable minerals which are used in jewelry but which are not quite as precious as the four principal gemstones. In fact, some precious stones are not stones at all. The pearl, for example, is a substance formed by an oyster. Some varieties of coral are rare and beautiful enough to be precious. Many relatively common minerals are particularly attractive. Such minerals are called semiprecious stones, since these minerals are not particularly expensive.

Many people have made a very enjoyable hobby of cutting and polishing semiprecious stones. There is a special thrill in finding a semiprecious mineral, and a special pleasure in polishing it and cutting it to create a beautiful jewel. Searching for, collecting, and polishing semiprecious stones is one of the most enjoyable ways to become involved in the study of geology.

Lapidary art. An individual who cuts and polishes stones is called a *lapidary* (lap' ə dər'i). The history of lapidary art is as ancient and fascinating as the history of jewelry itself. Profiles of emperors have been carved

in beryl and *carnelian* (kär nēl'yən)—a reddish-brown, semiprecious stone. In the Renaissance, rich men vied with one another to see who could give the most beautiful jewelry to the church. Artists of the time, such as *Botticelli* (bät ə chel'ē) and *Cellini,* (chə lē'nē), practiced their art in gold and jewelry as well as with paint. Superstitious people believed that sapphires would prevent insanity and amber would cure goiter. Even today the power and wealth of the British Empire is symbolized by the crown jewels.

Thus, the materials man has taken from the earth have provided tools, equipment, heat, power, and beauty. It seems as if civilization has progressed in direct proportion to mankind's knowledge of the nature and use of the wealth buried within the earth.

What minerals and ores can you think of that are important today that were not considered important 50 years ago?

Figure 24-14. A large, uncut crystal of emerald, decorated with gold figurines, is shown in the top picture. The lower-left picture is of a large, uncut ruby surrounded by smaller gems. The lower-right picture shows several gems called star sapphires.

Checking Your Knowledge

IMPORTANT IDEAS

1. Large amounts of metals are used by man in today's highly industrialized society. However, few metals are found uncombined in nature. Most metals must be obtained from mixtures of minerals called ores.

2. Although geologists are able to describe the origin of some ore deposits, the origin of most ore deposits is not known with a high degree of certainty.

3. The processes involved in the formation of coal are not completely known, but geologists are fairly certain that coal formed from the remains of tropical plants.

4. The processes in the formation of petroleum are even less well known than those for coal. However, petroleum is believed to be the remains of tiny marine organisms that lived in shallow seas long ago.

5. In general, precious and semiprecious stones are crystalline forms of common minerals. Their color is usually due to minute quantities of impurities in the crystal.

USING NEW WORDS

Study the words listed below. On your paper write the numerals *1-5*. After each numeral write the correct word or words to answer the question having the corresponding numeral.

lapidary	iron	chromium	diamond
sapphire	ore	aluminum	beryl
anthracite	ruby	bituminous	lignite
petroleum	peat	beryllium	corundum

1. Which words are names of elements?
2. Which word refers to a person who cuts and polishes stones?
3. Which words refer to fossil fuels?
4. Which words relate to precious stones?
5. Which word refers to a source of metal?

TEST YOURSELF

Study the test below. On your paper write the numerals *1-20*. Beside each numeral write the word or words that best complete the sentence having the corresponding numeral.

1. The hardest mineral is ____.
2. The impurity which gives emerald a green color is the element ____.
3. The main compound in ruby and sapphire is ____.
4. Diamond is composed of ____.
5. Petroleum is found in formations of ____ rock.
6. One semiprecious material that is not really a stone is ____.
7. The best grade of coal is called ____.
8. An ____ is a mixture of minerals from which a metal is profitably obtained.
9. The metal most used is ____.
10. Geologists believe that natural gas is probably derived from ____.
11. The most common type of coal is ____.
12. Hematite is an ore of ____.
13. Geologists believe that ore deposits *(do, do not)* result from metamorphism.
14. Two materials that seem to be incompletely formed coal are peat and ____.
15. A ____ is a person whose hobby is cutting and polishing rocks.
16. Rock, such as shale, through which gases and liquids cannot pass is ____ rock.
17. The most valuable gemstone is ____.
18. An early step in the process of coal formation involves the action of ____.
19. Concentrations of minerals from which a useful metal can be economically obtained are called ____.
20. The geologic periods during which the plants that formed coal grew were the Mississippian and the ____.

Extending Your Knowledge

QUESTIONS TO EXPLORE

1. Are there natural resources in your locality that are not being used wisely? If so, how could they be used to better advantage?

2. What is the present status of the petroleum and natural gas reserves in this country? What are some ways of conserving these important resources?

3. What will happen when the high-grade iron ore in this country is used up? Are the many, unsightly junkyards in the United States an important source of iron?

4. How would you explain why diamond and graphite are different minerals, although their chemical composition is identical?

5. How would you explain the fact that impurities can impart color to a gemstone? Is color always desirable in a gemstone?

SOME THINGS TO DO

1. Find out if anyone in your class or in your community is a lapidary. If you can find someone who is a lapidary, ask him to bring some samples of polished and unpolished stones to your class. Also ask him to explain the procedures, equipment, and materials used to cut and polish stones.

2. Obtain samples of various types of cable, such as telephone cable, cable that is used in a suspension bridge, and cable used in a high-voltage, electrical power line. Determine what metals are used in each type of cable. From measurements of the weights and lengths of your samples, determine the weight of a mile of each type of cable. Find out the cost per pound of the metals used in the cables. Then, compute the cost of a mile of each type of cable.

3. Make models of the crystal structures of graphite and of diamond. Use small, Styrofoam balls to represent carbon atoms and short sticks to assemble the balls in the proper crystal lattice. Use the models to explain to the class why diamond is very hard, and why graphite feels slippery when it is rubbed between your fingers.

4. Make a display showing many of the products that are obtained from petroleum. Also explain how petroleum is refined to produce these many products. Find out what oil-bearing shale is and explain how it may be important in the future.

CHALLENGES IN SCIENCE

1. List the ores of the following metals: iron, lead, aluminum, copper, silver, gold, zinc, and uranium. Some of these metals have several different ores. Describe the chemical composition of each ore and the process by which the metal is obtained from the ore.

2. Find out what materials from the earth's crust are considered vital to our country's needs. Of these materials, which are available in our own country and which must be imported? Is there an overabundance of any of these materials in our country?

3. At present, most of the energy we use for transportation, industry, and temperature control is obtained by burning fossil fuels. What are some disadvantages of burning large amounts of fossil fuels? What other sources of energy might we use in place of fossil fuels? What are the advantages and disadvantages of these energy sources?

4. Ordinary clay, which is plentiful in the United States, contains about 20 per cent aluminum. Explain why we import bauxite that contains about 45 per cent aluminum from South America, instead of using the material closer at hand.

Clues to the past are contained in the earth.

CHAPTER 25

The History of a Rock Formation

In your study of the earth, you have learned many things about the earth that you did not know before this study. Furthermore, you have studied the methods of geology. You have learned that by making and checking inferences, man has reached some interesting conclusions about events and conditions in the very distant past.

The only way we have of learning about the past history of any area is to study the rock formations found there. We must carefully observe, record, and interpret any evidence of geologic activity that we can find. In some instances and in some places, there is abundant evidence of the geologic processes that have occurred. Then, the history of a region is easy to reconstruct. Sometimes, however, the evidence is not so abundant, and we cannot be certain of the history of the region.

In Chapter 25 we will study a particular rock formation. We will observe and record any information we can about the materials in this formation. Then, by combining our detailed observations with our knowledge of geologic processes, we will make inferences about how this particular formation came into existence. In short, we will discover as much as we can about this particular formation. Of course, there are many uncertainties in this type of study, and you may wonder how much we will be able to learn about the history of this formation. You may be surprised.

1. Observing a Rock Formation

Why study a rock formation? Imagine yourself as a geologist. You are examining a cut through a hill where a road has been built. You are interested in a particular stratum of conglomerate, a type of sedimentary rock. Perhaps you are trying to locate a mineral deposit that you think is related to this stratum of rock. Perhaps you are searching for signs of an oil deposit and wish to map all the rock layers for miles around. Or perhaps you are just curious, and wish to learn as much as you can about this rock layer simply because of your interest in the details of the earth. Whatever your reason, you will want to examine both the layer itself and the rocky material of which it is composed. In carrying out this examination, you will make use of all the information and of all the tools which are available for a modern geologic study.

General observations of a rock formation. The photograph on page 460 is of an actual formation of conglomerate. In *Figure 25-1* you see a drawing illustrating the hypothetical formation discussed in this chapter. We use a hypothetical formation so we can include specific details that illustrate different geologic processes. Keep *Figure 25-1* in mind, because it is this hypothetical formation of conglomerate that is the basis for our discussion in Chapter 25.

As you examine the formation exposed by the road cut, you see that its strata are slightly tilted. This is indicated by the well-marked bedding plane that runs through the formation. This bedding plane indicates the position of the level surface at the time the material in the stratum was deposited. Notice, too, that the conglomerate extends to the bottom of the cut, so that it is impossible to determine what type of rock lies beneath the conglomerate. It is also impossible to determine the depth or thickness of the conglomerate without

Figure 25-1. This drawing illustrates the hypothetical rock formation to be studied in this chapter. Note the slight tilt of the layers, as indicated by the bedding plane. Note, too, the distribution of cobbles and boulders.

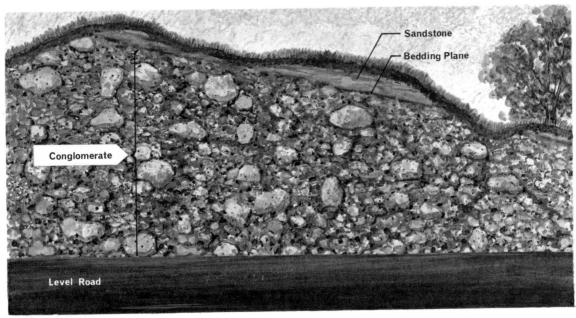

Sandstone

Bedding Plane

Conglomerate

Level Road

Figure 25-2. The conglomerate shown above is cobble conglomerate. Note that the cobbles are smooth and rounded. Notice, too, the fine texture of the matrix in this sample of conglomerate.

doing some more digging. The conglomerate extends almost to the top of the cut, too, but here and there a layer of reddish sandstone is visible above the conglomerate.

Examination of the conglomerate shows that it contains stones of a wide variety of sizes. These stones range in size from pebbles about one-half inch in diameter up to boulders which are more than ten inches in diameter. But most of the rock particles are between two and one-half inches and ten inches in diameter. Geologists call stones of this size *cobbles*. A conglomerate which contains a predominance of such stones is called a *cobble conglomerate*.

You will also examine the material of the *matrix* (mā′triks). The matrix is the fine-grained material that holds the cobbles together. This material has a texture like that of very fine sand and is a light tan color. You notice that this material is rather soft. You can actually rub fine particles off it with your fingertips.

You will undoubtedly wish to take samples of the various materials to a laboratory for more detailed study. But, already, your examination has given you some information. In your notebook you record your observations and the things you know. The first thing you record is your location—which you determine by studying a map of the region. By using a protractor and a plumb line, you measure and then record the tilt of the rock layer that you are examining. This is measured in degrees of the slope of the stratum compared to the horizontal. Note, too, the direction of the tilt. You measure and record the vertical extent of the bed of conglomerate, carefully noting that you cannot measure the layer's total thickness, since the lower portion is still concealed. You also note and record the type of layer which occurs on top of the one you are examining. You will probably want to take samples of that layer back to the laboratory for examination also.

You also include in your notebook the information that the material you are interested in consists mainly of cobbles inbedded in a sandstone matrix. The matrix is light tan in color, is composed of very fine sand particles, and is quite *friable* (fri′ə bəl). That is, the matrix is soft enough to be easily scratched and rubbed away.

What reasons can you give for taking a sample of the overlying rock back to the laboratory?

Components of the rock formation. In walking back and forth and in climbing over the rock formation, you notice that the cobbles not only differ in size but also in color. Perhaps this means that the various cobbles in the conglomerate differ in composition.

In order to make a more detailed study of the components of the formation, you will take samples of the rock to your laboratory.

You will want to take several samples from various portions of the exposed face. You select a variety of types for your samples, perhaps ten or twenty. You also record in your notebook the approximate percentage of the various stones in the exposed rock face. Thus, your notebook might contain the following information.

1. About 5 per cent dark black cobbles—mostly small
2. About 10 per cent greenish-black cobbles—mostly about five to ten inches in diameter—apparently olivine
3. About 30 per cent tan and brown cobbles—large sizes—apparently limestone —most larger boulders this material
4. Remaining cobbles and boulders (more than half) grayish-white with black flecks—apparently granite

In addition, your notebook would contain the information that the cobbles and boulders are well-rounded. None have jagged edges. You would also record that the distribution is not completely regular. There seems to be a few more of the small, black cobbles near the lower portion of the stratum than there are near the top. The greenish-black cobbles seem to be somewhat more abundant near the top than they are near the bottom. Apart from the rather slight tendency toward concentration of these two types, the pebbles and boulders are evenly scattered throughout the portion of the deposit that you can see.

How, do you suppose, did all the boulders and cobbles in this formation become well-rounded? Are the components of conglomerate always well-rounded stones?

2. Determining the Origins of Components of the Formation

The igneous origin of all rock. According to modern geologic theories, all the earth's crustal material was, at one time, igneous rock. Most of it still is. Thus, the material in the conglomerate rock which we are examining was, at one time, igneous rock. But, how can we learn about the igneous origins of the samples we have gathered from the formation?

The origin of sample cobbles. The first step in understanding the origin of our samples of rock is to determine what mineral forms the samples contain now. The components of the conglomerate are all well-rounded. That is, they have become so worn that their original shape and surface texture have long since disappeared. Therefore, to determine the crystal structure and appearance that each of these stones had in its original form, we must crack open the separate cobbles. Then we can examine the material exposed in the break.

Some of the cobbles break more easily than others, and the fracture patterns of the various cobbles differ. Of course, you record your observations concerning fractures in your

Figure 25-3. Rock is often cracked open in order to find fossils embedded in the rock or to examine the mineral forms and crystal structures of the rock.

HAYS FROM MONKMEYER

Figure 25-4. Gabbro (right) is similar to basalt (left) in some respects. As you can see, however, gabbro has a somewhat coarser grain structure than basalt.

notebook. The small black rocks break with a gently curved fracture, like the inside of a shell. The broken surface appears shiny, like a piece of broken glass. There is no crystal structure apparent. You recognize these small black cobbles as obsidian. They were formed from lava. See *Figure 14-8.*

The greenish-black cobbles are hard to crack. When you finally manage to break one open, you see that its fractured surface shows a granular pattern with a few very small crystals of light and dark materials. This is apparently a cobble of gabbro, a rock similar to basalt, and which contains such minerals as olivine. *(Figure 25-4.)*

When you crack open a sample of the rock that you have tentatively identified as granite, you see that your tentative identification was correct. The surface exposed by the break is rough, with many small crystals showing. Most of them are light in color, but a few are dark or black. A few shiny specks of mica are scattered through it, as in *Figure 22-2.* If you crack open several granite cobbles, you find that some of them have a slightly pinkish tinge, and some are darker than the average. This indicates that the cobbles you have taken from the conglomerate formation represent a variety of different types of granite and originally came from different igneous formations.

Testing for limestone. You have tentatively identified the light-colored or tan-colored smooth cobbles as limestone. When you crack open the first one, you are pleased to find that this seems to be correct. The surface exposed by the break is irregular but generally smooth. No small grains or crystals are apparent. You can further check this result with a little hydrochloric acid. A drop of weak hydrochloric acid on the calcium carbonate of limestone will produce a foaming action as carbon dioxide is produced.

The second such tan-colored cobble you crack open gives you a surprise. The appearance of the fractured surface is quite different from that of the first tan cobble you broke. This time the broken surface is smooth across a portion of the break, but then the break turns at a rather sharp angle to another smooth face. It appears as if the cracked portion were the face of a large crystal. Certainly, limestone would not fracture this way. A test with hydrochloric acid does not cause any foaming of carbon dioxide. A geologist would recognize the material in this cobble as a piece of a large crystal of feldspar. You may crack open several more light-colored cobbles before finding another one which turns out to be feldspar. Most of them are, as you first guessed, limestone.

JEROME WYCKOFF

Figure 25-5. Feldspar is a mineral that breaks along certain, well-defined cleavage planes, as shown here. This is one way that feldspar may be identified.

Age determinations. You may wish to know how old the various stones are. Of course, you already know that the cobbles are older than the conglomerate formation that now holds them.

Suppose you give your collection of cobbles to a geochemist and ask him to determine their ages. It will be quite an undertaking, and will probably represent a research project of some months' duration. But if the particular formation of conglomerate rock is important enough, then the research project is worth the time. Suppose he finds the obsidian to be between 300 million and 500 million years old, the granite to be between 800 million and 900 million years old, and the gabbro to be between 1.1 billion and 1.7 billion years old. He is unable to determine the ages of the limestone and the feldspar.

In what geologic time period was the obsidian formed? In what period was the gabbro formed? In what period was the granite formed?

3. The Effects of Weathering and Erosion

Mechanical weathering. An analysis of the components of the conglomerate has revealed that the various components are from different types of rock formations. Now we must consider how these components were broken loose or separated from their original formations to become available for inclusion in the formation we are studying.

You will recall that the process by which rock formations are broken down into smaller and smaller pieces of rock is called weathering. One type of weathering—*mechanical weathering*—occurs when the rock formation is actually cracked apart and the pieces are separated by some force. The forces which cause mechanical weathering may result from the freezing of water, the contraction and expansion caused by temperature changes, or the growth of plant roots. Examples of these types of weathering are shown in *Figure 25-6*.

Figure 25-6. Mechanical weathering occurs in several ways. The boulder in the picture on the left has been cracked open by the action of freezing water. Changes in temperature often cause layers of rock to split off from a large mass of rock, as shown in the center picture. The picture on the right shows an example of the splitting of a rock by tree roots.

ALASKA PICTORIAL SERVICE   JEROME WYCKOFF   HAROLD R. WANLESS

How would you explain weathering as a result of the freezing of water? Of changes in temperature? Of growing plants? What other types of mechanical weathering can you think of?

Chemical weathering. Not all rock formations crumble because of the application of some force which pushes portions of the rock formation away from each other. In the type of weathering called *chemical weathering,* various chemicals (usually dissolved in water) react with certain materials in a rock formation. Materials which are not affected are loosened from each other as the affected material is removed.

Not all rock formations are affected to the same degree by chemical weathering. Limestone, however, is particularly susceptible. As you know, there is a small percentage of carbon dioxide in the atmosphere. Carbon dioxide dissolves in water to form *carbonic*

Figure 25-7. Certain types of material are more susceptible to chemical weathering than others. As portions of this rock formation weathered, the pattern of holes developed.

RATHBONE FROM MONKMEYER

acid, H_2CO_3. Therefore, a typical raindrop is a very dilute solution of carbonic acid. Carbonic acid reacts with the calcium carbonate in limestone to form calcium bicarbonate, which readily dissolves in water. Thus, raindrops carry carbonic acid to the limestone. Then, calcium bicarbonate is carried away as the water moves off the limestone. Gradually, the limestone is worn away.

Another process of chemical weathering is *hydration*. Hydration is the process by which a mineral changes its chemical structure by absorbing water. To illustrate how hydration can affect a rock formation, consider what might happen to a formation of granite which contains the mineral feldspar as one of its components. Feldspar absorbs water easily. It then reacts with carbonic acid to form a clay. Eventually, the feldspar grains in a block of granite turn into soft particles of clay. Most of the remaining grains are quartz, which are not affected. However, the remaining grains in the granite are then loosened from each other. The clay is washed away, leaving a residue of sand.

What can you infer about the sizes of rock particles produced by mechanical weathering? By chemical weathering? Do you think the conglomerate we are considering represents the results of both types of weathering? Explain.

The role of gravity. Weathering is an explanation of how the various components of a formation of conglomerate are broken away from the formations of rock in which they originally formed. But how, you might ask, were these various components transported from their original locations to form a layer of conglomerate? The process which we usually associate with the moving of earth material from one place to another on the earth's surface is erosion.

W. F. LABAHN   JEROME WYCKOFF   SAN FRANCISCO CHRONICLE

Figure 25-8. The photographs above illustrate three types of downhill movement of earth materials. The stream of boulders shown at the left moves downhill very slowly. In the center picture, the accumulation of fragments broken off the rocky cliff forms a talus slope at the base of the cliff. The picture on the right shows the result of a landslide, which is a rapid downhill motion of a mass of earth materials.

Usually, when we think of erosion we think of streams or glaciers carrying away material as they erode the valley through which they travel. Another agent of erosion that we sometimes overlook is wind. Wind often picks up and carries away particles of dust and sand. In fact, when moving air contains grains of dust and sand, it is a very effective agent of weathering and erosion. *(Figure 22-8.)*

However, a large amount of material is transported without the aid of moving water, ice, or air. The motion of material from a higher point to a lower point requires only the force of gravity. The simple downhill motion of material due to gravity is the most common way for earth material to be moved.

The downhill motion of earth material may proceed rapidly or very slowly. Furthermore the material moved may differ. See *Figure 25-8.* Sometimes streams of boulders, often called rock rivers because of their appearance, move slowly downhill in a motion called *creep*. Piles of rock fragments called *talus* (tā′ləs) are the result of the downhill movement of pieces of rock which have broken off a cliff. Often huge masses of mud or earth slide downhill.

Thus, one of the commonest observations of geology is this. If material is loose, it will move downhill. There are many factors which aid this movement, but one way or another, slowly or rapidly, it will happen.

DO IT YOURSELF

Study the downhill movement of earth materials

From various reference materials, find answers to these questions. What factors determine the rate at which materials flow downhill? What factors are important in starting the downhill movement? What can be done to control downhill movement of material in large construction projects, such as in the building of the Panama Canal?

467

Figure 25-9. Notice the rocks which line this stream. Being tumbled about in a rapidly moving stream is one way by which rocks become smooth and rounded.

Explaining the well-rounded stones. We know that several different rock formations contributed the materials that make up the particular layer of conglomerate we are studying. Can we learn anything about the processes of erosion and weathering to which these materials were subjected? When the materials in this conglomerate first broke loose from their original formations, each piece was undoubtedly rough and irregularly shaped. But now they are smooth and well-rounded. Their smooth appearance must be the result of a long period of erosion, or perhaps a series of erosion processes. Naturally, we cannot be certain of what these processes were. How-

ever, our observations of rock and of the processes which are now acting on the earth's surface aid us in making a very good guess.

Probably, the first movement of the pieces of rock, after they broke off from their original formation, was simply downhill movement. Large blocks may have been broken into smaller ones during this movement, but such downhill movement would not result in smooth, well-rounded pieces of material.

In becoming smooth and rounded, the material in the conglomerate we are studying may have spent some time in a stream bed. In a stream bed, the cobbles and pebbles may have been washed along and tumbled about. Such a process would wear off their sharp edges. Or perhaps the material spent a long time on a shore of an ocean, being washed back and forth by the waves. This, too, would smooth off the sharp edges. Furthermore, the sandy material of the matrix must also have gone through such processes to be worn down into very fine particles.

We assume that rocks in this conglomerate first moved downhill by gravity and were then smoothed by stream or wave action. Could moving water have been the only agent which acted on these rocks from the time they left their original formation till they became part of this conglomerate?

4. Deposition, Solidification, and Uplift

The effects of turbidity currents. You know that sedimentary rock requires a long time and much pressure from overlying material in order to form. We have concluded that the cobbles we observe were once in a stream bed or on a seashore or both. How did they become deeply buried?

One way in which this could have happened is through the action of turbidity currents. In Chapter 17 you learned how turbidity currents can carry material from the shallow portion of the continental shelf down to the deepest parts of the sea. Thus, the cobbles, mud, and sand from the shoreline could be carried down to a deep portion of the ocean and deposited there in the undisturbed silence of the abyssal plain.

As more turbidity currents acted, more material would be carried down. Layers put down earlier would be buried. Eventually the early layers would be compressed, forming layers of sedimentary rock.

The effects of a subsiding ocean floor. A second way in which material from a rocky shoreline could become the floor of a deep part of the ocean is for the ocean floor to subside, or for the level of the ocean to rise. Either condition would result in the same type of rock formation. Such a change would take place over an extended period of time. The result would be to move material which was once in shallow water down to much greater depths.

But if the shoreline subsided, or if the ocean rose, would sediment be washed into the ocean and cover that which was already there? Perhaps the later-arriving sediment would be deposited in a different location. Where the sediment would be deposited would depend upon the nature of the land near the ocean shore. If land was being uplifted as the sea floor was sinking, a cliff would form along the shore. Layers of material would be deposited one on top of the other at the base of the cliff.

However, if the land near the shoreline was fairly level and was stable—that is, with no new mountain ranges forming—the result would be a steady change in the position of the shoreline. The shoreline would continually move inward. New sediment would not be deposited on top of old sediment, but rather in the area newly claimed by the sea.

Conditions affecting the conglomerate we are studying. Thinking back over the description of the conglomerate formation, we remember that it contains several different types of cobbles. The different types have various ages. Furthermore, the different types are not completely mixed together. The obsidian is somewhat concentrated near the bottom and the gabbro near the top. This implies a long period of deposition. First, lava fragments (obsidian) were broken from their formation, washed to the shore, and then carried somehow to a lower depth. Next came the granite and limestone cobbles. These came from a different source than the obsidian. The granite cobbles, in particular, came from an older source. They may well have come from deeper layers in the same mountain range which gave birth to the lava.

Finally, after the deposition of the granite and limestone cobbles was nearly completed, the older cobbles of gabbro were deposited. Throughout this extended series of events, the area in which the materials settled had remained the same.

From this evidence, we are led to two possibilities. One possibility is that the area of deposition was an abyssal plain and the materials were transported by turbidity currents. The other possibility is that the area of deposition was a subsiding ocean basin near a young and growing mountain range. If there were fossils included in the conglomerate, we might be able to choose between these two possibilities. But with the evidence that we have, we cannot make a justifiable choice.

Deposition of matrix material. As the cobbles were being deposited, so were the sand and mud in which they were finally solidified. If we were to conduct a careful chemical analysis of the sand matrix, we might find that it contained a little bit of iron oxide, a typical cementing chemical for sedimentary rock. Another typical cementing material is quartz. This is the same material that makes up sand.

Possibly, these cementing materials were originally dissolved in the water of the ocean.

Slight changes in the chemical nature of the ocean or in its temperature would cause these dissolved minerals to solidify and cement our sample of conglomerate rock together.

Evidences of uplift. We have concluded that the conglomerate rock formed under the ocean, perhaps very deep in the ocean, as part of an ancient abyssal plain. Now we find it on a hillside far above sea level. Clearly, some vertical movement has taken place. Either the sea has subsided, or the land has lifted. Probably, a combination of these two effects has brought the rock into its present position.

There is much evidence for such up-and-down movement of various portions of the earth's surface. One interesting piece of evidence is contained in Roman ruins. In ancient Naples there was a public market called the Temple of Jupiter Serapis. Many of the original columns still stand. It has been discovered that sea snails have bored holes into the columns six meters above the floor of the temple. Today the columns are above the level of the water, just as they were about two thousand years ago, when the temple was built. During the intervening two thousand years, this region apparently sank six meters below the water level and then rose again.

The first attempt to make a direct measurement of the rate of such movement started in 1731. Special marks were made near sea level on the rock cliffs along the coast of Sweden. Today, these marks are about 2.5 meters above sea level. This amounts to an average rise of about one centimeter per year. If such a rise were to continue steadily for a million years, this portion of the coast of Sweden would be 10 km above sea level. Then, this region would be higher than Mt. Everest is now.

As we know, earth movements are not steady over long periods of time. However, over extended periods of time a total movement of several kilometers could easily be accumulated. Thus, it is feasible for rock which was once deep in the ocean to now be exposed high up on a hillside in the middle of a continent.

A never-ending study. We have already learned something of the history of this particular rock formation and of the histories of its component parts. A continuing examination of the nature and materials of this conglomerate rock formation would undoubtedly reveal much more information. Furthermore, a study of other formations in this vicinity would also reveal their stories. In this way, detail by detail, geologists have been able to discover the histories of large areas of the crust of the earth.

What aspects of this conglomerate, other than those we have studied, might be considered important to other geologists?

Figure 25-10. Marks on the columns of a temple built two thousand years ago are an indication of changes in the elevation of this part of the earth's crust relative to the level of the sea.

SAWDERS FROM CUSHING

470

Checking Your Knowledge

IMPORTANT IDEAS

1. Careful study of rock formations in a given area will provide clues to the geologic history of that area.

2. All the earth's crustal material was, at one time, igneous rock. Much of this rock has undergone change since it first formed.

3. Mechanical and chemical processes are responsible for the weathering of rock—that is, for the breaking up of a mass of rock into smaller pieces. Weathering is usually a very slow process.

4. The force of gravity and other agents of erosion (wind, water, and ice) move materials from one location to another.

5. The process of being tumbled about in a stream bed or on a wave-washed beach smooths and rounds pieces of rock.

6. Some materials are carried to the deep ocean floor by turbidity currents. Other materials become part of the ocean floor due to the subsiding of the ocean floor or the rising of the level of the ocean.

7. Rock formed beneath the ocean floor may be uplifted to become part of a continent.

USING NEW WORDS

Study the six groups of words below. Each word is related to the study of a rock formation. Write the letters *a* through *f* on your paper. Following each letter, explain the relationships or similarities and differences in the meanings of the words in the group designated by that particular letter.

a. conglomerate — cobble — matrix
b. hydration — carbonic acid
c. creep — talus — landslide
d. gabbro — obsidian — granite
e. feldspar — quartz — clay — sand
f. turbidity current — erosion — gravity

TEST YOURSELF

Study the test below. On your paper write the numerals *1-10*. After each numeral write the correct response to that part of the test having the corresponding numeral.

1. A material, such as sandstone, that crumbles very easily is said to be _____.

2. The material of a conglomerate rock formation which binds the various parts together is called the _____.

3. As carbon dioxide from the air is dissolved in raindrops, they become drops of very dilute _____ acid.

4. When the feldspar in granite is removed by chemical weathering, the remaining grains of quartz form _____.

5. Which one of the following types of rock can be identified by its reaction with dilute hydrochloric acid? (a) basalt, (b) limestone, (c) granite.

6. Which of the following produces smooth, well-rounded pebbles? (a) deposition, (b) tumbling action of stones in a stream bed or on a wave-washed beach, (c) uplift of a rock formation.

7. Which of the following terms refers to the sloping piles of weathered rock which form at the base of a steep cliff? (a) matrix material, (b) talus, (c) friable.

8. Which of the following is not a factor in mechanical weathering? (a) temperature changes, (b) freezing of water, (c) roots of growing plants, (d) hydration.

9. Which of the following words refers to pieces of rock larger than ten inches across? (a) cobbles, (b) boulders, (c) matrix.

10. Which of the following words refers to pieces of rock having sizes ranging from two and one-half inches to ten inches across? (a) cobbles, (b) boulders, (c) matrix.

Extending Your Knowledge

QUESTIONS TO EXPLORE

1. Do you think the history of all rock formations can be determined easily? If not, what factors make the history of one rock formation easier to determine than that of another rock formation?

2. What explanation can you suggest for the occurrence of rock particles coarser than sand, but smaller than cobbles?

3. What evidence could a geologist use to determine whether a rock formation became exposed because the ocean level dropped or the coastline was raised?

4. Do you think there are any types of conglomerate other than cobble conglomerate? If so, how do they differ from cobble conglomerate?

5. Why, do you think, would a geologist ask a geochemist to determine the ages of rock samples, rather than make the determinations himself?

6. What are some methods by which the age of a formation of conglomerate might be determined?

SOME THINGS TO DO

1. Build an apparatus in which you can put pieces of rock and tumble them over and over. Some sort of rotating drum is generally used for this purpose. Use your apparatus to obtain answers to questions such as these. How rapidly do pieces of rock wear down? Do the types of rock wear down at the same rate? (If you weigh the pieces of rock before and after you tumble them in your apparatus, you can determine the weight of rock that has been worn away.) Does adding water to the tumbling rocks in the drum affect the rate of wear? What substances could be added to increase the rate of wear?

How far do pieces of rock travel in the apparatus in becoming smooth and rounded? Do you think that traveling this same distance in a stream bed would cause similar rock fragments to become smooth and rounded?

2. Study the rock formations and other geologic features near your community. From your observations, attempt to describe some of the past history of your locality. Was your area ever mountainous? Was it ever beneath the surface of the ocean? Did glaciers ever cover your locality? What evidence would you look for to answer such questions? Contact geologists in your State Geological Survey and ask for information about the geology of your state. When you get the information, compare it with your own findings.

CHALLENGES IN SCIENCE

1. A granite obelisk, called Cleopatra's Needle, stood about 3,500 years in Egypt. During this time, the effects of weathering were slight. In about 1880 the obelisk was brought to New York City and placed in Central Park. Since then, despite the application of preservatives, the granite has become severely weathered, and many of the inscriptions have been obliterated. Explain why the effects of weathering have been so much greater in 90 years in New York than they were in 3,500 years in Egypt.

2. Describe regions of the earth where you think conglomerate may be forming today.

3. Explain the differences between weathering and erosion. Do you think weathering occurs more rapidly in tropic regions or arctic regions? In dry climates or humid climates? In urban areas or rural areas? Compare the rates of erosion in these various localities. Give reasons for your answers.

BREAKTHROUGHS IN SCIENCE

Aluminum seems like the ideal metal in many ways. It is lightweight. It resists corrosion. It is an excellent conductor of heat and electricity. It can be mixed with other metals to form alloys that have great strength. No wonder aluminum is used in so many different ways and in so many different products. Because of its wide variety of uses, you may have the idea that aluminum has always been available for man's use. This, however, is certainly not true.

Scientists discovered aluminum in the 1800's. We now know that aluminum ranks third in abundance of the elements which compose the earth's crust. In fact, all soils and many minerals and types of rock contain aluminum compounds. However, aluminum is never found in the earth as a pure metal. Miners and prospectors can find pieces of gold and copper, but no one has ever dug up a piece of aluminum. It exists in nature only as a component of chemical compounds, usually with oxygen and silicon. Furthermore, separating the aluminum from its compounds is a difficult task. Therefore, the first aluminum—costing more than $500 per pound—was more precious than gold. Napoleon III had a set of aluminum forks and spoons for his most honored guests. Less important guests used gold and silver tableware.

Then, in 1886 an important discovery was made. As a matter of fact, two men working independently made the same discovery at about the same time. These men—Charles Hall of Thompson, Ohio, and *Paul Heroult* (ā rü') of Paris, France —developed an economical process for extracting aluminum from one of its ores. The ore they used was bauxite, which contains more than 32 per cent aluminum oxide. In the Hall-Heroult process, bauxite is dissolved in molten cryolite. Cryolite is a mineral containing sodium, aluminum, and fluorine. Then a direct current of electricity is passed through the solution. The electric current causes the aluminum oxide to decompose. Pure aluminum settles to the bottom of the container.

As you can imagine, the production of aluminum by this process requires great amounts of electrical energy. Each pound of metal produced requires from eight to ten kilowatt-hours of electrical energy. Since the cheapest source of electrical energy is hydroelectric power, many aluminum plants are built near rivers that can provide plenty of power.

Thus, the widespread use of aluminum has been made possible through the development of the Hall-Heroult process. The cost of aluminum has been reduced to as low as twelve cents a pound, and man has benefited in many ways. The methods of rapid transportation we use in the twentieth century result, to a large extent, from the use of aluminum. Our food is often preserved in aluminum wrappers and cooked in aluminum utensils. Many of our homes have aluminum doors, window frames, and screens. Aluminum in paint protects metal buildings. There are already many uses for this metal, and new uses are continually being discovered. The Hall-Heroult process has made the widespread use of aluminum possible and, therefore, the development of this process may be considered a breakthrough in science.

REVIEWING UNIT SIX

SUMMARY

1. Scientists believe that the original rock of the earth was igneous. Some of this igneous rock was broken down and formed into sedimentary rock.

2. Igneous and sedimentary rock are changed into metamorphic rock when subjected to very great pressure and high temperature.

3. The study of fossils reveals the geologic history of the earth, and the history of life on the earth as well.

4. Several methods of radioactive dating are used in determining the ages of rock and of fossil remains.

5. Our industrial society depends upon man's ability to locate and use wisely the resources buried in the earth. These resources include ores of various metals, fossil fuels, and precious and semiprecious stones.

6. The history of a region of the earth can be inferred from a study of the rock formations in that region.

QUESTIONS TO DISCUSS

1. In terms of career opportunities, which area of earth science do you think is the most attractive?

2. Which of our natural resources are renewable? Which are nonrenewable? Is there a chance that shortages of nonrenewable resources will occur in the near future?

3. Why is the potassium-argon method of radioactive dating so very useful?

4. How would you explain the observation that certain areas of the earth's surface seem to alternate between being above sea level and below sea level?

5. What differences are there between potassium 40 and potassium 39?

UNIT TEST

Study the test below. Read the instructions for each portion of the test. Then, on your paper write the numerals *1-20*. Beside each numeral write the letter of the correct response to the part of the test having the corresponding numeral.

1-4. Indicate whether each of the materials listed below is a product resulting from (a) volcanism, (b) metamorphism, or (c) sedimentation.

1. coquina
2. shale

3. obsidian
4. gneiss

5-10. Classify each rock or rock formation listed as (a) intrusive, (b) extrusive, (c) sedimentary, or (d) metamorphic.

5. batholith
6. marble
7. dike
8. the island of Hawai

9. walls of the Grand Canyon
10. lava flows in Oregon

11-14. Indicate which method of dating—(a) uranium-lead method, (b) potassium-argon method, (c) carbon 14 method, or (d) index fossils—could be used most effectively in determining the ages of each of the objects listed below.

11. a pharaoh's grave in Egypt
12. a fossil-bearing strata of sedimentary rock
13. a bone found under an ancient lava flow, believed to be 500,000 years old
14. rock from the Canadian shield

15-20. Classify each object listed as (a) an ore of a metal, (b) a precious or semiprecious stone, or (c) a fossil fuel.

15. anthracite
16. aluminum oxide crystals
17. petroleum

18. bauxite
19. hematite
20. beryl

ENRICHING YOUR SCIENCE EXPERIENCES

INVESTIGATIONS TO CARRY OUT

1. Make a study of the major industries in your area. Determine what raw materials are used by these industries. To what extent are the materials used by these industries obtained locally? To what extent are locally available resources shipped to other regions? From your investigations, what would you say are some factors that determine the location of large industrial areas?

2. Sand, gravel, soil, or any loose material, when piled as steeply as it can be piled, makes an angle with the horizontal called the angle of repose. What is the angle of repose for dry sand? For wet sand? For sand under water? Experiment with various materials. Is the size of the particles of material related to the angle of repose? If so, what is the relationship? What value is there in knowing the angle of repose for various materials?

3. Ordinary soda water, such as that dispensed at a soda fountain or that which you can buy in bottles at the grocery store, is a solution of carbon dioxide in water. As you know, this solution is carbonic acid. Obtain some soda water, and conduct some experiments to determine the effect of carbonic acid on various materials. In your experiment, use materials such as granite, limestone, sand, an iron nail, or any other sample of rock or mineral that you have. What materials are affected by the carbonic acid? How can you determine if a certain material is affected? Does its color change? Is it dissolved in the acid? Is there a visible chemical reaction between the acid and any of the materials? In what way could carbonic acid be formed in nature?

ADDITIONAL READING IN SCIENCE

Beiser, Arthur, *The Earth*. New York, Time Incorporated, 1963. 192 pp.

Fenton, Carroll Lane, and Fenton, Mildred Adams, *Rocks and Their Stories*. Garden City, New York, Doubleday & Company, Inc., 1951. 112 pp.

Harbeck, R., and Johnson, L., *Earth and Space Science*. New York, Holt, Rinehart and Winston, 1965. 296 pp.

Holden, Alan, and Singer, Phylis, *Crystals and Crystal Growing*. Garden City, New York, Doubleday & Company, Inc., 1960. 320 pp.

Ordway, Richard H., *Earth Science*. Princeton, New Jersey, D. Van Nostrand Company, Inc., 1966. 720 pp.

Pearl, Richard M., *How to Know the Minerals and Rocks*. New York, McGraw-Hill Book Company, 1955. 192 pp.

Spencer, Edgar Winston, *Geology, A Survey of Earth Science*. New York, Thomas Y. Crowell Company, 1966. 653 pp.

Viorst, Judith, *The Changing Earth*. New York, Bantam Books, 1967. 244 pp.

Zumberge, James H., *Elements of Geology*. New York, John Wiley and Sons, Inc., 1964. 342 pp.

NASA

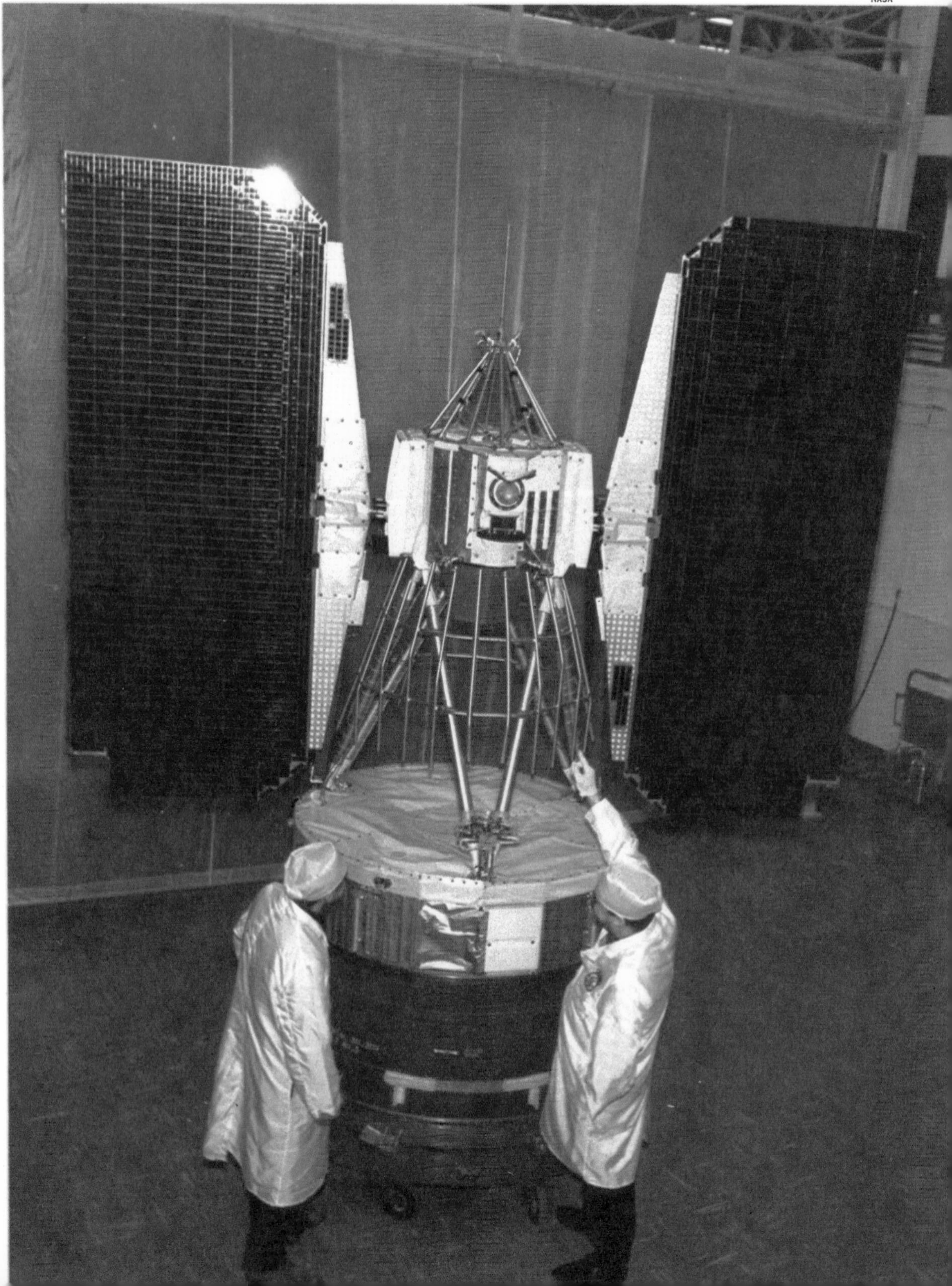

UNIT 7

THE EARTH'S ENVIRONMENT

Chapters

We now come to the last unit in this book. We first studied various fields of science and types of scientists. Then, we studied the universe in general, emphasizing its vast size and great number of galaxies. From the Milky Way Galaxy, we singled out the solar system for study. Then, we narrowed the range of our study further and made a detailed study of the earth.

One important thing we learned about the earth and about man's study of the earth is this. In spite of the fact that man lives on earth, there are still many things that he has not yet learned about its surface, its interior, its atmosphere, and the space that surrounds it. Scientists will be striving for many more years to find answers to questions that have already been asked. And, as has always been the case in scientific study, in answering these questions, other questions about the earth and its environment will be asked.

UNIT 7 is about some of the things that scientists have recently learned in their continuing exploration of the vast, unknown realms of the earth's environment. You will find out some things that were learned from recent space flights of unmanned satellites, such as *OGO* and *Surveyor,* as well as that which has been learned by astronauts in manned spacecraft. The exploration of the moon is discussed. You will discover something about the matter—other than planets, moons and stars—that exists in space, and how that matter is affected by gravitational force. You will also read about the frontiers of research—attempts to explore farther up and farther down. Finally, you will be challenged to think about problems associated with long-term space expeditions, both manned and unmanned. The mind of man makes it possible to explore our universe. Imagine the excitement and adventures that lie ahead!

◄ One way of studying the earth's environment is through the use of satellites.

The upper atmosphere is studied by using rockets and satellites.

CHAPTER 26

The Upper Atmosphere and Beyond

The properties of the atmosphere discussed in Chapter 18 were related to the lower atmosphere—that is, to regions below an altitude of 100 km. The upper atmosphere, then, is that portion of the atmosphere above an altitude of 100 km. There is no distinct boundary to the upper atmosphere. However, above an altitude of about 1,000 km, the atmosphere is so rare that the measurement of any physical property except the magnetic field is very difficult. When scientists discuss the upper atmosphere they are usually referring to the region between the altitudes of 100 km and 1,000 km.

Only in recent years has man been able to travel into the upper atmosphere and beyond. But now, through space exploration with manned and unmanned satellites, man has learned a great deal about the ionosphere, the upper atmosphere, and the regions beyond. However, much remains to be learned.

In Chapter 26 you will find out some of what has been learned about the region more than 100 km out from the earth. Furthermore, you will discover how this information was obtained. As you learn the answers to some questions about the density, temperature, and composition of the upper atmosphere, other questions will be raised. As you should know by now, that is the usual result of any scientific inquiry. Hopefully, some of you may be challenged to choose as your career the study of the upper atmosphere and beyond. If so, you will have a part in many exciting events that will occur during the decades ahead.

1. The Ionosphere

Ionization in the ionosphere. You will recall that the ionosphere is a portion of the atmosphere which exists between about 80 km and 500 km above the surface of the earth. Thus, most of the ionosphere is in the upper atmosphere—that is, above an altitude of 100 km. As the name of the region implies, many atoms and molecules in the ionosphere are ionized—that is, broken down into electrically charged particles.

When an atom is ionized, it loses at least one of its electrons. The electron, carrying a negative charge, then moves off and is no longer part of the original atom. The remainder of the atom, now called an ion, is left with a positive charge.

Molecules can also be ionized. Consider a molecule of nitrogen dioxide, NO_2. It can be separated into nitric oxide (NO) and an atom of oxygen (O). But when this separation occurs, the NO molecule will often carry with it an extra electron. It is thus a negative ion, NO^-. The oxygen atom, then, will have one electron less than it normally has. It is thus a positive ion, O^+.

Discovery of the ionosphere. Long before the ionosphere was actually discovered, its existence was predicted by several scientists. Michael Faraday made such a suggestion in 1832; the great mathematician *Karl Friedrich Gauss* (gous) in 1839; and the British physicist Lord Calvin in 1860. It was Gauss who first published the suggestion. Although Faraday apparently thought of it first, he put his suggestion in the form of a letter to an associate, and the letter remained unopened until 1937, more than a century after it had been written.

The idea that a region such as the ionosphere might exist was responsible for the first large-scale, international program of scientific endeavor. This program was called the International Polar Year, and it started in 1882. It involved scientists from ten European countries and the United States in a cooperative program to study the weather, the ocean, and many other characteristics of the earth, as well as of the sun. This project was so successful that it has been repeated in later and more ambitious projects. In fact, the organization of the International Geophysical Year (IGY) in 1957 was the direct result of this earlier attempt.

The International Quiet Sun Year recently ended. How could IQSY findings be related to studies of the upper atmosphere?

Even though an interest in the upper atmosphere and the possibility of proving the existence of the ionosphere was one of the reasons for the first International Polar Year, no data about the ionosphere were collected. The reason was that no one knew how to collect such data. Conditions and characteristics of the ionosphere could only be discussed in theory for another twenty years.

Figure 26-1. Faraday (holding a magnet) and Gauss (right) predicted that ionized gases surrounded the earth. During their lifetimes, however, no evidence of the existence of the ionosphere was found.

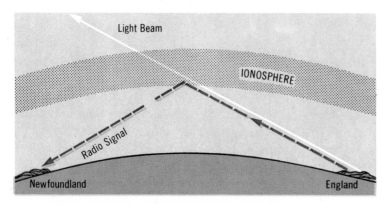

Figure 26-2. The radio signal sent from England by Marconi was reflected toward the surface of the earth by the ionosphere. Thus, the signal could be received in Newfoundland. A beam of light would not have been reflected. A beam of light would travel straight out into space instead.

In 1901, however, an important achievement was made by Guglielmo Marconi, the inventor of the radio. He succeeded in sending a message from Cornwall, England, to Newfoundland, Canada. Many scientists had predicted that sending a radio signal that far over the earth's surface would be impossible. They reasoned that in order for radio signals to travel between those two points, the signals could not travel in a straight line, as light would. They would somehow have to get around the curve of the earth. Other scientists, however, understood what had happened. They realized that evidence for the existence of the ionosphere had at last been discovered. They understood that charged particles in the upper atmosphere would bend radio waves and send them back down to earth again. See *Figure 26-2*.

Studies of the ionosphere. Many scientists then began to make more detailed studies of the ionosphere. These studies have continued up to the present day and still go on. Scientists have learned that the ionosphere is a turbulent, changing region of the earth's environment. Even though it is extremely rarefied, the ionosphere is of great practical importance and enormous scientific interest.

Early data concerning the ionosphere were obtained by using radio signals. Special radio transmitters and receivers called *ionosondes*

(ī on'ə sondz) were, and still are, used in the following way. A radio signal is sent straight up into the sky. It reflects from the ionosphere and returns to the receiver. By using various techniques, the time for this round trip is measured. Since radio signals travel at the speed of light, the time measurement can be used to determine the altitude at which the signal was reflected.

Studies made using ionosondes can reveal something about the structure of the ionosphere. The ionosphere differs from one altitude to another. Primarily, this difference is in the density of ions and electrons. At the base of the ionosphere, about 80 km above the surface of the earth, there are about 10^4 ions in each cubic centimeter. In comparison, at this point in the atmosphere there are about 2×10^{16} nonionized (or neutral) particles per cubic centimeter. Thus, at 80 km above the earth, the ratio of neutral particles to ions is about $2 \times 10^{12}:1$.

At an altitude of 300 km there are about 20 times more ions per cubic centimeter than there are at 80 km, and the atmosphere has about 10^9 particles per cubic centimeter. Between these two altitudes, the structure of the ionosphere is usually quite irregular. That is, the number of ions per cubic centimeter at any particular location changes from day to night and from one season to another.

DO IT YOURSELF

Make a computation

Fill a 100 milliliter (ml) graduate with dried beans. Count the beans. Then determine the number of beans per ml. Compute how large a container would have to be to hold 2×10^{16} beans of this same size. Imagine that you had such a container filled with 2×10^{16} beans. If you mixed 10^4 kernels of corn with the beans, how long, do you think, would it take to find 10 of the corn kernels?

Determining the structure of the ionosphere. How is an ionosonde used in determining the ionosphere's structure? Many radio signals will penetrate a little way into the ionosphere and then be reflected back again. The point at which this reflection takes place depends upon two things: the frequency of the radio signal and the number of electrons per cubic centimeter at that point. Scientists know the relationship between the frequency of a radio signal and the number of electrons per cubic centimeter needed to reflect that signal. A low frequency radio signal can only penetrate into a portion of the ionosphere where there are few electrons per cubic centimeter. A high frequency signal, however, will penetrate much farther into the ionosphere—that is, to a point where the density of electrons is much greater. So, scientists send out radio signals of various frequencies. The time required for each signal to make the trip from the surface of the earth to a particular level of the ionosphere and back is measured. Using these measurements, scientists can determine the electron density at various levels of the ionosphere.

In recent years, another technique has been used to probe the ionosphere. This new technique involves the use of instruments carried on rockets. The use of instrument-bearing rockets is not as convenient as the use of ionosondes is, but instruments on rockets give a much more complete picture.

NASA FROM ESSA

Figure 26-3. The rocket shown here is a RAM (Radio Attenuation Measurements) vehicle. This vehicle is used to propel instruments through the atmosphere to obtain data on ionization and its effects.

Changes in the ionosphere. Scientists have discovered that the ionosphere changes greatly from day to night. A graph of ion densities between altitudes 50 km and 200 km in the

481

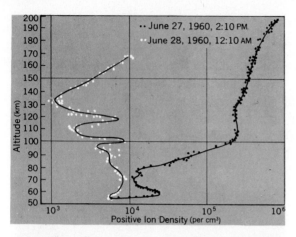

Figure 26-4. The data represented here indicate that ion density varies not only from one altitude to another but also from daytime to nighttime.

early afternoon and a little after midnight is shown in *Figure 26-4.*

Evidence such as this shows pretty clearly that the structure of the ionosphere depends upon sunlight. But exactly how does this dependence work? After a considerable number of observations and laboratory measurements, scientists concluded that the ultraviolet radiation and X rays from the sun are responsible for the creation of most of the ions in the earth's atmosphere. As high-energy radiation, either ultraviolet or X ray, strikes an atom or molecule, it "knocks off" an electron. This effect is called *photo emission.* This same effect makes a photoelectric cell work.

Photoelectric cells are coated with very special metals which are particularly susceptible to ionization by light. However, the gases in the earth's atmosphere are much harder to ionize than these special metals. Visible light will not do it. Ionization of gases requires the high-energy portion of the sun's spectrum— that is, ultraviolet radiation and X rays.

As radiation in this portion of the sun's spectrum passes through the atmosphere, it ionizes many gas molecules. At the same time,

this radiation is almost completely absorbed. Fortunately for us, very little of it reaches the surface of the earth. Life as we know it on earth could not survive if it were exposed to the full intensity of the ultraviolet radiation and X rays from the sun.

In the presence of the dangerous ultraviolet radiation and X rays in space, how can astronauts survive?

After ions are formed in the ionosphere, what happens to them? The ion has a positive charge and the electron a negative charge. Unlike charges attract each other, so there is a force tending to pull positive and negative ions together. If they were to come close to each other, it is very probable that the ion would recapture the electron and become a neutral atom again. In the lower portion of the atmosphere, this is exactly what happens. At low altitudes, there is a higher density of particles than at high altitudes. The electrons and ions are much closer to each other. Therefore, the ionosphere almost never extends below an altitude of 80 km. Below this altitude, the ions and electrons combine with each other (to form neutral atoms and molecules) as rapidly as atoms and molecules are split apart to form ions. Thus, no ionosphere exists at this low level.

Above an altitude of about 80 km, however, the air density is low enough so that the ions and electrons are separated for a short time before they recombine. Thus, sunlight will produce ions faster than they disappear by recombination, and an ionosphere will form. However, over the nighttime side of the earth no ions are created in this way. As an example, ionization in the atmosphere over North America decreases after sunset. Gradually the ions and electrons recombine, and the ion density decreases until sunrise the next morning. Then the process of ionization

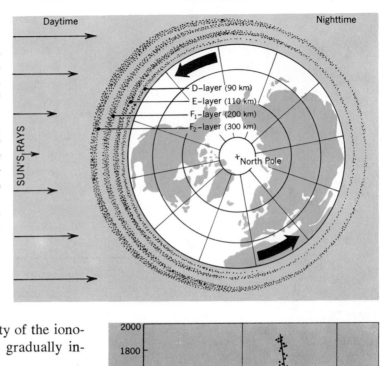

Figure 26-5. Four layers of the ionosphere and their altitudes are indicated in the diagram. Each altitude indicated is the average altitude of the maximum ion density in that layer. The ion density and the altitude of a layer change frequently, particularly during periods of sunspot activity. For example, after a solar flare the D-layer may extend to a level lower than 90 km. Other changes also occur. The D-layer and the F_2-layer are present only during the daytime. The E-layer and the F_1-layer decrease in ion density at night, but do not disappear.

begins again, and the ion density of the ionosphere over North America is gradually increased.

At higher altitudes where the atmosphere is even less dense, ions have a chance for an even longer life. Consequently, the ion density is greater. However, the ion density does not continue to increase as the altitude increases. A graph illustrating the relationship between ion density and altitude at night, as determined by ionosondes and instrument-carrying rockets, is shown in *Figure 26-6*. As you can see, the ion density has a maximum point at around 300 or 350 km. Above that level, there are fewer ions per cubic centimeter.

How might data obtained during the day concerning ion density and altitude be different from data collected at night in the same region of the atmosphere?

There are several reasons why the ion density decreases at very high altitudes. One reason is that the atmosphere is so rarefied at these high altitudes that not many atoms are available to be ionized. Another reason is that the content of the atmosphere is quite different at high altitudes than it is at low altitudes.

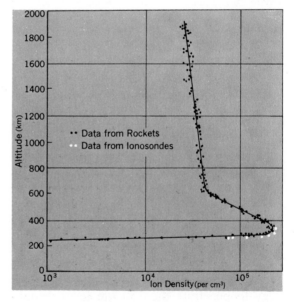

Figure 26-6. This graph is composed of data collected in two different ways. Notice that the maximum ion intensity is at an altitude of about 350 km. Note, too, that no data from above this point was obtained through the use of ground-based ionosondes.

For example, although hydrogen and helium are very rare in the atmosphere near the surface of the earth, they predominate at altitudes above 1,000 km.

Figure 26-7. Complex electronic equipment, such as that shown above, is used in studies of variations in ionospheric conditions.

In addition to the regular variations of the ionosphere, there are a number of erratic ones. These erratic variations are related to solar activity. Whenever flares occur on the surface of the sun, the earth's ionosphere is affected. Solar flares are usually accompanied by a strong burst of X rays. These extra X rays create more ions, thereby increasing the ion density of the ionosphere.

Sometimes changes in the ionosphere have an effect on radio communication. If ions are created below 80 km—the usual bottom of the ionosphere—these ions will absorb radio signals rather than reflect them. This means that radio signals, instead of being bounced around the earth, will simply be stopped. Thus, solar storms interfere with radio communication on earth.

2. Observing the Upper Atmosphere

Studying the ionosphere from above. Much has been learned about the ionosphere by observing radio signals sent out from the surface of the earth. But there is a limitation to this method. As shown in *Figure 26-6,* the greatest ion density occurs at an altitude of about 350 km. Suppose a radio signal were sent upward and this signal had enough energy to penetrate the 350 km level. Would such a signal be reflected back again from higher regions? No, above this point of maximum ion density, there are fewer ions and electrons present. If a radio signal had enough energy to penetrate the level of maximum ion density, the signal would continue on into space. Thus, nothing can be learned of the structure of the ionosphere above the point of maximum density by sending radio signals from the earth.

Figure 26-8. The picture below is an artist's conception of the hardware used in a space probe. The instruments are shown just after separation from the rocket that put the hardware into orbit. The spherical object is designed to measure air density. The satellite with the flat surfaces is the Injun Explorer. It has sixteen separate sensors for measuring radiation of various kinds and intensities.

AUTHENTICATED NEWS INTERNATIONAL

Figure 26-9. The Alouette satellite, shown as technicians make last-minute checks on its operation, is designed to study the ionosphere from above (topside sounding). As shown at the right, data is also obtained by ground-based radio signals (underside sounding). Still more information is obtained by rocket probes which pass through the ionosphere.

AUTHENTICATED NEWS INTERNATIONAL

If radio signals sent from the earth cannot be used to get information from above an altitude of 350 km, how can information about the high-altitude portion of the ionosphere be gained? Data concerning the very high reaches of the atmosphere are obtained through the use of rockets and satellites. Characteristics of other parts of the atmosphere are determined, as well as those of the ionosphere.

The density of ions at high altitudes is measured by putting an ionosonde in a rocket or a satellite, and sending it above the 350 km level. With the ionosonde above the alti-tude of 350 km, a radio signal can be sent toward the earth. If the signal is of the right frequency, it will be reflected back to the satellite by the intervening layer of ions. In this way, ion densities at altitudes above 350 km are measured. Measurements made from above the ionosphere are called "topside soundings." Measurements of this type were made by the Canadian satellite *Alouette* (al lù et′).

How would you explain the relationship between the energy of a radio wave and the frequency of the wave?

DO IT YOURSELF

Make a report

Find out what you can about the *Alouette* satellite. When and where was it launched? Was it placed in an equatorial orbit or a polar orbit? Why was this type of orbit chosen? Is the satellite still operative? Organize your findings into a report to present to the class.

Chemical composition of the upper atmosphere. The nature of the ionosphere is not the only important characteristic of the upper atmosphere. For many years the ionization of the upper atmosphere was the only characteristic which could be studied, since it was the only thing that could be observed with equipment located on the surface of the earth. Now, however, since rockets and satellites are being sent into this region, we are beginning to learn a great deal more about the upper atmosphere.

Only a small fraction of the total number of atoms and molecules in the upper atmosphere is ionized. Most of them are ordinary atoms and molecules. However, the relative proportion of the various elements is quite different in the upper atmosphere than it is near the earth's surface.

Determining constituents of the upper atmosphere has been done through the use of instruments aboard rockets and satellites. In many cases spectrometers have been used. As you may recall, these same instruments are used on earth to determine the composition of the atmospheres of stars. Spectrometers carried to high altitudes in a satellite can be used to determine the constituents of the earth's atmosphere. By analyzing the sunlight shining through a region of the atmosphere, it is possible to determine what elements are present in that region.

Studies such as this have revealed that up to an altitude of about 80 km the composition of the atmosphere is relatively uniform, as was described in Chapter 18. Above the mesopause, however, the atmosphere seems to be formed of layers. In each layer, a different element predominates. In *Figure 26-10*, the diagram indicates the depth of each layer and what element is most important in each layer.

In considering the portion of the atmosphere above 80 km, you must keep in mind that less than one thousandth of one per cent of the total mass of the atmosphere is in the portion above an altitude of 80 km. The gas particles in the layers of nitrogen, oxygen, helium, and hydrogen are very far apart. The entire portion above 80 km resembles a vacuum. Thus, even though one layer consists mainly of oxygen, the atmosphere in that layer is far too rarefied to permit man to live there—unless he carried his own supply of oxygen.

There is another way in which the gases of the upper atmosphere differ from those near the earth's surface. Near the earth's surface, the particles of most gaseous elements are molecules. These molecules contain two atoms of that particular element. However, beginning with the layer of oxygen in the upper atmosphere, the particles which make up the gases in the upper atmosphere are individual atoms of the elements, rather than molecules made up of two atoms joined together.

What reasons can you give to explain why the particles of gases in the upper atmosphere are individual atoms, while the particles in the lower portions are molecules?

Temperature, density, and pressure. Instruments carried by rockets have also been used to measure temperature. Can you imagine

Figure 26-10. Below the mesopause, the atmosphere is a mixture of gases. Above the mesopause, the atmosphere is formed of layers of various gaseous elements.

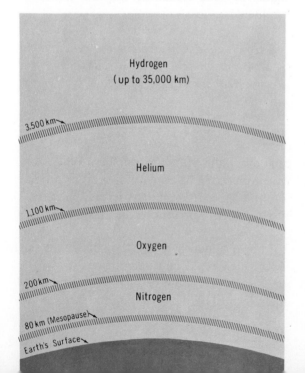

Hydrogen
(up to 35,000 km)

3,500 km

Helium

1,100 km

Oxygen

200 km

Nitrogen

80 km (Mesopause)

Earth's Surface

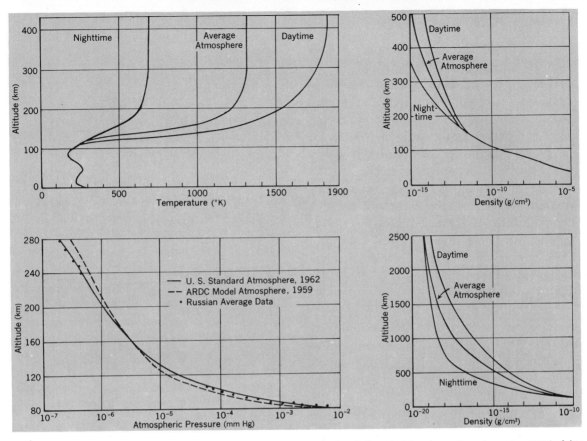

Figure 26-11. Some data concerning conditions at various levels of the earth's atmosphere are represented by these graphs. Much of this data was obtained through the use of instrument-carrying rockets and satellites.

how this might be done? After all, the air is extremely rarefied at these altitudes, and an ordinary thermometer would not work. It is possible, however, to use other natural phenomena to measure temperature.

The speed of sound depends upon the temperature of the gas through which the sound is moving. The warmer the gas, the faster the speed of sound. Temperature measurements in the upper atmosphere have been made using this relationship. In one such technique, a rocket is sent up and carefully tracked so that its position is accurately known at all times. At a precise time, a small bomb is set off in the rocket. The sound which it makes is recorded a short time later at several other stations. From information about the distance

and time, the speed of sound can be determined. Then, the average temperature between the rocket and the other recording stations can be calculated.

This method works up to an altitude of about 90 km. Above that, the air is so rarefied that sound waves are not transmitted well enough for this technique to be useful.

It is possible to figure out the temperature in another way. This second method requires knowing the pressure of the gas, its density, and the type of chemicals that are present. Then a physical principle known as the gas law can be used to calculate temperature.

Some unusual ideas have been employed to measure pressure and density. One of these is the "falling-sphere method." A balloon is carried very high into the upper atmosphere by a rocket, and then inflated. In one such measurement, a balloon ten feet in diameter was released from a rocket at an altitude of about 100 km over Eglin Air Force Base in Florida. As the balloon fell toward the ground, its motion was carefully determined by small instruments attached to the balloon. Information from these instruments was sent to the earth by means of a radio. The radio signals revealed how much the balloon was being slowed by air resistance. The experimenters were then able to calculate the density of the air which would cause this particular rate of slowing.

Pressure measurements can be made with pressure gauges carried to high altitudes by rockets. This procedure is usable only up to an altitude of about 90 to 100 km. Above this altitude, the measurement of pressure is extremely difficult. However, there are some types of equipment that can be used to make density measurements at high altitudes.

Upper atmospheric weather. Just as the lower portion of the atmosphere has winds and storms, so does the upper portion. So far, very little is known about this "weather" in the upper atmosphere. However, some interesting measurements have been made concerning wind velocities. These measurements were also made through the use of rockets. For these measurements, sodium pellets are carried in the front end of a rocket. At a high altitude, the sodium is heated, vaporized, and then released into the atmosphere. The

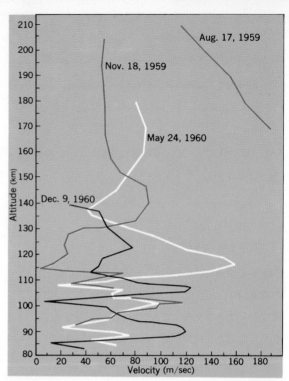

Figure 26-12. The data represented on this graph indicate the variation of wind velocity with altitude on several different days.

result is a large cloud of sodium vapor. Sunlight striking the sodium vapor causes a distinct, yellow glow. This permits the sodium cloud to be observed from the ground. By observing the motion of the sodium vapor cloud, scientists study the winds in the upper atmosphere. The observation must usually be carried out just before sunrise or just after sunset. Otherwise, the bright sky would make the sodium vapor cloud almost invisible. The results of some of the measurements of high-altitude winds are shown in *Figure 26-12*.

3. Magnetic Fields in the Upper Atmosphere

The nature of the atmosphere at very high altitudes. Knowledge of the outermost region of the atmosphere has been gained very recently and almost entirely through the use of man-made satellites. As you know, there is no sharp boundary where the atmosphere of the earth stops and space begins. Instead, there is a broad region of gradual transition. As the altitude increases, the density of the atmosphere becomes less and less. The chemical nature of the atmosphere also changes with the altitude.

There are two important factors that determine the nature of the atmosphere at altitudes above 1,000 km. These factors are the magnetic field of the earth and the solar wind. The solar wind is composed of charged, subatomic particles. These particles are, for the most part, protons and electrons. As was described in Chapter 8, these streams of charged particles moving out from the sun constitute an electric current. Consequently, they create a magnetic field which moves with them.

When these charged particles and the magnetic field which travels with them reach the

Figure 26-13. The satellite below is an OSO (Orbiting Solar Observatory) satellite. The data from OSO satellites will be the subject of intense scientific interest for years to come.

vicinity of the earth, they interact with the magnetic field of the earth. The result of this interaction is not yet fully understood. However, by using instrument-carrying satellites, scientists have obtained information about the conditions in the region of this interaction. One result of the interaction is that the magnetic field of the earth is compressed on the side facing the sun, and extended out into a long tail on the opposite side as shown in *Figure 26-14*.

Near the surface of the earth these compression and streaming effects are impossible to observe. In fact, even several thousand kilometers out from the surface of the earth, there is little indication that the field of the earth does not have a regular shape. But at an altitude of about 20,000 km, the irregularities begin to show up.

Do you think the solar wind reaches the other planets? If so, how might its effect on other planets differ from its effect on the earth?

The magnetopause and the magnetosphere. Suppose we imagine ourselves in a satellite orbiting the earth at an altitude of about 50,000 km. As our satellite moves into a position between the earth and the sun, our magnetic detectors would show a sudden change in the magnetic field through which we are

Figure 26-14. The solar wind, represented by the dashed arrows, distorts the earth's magnetic field, represented by the solid lines. However, only that region of the earth's magnetic field farther than 20,000 km from the earth is affected.

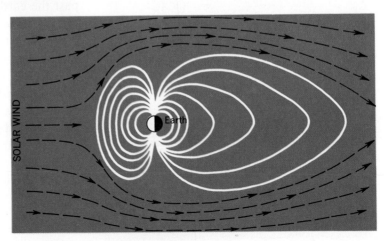

traveling. The field would suddenly become irregular. The direction of the north magnetic pole would fluctuate rapidly. As we continued our flight around earth, these fluctuations would stop, and we would find ourselves again in a stable magnetic field.

Suppose we went to a still higher orbital altitude, say 100,000 km. Now we would find the field irregular around almost all of the orbit. The magnetic field would be regular only during a small portion of the orbit on the side of the earth away from the sun.

If we continued to make such exploratory flights at different altitudes, we would eventually be able to map all of the regions where the field was irregular and where it was regular. If we drew a line through the points where the change from an irregular field to a stable field was observed, we would get a pattern such as that shown in *Figure 26-15*. The boundary between the two kinds of magnetic

fields is called the *magnetopause* (mag nē′tō pôz). Inside this boundary, the magnetic field appears to be dominated by the earth. Outside of it, the magnetic field is dominated by the solar wind.

Thus, the magnetopause is a boundary between two regions of space with different characteristics. In Chapter 18 you learned that the tropopause is the boundary between the troposphere below and the stratosphere above. You can think of the magnetopause the same way. Below it is the *magnetosphere* (mag nē′tō sfir) in which the earth's magnetic field dominates, and above it is interplanetary space.

If we continued to make satellite flights day after day, we would discover that the magnetopause is not a fixed boundary. Its position fluctuates from one day to another. Some of these fluctuations are related to occurrences on the surface of the sun. A strong flare which sends out a burst of particles will cause the magnetopause to change its position. But there will always be a boundary with the regular field of the earth inside and the irregular field of interplanetary space outside.

Where, do you think, is the lower limit of the magnetosphere?

Motions of charged particles. It seems that many particles of the solar wind do not speed past the earth. Instead, they become trapped in the magnetosphere. Many of these particles then spend their time circulating in a narrow region near the magnetopause. Others penetrate more deeply into the magnetosphere. Once these particles come under the influence of the earth's magnetic field, they tend to move back toward the sun. A diagram of the motions of charged particles in and around the magnetosphere is shown in *Figure 26-16*. The motions indicated in *Figure 26-16* are largely speculative. Only a few observations have

Figure 26-15. The circles represent orbits at various distances above the earth. The solid portion of each orbit indicates the region in which the magnetic field is stable. The dashed portion indicates the region in which the magnetic field fluctuates.

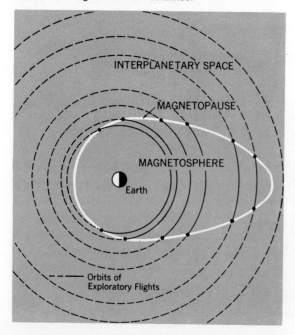

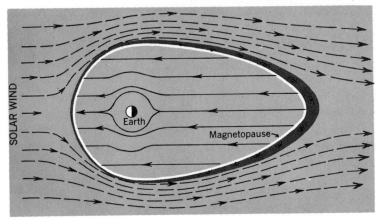

Figure 26-16. This diagram represents a possible pattern of the motion of charged particles far from the earth. Some particles of the solar wind (dashed arrows) stream past the earth. Some particles do not continue past the earth, but circulate in a narrow region near the magnetosphere (shaded area). Inside the magnetosphere, particles move in a direction opposite to that of the solar wind, but stay about 20,000 km away from the earth.

been made of the motions of particles in this region. Scientists believe that the motions may be somewhat like those shown in the diagram, but they are not at all certain. Many more observations must be made before an accurate picture can be drawn showing the interaction of the solar wind and the magnetosphere.

The boundary between the atmosphere and space. It would seem that the magnetopause is as much like a boundary between the atmosphere of the earth and outer space as anything else we can observe. Thus, we might say that the magnetopause is the upper edge of the earth's atmosphere.

But this description is not completely satisfactory. First of all, the position of the magnetopause changes greatly from day to day. For example, the long tail behind the earth waves back and forth and sometimes seems to stretch out for hundreds of thousands of kilometers. The principal difference between the regions inside and outside the magnetopause is just the magnetic field itself.

In spite of our limited knowledge of the upper atmosphere, we do know that phenomena going on in this region have spectacular and important effects on the atmosphere much closer to the surface of the earth. Thus, studies of the upper atmosphere may have some immediate benefits for mankind. Such studies may aid in weather prediction and control.

Figure 26-17. Upper atmosphere research also yields information about the lower atmosphere—the region where our weather occurs. Recording and interpreting the data collected by a satellite such as TIROS (Television InfraRed Observation Satellite) requires many hours of painstaking work.

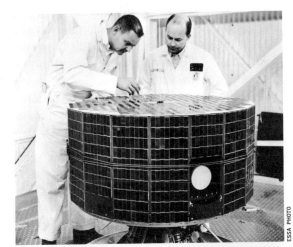

Checking Your Knowledge

IMPORTANT IDEAS

1. The ions in the ionosphere are produced as high-energy radiation (ultraviolet and X ray) from the sun interacts with atoms and molecules in the upper atmosphere.

2. The absorption of ultraviolet radiation and X rays by the atmosphere enables life to exist on the earth.

3. Radio signals of various frequencies are affected in different ways by the layers of ions in the ionosphere. These effects make possible the study of the ionosphere through the use of radio signals.

4. Upper atmospheric winds are studied by releasing sodium vapor in the upper atmosphere and observing its movement.

5. The magnetic field associated with the solar wind interacts with the earth's magnetic field, causing fluctuations and distortions in the earth's magnetic field.

6. The magnetopause may be considered as the boundary between the earth's atmosphere and interplanetary space.

USING NEW WORDS

Study the terms listed below. On your paper write the letters *a* through *d*. Beside each letter, answer the question or questions having the corresponding letter.

magnetosphere	ion
photo emission	ionosonde
falling-sphere method	magnetopause

a. Which term names a charged particle?

b. Which terms are related to methods of studying the upper atmosphere? How would you describe each relationship?

c. Which term refers to ion production?

d. Which terms are related to the region in space dominated by the earth's magnetic field? What are the relationships?

TEST YOURSELF

Study the test below. On your paper write the numerals *1-10*. Beside each numeral write the correct response to that part of the test having the corresponding numeral.

1. The first internationally sponsored program of scientific endeavor was the _____, begun in 1882.

2. The upper atmosphere is that region above the earth between the altitudes of _____ km and 1,000 km.

3. Early data concerning the ionosphere were obtained by using devices called _____, which are special types of radio transmitters and receivers.

4. The production of ions in the atmosphere is the result of an interaction between atoms or molecules in the atmosphere and several forms of _____ radiation from the sun.

5. The region of space in which the magnetic field of the earth predominates is the (*magnetosphere, magnetopause, ionosonde*).

6. The boundary between interplanetary space and the region in which the magnetic field of the earth predominates is the (*magnetosphere, magnetopause, ionosonde*).

7. Atoms from which electrons are emitted become (*positive, negative, neutral*) ions.

8. As altitude increases, the ratio of the number of neutral particles to the number of ions in the earth's atmosphere (*increases, decreases, remains unchanged*).

9. The ionosphere does not usually extend below an altitude of 80 km because (*no ions form, ions recombine rapidly, no radiation reaches*) below this level.

10. Ion density in the ionosphere over a particular place is greatest (*during the daylight hours, during periods of violent thunderstorms, at night*).

Extending Your Knowledge

QUESTIONS TO EXPLORE

QUESTIONS TO EXPLORE

1. How would you explain the layers of various elements in the upper atmosphere?

2. Why has most of the information we now have concerning the ionosphere been collected since 1955?

3. Why do scientists use sodium vapor instead of some other colored substance in their studies of high-altitude weather?

4. What are some of the factors that make it difficult for scientists to determine the boundary between the upper atmosphere and interplanetary space?

5. What are some very recent, internationally sponsored, scientific research projects? What subjects did these projects deal with? When were these projects carried out?

6. How would you explain why it was impossible to study the atmosphere above 350 km until man was able to send rockets and satellites above this altitude?

SOME THINGS TO DO

1. Compare the graphs in *Figure 26-4* and *Figure 26-6*. From the values of ion density at night as shown in *Figure 26-4,* estimate what the ion density would be at an altitude of 250 km. Does this value agree with that shown in the graph in *Figure 26-6?* Explain.

2. Find out if someone can bring to class an air purifier that operates by emitting ultraviolet radiation. If so, operate the air purifier in the classroom. Can you detect an unusual odor when the purifier is operating? Have you ever experienced this odor before? If so, what were the conditions? Explain to the class how the emission of ultraviolet radiation can purify the air.

3. Collect as much information as you can about the effects which solar disturbances have on communications on the earth. How are television transmission and reception affected? How are radio signals affected? Are telephone and telegraph communications affected? If so, how? If not, why not?

4. Explain what scientists mean when they refer to "windows" through which earthbound scientists can observe the remainder of the universe. Is the view through each window the same? Are there any new windows which have come into use in recent years?

CHALLENGES IN SCIENCE

1. Examine the graph of altitude and temperature in *Figure 26-11*. Then consider that several manned and unmanned space flights have reached altitudes of 300 km and above. What temperatures might be expected at these altitudes? Do such temperatures create a hazard to astronauts and spacecraft flying above 300 km? If so, what precautions may be taken to reduce the danger?

2. Examine the graphs of altitude and density in *Figure 26-11*. Estimate the number of gas particles per cubic centimeter at altitudes of 150, 200, and 300 km. HINT: The density of air at sea level is about 1.25×10^{-3} g/cm^3, and each cm^3 contains approximately 2.7×10^{19} gas particles. At what altitude would the density of the atmosphere be 10^{-3} of its density at sea level? At what altitude would its density be 10^{-6} of its density at sea level? At what altitude would its density be 10^{-9} of its density at sea level.

3. Suppose one cubic centimeter of air from sea level was carried at an altitude of 400 km and then allowed to expand. What volume would this amount of gas have at an altitude of 400 km? What would be the length of one side of a cube having this volume?

CHAPTER 27

Auroral displays are not completely understood.

Belts of Particles

In previous chapters we have discussed the atmosphere and the upper atmosphere of the earth. We will now turn our attention to that region of space above the earth's upper atmosphere. Many surprising facts have been learned about this region of the earth's environment.

As man learns more and more about the universe, more and more questions are raised. The study of the region above the earth's upper atmosphere is no exception to this statement. What was thought to be a vast, empty space has been found to contain belts of charged particles that are of potential danger to astronauts traveling through this region of space.

In Chapter 27, you will learn how these belts of particles were discovered. You will read about several theories that have been proposed to explain the existence of these belts. You will soon realize, however, that scientists are not certain about the explanations they give for the formation of these belts. You will also read about the northern lights. Scientists are not certain about the origin of these spectacular displays either, but some theories have been suggested.

As you finish studying Chapter 27, you will undoubtedly realize that man needs to learn much more about the belts of particles surrounding the earth. It is very probable that someday he will know their origin and how they affect our lives. Perhaps you will have a part in acquiring that knowledge.

1. The Strange Discovery

Explorer I. On January 31, 1958, the United States launched its first artificial satellite, *Explorer I,* into orbit about the earth. See *Figure 27-1. Explorer I* was small. Its working section, or *payload,* weighed only 18 pounds. Compared with the large, complex pieces of equipment which have carried man and instruments into space in subsequent years, *Explorer I* was, indeed, a midget. And yet, data from *Explorer I* enabled scientists to make one of the most important discoveries of the space age.

The principal instrument aboard *Explorer I* was a Geiger counter intended for the study of cosmic particles above the earth's atmosphere. For many years scientists had been sending Geiger counters up on balloons and small rockets to investigate the charged, subatomic particles from space that bombard the upper atmosphere of the earth. Most of these particles interact with the atmosphere at very high altitudes and are destroyed. Very few of them reach the earth's surface. The charged particles that do reach the surface are not the same as the original ones which came from space. In the interaction with atoms in the atmosphere, the primary particle is destroyed,

Figure 27-1. Explorer I, although small by present standards, was an important step in man's exploration of space.

NASA

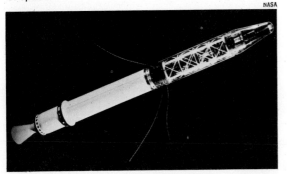

and many subatomic particles, called secondary particles, are produced. Scientists wanted to learn more about the primary particles. They thought they could do so with the instruments aboard *Explorer I.*

Do you think the cosmic particles mentioned in the preceding paragraph are the same as cosmic rays? If so, why, do you suppose, are they called by two different names? If not, how do cosmic particles differ from cosmic rays?

Collecting data. After *Explorer I* was launched, the first indications were that its instrumentation was working perfectly. By means of a small radio, information collected by the Geiger counter was reported to scientists on earth. The data indicated that cosmic particles were passing through the shell of the satellite and into the counter.

But then, as time passed and more data were collected, some peculiar results were observed. During some intervals of time, the Geiger counter seemed to be operating very well. At other times, it seemed to stop operating completely. It was as if there were no particles present at all. The scientists knew that this was a very unreasonable situation. The first guess was that the Geiger counter was damaged in some way.

Dr. James Van Allen, who designed the experiment, was not satisfied with this explanation and continued to study the data. He noticed that there were times when the data showed a steady increase in the number of charged particles and other times when they showed a steady decrease. The apparent failure always took place following a steady increase. That is, as reports from the Geiger counter began to show extremely high counting rates, the reports suddenly stopped. The radio was silent. When reports again began to be received, the counting rate was at about the same level as when the reports had stopped. But now, the counting rate was decreasing.

In order to determine what was happening in space, Dr. Van Allen subjected a Geiger counter to a beam of charged particles in a laboratory. He steadily increased the number of particles striking the counter, copying the increase reported by the satellite instrument. When he reached a particular level, he discovered that the Geiger counter "saturated." That is, particles were coming through so fast that the instrument was unable to respond to all of them and stopped responding to any. The counter had broken down, but not because the counter was faulty. The counter had failed because of the great number of particles striking it. This number was far greater than had been anticipated. Therefore, the number was far greater than that which the Geiger counter was designed to count.

NASA

Figure 27-2. Dr. James Van Allen designed the experiment and analyzed the data that resulted in the discovery of a belt of particles about the earth.

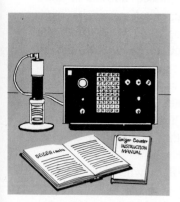

DO IT YOURSELF

Study the operation of a Geiger counter

Use various reference materials to obtain information about the principles of operation of a Geiger counter. Perhaps your school has a Geiger counter you can use, or perhaps you can obtain one from local civil defense officials. If so, learn how to operate the apparatus. Find answers to these questions. What does a Geiger counter count? Is the same apparatus used for detecting and counting? Why does the counter not respond when it is saturated? What are some uses of Geiger counters?

The Van Allen belt. After *Explorer I* had orbited the earth a few times, data received from tracking stations had been processed through electronic computers. The satellite's orbit was accurately determined. Dr. Van Allen already had a record of the times at which the data were obtained. Now, with the satellite's orbit known, he could determine exactly where the satellite was in space when each bit of information was obtained. He discovered that the periods during which the counter saturated (which he now believed indicated an unusually great number of charged particles) occurred at the highest altitudes reached by the satellite. At lower altitudes, the number of particles was within the predicted

Figure 27-3. Data obtained in studies
of regions high above the earth are
represented in the diagram. The contours connect points containing equal
densities of charged particles. Notice
that within the area observed, the density of particles increases with altitude. Notice, too, that away from the
equator, charged particles are detected at lower altitudes.

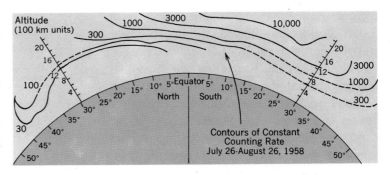

estimates and could be measured by the counter aboard the satellite.

The picture was now clear. The number of charged particles surrounding the earth was, at some altitudes, much greater than had been anticipated. Unusually great numbers of particles were counted in regions near the equator between the altitudes of 1,000 km and 2,520 km. Perhaps the number would also be great at higher altitudes, but 2,520 km was the *apogee* (ap′ə jē), or maximum altitude, of the satellite's orbit.

The satellite did not orbit directly above the equator. It traveled between the latitudes 30° N and 30° S. The data obtained revealed that the lower limit of the region of high particle count was closer to the earth away from the equator. The newly discovered region of high particle count became known as the *Van Allen belt*.

Further studies. Another satellite launched a few months later carried two Geiger counters designed to count the unusually high number of particles believed to be in the Van Allen belt. The data from these Geiger counters confirmed Dr. Van Allen's earlier findings. There was, indeed, a belt containing a very high concentration of charged particles around the earth at an altitude of about 1,000 km over the equator. This second satellite, and others which soon followed, also indicated that the region of high counting rate was closer to the surface of the earth at latitudes north and south of the equator. See *Figure 27-3*.

There were also data to indicate that at still higher altitudes, the counting rate was less. And, there was another surprise. Data received from the satellite indicated that a second belt of charged particles might ·exist above the one originally discovered.

2. Explanations and Theories

Questions raised. How can the discovery of a belt of charged particles about the earth be explained? What is the source of these charged, atomic particles? What keeps them high above the surface of the earth? Why don't many of these particles strike the upper atmosphere, where they could be observed by instruments aboard rockets and balloons? What kinds of particles are they?

This last question has been the subject of continuing satellite experiments for many years. On the basis of data collected so far, scientists believe that most of the particles in the lower region of the Van Allen belt are protons—that is, the nuclei of hydrogen atoms. On the other hand, most of the particles in the outermost region are electrons. There seems to be a division between these two regions. Between them, at altitudes of from 3,000 km to 5,000 km, there are fewer trapped particles of either type.

The shape of the Van Allen belt. Scientists recognized that the shape of the Van Allen belt, as revealed by the satellite measurements, closely resembled the inferred shape of the earth's magnetic field. Of course, they did not know the shape of the earth's magnetic field, since studies of the earth's magnetic field at high altitude had not yet been made. But they reasoned this way. Measurements on the earth's surface indicate that the magnetic field of the earth is like that of a huge bar magnet. Above the atmosphere, the pattern of such a field would be similar to the field shown in *Figure 12-12*.

As you have learned, the motion of charged particles is strongly affected by a magnetic field. Thus, such a relationship between the distribution of these particles and the magnetic field was to be expected.

What ways can you think of to demonstrate that the motion of charged particles is affected by a magnetic field?

The direction of a magnetic field. The way a charged particle moves in a magnetic field is well understood on the basis of theoretical studies and many laboratory experiments. A magnetic field causes a charged particle to move in a curved path. The exact nature of the curved path depends upon two factors. The first is the relationship between the direction of the particle's motion and the direction of the magnetic field.

But what, you might ask, is the "direction" of a magnetic field? It is the direction along which another magnet would line up if it were allowed to move freely in the field. As you know, a compass needle lines up with the magnetic field of the earth. But an ordinary compass needle does not give all the

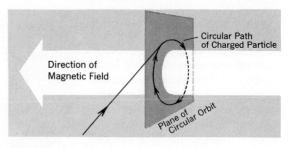

Figure 27-4. A charged particle moving across a magnetic field is deflected. The plane of its circular path is perpendicular to the direction of the field.

needed information about the field's direction. The compass needle is not free to move in all directions. It can rotate, but it cannot tip up and down. However, a compass needle can be mounted so that it can tip up and down. With the help of such a compass needle, called a *dip needle,* the true direction of the earth's magnetic field at any point can be determined. The drawing of the earth's magnetic field shown in *Figure 12-12* is actually a diagram of the direction of the field at different points in space. Suppose you were free to move about in this area of space near the earth and could carry a dip needle with you. Wherever you went, you would find the dip needle pointing in the direction of the lines in *Figure 12-12*.

Factors affecting the motion of a charged particle. Suppose a charged particle is moving in the same direction as a magnetic field. Then the magnetic field will have no effect on the particle's motion. If, however, the particle is moving perpendicularly to the field direction, the particle will be deflected so that it moves in a circular path. The plane of the circle will be perpendicular to the direction of the magnetic field, as shown in *Figure 27-4*. If the particle is moving at an angle other than 0° or 90° to the direction of the field, the particle's path will be a *helix* (hē′liks), or a corkscrew shape, as shown in *Figure 27-5*.

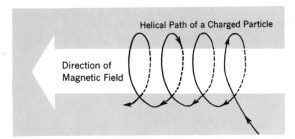

Figure 27-5. If the motion of a charged particle is not perpendicular to the magnetic field, the deflected particle's path is the shape of a helix.

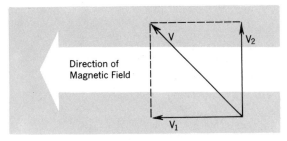

Figure 27-6. The arrow V represents the velocity of a particle. This velocity has components parallel to the magnetic field and perpendicular to the field.

The second factor that determines the path followed by a charged particle moving in a magnetic field is the ratio of the speed of the particle to the strength of the field. In considering this ratio, we are concerned with only one component of the particle's motion—the component that is perpendicular to the direction of the field.

The diagram in *Figure 27-6* shows how the velocity—that is, speed and direction—of the charged particle is represented by two components. One component, V_1, is parallel to the magnetic field. The other component, V_2, is perpendicular to the magnetic field. The two components added together as vectors make up the total velocity, V, of the particle. A magnetic field affects only the component of the velocity that is perpendicular to the direction of the field.

The radius of the curved path which a charged particle follows is proportional to the ratio between the perpendicular component of its velocity and the strength of the magnetic field. Thus, if the perpendicular component of velocity is high, the radius of the curve will be large. If it is low, the radius will be small. If the magnetic field is quite strong, then the radius will be small. If the magnetic field is weak, the radius will be large. This relationship between velocity and field strength governs the radius for either a circular motion or a helical motion.

Knowing the two factors that determine the path of a charged particle in a magnetic field, we can predict how a charged particle would move in the magnetic field of the earth. Very few particles would be moving exactly parallel to or exactly perpendicular to the

Figure 27-7. The strength of the magnetic field and the velocity of the particle are two factors that influence the radius of the curved path of a charged particle in a magnetic field. The radius is inversely proportional to the field strength and directly proportional to the perpendicular component of the particle's velocity.

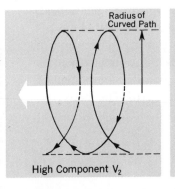

High Component V_2

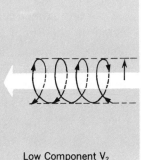

Low Component V_2

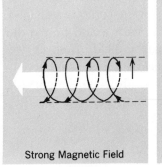

Strong Magnetic Field

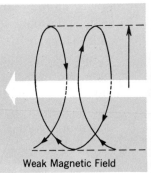

Weak Magnetic Field

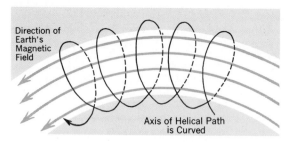

Figure 27-8. The axis of the helical path of a trapped, charged particle is the direction of the earth's magnetic field. The earth's magnetic field is curved.

Figure 27-9. The radius of the helical path of a trapped, charged particle is greater far from the earth than it is near the earth.

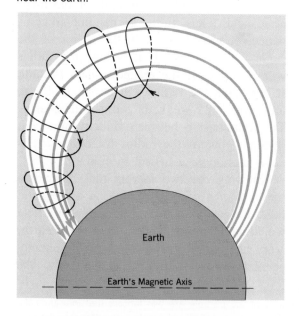

Figure 27-10. As the helical path of a charged particle brings the particle closer and closer to the earth, the helix becomes flatter and flatter. The helical motion becomes circular motion.

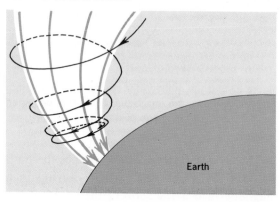

A charged particle in the earth's magnetic field. Far out from the earth, the earth's magnetic field is weaker than it is close to the surface. Scientists usually diagram this by showing the magnetic field lines farther apart in the weak regions and closer together in the strong regions, just as we have shown them in *Figure 12-12*. We know that the radius of a particle's motion in the stronger region of the field will be smaller. How does this affect a particle following its helical path? It means that the helix will get tighter and tighter as the particle moves down closer to the surface of the earth. This situation is illustrated in *Figure 27-9*.

It is possible to calculate what will happen as the helical motion becomes tighter and tighter. The calculations show that the component of motion parallel to the field becomes lower and lower. In a steady magnetic field, the parallel component of velocity is not affected at all. But if a particle moves into a steadily increasing field, this component is decreased. Finally, the parallel component of motion is decreased to zero. The helix has been flattened out into a circle, as shown in *Figure 27-10*.

magnetic field. Almost all of them would be moving at other angles to the direction of the field, and would follow a corkscrew-shaped path. The axis of this path would be the direction of the magnetic field. But, as we know, the magnetic field of the earth is curved. Thus, the axis of the path would be curved. The motion of a particle would be like that shown in *Figure 27-8*.

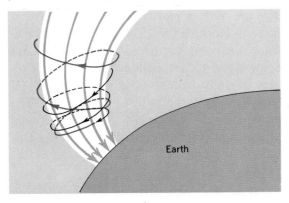

Figure 27-11. After its helical path has become flattened, the particle continues to circle in the same direction. Then the path becomes helical again. Now, however, the particle moves away from the earth (blue arrow).

Earth

But the motion of the charged particle cannot remain in this condition. It is an unstable condition that may be compared to a pendulum at one end of its swing. The pendulum stops, then swings back. Similarly, the particle stops moving toward the earth and starts moving away from the earth. The particle does not stop circling, but its helical motion reverses, carrying it back in the opposite direction, as shown in *Figure 27-11*. In this manner it travels all the way back to the other end of the magnetic field where its motion again becomes flattened and is again reversed. In other words, the particle moves back and forth between the Northern and Southern Hemispheres of the earth. The time required to go from one point of reversal to the other varies, depending upon the particle's velocity and also upon the kind of particle it is. But, in general, the time has been calculated to be between 0.1 second and 10 seconds. The particle will continue this motion indefinitely unless it collides with some other particle and either becomes slowed down or loses its electric charge.

In what regions will a trapped, charged particle, moving under the influence of the earth's magnetic field, be closest to the earth?

3. Trapped Particles

Colliding particles. So far we have been discussing the motion of a single particle in the earth's field. But now we must imagine that there are billions of billions of these particles trapped in the earth's magnetic field. Each one of them is moving back and forth along its own helical path between the Northern Hemisphere and the Southern Hemisphere of the earth. As we have said, each particle will continue moving back and forth in this manner until it collides with some other particle. But how often do such collisions occur?

The likelihood that a charged particle will run into another particle depends, of course, upon how many other particles are around. In spite of the fact that great numbers of charged particles are following these paths, the distance between the particles is very great compared to their size. The likelihood that one charged particle will run into another charged particle is very small. A much more likely occurrence is that a particle will run into an atom or molecule in the earth's upper atmosphere. As you know, the earth's atmosphere extends a long way out into space. But at an altitude of a few hundred kilometers, the atmosphere is very rarefied. There is little chance for a charged particle to collide with an atom of the earth's atmosphere when the charged particle is on that part of its path far from the earth's surface.

Do you think the Van Allen belt should be considered as part of the earth's atmosphere? If so, why? If not, why not?

Where do collisions occur? The most likely place for collisions to occur is the place where the particles reverse their motion. It is there that the particles are closest to the earth's surface. How close, then, will a charged particle get to the surface of the earth before its path reverses and it starts back again?

The place where a particle reverses its motion depends primarily upon the component of the particle's velocity parallel to the earth's magnetic field. The greater this component is, the farther the particle will descend toward the earth's surface before it reverses and starts back. Thus, each component of the particle's velocity is a factor in determining the path of the particle. The component perpendicular to the earth's magnetic field determines the radius of the helix. The component parallel to the magnetic field determines how close to the earth's surface the particle will come before reversing its direction.

Some particles make only one trip between the points of reversal. That is, some particles collide with an atom or molecule of the earth's atmosphere before their first reversal. But most particles do not come very close to the earth, and so can make several trips back and forth before colliding with another particle.

The situation is best described in terms of probability. Each trapped particle has a certain probability of running into an atom or molecule in the earth's atmosphere. This probability is greatest when the particles are closest to the earth's surface—that is, at the place

where they reverse their direction of motion. Some particles descend so far that the probability of their being destroyed at each reversal is, say, 10 per cent. Thus, on the average, such a particle could expect to last through ten reversals. The probability of collision for other particles—those that do not come down to low altitudes before being reversed—may be only one in a million. Of course, such particles last much longer. The probability of collision is directly proportional to the density of the atmosphere at the altitude of reversal.

What are other areas of science that you can think of in which probability is an important factor?

The origin of trapped particles. No matter how low the probability of collision might be, it is never quite zero. No particle can last forever in this region. Collisions occur continuously. Thus, some of the charged, trapped particles are constantly losing their charge. How, then, is the great number of charged particles maintained? What is the source of new, charged particles? These questions have not been satisfactorily answered. A number of ideas have been suggested. One idea is that electrons and protons in the solar wind are caught by the earth's magnetic field and become trapped particles, traveling back and forth as part of the Van Allen belt.

Suppose a charged particle in the solar wind is moving toward the earth's magnetic field. As it comes closer and closer to the earth, its path will be bent. *(Figure 27-12.)* Eventually, it will be bent so much that the particle will curve away and fly back out into space. Or, if it is traveling fast enough and coming in at the right angle, its path may be bent so that the particle will move toward the surface of the earth.

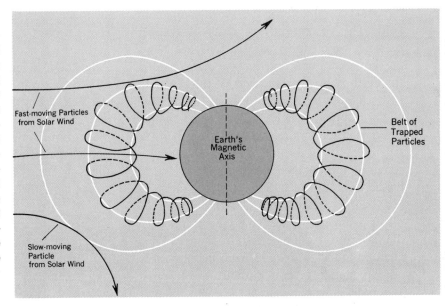

Figure 27-12. The earth's magnetic field affects the charged particles of the solar wind in various ways. Some fast-moving particles are deflected away from the earth and out into space. Other fast-moving particles are deflected, but still manage to get through the magnetic field to the earth. Slow-moving particles are deflected before they have a chance to get to the region of trapped particles. Only a very small percentage of the particles have just the right speed to become trapped.

Fast-moving Particles from Solar Wind

Earth's Magnetic Axis

Belt of Trapped Particles

Slow-moving Particle from Solar Wind

In order for a particle to become trapped, the radius of its curved path would have to be small enough to fit into the region of trapped, charged particles. In order for the radius to be that small, the particle must be a comparatively slow-moving particle, since the radius of the curved path is proportional to the speed of the particle. However, a slow-moving particle cannot penetrate far enough into the earth's field to get near the region of trapped, charged particles. Particles which can descend this far into the field are moving much too rapidly to become trapped. So, there must be some other explanation.

A second suggested explanation is this. Cosmic particles—that is, particles from far out in space—are constantly raining down upon the earth's atmosphere. When such a particle strikes an atom in the earth's atmosphere, a nuclear reaction occurs. Subatomic particles are scattered in all directions. Some of these are neutrons. Most of the subatomic particles descend toward the surface of the earth. However, some—including some neutrons—could fly out toward space. Since a

neutron is a neutral particle, its motion would not be affected by the earth's magnetic field. Its path through the magnetic field would be straight.

However, a neutron all by itself is not a stable particle. A neutron has a half-life of about 12 minutes, decaying into a proton and an electron. Suppose a neutron flying out into space undergoes this decay while it is still in the earth's magnetic field, in the region of the trapped particles. The result would be a proton and an electron. Both of these are charged particles. Therefore, their motion would immediately be affected by the magnetic field. If they were moving at the right speed, they would become trapped in the earth's magnetic field.

This explanation might account for the protons trapped in the Van Allen belt, but not for the electrons. The electrons that result from a neutron decay are moving much too rapidly to be trapped.

Another explanation is based on the fact that the magnetic field of the earth is not constant in position or strength. As you know, the solar wind affects the earth's magnetic field. The descriptions of belts of trapped particles in the previous sections are based on the assumption that the magnetic field of the earth is steady. However, if the magnetic field changes from time to time, the motions of the trapped particles will be more complicated than the motion we have described. As the strength of the magnetic field changes, some of the trapped particles could be released out into space. Some of them could be sent to the earth. At the same time, particles moving through space could be trapped by the field during these periods of change. Thus, changes in the earth's magnetic field could be an explanation of how particles are trapped. When the magnetic field of the earth changes, particles moving through space are caught by it and become trapped particles.

Unfortunately, none of these explanations seems satisfactory. Particles in the solar wind move too fast to be trapped by the earth's magnetic field. The explanation having to do with neutron decay does not seem to provide enough particles. There are not enough neutrons flying out into space to provide the necessary protons, and, of course, neutrons would provide no electrons at all. The explanation having to do with sudden changes in the earth's magnetic field is also questionable. Calculations indicate that more particles would be lost than gained. In other words, the net result would be fewer trapped particles rather than more. As you can imagine, the behavior of charged particles in a changing magnetic field is a very complex problem. Scientists are a long way from explaining all the data that have been collected concerning the Van Allen belt.

Continuing studies of the Van Allen belt. Studies of the belt of charged particles above the earth are both theoretical and experimental. While theoretical studies are made on such ideas as those we have just described, space probes and satellites are being used to learn more about the properties of the Van Allen belt. Scientists wish to know the ratio of protons to electrons in various portions of the belt. They also attempt to measure the energies of these particles. These measurements have shown that the region of trapped particles extends far out into space, sometimes as far as 50,000 km above the earth's surface. In the outermost regions, the number of particles (mostly electrons) is quite variable. On some occasions, satellites moving through this region have detected about the same number of particles as that detected by instruments on balloons. The balloons, of course, were not nearly high enough to detect charged particles in the Van Allen belt. The particles detected by the balloons were cosmic particles that penetrated through the Van Allen belt.

From such results, scientists infer that, at certain times, only cosmic particles are present in the outermost region, and not trapped particles. At other times, however, the number of particles found in this same region is several times greater than it would be if only cosmic particles were present. Obviously, the nature of the outermost region of the Van Allen belt undergoes great changes from one time to another.

The inner region of the Van Allen belt consists mostly of protons and is much more stable than the outer region. This inner region is located near the equator at altitudes of from one thousand to five thousand kilometers. The total number of trapped, charged particles in this region changes only slightly from one time to another.

Since the inner and outer regions of the Van Allen belt are so different, many scientists prefer to think of them as two separate belts. They use the term Van Allen belts.

DO IT YOURSELF
Make a report

Obtain as much information as you can concerning man's studies of the Van Allen belt. What types of instruments and spacecraft were used to collect data? List in chronological order some of the important findings that have been made concerning the Van Allen belt. What is the most widely accepted explanation concerning the origin of the charged particles in the Van Allen belt? Prepare a large diagram in which you represent the earth, the Van Allen belt, the magnetosphere, the magnetopause, and the solar wind. Use the diagram as a visual aid in reporting your findings to the class.

4. Auroral Displays

Northern and southern lights. People who live in the northern portion of the United States and in Canada are often privileged to see one of nature's most beautiful displays, the *northern lights* or the *aurora borealis* (ô rôr′ə bôr′i al′is). These beautiful displays in the nighttime sky are usually of a greenish color and often have the appearance of a slowly waving curtain of light, stretching for miles in a general east-west direction. The same type of phenomena occurs in far southern latitudes. There, auroral displays are called the *southern lights,* or the *aurora australis* (ô strā′lis).

The cause of auroral displays. For years scientists have tried to determine the cause of auroral displays. Auroral displays occur most frequently during periods of intense sunspot activity. You also learned that solar flares accompany sunspots. Solar flares, you will recall, are responsible for the discharge of intense beams of charged particles—that is, protons and electrons—out into space. Thus, it seems reasonable that there is some connection between the charged particles leaving the sun and the occurrence of auroral displays on the earth.

Formerly, scientists believed that charged particles moving from the sun toward the earth would be affected by the earth's magnetic field in the following way. As the particles interacted with the earth's magnetic field, the particles would be deflected downward and would strike the atmosphere near the north and south magnetic poles. An interaction

Figure 27-13. Auroral displays vary in color and in form. Red displays, such as that shown below, are not as common as those which are all green in color.

ZENTRALE FARBBILD AGENTUR

Figure 27-14. A great amount of energy is needed to produce brilliant auroral displays. Scientists would like to know the source of this energy.

PRO PIX FROM MONKMEYER

between the deflected particles and the earth's atmosphere was believed to cause the northern and southern lights.

This explanation, however, leaves much to be desired. The earth's magnetic field does not make a very efficient deflector for particles moving in from the sun. A few particles would undoubtedly be deflected in this manner and spiral down toward the earth's surface like water going down a drain. But, calculations indicate that the number of deflected particles would not be great enough to account for the tremendous amount of energy represented by brilliant auroral displays.

How, do you suppose, can the amount of energy released during an auroral display be calculated?

Shortly after the discovery of the Van Allen belt, many scientists thought that the particles trapped there were responsible for the northern and southern lights. The explanation they suggested was this. The earth's magnetic field

is greatly disturbed by solar flares. As a result, the motion of the particles trapped in the Van Allen belt is changed. In particular, the reversal points are changed. These reversal points are lowered, because the magnetic field is compressed or squeezed down toward the earth's surface. When this happens, huge numbers of particles which had previously been safe from collision are carried down into the upper portion of the atmosphere. When a charged particle collides with an atom or molecule in the atmosphere, a photon of light is released. Such a process might account for the northern lights. Then, between displays, the number of trapped particles in the Van Allen belt would return to normal, as particles gradually come in from outside the belt. (Although, as you learned previously, how this build-up of particles would happen is still a mystery.)

At first, this seemed to be a reasonable explanation. But as more data concerning the Van Allen belt were obtained, this explanation was gradually abandoned. As data became available, scientists could determine how much energy was in the particles of the Van Allen belt. They found that there was only enough to cause a fifteen-minute auroral display. At the end of that time, the Van Allen belt—if it were the source of the energy—would be completely drained.

Then, an important observation was made. Satellites probing the Van Allen belt were collecting data at the same time that an auroral display was occurring. It was found that the number of particles in the Van Allen belt increased while the aurora display was in progress. In other words, the Van Allen belt was not giving up electrons and protons to cause the aurora, but was somehow or other gaining them.

Although this observation meant that the Van Allen belt was not causing auroral displays, some new ideas to explain both the aurora and the Van Allen belt were developed from this observation. Some scientists now believe that it is possible for still another belt of charged particles to exist. This belt would be outside of the region in which trapped particles have so far been observed. It would be a very temporary belt. Somehow, by a mechanism which has yet to be explained, particles approaching the earth from a solar flare would be temporarily trapped in this region. Perhaps, such particles would be trapped for less than a day.

Streams of particles coming from additional solar flares would have a number of effects on this temporary region. First, these additional incoming particles would disturb the earth's magnetic field. Many of the temporary particles would be deflected down into the atmosphere, causing auroral displays. However, some of the particles would become trapped in the region of the Van Allen belt, thereby causing an increase in the number of trapped particles there. At the same time, the streams of particles from the sun would repopulate the temporary belt. Another burst of solar activity would repeat the cycle, causing more auroral displays, more particles in the Van Allen belt, and another supply of particles in the temporary zone.

DO IT YOURSELF

Conduct a library research project

In 1958, scientists working under the direction of the U. S. Atomic Energy Commission, carried out an experiment called the *Argus experiment*. Find out what you can about this experiment. Try to find answers to the following questions. What was the purpose of the experiment? What procedure was followed? How were data collected? How was this experiment related to a study of auroral displays? Have similar experiments been conducted more recently?

Do auroral displays affect us? The lower edge of the aurora borealis is normally about 80 to 90 km above the surface of the earth. Sometimes the brightest region of display is as high as 130 km above the surface. So, it does not seem that this phenomena, spectacular as it is, would have any great effect upon atmospheric conditions near the surface of the earth. And yet, we cannot rule out the possibility that auroral displays may have some effect on our weather. Thus, there seems to be some relationship between solar activity, the earth's magnetic field, the ionosphere, the northern lights, charged particles trapped in belts above the earth, and perhaps even our weather.

As you no doubt realize, scientists have a long way to go before they determine all of the mechanisms that are involved in these various phenomena and what relationships these phenomena have to one another. We have, as yet, only a very slight understanding of how occurrences in distant regions of space affect us. We are not even certain that an understanding of these occurrences will help us to improve man's environment here on the surface of the earth. But man will continue his studies and investigations. Whether or not the knowledge gained has any practical value makes little difference. Human nature is such that man must know as much as possible about his environment.

Checking Your Knowledge

1. The Van Allen belt, a region in space where charged particles are trapped by the earth's magnetic field, was discovered by analyzing data received from *Explorer I*.

2. The portion of the Van Allen belt nearest the earth consists mainly of protons and is relatively stable. The outermost portion consists mainly of electrons, but the concentration of electrons varies greatly.

3. Because the lower and upper portions of the Van Allen belt differ, some scientists prefer to speak of the Van Allen belts, rather than of the Van Allen belt.

4. The origin of the particles in the Van Allen belt and the way in which they become trapped there are not completely understood.

5. Auroral displays are related in some way to the earth's magnetic field, the Van Allen belt, and sunspot activity. Much research is being done to discover the exact nature of the relationship.

USING NEW WORDS

Study the groups of terms listed below. On your paper write the letters *a* through *e*. Beside each letter write a short paragraph concerning the group of terms having the corresponding letter. In the paragraph, tell how the terms in each group are related—that is, why they should be grouped together, although they name different objects or have different meanings.

a. Van Allen belt—*Explorer I*—Geiger counter
b. aurora borealis—aurora australis
c. velocity—vector diagram—component
d. charged particle—magnetic field—helix
e. secondary cosmic particles—primary cosmic particles

TEST YOURSELF

Study the test below. Write the numerals *1-10* on your paper. Beside each numeral, write the correct response to that part of the test having the corresponding numeral.

1. The (*Van Allen belt, aurora borealis, magnetosphere*) can easily be observed from the earth's surface.

2. The (*lowest portion of the, outermost portion of the, entire*) Van Allen belt is composed mainly of protons.

3. The (*lowest portion of the, outermost portion of the, entire*) Van Allen belt is subject to unpredictable fluctuations in particle concentration.

4. Auroral displays are (*more spectacular, less spectacular, unaffected*) during periods of sunspot activity.

5. Particles that travel through space and that have extremely high energies are called _____ particles.

6. The instrument used to detect and count charged particles in the Van Allen belt is the _____ counter.

7. Charged particles trapped in the Van Allen belt lose their charge and escape as a result of _____ with other particles.

8. Auroral displays seen in Canada and in the northern part of the United States are called the northern lights or the _____.

9. The component of a charged particle's velocity that is _____ to the direction of the earth's magnetic field determines the radius of the helical path followed by the particle as it travels in that field.

10. The component of a charged particle's velocity that is _____ to the direction of the earth's magnetic field determines the distance above the earth at which the particle's helical motion is reversed.

Extending Your Knowledge

QUESTIONS TO EXPLORE

1. Do you suppose that any other planets in our solar system are encircled by belts of charged particles? How might such belts be detected? What are some inferences that could be made about any planet that is encircled by a belt similar to the Van Allen belt?

2. How would you justify the expenditures made on studies of the Van Allen belt, auroral displays, and other phenomena that are so far from the earth?

3. How would the Van Allen belt be affected if the strength of the earth's magnetic field increased? If the strength decreased? If the magnetic field disappeared?

4. How does the presence of the Van Allen belt complicate future space explorations?

5. How would you explain the term "saturated," as used in explaining a condition in the operation of a Geiger counter?

SOME THINGS TO DO

1. Hold a horseshoe magnet in a position near the picture tube of a black and white television set. Is the picture affected? If so, describe the effect. Experiment by moving the magnet around, or by reversing the poles of the magnet. Describe any effects. How would you explain the effects (if there are any)? From your findings, what can you infer about the operation of a television set?

2. Make a study of auroral displays. Collect photographs and drawings depicting various auroral displays. Does the "curtain of light" always have the same general shape, or can an auroral display take on various forms? Is the color always the same? Do auroral displays appear most often during certain seasons of the year? What other phenomena seem to be associated with auroral displays?

3. Find out what "magnetic bottles" are and in what type of research they are used.

CHALLENGES IN SCIENCE

1. We have spoken of "particles" in the Van Allen belt. Other books speak of "radiation" in the Van Allen belt. Still others use the terms radiation and particles interchangeably. Explain this inconsistent terminology.

2. Build your own Geiger counter. The diagram below shows a circuit for a simple Geiger counter. In addition to the materials indicated on the diagram, you will need a Geiger tube and headphones. The total cost, including the headphones and Geiger tube, should be about $25. The unit will operate from a regular 110 volt, a. c., electrical outlet. The circuit will boost the peak voltage to just over 300 volts—enough to operate a low-voltage Geiger tube. CAUTION: Most Geiger tubes are designed to operate at voltages higher than 300 volts. Be certain that the Geiger tube you get operates at 300 volts.

The counter you build can detect several types of particles and radiation. How could you modify it so that it would detect only cosmic particles?

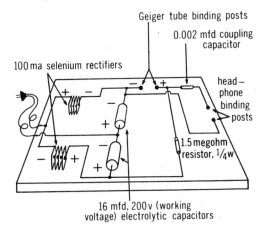

Geiger tube binding posts

0.002 mfd coupling capacitor

100 ma selenium rectifiers

head-phone binding posts

1.5 megohm resistor, 1/4 w

16 mfd, 200 v (working voltage) electrolytic capacitors

Man has learned much about the moon's surface.

CHAPTER 28

The Moon

We have witnessed one of the greatest scientific achievements of all time—man's arrival on the moon. Man has always wondered about the nature of the moon and about its origin. But he has done more than just wonder. He has observed and investigated the moon as thoroughly as he could. As early as the seventeenth century, for example, Galileo described the moon's surface appearance in detail. Later, Newton determined the force which controls the moon's orbit.

Until fairly recently, however, scientists knew little more about the moon than Galileo knew more than 300 years ago. Until scientists could send space probes to the moon and actually land and bring back samples, they were only able to guess about the nature and composition of the moon's surface materials. Now, man is learning about the moon's surface materials. This knowledge may help answer questions about the moon's origin. Did the moon condense from a collection of materials in space, or was it torn from the earth? Could it have been formed as a small planet that was later "captured" by the earth's gravitational attraction?

Chapter 28 contains recent information that has been collected about the moon, including information obtained by Ranger and Surveyor space probes and by the Apollo astronauts. The stage is set for obtaining more information about the moon and its origin. In the next decade we can expect that man will gain much important knowledge about the moon and its origin. From this knowledge, he will understand more about the origin and history of the earth and the rest of the solar system.

1. Observations of the Moon

Galileo's description. Early in the 17th century, in the year 1609, Galileo Galilei began studying the moon with the first astronomical telescope. Several years later, he described what he saw in one of the famous books in the history of science, *Dialogues Concerning the Two Chief World Systems.*

> The prominences there are mainly very similar to our most rugged and steepest mountains, and some of them are seen to be drawn out in long tracts of hundreds of miles. Others are in more compact groups, and there are also many detached and solitary rocks, precipitous and craggy. But what occur most frequently there are certain ridges (I shall use this word because no more descriptive one occurs to me), somewhat raised, which surround and enclose plains of different sizes and various shapes but for the most part circular. In the middle of many of these there is a mountain in sharp relief and some few are filled with a rather dark substance similar to that of the large spots that are seen with the naked eye; these are the largest ones, and there are a very great number of smaller ones, almost all of them circular.

In the 350 years since Galileo began his study of the moon, telescopes have been greatly improved. The use of photography has enabled astronomers to record on film the details of the subjects of their observations. And yet, suppose you asked a modern astronomer to give a general description of the moon's surface. Suppose, too, that he must base his description only on information gained by telescopic observations made in the past three and a half centuries. He could hardly give a better description than that given by Galileo. No matter how good the telescopes or how accurate the instruments, astronomers have always been faced with one insoluble difficulty —the effects of the earth's atmosphere.

Figure 28-1. Galileo Galilei was the first scientist to use a telescope to study the moon. His detailed observations were recorded with care and accuracy.

BROWN BROTHERS

Astronomical seeing. The atmosphere distorts our view of the sky. Turbulent air currents between the telescope and space refract light rays in such a manner that the image of a star or planet cannot be perfectly clear. Thus, the condition of the atmosphere determines *seeing.* Seeing is the term used by astronomers to describe the degree to which details may be observed. When the seeing is good, a great amount of detail can be observed. However, certain weather conditions make the seeing bad. That is, details are lost.

When an observatory is to be built, astronomers study many locations. They try to find places that have the best seeing conditions

Figure 28-2. Lick Observatory, like many other major observatories, is situated high in the mountains. The air is clear, and the seeing is consistently good.

night after night. Usually, such favorable locations are high in the mountains. Of course, other characteristics, such as the clarity of the air, the stability of the ground, and convenience for travel and for bringing in supplies, must also be considered in selecting a site. Telescopes located at the very best seeing positions are usually used for observing the moon and the planets.

What reasons can you give to explain why seeing must be better for observing the moon and the planets than for observing the stars?

Lunar surface features. How much detail can an astronomer see, observing the moon from the most favored positions on the surface of the earth? Actually, any detail smaller than 400 or 500 meters across is blurred by atmospheric turbulence, even at the most favorable location. In fact, observing details this small is unusual. Most of the time the smallest observable detail is about one, or perhaps two, kilometers across.

Thus, astronomers can see the circular features which Galileo described. We call them *craters.* Many craters can be seen. On some portions of the moon, called the *highlands,*

there are so many craters that they overlap each other, as you can see along the right-hand side of *Figure 28-3.*

There are areas of the moon which appear to be both darker and smoother than the highlands regions. Such an area is shown in the upper left-hand corner of *Figure 28-3.* An area such as this is called a *mare* (mãr′ē), the Latin word for sea. Some early astronomers believed these areas were filled with water.

Today, modern astronomers can see many more craters than were visible to Galileo through his comparatively small telescopes. And yet, they have not been able to gain much more information about the nature of the surface on which these craters appear. Nor have they determined the cause of the craters.

The lunar atmosphere. Some things have been learned about the moon since Galileo's

Figure 28-3. Several types of lunar features are shown below. Notice the mare (upper left) and the many craters in the highlands region (lower right).

time. For example, astronomers have long known that the moon has little, if any, atmosphere. The possibility of a lunar atmosphere can be checked from here on earth. As the moon moves about the earth, it passes between us and various stars. When this happens, of course, the stars disappear from view. What does such a star look like just before it disappears? Suppose the moon had an atmosphere similar to that of the earth. The disappearing star would turn red, just as the setting sun does. Furthermore, much of the star's light would be absorbed by the moon's atmosphere, so the star would get dimmer just before it disappeared. The lunar atmosphere would also diffract the light coming from the star to the earth, so the star's position would appear to shift slightly. These possibilities have been checked. So far, nothing that would indicate the presence of a lunar atmosphere has ever been observed. Therefore, astonomers place an upper limit of 10^{-14} *millibars* as the amount of pressure exerted by the lunar atmosphere. (A pressure of 34 millibars is about the same as that of 1 inch of mercury.)

What does this upper limit mean? If there were an atmosphere on the moon with a pressure greater than this, then one or another of the many observations would have shown some positive indication. Since no instruments have ever shown any indication of an atmosphere, the conclusion is that the pressure cannot be greater than this limiting value.

The possibility exists that the pressure is even less than 10^{-14} millibars. The earth's atmosphere exerts a pressure of about 10^3 millibars at sea level. Thus, atmospheric pressure at the earth's surface is at least 10^{17} times greater than that at the moon's surface. We would have to go out from the earth's surface more than 1,000 km to find the atmosphere so rarefied. The moon's atmosphere is more nearly like a vacuum than anything which can be produced in a laboratory.

Other information. Scientists have collected much information about the moon in addition to learning about its surface features and its atmosphere. Astronomers have also measured the moon's *albedo* (al bē'dō)—that is, the ratio of light reflected to light received. On the average, the surface of the moon reflects about eight per cent of the sunlight that strikes it. Thus, the surface of the moon is not much brighter than the surface of a lump of coal. The lunar surface material is like basalt, a dark kind of rock. See *Figure 28-16.*

This seems somewhat surprising, since the moon appears to be so white and silvery in the sky. However, we must remember that there is nothing nearby with which we can compare the moon's brightness. If a second body—one about the same size but one having a surface more like that of the earth, complete with oceans and clouds—were nearby, such a body would appear five times as bright as the moon.

Astronomers can measure the insulating properties of the moon's surface materials. Quite often, the moon passes into the shadow of the earth. This is called a *lunar eclipse.* Sunlight is suddenly cut off from the lunar surface. The moon's surface begins to cool,

Figure 28-4. The diagram below shows the relative positions of the sun, the earth, and the moon during a lunar eclipse. Obviously, the sizes and distances are not shown in the correct proportions.

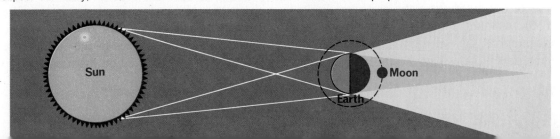

because no heat is coming in and heat continues to be radiated directly out into space. (Remember, the moon has no atmosphere.) Astronomers can measure this cooling rate by measuring the infrared radiation from the moon's surface. Now, suppose that the surface materials of the moon conduct heat quite readily. The outermost layer would take a long time to cool off, even after the sunlight was not striking it. Heat from deep in the moon would be conducted to the surface to replace the heat that was being radiated away. Thus, the cooling process would have a huge reservoir of buried heat to work with. On the other hand, if the materials were very good insulators, then heat from the inner layers could not reach the surface easily. The moon's surface would cool very quickly in the absence of sunlight. Measurements have shown that the moon's surface does cool quickly. Therefore, the materials of the moon's surface do not conduct heat readily.

Scientists, then, have learned much about the moon, in spite of the fact that they have had to make their observations from the earth. See *Figure 28-5*. But such observations cannot tell us what materials are on the surface. Nor can they reveal any of the small details of the surface structure. Other methods must be used to obtain that information.

Figure 28-5. The data in the table below represent some of the information that man has obtained from observations made here on earth.

LUNAR DATA	
Diameter	3,478 km
Mass	7.12×10^{25} grams
Density	3.31 g/cm^3
Apogee	407,000 km
Perigee	357,000 km
Period of Revolution	27.3 days
Surface Temperature (max.)	104°C
Surface Temperature (min.)	−151°C

FIND OUT BY TRYING

Materials you will need: binoculars or a small telescope, pencil, paper

Use binoculars or a telescope to observe the moon during several different phases. What features can be observed during full moon? What features can be observed during other phases? Make sketches of the surface features that you can observe. Compare your sketches with photographs and sketches in various books. Can you locate and identify features such as the craters Copernicus and Kepler? Can you identify Mare Crisium and Mare Imbrium? Does the same side of the moon seem to be facing the earth during each of your observations?

2. Conflicting Theories

Explaining lunar craters. Although observations of the moon from the earth are limited in the amount of detail they reveal, the imaginations of scientists have no limits. Numerous theories have been proposed to account for the lunar features which can be observed. Naturally, in formulating such theories, scientists make use of what has been learned about the surface of the earth as well as what can be observed on the moon.

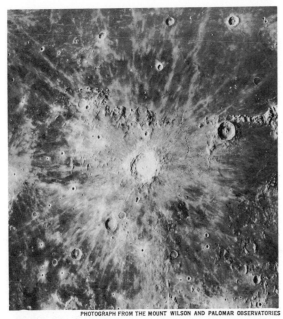

Figure 28-6. The origin of the rays that are about some craters on the moon is a controversial subject. Today, most persons who study the moon believe that the rays consist of material ejected from the craters at the time of crater formation.

The lunar craters have received the most attention in the development of these theories. There are two principal explanations for the craters: meteorite impacts and volcanism.

Meteorite impact. If a meteorite were to fall from space onto the surface of the moon, it would be going at least 2.4 km per second just before striking the moon's surface. The meteorite would acquire this amount of speed in falling through the moon's gravitational field. It might be going at considerably greater speed just before impact, depending upon the meteorite's velocity before being affected by the moon's gravitational attraction.

Such a high speed has an important effect. A speed of 2.4 km per second is greater than the speed of sound in ordinary rock. Because of this, such an impact would result in an explosion. The impact would not be at all like the impact of a pebble dropped into wet sand. It would be much more like a bomb burst.

Scientists have never been able to observe the results of such a collision. However, the effects of large nuclear explosions have been studied. Furthermore, using special equipment in laboratories, scientists have been able to accelerate small particles to extremely high speeds. Then they observe what happens when the rapidly moving particles strike various kinds of materials. Experiments such as this indicate that the crater resulting from a meteorite impact would be ten to twenty times the diameter of the meteorite.

If meteorites have been striking the moon and creating craters, meteorites must also have been striking the earth. Are there any such craters on the earth? As you probably know, the answer to this question is yes. A famous meteorite crater is located in Arizona. See *Figure 9-17*. But this crater is only about 1.3 km in diameter. If viewed from the earth, a crater of this size would scarcely be visible on the surface of the moon. Are there any very large craters on the earth?

The search for large meteorite craters on the earth has been frustrating. In some places, what appear to be large meteorite craters have been found. However, these craters have been greatly affected by erosion. Their edges are gone. Nevertheless, circular rock formations indicate that there have been craters 80 to 160 km across on the surface of the earth.

These observations point out the importance of the moon's lack of atmosphere. Wind, rainfall, rivers, and oceans cannot exist without an atmosphere. Thus, the moon's surface has not been subjected to the same kinds of erosion that have been steadily wearing away the surface features of the earth.

Not all meteorites striking the moon will strike it at right angles. Many would strike it obliquely. Why, then, are all the craters nearly circular?

Volcanism. Many years ago most scientists believed that the craters of the moon were volcanic in origin. In recent years, however, this idea has become less and less popular. One problem concerns the relative sizes of the volcanic craters on the earth and the craters on the moon. It seems logical that volcanic craters on the earth should be about the same size as those on the moon. Large volcanic craters on the earth are about 1.5 to 2 km across. Most of the earth's volcanic craters are much smaller. And yet, many craters on the moon are 15 to 80 km in diameter. How volcanism could have caused such large craters is hard to imagine.

Of course, this does not rule out the possibility of volcanism on the moon. Many small craters—some even too small to be observed from the earth—may have been caused by volcanic action.

Theories concerning materials on the moon's surface. Many scientists believed the surface of the moon was covered with small particles and broken-up rock fragments resulting from the meteorite impacts. In fact, one scientist suggested that the large, dark areas on the moon, the *maria* (plural of mare), are actually seas of rock dust.

However, many scientists did not accept the picture of the lunar surface as being covered with the debris of exploded meteorites. They believed the lunar surface to be covered with lava or volcanic ash. Many of the scientists on this side of the controversy thought that the surface of the moon would be quite rugged.

D. APPENBRINK

Figure 28-7. If the moon is, or was, an active volcanic body, then the moon's surface might be rough and rugged like this lava field in Idaho.

They visualized it as being much like the lava fields in the northwestern part of the United States. See *Figure 28-7*.

Clearly, the differences between these two theories could not be resolved by earth-based observations. In fact, it probably would be necessary to actually land on the moon's surface and analyze the material. How scientists have studied the moon's surface is one of the most fascinating portions of the story of space exploration.

Is it possible that scientists on both sides of this controversy may be correct? Justify your answer.

3. Lunar Spacecraft

Finding a landing site. One of the most ambitious projects of space exploration was landing men on the surface of the moon. However, before such a landing could be suc-

cessfully carried out, it was necessary to know much more about the moon's surface than could be observed from the earth. Therefore, a number of unmanned spacecraft were de-

Figure 28-8. Ranger spacecraft (*Ranger 1* shown above) photographed the moon's surface, relayed the pictures to earth, and then made hard landings on the moon.

signed and launched to the moon. Their primary mission was to investigate the moon's surface. Particular attention was given to those areas of the moon's surface which appeared, on the basis of earth-based observations, to offer the best possible landing sites.

Some of these spacecraft made "hard" landings on the moon. That is, they simply crashed onto the moon's surface. Other spacecraft orbited the moon. A third type made "soft" landings on the moon. A soft landing is a controlled descent. The craft is not destroyed by the landing. The equipment aboard the craft can be operated after the landing.

Why not continue to use unmanned satellites to gather information about the moon, so that an astronaut's life is not endangered by attempting to land on the moon?

The Ranger series. The first spacecraft to provide us with detailed pictures of the lunar surface were those in the Ranger series. The last spacecraft in this series, *Ranger 9,* was sent to the crater Alphonsus. This crater is near the center of the visible side of the moon. Pictures of this crater taken from the earth and from *Ranger 9* are shown in *Figure 28-9.*

Figure 28-9. The two photographs below are of the same general area of the moon's surface. The picture on the left was taken through a large telescope on earth. The one on the right was taken by *Ranger 9* from an altitude of 424 km above the moon's surface.

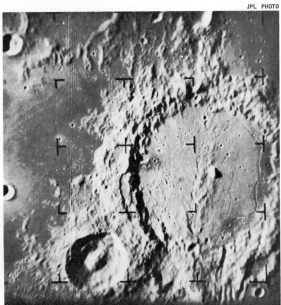

Figure 28-10. The photograph above is one of the last ones relayed back by *Ranger 9*. Scientists have calculated that the smallest details that are recognizable in this photograph are only 18 inches in diameter.

Even at a distance of 480 km, the television cameras of *Ranger 9* showed much more detail than any photographs of this crater taken from the earth. Before *Ranger 9* had completed its mission and crashed onto the moon's surface, it sent back a series of pictures taken at successively smaller distances above the moon's surface. One of the last photographs showed details as small as eighteen inches in diameter. See *Figure 28-10*.

Such photographs showed that the surface was not a rugged lava field as some scientists had suggested. But the pictures did not rule out the possibility of a surface covered with volcanic ash. Nor did the pictures disprove the competing notion of meteorite dust. However, the photographs did satisfy the primary objective of the Ranger series. They showed that there were, indeed, large areas of the surface of the moon which were smooth enough for the safe landing of a larger spacecraft. See *Figure 28-11*.

Figure 28-11. This photograph of the lunar surface was taken by the *Apollo 8* astronauts. It shows a portion of the mare known as The Sea of Tranquillity. Several interesting features are visible, including several craters and two long, narrow features called rills. Of great importance is the fact that much of the area shown is smooth enough for the safe landing of a manned spacecraft.

The Lunar Orbiter series. Another series of spacecraft was placed in orbit about the moon. These orbiting spacecraft took photographs of the lunar surface. The information was sent back by radio so that scientists on earth could begin the construction of detailed lunar maps.

In general, the Orbiter photographs showed surface detail much more clearly than any earth-based observation could. But still, with all these detailed photographs, the fundamental controversy could not be resolved. Is the surface of the moon covered with lava-like material, or is it covered with meteorite dust? Even if it is granular, as indicated by later photographs, it could still be lava. Over millions or billions of years, constant pounding by small meteorites would be expected to break up the surface of a lava field into granular particles. Photographs alone could never provide the information necessary to choose between these possibilities. The information must come from a chemical analysis of the material, and a chemical analysis would require a soft landing on the moon's surface.

Luna 9 and the Surveyor series. The first spacecraft to land safely on the surface of the moon was the Soviet Union's *Luna 9*. *Luna 9* sent back photographs of the surrounding surface, such as that shown in *Figure 28-12*. On photographs taken from *Luna 9*, the lunar surface appears to be generally smooth. However, some small pockmarks, probably small craters, were visible.

A much more detailed examination of the lunar surface was made possible by the Surveyor series of spacecraft, launched by the United States. *Surveyor I* landed in a mare and gave some indication of the nature of the lunar surface material. *Surveyor I* photographed its own foot resting in the lunar soil. *(Figure 28-13.)* The granular nature of the soil is quite evident in this picture. The picture

Figure 28-12. One of the photographs of the lunar surface taken by *Luna 9* is shown below. The picture was received at the Jodrell Bank radio telescope in England. Note the apparent craters and the protruding rocks on the lunar surface.

WIDE WORLD PHOTOS

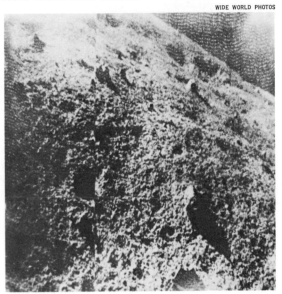

NASA

Figure 28-13. This close-up of one of the footpads of *Surveyor I* indicates that the lunar surface is made up of small particles that tend to stick together. Note the depression in the lunar surface.

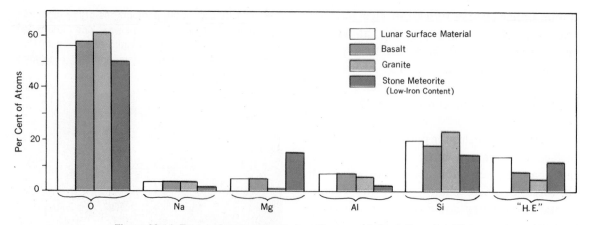

Figure 28-14. Even before man landed on the moon, information about the moon's composition was obtained with instruments aboard the Surveyor spacecraft. It is believed to be accurate to within 3 per cent. The "H.E." stands for heavy elements (heavier than silicon).

also proves that the surface can support the weight of the spacecraft.

Subsequent Surveyors were provided with digging tools which could better test the soil. In addition, three of the Surveyors carried small chemical analysis units. These chemical analysis units were able to determine the relative abundances of a number of the lighter elements. The results are shown in *Figure 28-14*.

The bar graphs in *Figure 28-14* show comparisons between the composition of the moon's material and the composition of various kinds of rock found on earth. From these data, the moon's surface material seems to be similar to basalt. It is not like granite, and it is not like meteorites. Although the three Surveyors that carried chemical analysis units landed at widely separated places on the moon, they all returned similar data.

The Apollo project. The main purpose of all the unmanned spacecraft that had been sent to the moon was finally realized on July 20, 1969. On that day, *Apollo 11* landed on the surface of the moon, carrying with it the first men ever to walk on another world. See *Figure 28-15*. They placed instruments on the

Figure 28-15. This photograph, taken during man's first walk on the moon, shows astronaut Edwin Aldrin walking near the lunar module. Notice the reflection in the face mask of his helmet.

NASA

moon which would stay there after the men had returned to the earth. They also brought back samples of lunar materials.

The equipment the astronauts left behind sends information back to the earth in the form of radio signals. Thus, scientists on the earth can continue to conduct experiments even after the astronauts leave the moon.

One piece of equipment left on the moon is a seismograph which detects vibrations at the moon's surface. Such vibrations might come from moonquakes or from the impact of meteorites on the moon's surface. Another piece of equipment is a reflector for laser beams. Laser beams can be aimed at the moon from the earth, reflected off the equipment left by the astronauts, and detected again when the light returns to the earth. By measuring the time of the round trip, scientists can determine how the distance between the earth and the moon changes as these objects move in their orbits.

The samples of moon materials which the astronauts brought back are very much like basalt. Scientists have managed to duplicate lunar rock samples by melting mixtures of minerals in a laboratory and allowing them to solidify. From these experiments scientists have determined something about conditions on the moon at the time the rock solidified.

Other important information concerns the age of the lunar samples. Some of the rock samples are rather massive, and they contain large crystals. See *Figure 28-16*. These samples were found to be 3.7×10^9 years old. Other samples are made up of small crystals compacted together. Some of the lunar dust samples were found to be 4.6×10^9 years old.

Meaning of the results. Basalt is a typical volcanic rock on the surface of the earth. It is not the most common rock on the continents. Granite is more plentiful. However, basalt is common in some regions, such as in

Figure 28-16. The *Apollo 11* astronauts brought back 48.5 pounds of lunar materials. Some were rather large pieces (top). Others were small and granular (bottom).

northwestern United States and in Hawaii. It is also typical of the materials underlying the ocean basins.

Many scientists were discouraged by the first Surveyor data. These data showed that the moon's surface material was like basalt. They felt that this probably meant the moon's surface had been covered by lava at various times in its history. Therefore, evidence of the moon's formation would not be easy to find. Now they have been reassured by the information about the age of the lunar rocks.

The oldest samples, dating back 4.6×10^9 years, probably formed at the same time that the moon formed. The younger rocks seemed to have formed about one billion years later. Thus, some lava has been created since the formation of the moon. There must have been a second period of melting. But this second period of melting did not affect the entire moon. Therefore, large areas of the lunar surface might still be in their original condition. Scientists guess that these original surface areas must be in the lunar highlands. Most likely, the lunar seas, or maria, are where the second phase of melting took place.

Scientists look forward to a more thorough examination of the lunar highlands. Here they believe they will obtain more information to unravel some of the secrets of the solar system's origin.

Besides spewing out dust and lava, volcanoes also give off many gases. The moon probably had volcanoes, but the moon has no atmosphere. How would you explain where these gases have gone?

4. The Origin of the Moon

Why study the moon? Why are scientists so interested in studying the moon? It is almost a quarter of a million miles away from the earth. It has no atmosphere. The appearance of its surface is quite different from that of the earth's surface. Can we learn anything about the earth by studying the moon? Or should we consider the moon as a completely separate body, interesting for its own sake?

Scientists study the moon for both of these reasons. They believe they can gain information about the earth, and they are also interested in the moon itself. These two separate interests are brought together in a study of two major questions about the moon. (1) How did the moon originate? (2) What has been the history of its development?

What could scientists possibly learn about the earth by studying the moon?

Theories of the moon's origin. We will discuss three different theories about the origin of the moon. One theory holds that the moon was once a part of the earth. Somehow, the moon was spun out from the earth. At first, the moon was in a close orbit about the earth. Gradually, over billions of years, the moon's orbit increased to its present size, as shown in *Figure 28-18.*

A second theory holds that the moon was formed at the same time as the earth. Furthermore, the moon was formed at about its present orbital location. In Chapter 11, we described various theories about the origin of the solar system. The theory that all of the bodies of the solar system condensed out of an original cloud of gas and dust was included in Chapter 11. So, the second theory about the moon suggests that the moon condensed out of a cloud of gas and dust which was swirling about the protoearth.

A third theory holds that the moon condensed as a completely separate planet. Then, about one or two billion years ago, it was

Figure 28-17. The diagram below illustrates several stages in the development of the moon, based on the theory that the moon was once part of the earth. As the spin rate of the earth increased (perhaps due to the accumulation of the heavy materials near its center), the earth assumed the shape of a very flat, oblate spheroid (A). The motion became unstable, resulting in a bulge (B and C). The bulge separated from the earth (D), and both parts returned to stable shapes (E). Tidal friction reduced the energy of the system. The earth and moon gradually assumed their present shapes and positions (F).

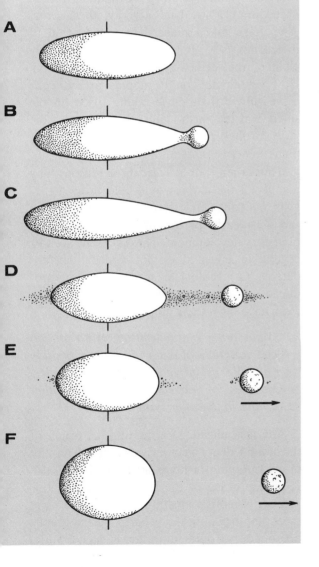

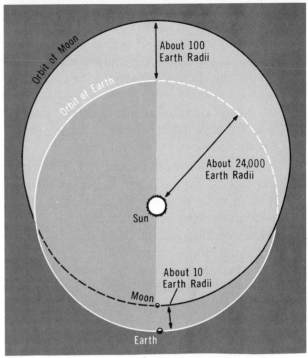

Figure 28-18. The moon may have formed as a planet that was later "captured" by the earth. However, the circumstances under which this could have happened are unique. The path followed by the moon during the capture process must have been very complex. A top view of the orbits of the earth and the moon as they may have been before capture is shown above. The distances are included since it is not possible to draw such a diagram to scale in a limited space. The capture would have occurred when the earth and the moon were closest together—that is, at the locations indicated in the diagram. The plane of the moon's orbit is tilted with respect to that of the earth's orbit. Although the angle of tilt cannot be shown in a top view, the angle of tilt is about 5°.

"captured" into an orbit around the earth by a gravitational interaction between the earth, the sun, and the moon. Analysis—made with the help of modern computing machines—of this last theory indicates that such a capture process would have to be very complicated. *Figure 28-19* shows the orbits that the moon and the earth might have had before the capture occurred.

Each of these theories is important for developing an understanding of the origin and nature of the earth. If the moon were once part of the earth, then a study of it will tell us something about the nature of the earth in its earlier years. Furthermore, a study of the moon will give us a sample of earthly material which is quite different from any we can obtain on the surface of the present earth.

If the moon were created out of the same dust cloud that resulted in the protoearth, then a study of lunar materials may tell us something about the original earthly materials. These earthly materials may now be buried too deeply for us to sample them, or they may have been changed by important earth processes which we need to learn more about.

If the moon were created as a completely separate body, then it offers us a very convenient second planet to study. At present, we have only one planet, our own, on which we are basing most of our theories about the nature of the solar system and the universe. The moon might be an independent second case. If so, a study of the moon would help us to better understand our own planet and the rest of the universe.

What we might learn from lunar studies. The riddle of the moon's origin and development will not be solved for many years. If it is eventually solved, how can it help us? With knowledge about the moon, we might be able to better understand the process of differentiation on the earth. We might better understand how earthly continents are formed. We might gain some knowledge about the structure of the earth's mantle. Knowledge of these matters would help us to better understand such phenomena as earthquakes and volcanoes. Undoubtedly, there are other ways in which knowledge of the moon will benefit man. In fact, one geologist has suggested that knowledge of the moon will even help us in prospecting for essential minerals here on the earth.

Why is it that the moon offers such important possibilities? The moon has two special characteristics that make it of special interest to geologists. First, it is completely free of vegetation. Thus, all rock formations are exposed for study. As far as we know, biological processes have not taken place at all on the moon. Everything that we see there now is a result of geological processes alone.

The second important characteristic is the lack of an atmosphere. This means that weathering and erosion on the moon have been exceedingly slow. Undoubtedly, these processes have taken place. The steady rain of meteorites of all sizes has continuously changed the surface appearance of the moon. However, changes on the moon's surface occur more slowly than those taking place on the surface of the earth. Thus, the surface of the moon probably represents a very early stage in planetary development.

Thus, there are at least three reasons why a study of the moon would help bring geologists to a better understanding of conditions in the very early period of solar system and planetary development. These reasons are (1) vegetative cover does not conceal surface details, (2) biological activity has not produced any changes, and (3) erosional processes have been exceedingly slow.

What other characteristics of the moon can you think of that would make its study valuable as an aid to increased understanding of the earth and of the other bodies in the solar system?

The task ahead. Determining the origin of the moon will not be an easy task. It will require much sampling of lunar material. It will also require probing of the lunar interior. In this process, scientists must use many of the same tools that they now use on earth. Seismographs are, of course, quite important in such a study.

Figure 28-19. Astronauts from both *Apollo 11* and *Apollo 12* left apparatus on the moon. In this way, scientists on earth could continue studies of the moon even after the astronauts had returned to the earth. These pictures show astronauts from *Apollo 11* (left) and *Apollo 12* (right) setting up various types of equipment on the lunar surface.

NASA   NASA

Scientists will wish to collect samples from a wide variety of regions on the lunar surface and to place seismographs and other instruments at a number of different points.

Experiments may turn out differently on the moon than they do on the earth. Therefore, scientists will have to be very clever in interpreting the results of their experiments. For example, one experiment by the *Apollo 12* astronauts produced some unexpected results. After the astronauts were back in the command module, they sent the lunar module crashing onto the moon. The impact caused the seismograph they had left behind to react in a way that could not be explained in terms of seismographic data obtained on the earth.

In addition, the lunar samples—being similar to basalt—pose some questions. They indicate that volcanism occurred on the moon at some time in the past—at least 3.7×10^9 years ago. But these samples are from only two locations. Could there be active volcanoes at other locations on the moon now? Or has the moon become a totally cold, inactive body? If the moon has become inactive, how long ago did this occur? Answers to questions such as these will reveal something about the moon's interior and about its history.

By now, your study of the earth-space sciences should have made you understand that knowledge of any portion of the universe helps us to understand all other portions. So it is no wonder that scientists are taking advantage of every opportunity to gain a better understanding of the moon.

What techniques are used by scientists in determining the ages of lunar materials?

DO IT YOURSELF

Report on Project Apollo

Use periodicals and scientific journals to learn about Project Apollo. How many trips to the moon are planned? When is the project scheduled for completion? What will the entire project cost? What progress has been made so far? Have there been any major setbacks in the project? Organize your findings into a report to be given to the class.

Checking Your Knowledge

1. To obtain good seeing, observatories are often located on mountain tops.

2. Some scientists think the moon's craters are the effects of meteorite impacts. Others believe the craters are of volcanic origin.

3. In preparation for man's landing on the moon, the surface of the moon was investigated through the use of various types of unmanned spacecraft.

4. Three suggested theories of the moon's origin are (1) it was once part of the earth, (2) it formed from a protomoon, and (3) it formed as a planet and was later captured by the earth's gravitational field.

5. Through continuing studies of the moon, scientists hope to improve their understanding of the origin of the earth and other objects in the solar system.

6. Scientists think that the moon will be a good place to study geologic processes because the absence of an atmosphere on the moon has caused erosional processes to be slow and has prevented biological activities.

USING NEW WORDS

Study the terms listed below. On your paper write the numerals 1-4. After each numeral write terms or statements to satisfy the instructions having the corresponding numeral.

seeing	crater	Ranger
mare	millibar	Lunar Orbiter
Surveyor	highlands	albedo

1. List the terms that refer to spacecraft. Describe the mission of each type.

2. List the terms that refer to lunar surface features. Describe each feature.

3. List the terms that may be related to atmospheric conditions. Define each term.

4. Select a term related to reflection.

TEST YOURSELF

Study the test below. On your paper write the numerals 1-10. After each numeral write the correct response to that part of the test having the corresponding numeral.

1. The greatest limitation to seeing details on the moon's surface when viewing the moon from the earth is imposed by (the size of the telescope, the earth's atmosphere, the motion of the moon).

2. The smallest details on the moon's surface that can be seen through earth-based telescopes are approximately (50 meters, 500 meters, 5,000 meters) across.

3. A large, flat, dark-appearing expanse on the moon is known as (a mare, an albedo, an abyssal plain).

4. One shortcoming of the theory of volcanism as the cause of lunar craters is that the craters appear to be (too small, too large, too numerous) to have been caused by volcanic activity.

5. The surface of the moon is (nearly white, yellow, very dark).

6. Analysis of the moon's surface materials indicates that the materials are similar to (basalt, granite, limestone).

7. The regions of the moon that appear to be light colored are known as the _____.

8. Spacecraft of the _____ series were designed and built by American scientists and engineers to collect data after making soft landings on the moon.

9. The absence of an _____ on the moon retards the processes of weathering and erosion and prevents biological activity.

10. The ratio of the amount of light reflected by a body to the amount of light which falls on the body is referred to as the _____ of that body.

Extending Your Knowledge

QUESTIONS TO EXPLORE

1. Why are there so few positively identified meteorite craters on the earth, when so many may be observed on the moon?

2. If you had been the first person to go to the moon and back, what materials would you have selected to bring back for analysis?

3. What would be some benefits of having a permanent "moon base"? What difficulties will have to be overcome before such a base can be established?

4. Since the moon has no atmosphere and no water, how would you explain how changes on the moon's surface could occur?

5. Do you think that there is such a thing as twilight on the moon? How would you justify your answer?

6. Do you think the term mare is an appropriate name for a lunar feature? How would you justify your answer?

7. Do you think that an astronomical observatory on the moon would be more useful or less useful than an observatory on a space platform orbiting the earth? How would you justify your answer?

SOME THINGS TO DO

1. Use the formula on page 180 to calculate the gravitational force between the moon and the earth. Then calculate the gravitational force between the sun and the earth. Which of the two forces is greater? By how much? Explain your results.

2. Study maps of various parts of the world. Look for surface features that might possibly be meteorite craters. Check your findings with a list of known craters to see if you have identified any meteorite craters.

3. Drop various sized objects, such as marbles or ball bearings, from various heights into clay or soil mixtures. Study the craters formed. Is there any relationship between the size of the crater and the size of the object dropped? Between the size of the crater and the height from which the object was dropped? How are these effects similar to meteorite impacts on the moon? How are they different?

4. Prepare several trays containing mixtures of various combinations of rock and soil. Place a thermometer on the surface of each tray of material. Then, immerse another thermometer just under the surface of the water in a pan. Place the trays and the pan of water in the bright sun or under a heat lamp for several hours. Then remove the trays and the pan from the light. Record the rate of temperature drop in each of the materials. Can your data be related to the rate of cooling of the lunar surface? If so, how? If not, why not?

CHALLENGES IN SCIENCE

1. Explain why a baseball pitcher could not throw a curve on the moon.

2. The crater Alphonsus (*Figure 28-9*) is slightly more than 100 km across. The Great Meteor Crater in Arizona (*Figure 9-17*) is about 1.3 km across. Try to find a crater in *Figure 28-9* that is approximately the same size as the Great Meteor Crater in Arizona.

3. Find out how the Surveyor chemical analysis unit, called the alpha-scattering experiment, operated. What advantages does this type of analysis have for unmanned space missions? What are its limitations?

4. Explain why the impact of an object traveling at an extremely high rate of speed would produce an explosion.

5. Suggest a theory, other than those outlined in Chapter 28, to account for the origin and development of the moon.

A meteor is one type of particle in "empty" space.

CHAPTER 29

The Nature of Space

Suppose someone asked you, "What is the nature of space?" Your first reaction might be to say that space is the vast, empty region that lies between the earth and the other large objects—such as the stars, planets, and moons—that we can see in the universe.

But, is the region between the planets and between the stars really empty? Might there be objects in this region that we cannot see, simply because they do not emit or reflect enough light to be seen? Perhaps there are objects too small or moving too fast to be seen by observers on the earth.

As you study Chapter 29, you will discover the nature of some particles that do exist in that "vast, empty region" of space. You will find out how these particles were discovered and what happens when these particles interact with the earth's atmosphere or with the earth itself. You will also read about some theories by which scientists attempt to explain the nature and origin of these particles. After studying Chapter 29, you will probably still refer to space as a vast region, but chances are that you will no longer refer to space as an empty region.

528

1. "Invisible" Objects in Space

The earth as a spacecraft. In recent years many satellites and spacecraft have been launched in efforts to study space beyond the earth's atmosphere. However, we could easily think of the earth itself as a gigantic spacecraft. The earth moves through space carrying all of us along with it. From here on the earth's surface, we are able to make many observations concerning the characteristics of the space through which we move.

In previous chapters we have described a large variety of objects in space which we have observed from the surface of the earth. A list of such objects would include galaxies, stars, planets, asteroids, comets, and so on. Furthermore, we have mentioned that scientists use precise measurements of magnetic effects to learn about the nature of space. In general, scientists obtain information about space by observing signals that reach the earth's surface. The signals are either light signals or signals produced by changes in magnetic fields. But how can scientists observe objects in space which are too small to be seen or sensed in this way?

If we think of our earth as a spacecraft, we realize that we can learn much about these "invisible" objects also. After all, the earth is constantly sweeping through space. The earth collides with—or we might say collects—samples of the objects which exist in space. The samples collected by our earthly spacecraft have permitted scientists to make a partial description of what space is like between the planets and between the stars.

Consider the earth, the moon, and a man-made, orbiting space platform. What advantages would each of these objects have if used as a base for conducting studies of the nature of space? What disadvantages?

Particles or rays? You have often heard the terms "atomic radiation" and "radiation in space." Perhaps you have discovered that in many cases the subjects being discussed were not rays in the usual sense. Instead they were small, electrically charged, subatomic particles. In fact, the Van Allen belts which we described as belts of trapped, charged particles are often called belts of radiation. Thus, the terms particles and radiation are used interchangeably by scientists.

Although this seemingly inconsistent usage may be confusing at first, there are at least two good reasons for it. The first reason is historical. When scientists first noticed the effects of cosmic rays, they had no idea what was producing the effects. All they knew was that something was affecting their instruments. The effects were similar to the effects produced by X rays. However, the phenomenon seemed to originate not from the earth, but from outer space. So, the first name they used was cosmic radiation, or cosmic rays. We now know that most of this radiation is in the form of subatomic particles moving at high speeds. In fact, their speeds are nearly as great as the speed of light.

The second reason for using the terms radiation and particles interchangeably has to do with modern physics. Scientists have realized that there is no way to tell the difference between a wave and a particle. In some respects, for example, light behaves as if it were a train of waves. Then we can call it a *light beam.* In other respects, light behaves as if it were composed of tiny particles that we call photons. In a similar manner, electrons sometimes behave as waves and sometimes as particles.

This dual nature is really a very mystifying situation. Our intuition, gained on the basis of everyday experiences, does not serve us very well when we are dealing with the fundamental particles of nature. The result is that there is always some confusion in the language that we have to use. The following questions arise. What shall we call these objects? Are they particles or waves?

There is no hard and fast rule to apply in answering these questions. When scientists discuss the motion of one of these objects in a magnetic field, they usually use the word particle. When they are discussing the effect of a group of particles on a detecting instrument, they often use the term radiation. Thus, the Van Allen belt of trapped particles above the earth's atmosphere is often called the Van Allen radiation belt.

In considering the wavelike properties of cosmic particles or cosmic rays, how would you describe the wave length of cosmic rays?

2. Cosmic Rays

Why do scientists study cosmic rays? The study of cosmic rays is a good example of scientific research. The study began about the beginning of the twentieth century and continues today. Throughout all of this time, the physicists engaged in this study have been prompted by their own curiosity about the nature of the universe. Their inspiration has come from the mystery of the subject. They gave little, if any, thought to the benefits that might result from a study of cosmic rays. And yet, investigations of cosmic rays have resulted in much of our present-day understanding of the nature of fundamental particles and of atomic energy. Cosmic rays provided scientists with a natural key for unlocking the atomic nucleus.

What other studies do you know of that were undertaken only because of man's curiosity, but that resulted in important discoveries?

An effect of cosmic rays. The first scientists to observe the effects of cosmic rays did not know what was causing these effects. What they observed was that a charged *electroscope* left by itself would steadily discharge. A simple electroscope consists of a metal rod stuck through a cork in the top of a flask or of a bottle. At the bottom of the rod are two thin strips of metal foil. *(Figure 29-1.)* Normally, the two strips of foil hang straight down. However, if the end of the rod sticking

Figure 29-1. Investigations concerning the rate of discharge of a simple electroscope led to important findings concerning the nature of cosmic rays.

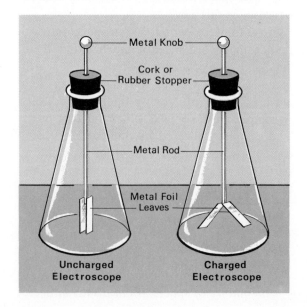

Metal Knob

Cork or Rubber Stopper

Metal Rod

Metal Foil Leaves

Uncharged Electroscope

Charged Electroscope

out the top of the bottle is charged with static electricity, the two pieces of metal foil stand out from each other, forming an inverted V. Then, after a time, the two pieces of metal foil gradually come back together. Somehow, the static electricity is leaving the electroscope. There are no electrical connectors attached to the rod or the metal foil to carry the electricity away. The electricity must be leaking away from the electroscope through the air surrounding the electroscope.

How could this happen? Air is not a conductor of electricity. Of course, when air is ionized it is a conductor. This condition exists in the ionosphere far above the surface of the earth. But, as we learned in studying the ionosphere, the air near the surface of the earth does not remain in an ionized condition. Any ions formed in the dense air would quickly recombine to form neutral particles. The air about an electroscope should not be ionized. And yet, it apparently is.

The scientists who first made this observation realized what was occurring. Some form of radiation in the earth's atmosphere was forming ions in the air about the electroscope. Although the ions would disappear quickly, more radiation was constantly bombarding the air to create more ions. Thus, a very small number of ions would always be present.

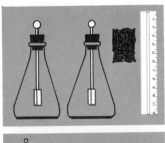
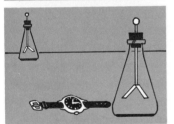

FIND OUT BY TRYING

Materials you will need: 2 electroscopes, plastic ruler, woolen cloth, clock or watch with luminous dial

Find out if the luminous material on a watch or clock face has any effect on the rate at which an electroscope discharges. Charge each electroscope in the following manner. Rub the plastic ruler vigorously with the woolen cloth. Then, touch the charged end of the ruler to the knob of the electroscope.

When both electroscopes are charged, set them aside. Observe the rates at which they discharge. After they have discharged, place the clock or watch having luminous material on it near one of the electroscopes. Charge the electroscopes as you did before. Does the presence of the luminous material have an effect on the rate of discharge? Explain the results of your experiment.

The nature of cosmic radiation. For some time it was believed that ion-producing radiation came from the earth itself. After all, the earth contains radioactive elements, such as uranium and radium. Scientists placed electroscopes in boxes with thick, lead walls. They wanted to see if the lead would prevent the radiation from getting to the electroscope. But the thick, lead walls made only a small difference. Finally, just before the first World War, two scientists took electroscopes up to high altitudes in balloons. They discovered that the electroscopes discharged much more rapidly at high altitudes than near the surface of the earth. This information was an important, and previously missing, piece of the puzzle.

On the basis of these high-altitude observations, scientists concluded that the radiation was coming from outside the earth's atmosphere rather than from the earth itself. The effect of the radiation was then measured at various altitudes, but the actual nature of the radiation was still a mystery. Some scientists thought the radiation consisted of *gamma rays*—a high-energy form of electromagnetic radiation. Others thought the radiation consisted of charged particles, such as electrons or protons.

Measurements made over different regions of the earth revealed that the radiation was more intense near the magnetic poles than it was between the magnetic poles. This finding was good evidence that the radiation was in the form of charged particles. Charged particles would be affected by the earth's magnetic field. Gamma rays would not.

Finally, the invention of the cloud chamber permitted scientists to observe the tracks of cosmic particles. As high-energy particles move through the vapor in a cloud chamber, they ionize the vapor. Small droplets of liquid condense around the ionized atoms. These droplets can be photographed, and they trace out the path which a cosmic particle—or cosmic ray—has followed.

If a magnet is placed next to the cloud chamber, charged particles moving through the cloud chamber follow a curved path. The direction of the curve reveals to scientists the sign of the electric charge on the particle. The radius of the curve tells the *momentum*—that is, the product of the mass and the velocity—of the particle.

By using the cloud chamber, scientists discovered that cosmic particles are not all alike. Many different types of particles were found in cosmic rays. Some of these types of particles

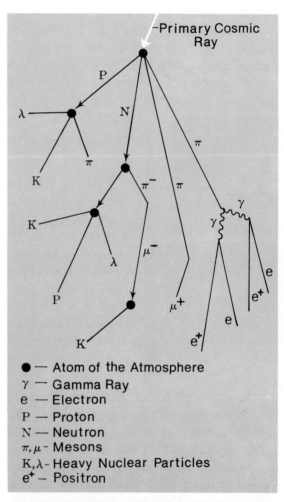

● — Atom of the Atmosphere
γ — Gamma Ray
e — Electron
P — Proton
N — Neutron
π, μ - Mesons
K, λ- Heavy Nuclear Particles
e^+ — Positron

Figure 29-3. Few, if any, primary cosmic rays reach the earth's surface. Instead, they collide with atoms in the atmosphere, producing secondary particles. Cosmic rays detected at the earth's surface are secondaries. How do scientists observe primary cosmic rays?

Figure 29-2. The paths of high-energy particles can be observed as the particles pass through a cloud chamber, or through a bubble chamber. Why are some of these paths—photographed in a bubble chamber— curved, while others are straight?

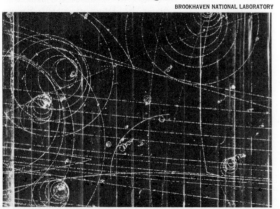

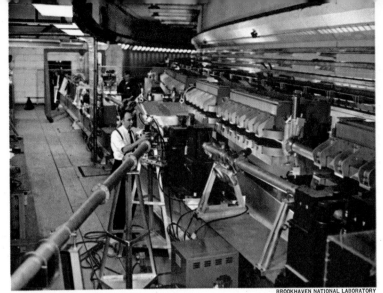

Figure 29-4. The great size and complexity of a particle accelerator are revealed by this photograph. The walls of the circular track around which the particles speed can be seen curving off to the right. Scientists are shown checking the pipe through which the beam of protons enters the accelerator. Even using such huge machines, man cannot give protons as much energy as primary cosmic rays have.

BROOKHAVEN NATIONAL LABORATORY

had never been observed before. They were completely new to scientists.

In recent years, cloud chambers and other instruments have been carried into space by rockets and satellites. It has been found that most of the cosmic particles reaching the top of the earth's atmosphere are protons moving with extremely great speeds. In fact, these cosmic particles—called *primary cosmic rays*—move with speeds that are more than 99.99999% of the speed of light. They are traveling at speeds very close to the absolute limit of speed.

One consequence of traveling at a very great speed is described by the theory of relativity. That is, from an earthly point of view, primary cosmic ray protons are more massive than protons which are at rest. When they enter the earth's atmosphere they may be considered as extremely powerful, subatomic bullets. As a primary cosmic ray smashes into the nucleus of an atom in the atmosphere, a shower of other particles called *secondary cosmic rays,* or just *secondaries,* is produced. *(Figure 29-3.)* By studying such collisions and the particles produced by such collisions, scientists have learned a great deal about the nature of atomic nuclei.

Today, scientists in many countries—particularly the United States and Russia—are building huge machines to accelerate protons to high energies. With these machines the scientists will be able to make studies much more conveniently than if they must rely on collisions between cosmic rays and atoms. They will be able to control the source of radiation and to make collisions occur where the collisions and their effects can be observed more conveniently.

The discharge of an electroscope is principally due to the secondaries produced when a primary particle strikes the nucleus of an atom in the atmosphere. As shown in *Figure 29-3,* the particles produced in the first impact go on to hit other nuclei and produce still more particles, and so on. This process keeps repeating all the way down to the surface of the earth. The shower of subatomic particles produced in this way amounts to about 10 to 15 particles passing into each square inch of the earth's surface every second.

How many cosmic rays are striking the top of your head every second? Are they primary or secondary rays? Might such rays affect your life in any way?

533

The origin of cosmic rays. Although scientists now know quite a bit about the nature and speed of cosmic particles, they are still mystified by the origin of cosmic particles. There have been many suggestions concerning the origin of cosmic rays. Some scientists believe that they were accelerated to their high speed at the time of the formation of the universe and have been flying through space ever since. Others believe that they are given off by supernovae—that is, by exploding stars. If this latter theory is correct, then one source for the cosmic rays now striking the earth might be the Crab nebula, shown in *Figure 4-14.*

Whatever the source of cosmic rays is, one thing seems clear. These extremely high-energy particles are related to the vast, cosmic phenomena of the universe and to the phenomena of minute atomic nuclei. Suppose we could observe all the phenomena associated with cosmic rays—from the time the primaries originate in space until the secondaries are absorbed by the earth. We would probably see all of the principles of physics demonstrated.

3. Meteorites

Early ideas about meteorites. On December 17, 1807, when Thomas Jefferson was President of the United States, two scientists from Yale University observed the fall of a meteorite. The meteorite landed close by, and they recovered it almost immediately. The story was told to Jefferson. His reply was, "I could more easily believe that two Yankee professors would lie than that stones would fall from heaven."

It may seem strange that Jefferson, one of the most educated men of his day, should have such an opinion about meteorites. And yet, such an opinion was common at that time. In those days, the strange-looking objects that we call meteorites were considered by most scientists to be ordinary stones which had been struck by lightning. That there could actually be stones flying through the heavens seemed as inconceivable to most educated people of that time as it did to Jefferson.

As years went by and as more and more accurate observations were made, the "rock struck by lightning" belief was finally set aside. Thus, for the past century, meteorites have not been regarded as objects to be viewed with suspicion or doubt. Rather, they are regarded as some of the best clues scientists can find about the nature of the solar system.

Sizes and classes of meteorites. The mass of an average meteorite is about 20 kg. However, the mass of an individual meteorite may differ greatly from this average. The largest known meteorite has a mass of about 60,000 kg—

Figure 29-5. The Hoba West meteorite, found near Grootfontain, South West Africa, is the largest meteorite ever found on earth.

that is, it weighs about 66 tons. *(Figure 29-5.)* The largest one ever found in the United States has a mass of about 14,000 kg. It weighs about 15.5 tons. Its surface is pitted with cavities, such as are commonly associated with meteorites. *(Figure 29-6.)* The smallest meteorites weigh less than one ounce. (There are other, very tiny particles called *micrometeorites* or *micrometeors*. These will be discussed later.)

Meteorites are commonly divided into three major classes. *Iron meteorites,* with a composition consisting of about 91 per cent iron and 8.5 per cent nickel, are one class of meteorites. *Stony meteorites* are another class of meteorites. This class of meteorites consists of meteorites having a composition of about 24 per cent iron. The remaining 76 per cent is similar to the silicate materials in the earth's crust. The third class of meteorites—the *stony-iron meteorites*—has a composition that is different from that of the other two classes. These contain more iron than the stony meteorites, but not enough iron to be classed as iron meteorites.

Figure 29-6. The Willamette meteorite, unearthed in Oregon's Willamette Valley in 1902, is the largest meteorite ever found in the United States.

COURTESY OF THE AMERICAN MUSEUM OF NATURAL HISTORY

Class	Falls (Per Cent)	Finds (Per Cent)
Iron	5.0	66.0
Stony-iron	1.5	7.5
Stony	93.5	26.5
Total	100.0	100.0

Figure 29-7. The table above shows the percentages of the 3 classes of meteorites that are falls and finds. Why, do you suppose, are there such differences in the percentages of falls and finds?

Scientists often group meteorites into two other kinds of groups called *falls* and *finds*. These groups are not based upon the composition of the meteorites. Instead, they depend upon the conditions under which the meteorites are found. Those which are called falls are ones which are seen to fall through the sky and are immediately picked up by someone. Their identification is not in question. Those that are called finds are those that are found on the ground sometime after they have fallen. The identification of such objects must be made through chemical analysis and comparison with other rocks, since no one actually saw them fall to earth.

Meteorite impacts. Meteorites enter the earth's atmosphere at various speeds. Some are traveling at 15 km per second. Others are traveling more than 70 km per second. As they streak down through the atmosphere, they leave behind them a bright trail of *incandescent* (in'kən des'ənt) *material.* Friction between the meteorite and the earth's atmosphere causes the meteorite to become so hot that the outer portion of the meteorite vaporizes and glows. Thus, the meteorite that reaches the surface of the earth is smaller than the object which began its passage through the earth's atmosphere. It is probable that, in some cases, a meteorite has lost more than half its mass in this manner.

Very large meteorites have struck the earth in prehistoric times. Such meteorites created huge craters on the surface of the earth, like those on the surface of the moon. Of course, over the years, the agents of weathering and erosion have been acting on these craters. Today, only a few of these craters are clearly recognizable and can be identified and studied. One of these is the Great Meteor Crater in Arizona, shown in *Figure 9-17*. Another is Chubb Crater in Canada, shown in *Figure 29-8*. Several other large circular features have been tentatively identified as the worn-down remnants of the rims of huge craters. One in Germany has a diameter of 25 km. Another in Africa is 80 km in diameter.

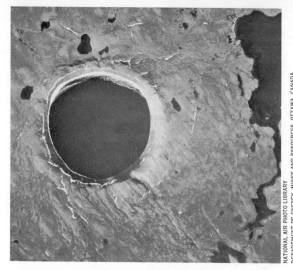

NATIONAL AIR PHOTO LIBRARY
DEPARTMENT OF ENERGY, MINES AND RESOURCES, OTTAWA, CANADA

Figure 29-8. An aerial photograph of Chubb Crater reveals the crater's nearly circular shape. This crater is more than 3 km across.

DO IT YOURSELF

Study meteorite impacts on the earth

Read articles in scientific journals and periodicals concerning meteorites and meteorite impacts on the earth. On a map of the world, mark locations that have been positively identified as sites of meteorite impacts. Mark locations which are suspected of being meteorite impact craters. Why isn't each site marked by a crater?

If a site or suspected site of meteorite impact is located near you, visit the site. What type of evidence would you search for in attempting to determine if a meteorite had impacted at that site?

The origin of meteorites. The chemical analysis of meteorites is considered in estimating the distribution of chemical elements in the universe. Scientists use the results of such analyses along with the results obtained by analyzing the spectra of various stars. The results of such analyses have also been compared with determinations of the distribution of chemical elements found in the crust of the earth. Thus, scientists include the composition of meteorites as an important part of their discussions of the composition of the universe. However, the origin of the meteorites is still a mystery.

Many meteorites have been tracked carefully by scientists using special cameras. In this way, scientists can estimate the meteorites' orbits, or at least the orbits they had before they encountered the atmosphere of the earth. In many cases, these orbits appear to have their farthest point about midway between Mars and Jupiter. As you may recall, this is the region containing the belt of asteroids. Thus, many scientists believe that the meteorites are actually small asteroids. There are other meteorites, however, with orbits that do not originate in the belt of asteroids. Therefore, it seems that the small-asteroid idea is not a complete explanation for the origin of meteorites.

In Chapter 11, we described one theory of the origin of the solar system based on a careful analysis of the chemical and mineral nature of meteorites. According to this theory, meteorites have had a complicated history. The material within them was once contained in a group of many small planets that orbited the sun. According to this theory, these planets collided with one another and were broken into much smaller particles, including many asteroids and meteorites. Thus, the meteorites

which fall to the earth now are, supposedly, pieces of these original planets.

Other scientists favor a less complicated theory. They feel that numerous, individual asteroids were formed at the same time the planets were formed. Subsequently, some of these asteroids collided with one another, and broke up to form the meteorites.

But neither theory is completely satisfactory. Although we know that meteorites do, indeed, "fall from heaven," their origin and many other details about meteorites are still mysteries.

4. Meteors

Observing meteors. How many "shooting stars" have you seen? Do you know what they are? Although they are called shooting stars, they are not stars at all. They are correctly called *meteors* (mē′ti ərs). They are not the same as meteorites, because for one thing, meteors never reach the surface of the earth. They are also much smaller than meteorites, and seem to be made of different materials.

A typical meteor is a small particle. Most meteors that you see on a clear night have a mass of only a small fraction of a gram. The mass of a meteor is determined by carefully measuring its speed and the brightness of the track it makes across the sky.

Most meteors strike the earth's atmosphere going at extremely high speeds, up to 70 km per second. At the time that a meteor makes its bright flash, it is about 100 km above the surface of the earth.

How can measurements of the speed and altitude of a meteor be made? Think back to the time you last saw a shooting star. Was there any way in which you could have determined how high it was and how fast it was going? Actually, such measurements are im-

possible for one observer alone. At least two people, located at different places on the earth's surface, must observe the same meteor. Then, using the principles of trigonometry, they can determine the altitude and the length of the meteor's visible path. See *Figure 29-9*. If the observers can measure the time the

Figure 29-9. The height and speed of a meteor can be determined if accurate observations of the same meteor are made from two different locations.

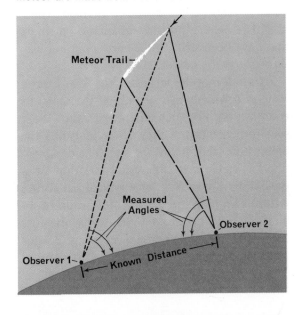

Figure 29-10. The photomicrographs at the right show particles believed to be meteor dust. Scientists search the world over for samples of meteor dust that have not been contaminated by industrial dust. Such samples have been found in Greenland and in sediment from the floor of the Pacific Ocean.

meteor takes to travel along the path, then the speed of the meteor can be calculated.

The nature of meteors. Apparently, meteors are small particles of dust. When they strike the atmosphere going at a high speed, friction between the meteor and atmosphere heats the material. The material gets so hot that it glows like the wire in an incandescent light bulb or in a flashbulb. Much of the material in the meteor is vaporized. The remainder is shattered into even smaller particles. These particles are slowed by friction. They finally fall to the earth, but they are too small to be seen without the aid of a microscope.

Scientists have examined samples of material that had lain undisturbed for hundreds of years. For example, samples of ice from Greenland and samples of sediment from the ocean floor have been examined. Such samples contain microscopic particles of iron which scientists believe are the remains of meteors that have been striking the earth continuously throughout the centuries.

By analyzing the incandescent light from a meteor, scientists can determine the meteor's composition. For such an analysis, they use a spectrometer, just as they do in analyzing the light of the stars and of the sun. The composition of meteors is different from that of a typical earthly rock or of a typical meteorite. After examining the spectra of a group of 44 meteors, scientists found that these meteors contained about 50 per cent calcium, 35 per cent iron, and small percentages of many other metals. However, not all meteors are alike in composition. Some meteors contain very little calcium, but a high percentage of magnesium and iron.

Would you consider the microscopic particles that reach the earth as micrometeors or as micrometeorites? Explain.

Are meteors common? Although you may think meteors are rare, they are actually very numerous. Astronomers estimate that 100 million meteors, each big enough to leave a visible trail, enter the earth's atmosphere each day. Of course, about half of these come in over the sunlit side of the earth. These cannot be seen. However, at least 50 million meteors are visible each night over the dark side of the earth. The smallest meteor that would leave a trail visible to the naked eye has a mass of about 0.001 grams. There are many meteors even smaller than that. In fact, if you consider how many meteors can be seen with a small telescope, the number is about 4 billion each night. There are meteors that are even smaller than those that are visible through a small telescope. In fact, scientists estimate that meteors carry about 1×10^7 kg, or about 10,000 tons, of material per day from space to the surface of the earth.

It is unlikely that meteors are more abundant near the earth than at any other location in the solar system. It is much more likely that meteors are common throughout the solar system. We see only those that enter the earth's atmosphere. Many spacecraft that have flown in interplanetary space have carried instruments to detect the impact of these tiny dust particles. They have found that dust particles are, indeed, scattered throughout the solar system. At least, they are scattered through those portions where spacecraft have flown.

How, do you suppose, could the presence of tiny dust particles in interplanetary space affect future space exploration?

5. Meteor Showers

Observing meteor showers. At certain times many meteors appear in the sky during a short interval of time. For example, many meteors occurred in the sky over America on November 12, 1833. In the late night and early morning hours, meteors were reported to be as thick in the sky as snowflakes in a storm. Many superstitious people believed that this was a signal for the end of the world. The drawing in *Figure 29-11* shows how this phenomenon appeared to one observer.

When many meteors appear in the sky in a short time, the phenomenon is called a *meteor shower.* Such meteor showers seem to occur each year at about the same time of the year. Furthermore, the tracks of the meteors in such a shower all appear to originate from a particular point in the sky. If so, all of the tiny dust particles that make up a meteor shower must be moving in the same orbit about the sun. The earth, traveling in its orbit about the sun, intersects the orbit of the meteors once each year. See *Figure 29-12.*

AUTHENTICATED NEWS INTERNATIONAL

Figure 29-11. The picture above shows the meteor shower of November 12, 1833, as portrayed by an artist of that time.

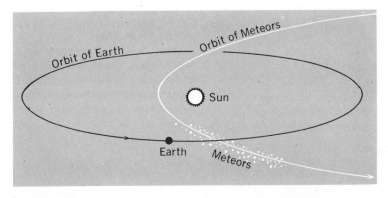

Figure 29-12. Suppose dust particles are spread out along an orbit about the sun. Suppose, too, that the orbit of the dust particles and the orbit of the earth intersect. Then, once each year, the earth would pass through the orbiting dust particles. The result would be a meteor shower.

If you have read about meteor showers in other books or in articles, you may have noticed that many regularly occurring showers have been given names, such as Geminids, Leonids, Orionids, etc. Use various references to determine the basis for such names.

Relating meteor showers and comets. Through the years, astronomers kept careful track of meteor showers, noting both the time of the year when the showers occurred and the direction from which they seemed to come. Eventually, it was possible to determine the orbit in which these small particles were moving.

Then, in 1862, an astronomer noticed that a newly discovered comet had the same orbit that had been determined for the particles of a particular shower of meteors. A few years later, the same relationship was found between another comet and a different meteor shower. During the next century, more and more observations indicated a relationship between comets and meteors. Today, astronomers believe that many meteors, especially those in meteor showers, originated from the comets. But if this is so, how did the meteors become separated from the comets they were once associated with?

No one knows exactly what a comet is. They appear very bright in the sky, but they do not seem to be solid bodies. By carefully examining a comet through a telescope, scientists can see bright stars shining through the comet. Thus, perhaps a comet is a loosely packed swarm of small particles. As the swarm passes the sun or any massive body, such as the planet Jupiter, the swarm of particles is subjected to tidal forces. That is, the gravitational force from the sun tends to pull more strongly on the portion of the swarm near the sun, and less strongly on the portion farther away. This is precisely the same effect that the moon has on the earth in causing tides in the ocean.

The earth, however, is a massive body and the moon's gravity can do no more than make a small bulge in the ocean a few feet high. In comparison, the mass of a comet is very small. Its own internal gravitational force is not enough to hold all of its pieces together. The tidal force of the sun pulls some of the pieces

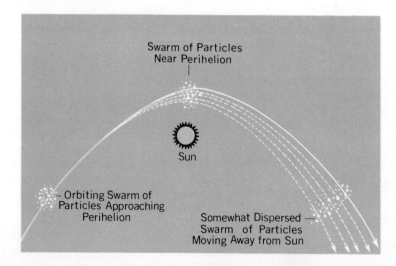

Swarm of Particles
Near Perihelion

Sun

Orbiting Swarm of
Particles Approaching
Perihelion

Somewhat Dispersed
Swarm of Particles
Moving Away from Sun

Figure 29-13. As an orbiting swarm of particles approaches perihelion, the sun's gravitational force attracts those particles closer to the sun more strongly than it does those farther from the sun. The gravitational force of the swarm is not great enough to hold the swarm together as closely as before. Thus, each time the swarm passes the sun, the particles in the swarm become more separated from one another.

away. The pieces then move in slightly different orbits, independent of one another. See *Figure 29-13.*

Although these pieces of the comet are now free of the main body of the comet, their orbit has not been changed very much. They still follow the same general path through the sky. The effect, then, is this. As a comet moves on in its orbit, it is preceded and followed by swarms of small dust particles.

Many factors will affect the subsequent motion of these dust particles and of the comet. Some factors that affect the particles are the gravitational attraction of planets near which they pass, the gravitational attraction of the sun, and the pressure of light from the sun. Various particles respond in various ways to these forces. Gradually, the swarm becomes more and more spread out. After hundreds of millions of years, the comet may become completely disintegrated. The particles which were originally in the comet might become spread out all along the orbit of the comet. The result would be a ring of dust particles following each other in an endless orbit around the sun.

In other cases, where the spreading-out effect has not become so great, the swarms of particles will be concentrated near the comet. We may pass through a meteor shower at the same time that we can see the parent comet in the sky.

Not all meteors are associated with meteor showers. What, would you say, is the origin of these individual meteors?

Distances between meteors. Although we have used the words "swarm of particles" in describing meteor showers, we must remember that we are dealing with very great distances and very high speeds. When a meteor shower occurs, so many meteors are seen that they appear to be very close to one another. And

WIDE WORLD PHOTOS

Figure 29-14. The nearly perpendicular streaks on the picture were caused by meteors. The film was exposed for two minutes during a 1966 meteor shower.

yet, even in the most intense meteor showers, the meteors are 30 to 40 km apart. For meteors that are not associated with a meteor shower, the spacing is even greater. The space between these meteors is about 500 km.

Since most meteor showers are closely associated with their parent comets, they are not equally intense each year. Some years when the earth passes through a comet's orbit, there are not many meteors there. After all, it takes a comet many years, in some cases hundreds of years, to complete one orbit. A comet, with its accompanying swarms of particles, may be far from the place where its orbit crosses the earth's orbit. However, when the timing is right—that is, when the meteors are moving along their orbit just in time to intersect the earth moving along its orbit—the showers can be spectacular. One shower that is often visible occurs every year in October. You can learn about the meteor showers predicted for any particular year from a local observatory or planetarium, from magazines such as *Sky and Telescope,* and even from your local newspaper. If possible, observe the next meteor shower that occurs. You will probably find it worthwhile.

If you were on the moon, would you expect to observe meteor showers? Give reasons for your answer.

Checking Your Knowledge

IMPORTANT IDEAS

1. Scientists use the terms particles and radiation interchangeably in describing certain phenomena.

2. One noticeable effect of cosmic rays is that they cause charged electroscopes to discharge.

3. Primary cosmic rays collide with atoms in the atmosphere, producing a shower of secondary cosmic rays. The secondaries are the rays we detect at the earth's surface.

4. Meteorites vary greatly in size and in chemical composition. Few meteorite craters are seen on the earth because of the effects of weathering and erosion.

5. As fast-moving dust particles encounter the earth's atmosphere, friction heats them to incandescence, producing bright streaks of light in the sky.

6. Whenever the earth intersects the orbit of a comet, a great number of dust particles enter the earth's atmosphere, producing a meteor shower.

USING NEW WORDS

Study the terms listed below. On your paper write the numerals 1-4. After each numeral write the term or terms to satisfy the instructions having the corresponding numeral.

incandescent	primary cosmic ray
meteor shower	secondary cosmic ray
momentum	iron meteorite
electroscope	cloud chamber
meteor	stony meteorite

1. List those terms that name particles entering the earth's atmosphere from space.

2. Select the term related to temperature.

3. Select the term related to velocity.

4. Write the terms that name instruments used in the study of cosmic rays.

TEST YOURSELF

Study the test below. On your paper write the numerals *1-10*. Beside each numeral write the correct response to that part of the test having the corresponding numeral.

1. An electroscope discharges, even when it is not touched, because cosmic rays _____ the air about the electroscope.

2. Primary cosmic rays consist of many different types of particles flying through space at very high speeds; however, the majority of these particles are _____.

3. When a primary cosmic ray collides with an atom in the earth's atmosphere, the result is a shower of particles called _____.

4. Meteorites which are seen to strike the earth and which are recovered almost immediately are called _____.

5. Craters produced by the impact of meteorites on the earth are *(often concealed by the effects of weathering and erosion, always easily recognized, never found in any region except the tropics).*

6. Most meteorites that are finds are *(iron meteorites, stony meteorites, stony-iron meteorites).*

7. As meteors streak across the sky, they become very hot because of *(cosmic ray activity, friction, their small size).*

8. The size of meteor particles is *(smaller than, larger than, the same as)* the size of meteorites.

9. Scientists now believe that meteor showers are related to *(phases of the moon, cosmic rays, orbits of comets).*

10. During a meteor shower, the meteors appear to be very close together; however, the average distance between meteors during such a shower is *(40 astronomical units; 40 meters, 40 km).*

Extending Your Knowledge

QUESTIONS TO EXPLORE

1. What observations indicate that cosmic rays are charged particles?

2. How would you explain why at least two observers must work together in determining the height and speed of a meteor?

3. What reasons can you give to explain why Galileo did not suggest that meteorite impacts formed the craters on the moon?

4. Do planets other than the earth intersect the orbits of comets? If so, would meteor showers be visible on these planets?

SOME THINGS TO DO

1. Find the volume of space you would need to search through to find a typical meteoric particle. Imagine each particle is in the center of a cube-shaped box, that each box touches the one next to it, and that each meteoric particle is 500 km from its nearest neighbor. What is the volume of each cube-shaped box?

2. Make a simple cloud chamber. You will need a small jar with a lid (a 12 oz. peanut butter jar is suitable), a small piece of black velvet, a piece of blotting paper, wire, a towel, alcohol, dry ice, and a bright flashlight. Cut a circular piece of velvet to fit inside the lid and a piece of blotting paper to fit the bottom of the jar. Bend a piece of wire to serve as a clip to hold the blotter in the bottom of the jar. Rinse the jar with hot water to get the jar warm. Then swish alcohol around on the sides of the jar and saturate the blotter. Pour off the excess alcohol and screw the lid onto the jar. Wrap the dry ice in the towel, so that only a small circle of dry ice is exposed. CAUTION: Wear gloves while handling dry ice. Place the jar, lid down, onto the exposed dry ice. Shine the light directly into the jar. Your apparatus should be set up as shown below. Look into the jar at the black velvet in the lid. You should see the trails of cosmic rays there.

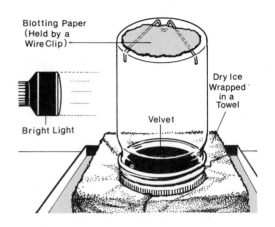

Blotting Paper (Held by a Wire Clip)

Dry Ice Wrapped in a Towel

Velvet

Bright Light

CHALLENGES IN SCIENCE

1. Estimate the total mass of all meteors in the solar system. Remember that the earth collects about 1×10^7 kg of meteor material each day. Compute the volume of space that the earth sweeps through each day. Next, compute the volume of a sphere with a radius equal to the radius of the orbit of Pluto. Assume that meteors are distributed uniformly throughout the solar system. Then, the volume of the solar system is to the volume of space the earth sweeps out in one day as the mass of meteor material in the solar system is to the mass of meteor material collected by the earth in one day. After finding the mass of meteor material in the solar system, compare this mass with the mass of the earth and with the mass of the sun.

2. Several types of particles have been identified as primary cosmic particles. Prepare a bar graph showing these types and what percentage of the total number of cosmic particles is represented by each type.

CHAPTER 30

The radio telescope is one tool used in exploring the frontier of space.

Frontiers—Above and Below

At the beginning of the 20th century, some scientists felt that man's knowledge of the physical world was almost complete. To be sure, there was work to be done in determining more accurate values of physical constants, distances, and sizes. For example, the speed of light would be more accurately determined, the distances to the stars and planets would become known with greater accuracy, and precise values for atomic radii would be obtained. However, these scientists thought that the really important discoveries in science had already been made. To say that this idea was a mistake is an understatement.

Nevertheless, many people today express a similar belief. They think of the discoveries of the early explorers and inventors with envy and yearning. They wonder about the future. Can we ever expect to experience the thrill and excitement that Columbus or Magellan felt in setting out to explore an unknown world? Will any of our inventions change man's way of life the way the steam engine did, or the way the use of atomic energy is doing now? Where can one find such exciting worlds to conquer? Where are today's frontiers of adventure and knowledge?

The title of this chapter implies answers to some of these questions. In the earth-space sciences, the frontiers are above and below. Of course, man's knowledge of the earth's surface is not complete either, but his quest for knowledge is constantly taking him deeper into the earth's interior and farther out into space. Chapter 30 should help you realize that there are many frontiers, even in today's world. Will you help explore them?

1. The Farthest Probe

The record distance. In the exploration of space, men have sent instrumented spacecraft far from the earth. Some have been sent toward the sun, to the vicinity of Venus. Others have gone away from the sun, to the vicinity of Mars. *Mariner IV,* which traveled past Mars in 1965, was one such spacecraft.

At the time *Mariner IV* passed Mars, it was 134 million miles from earth. Most of the data that *Mariner IV* was designed to collect were collected as the spacecraft passed Mars. However, some instruments on board were designed to measure the characteristics of interplanetary space. These instruments continued to operate for two years after *Mariner IV* passed Mars. During this time, *Mariner IV* proceeded on its orbit about the sun. At one point, it was on the far side of the sun as viewed from the earth. At this point, *Mariner IV* was 216 million miles from the earth. Data were still being sent back to the large radio telescopes designed to receive the signals.

In spite of the fact that its distance from the earth was very great, *Mariner IV's* position in the solar system was still what astronomers might call "close in." After all, it was just barely outside the orbit of Mars, and Mars is one of the closer planets that circle the sun.

How would you explain the fact that Mariner IV *traveled 325 million miles in getting to Mars, and yet* Mariner IV *was only 134 million miles from earth when it got to Mars?*

The Grand Tour. Since 1965, other space probes—for example, *Mariner VI* and *Mariner VII*—have traveled even farther from the earth than *Mariner IV* went. A *Grand Tour* of the outer planets has been conceived by scientists. In accomplishing this Grand Tour, scientists plan to use natural forces to help propel the spacecraft along its path. The spacecraft will not depend completely upon rocket power to attain a high speed.

The first leg of the journey will be to get near the huge planet Jupiter. The spacecraft will have to use its own propulsion system to make this portion of the trip. But thereafter, nature will provide the force necessary to carry the probe out to Saturn, Uranus, and Neptune.

What force can propel a spacecraft away from the sun? It is simply gravitational force. As the spacecraft nears Jupiter, the gravitational force of Jupiter will attract it. However, the spacecraft will be moving too fast to be captured by Jupiter's gravitational field. It will move past Jupiter and continue on into space. But, in the interaction with Jupiter, Jupiter's gravitational attraction will have increased the speed of the spacecraft and will have changed its direction slightly. If the spacecraft passes Jupiter at just the right point, going in just the right direction, the effect of Jupiter's gravitational force will be to speed the probe on to the vicinity of Saturn. There, gravitational attraction will again be used to speed up the probe as it passes Saturn. The spacecraft will proceed out farther, to pass Uranus and, finally, Neptune.

Do you think the Grand Tour will be a manned space flight? How would you justify your answer?

Conditions favoring the Grand Tour. The complicated orbit of the Grand Tour is shown

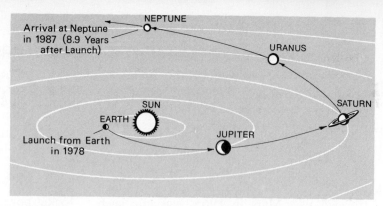

Figure 30-1. Can man explore the solar system without building rockets larger than those now available? One way would be to use the gravitational attraction of various planets to speed up the spacecraft as it flies by them. Such a proposal, called the Grand Tour, is represented in this diagram.

in *Figure 30-1*. As you can understand, the Grand Tour can occur only if all of these outer planets are in the proper positions. Furthermore, the spacecraft itself must be carefully guided. The guidance of the spacecraft can be accomplished from earth. Throughout its course, the spacecraft will be carefully tracked. Commands can be sent from earth to make slight changes in its course. These changes will be accomplished through the use of small rocket motors carried aboard the spacecraft. Thus, the spacecraft can be carefully steered to accomplish its mission.

However, the positions of the planets are beyond man's control. The planets are seldom in the proper positions to make such a flight possible. The planets will be in the proper positions for a launching in 1978. After that, however, it will be 174 years before they are again in the proper positions.

Of course, it would be possible to send a probe to the far reaches of the solar system by simply using a very powerful rocket. However, a rocket powerful enough to send a probe of several hundred pounds to the planet Neptune would be very big—much bigger than the giant rockets already being built to carry men to the moon. It is only with the help of the gravitational attraction of the planets that rockets of the type available now could be used to accomplish this mission. So, if a probe can be launched on such a trip in 1978, it may well set a distance record which will remain unmatched for many years.

2. The Deepest Hole

Why drill through the crust? Almost all the information we have about the interior of the earth has come from an analysis of seismograms. Scientists would like to be able to check this information by actually drilling down into and perhaps even through the crust of the earth.

The deepest oil well yet drilled is a little more than 6 km deep. This well is located in Wyoming—that is, in the center of a continental area. It does not reach through the crust to the Mohorovičić discontinuity.

Drilling through the earth's crust, of course, would be an extremely difficult task. But, if it could be accomplished, we would be able to bring samples of rock from below the Mohorovičić discontinuity to the earth's surface. We would be able to sample the upper edge of the mantle itself.

What are some properties and characteristics of the crust and of the mantle that might be determined if a hole could be drilled into the mantle?

Project Mohole. In 1957, a group of scientists suggested that it might be possible to drill a hole through the crust of the earth and into the upper regions of the mantle. The proposed project was called *Project Mohole*. These scientists suggested that the hole be drilled through the crust under the ocean rather than on a continent.

As you learned in Chapter 14, the crust of the earth is much thinner under the ocean than it is in the areas of the continents. In fact, there are places on the ocean floor where the crust is less than 5 km thick. In comparison, the continental region of the crust is about 30 km thick. Scientists involved with Project Mohole believed that it might be possible to drill through 5 km of rock. First, however, a way had to be found to operate a drilling platform from the surface of the ocean.

Difficulties encountered. As the project developed and as various designs were proposed, it became clear that one very difficult portion of the project would be the design of the drilling platform. The platform would have to be steady in spite of winds and waves.

Even if a steady platform could be devised, the drill shaft would have to extend through more than 10,000 feet of water before contacting the ocean floor. With nothing to constrain it from the sides, the shaft might bend and twist too much to operate properly.

In this drilling operation, the drilling rod would be a steel pipe, six inches to one foot in diameter. It might seem that a steel pipe of this size would have little tendency to bend and twist. But 10,000 feet is a long distance. Think of it this way. Imagine having a thin piece of steel wire 25 feet long. If you were standing on the third floor of a building and holding the wire out of a window, it would just about reach the ground. Now, imagine twisting the top end of the piece of wire between your fingers while you are trying to

push the other end into the ground, 25 feet below. This gives some idea of the nature of the problem. There was even the possibility that the steel pipe might actually twist itself into knots.

In order to prevent accidental twisting and bending, the platform on which the top of the drill was mounted would have to be very stable. The platform conceived of was, indeed, very big and probably would be very stable. See *Figure 30-2*.

As the years went by, the technical difficulties in Project Mohole became greater and greater. The amount of money estimated for successful completion also became greater and greater. Finally, the project was slowed down for a reëvaluation and redesign. At the present time, it appears that it will be many years before a hole will be drilled all the way through the crust of the earth.

Can you think of any difficulties, other than those mentioned, which might be encountered during the drilling of a very deep hole?

Figure 30-2. This proposed drilling platform (234 ft. × 279 ft.) would offer great stability. Drilling could be carried on even in winds of 38 miles per hour.

AUTHENTICATED NEWS INTERNATIONAL

3. Mysteries in Space

Strange objects in space. When astronomers discovered novae, nebulae, and the existence of galaxies beyond the Milky Way, they had come upon some fascinating mysteries. But more recently, with the development of radio astronomy, even stranger objects have been found in space. Two of the most curious of these are called *quasars* (quasi-stellar radio sources) and *pulsars* (pulsating stars).

The discovery of quasars. Quasars were discovered by detecting the very strong radio signals which they emit. Radio astronomers compared their data with that of their colleagues who worked with optical telescopes. It was found that sources of intense radio signals seem to be associated with what appear to be ordinary stars. However, a careful examination of the spectra of these "ordinary" stars indicates that the light from these stars shows a very large red shift. As you learned in Chapter 5, a large red shift in a star's spectrum implies that the star is moving away from us very rapidly. In fact, based on their red shifts, quasars appear to be receding faster than any other known object. Their speeds of recession are from 0.2 to 0.5 times the speed of light.

What could these objects be? In order to fit them into the theory of the expanding universe, they would have to be very distant galaxies. They would have to be 2 billion to 5 billion light-years away—much farther away than any other galaxy previously studied.

This great distance from us would account for the fact that these objects appear to be faint stars, although they might be, in fact, large galaxies. However, there are some problems with this idea. First of all, the amount of radio energy which is being received here on earth from these objects is very great. If these objects are so very far away from us, then the amount of radio energy that they are emitting must be truly enormous.

Furthermore, it has been noticed that the amount of energy emitted is variable. For most quasars the variation in energy occurs in a cycle going from strong to weak in just a few days. Does this variation mean that the whole galaxy is somehow pulsating? Could a wave of pulsation move across a galaxy in a matter of few days? If so, the galaxy must be quite small. But, this assumption creates still another problem. How could a small galaxy emit such huge amounts of energy?

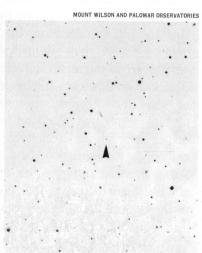

UNITED PRESS INTERNATIONAL

MOUNT WILSON AND PALOMAR OBSERVATORIES

Figure 30-3. Radio telescopes first detect the radio signals from quasars. Then, optical telescopes are pointed toward the source of radio signals. Pictures, such as the negative shown here, are obtained. In this picture, the faint dot indicated by the arrow represents the quasar 3C9.

Some scientists suggest that the physical forces involved are forces completely unknown to us. This might account for the tremendous output of energy. Other scientists suggest that the quasars are not as far away as their red shifts would indicate. According to these scientists, quasars may be members of our own galaxy flying away from us at tremendous speeds. If so, the red shifts of quasars should not be considered in relation to the red shifts of all of the other galaxies in the expanding universe. Instead, quasars should be considered as special cases. They might be special types of stars which had somehow been blasted out of our own Milky Way Galaxy and are now moving through intergalactic space at extremely high speeds. But what occurrence within our own galaxy could cause stars to be blown out in this way? There is no other evidence of such an occurrence to support this particular theory. Thus, the quasars remain something of a mystery.

Why, do you suppose, are some scientists reluctant to use a new, unknown force or an unknown principle in explaining the behavior of quasars?

Pulsars. Recently, another discovery, the pulsar, has created much interest. Pulsars, like quasars, were found by the radio astronomers. Pulsars not only emit radio signals, but they emit the signals in distinct pulses, at regularly spaced intervals. The pulses are received at the rate of about one pulse per second. The spacing of the intervals is so regular that some scientists have suggested the signals may be evidence of intelligent life in other parts of the galaxy. They have suggested that pulsars are gigantic radio beacons placed throughout the galaxy by some super civilization as guideposts for interstellar travel. Other scientists, inclined to be less imaginative, have tried to understand what kind of a star could put out pulses of energy at regularly repeated intervals. So far, no previously observed phenomenon in astronomy can account for it.

One suggestion to account for the pulses of radiation is that pulsars are extremely dense, rapidly rotating stars with strong magnetic fields. As they spin, their magnetic fields sweep across the sky. Radio pulses are sent out at regular intervals. However, the nature of such an extremely dense star cannot be explained. In order to have gravitational forces great enough to hold themselves together, such stars would have to be very dense. The gravitational force of an ordinary star would not be great enough to hold the star together if the star were rotating once each second.

Undoubtedly, other curious objects will be discovered in the sky as the techniques of radio astronomy are advanced. Larger telescopes, with more sensitive receivers are continually being built. In the future, the mysteries of outer space will probably be investigated more through the techniques of radio astronomy than through any other method.

What reasons can you give to explain why radio telescopes will be more useful than optical telescopes in the future?

4. Mysteries Within the Earth

Uncertainties concerning the core. You have read several chapters describing what is known about the interior of the earth. You have read various theories that scientists have proposed to explain their inferences about the earth's interior. Scientists have learned a great deal about the structure of the deep interior of the earth. However, there are many things they would like to know that they do not know as yet. In fact, the amount that is unknown seems to far outweigh the amount that is known. What is the composition of the core of the earth? Is it molten iron and nickel, as most geologists believe? Or is it some unusual, high-density form of silicate rock, as other geologists have suggested? How can scientists determine answers to these questions?

Uncertainties concerning the mantle. There are many uncertainties in man's concept of the mantle. The mantle is a complicated region. It may be as complicated as the crust. Some evidence, obtained in recent years, indicates that at about 100 km below the earth's surface, there is an unusual layer in the mantle. This layer appears to be more fluid than the material above it and below it. This layer may be the origin of volcanic material.

If such a fluid layer does exist, it has very important implications concerning the formation of the continents and the nature of the deep interior. As you will recall, in Chapter 20 we described a theory of convection currents in the mantle. These are currents of slowly moving, plastic rock. These currents start down near the boundary between the mantle and the core and move up to the Mohorovičić discontinuity. However, it is hard to imagine that such currents could penetrate a fluid layer 100 km below the Mohorovičić discontinuity. The energy and heat that convection currents carried from the deep interior would be rapidly dissipated in such a fluid layer. See *Figure 30-4*.

Effects on the earth's crust. As you recall, according to various theories, the formation of mountains and the growth of continents are the result of convection currents in the mantle. If such convection currents are stopped 100 km below the surface, does this mean that

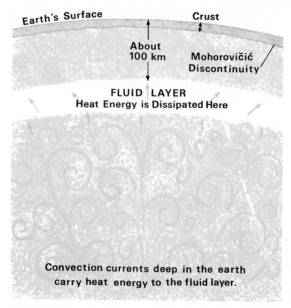

Convection currents deep in the earth carry heat energy to the fluid layer.

Figure 30-4. A fluid layer may exist in the mantle. If so, this layer would quickly dissipate heat brought to it from the earth's interior by convection currents.

Figure 30-5. Relatively fast-moving convection currents may exist above the fluid layer. Such currents would produce various effects at the earth's surface.

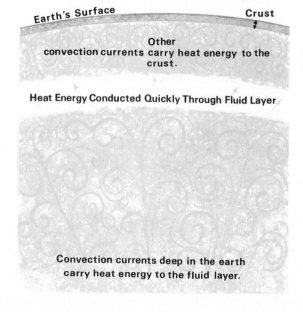

Convection currents deep in the earth carry heat energy to the fluid layer.

the convection theory of mountain building must be thrown out? Actually, it does not. Instead, the reverse may be true. It may be that a second set of convection currents exists in the top 100 km of the mantle, just above the fluid layer and just below the crust. *(Figure 30-5.)* Such currents might move rapidly. Perhaps the rock in this region is more plastic than that in deeper layers. Furthermore, these currents would have very little to impede them. That is, there would be a fluid layer beneath them and a fairly mobile crust above them.

As you can understand, the mystery about the detailed structure of the mantle is also closely related to ideas about the nature and development of the continents. In fact, the presence of a fluid layer within the mantle strongly supports the idea of continental drift that was described in Chapter 21.

Possibilities for the future. Perhaps the question of whether or not a fluid layer exists in the mantle will be resolved in a few years. The techniques of seismology are used to determine the nature of this region of the earth.

Therefore, as more and better seismographs are built, more complete data are continually being made available. In addition, computers are used to process these data. Therefore, scientists are able to make reasonable inferences much more quickly than before.

There is also some evidence that portions of the floor of the Atlantic Ocean are moving away from the Mid-Atlantic Ridge. If this evidence can be substantiated, it will give strong support to the theory of continental drift. As more and better oceanographic measurements are obtained, this mystery may also be solved.

But, will it ever be possible to obtain direct evidence about the huge convection currents in the mantle or in its upper and lower regions? So far, no one has thought of a way of making direct observations of much of the interior portion of the lithosphere.

Suppose the existence of a fluid layer in the mantle is proved. What effect will this have on presently accepted theories of the earth's origin and development?

5. Mysteries of the Universe

Cosmology. Ever since men began to think seriously about the nature of the universe, the greatest mysteries have seemed to lie in the field of cosmology. What is the nature of the universe? How did it all begin? Man has searched the skies and probed the earth trying to solve the mysteries of cosmology. Instead of solving them he has only succeeded in finding more mysteries. But one of the most fascinating mysteries in all of cosmology did not come from observations of the sky or of the earth. Instead, it came from the mind of a mathematician, Kurt Gödel.

Kurt Gödel was a close friend of Albert Einstein. They worked together on many problems of cosmology. As you may know, the theory of relativity is the basis for most modern theories of cosmology. Together, Gödel and Einstein would work out various mathematical "models" of the universe. Such a model is a picture that (1) agrees with what is known about astronomy and (2) is in accord with Einstein's theory of relativity. Many such models can be suggested. Because our knowledge of the universe is so limited, most of these models cannot be disproved.

An unusual model. One model that Kurt Gödel proposed is so baffling that scientists who have subsequently studied it have actually been shocked by its implications. What Professor Gödel suggested was this. We can actually see only a small fraction of the universe with our telescopes. Its total structure might be quite different from what we have observed so far.

After studying many possible structures for our universe, he discovered one with a very special property. Suppose a rocket ship could be built which would be capable of traveling at almost the speed of light. Suppose, too, that this rocket ship set off from earth, traveling in a straight line. The rocket ship would eventually complete a trip all the way around the universe. That is, even though it traveled in a straight line, the rocket ship would return to its starting point.

So far, this is not an unusual theory. Many models of a curved universe give the same sort of picture. But this model has an added feature. In this model, which is theoretically possible, the rocket ship would return to earth before it left!

So far, the strange model of the universe proposed by Professor Gödel continues to be a theoretical possibility. Observations that have been made in the many years since he developed this idea have not proved it wrong. Thus, for all scientists know today, we might be living in a universe in which traveling backward in time is possible.

The years ahead. The farther we look into space and the deeper we penetrate the earth's crust, the more we realize that there is a vast unknown to be explored by future generations. We have not reached a stage in the exploration of our environment that would compare with Leif Ericson's first visit to a new world. We have yet to send a Columbus to set foot onto other unexplored worlds.

Many opportunities lie ahead for ambitious and adventurous persons. The need for astronomers, astronauts, oceanographers, geophysicists, cosmologists, meteorologists, and geologists will increase manyfold.

In the years ahead, you will learn many things about the earth-space sciences—things that are not even known to scientists today. Whether you become a scientist or not makes little difference. The earth-space sciences will become increasingly important to the individual citizen. In our society, where the individual is asked to make important decisions about the future of himself and his neighbors, learning about the earth-space sciences will be an essential part of each individual's continuing education.

DO IT YOURSELF

Prepare a report

How would you compare your present idea of the earth and its environment in space with what you thought about this subject one year ago? What objects and phenomena do you now know of that you did not know of one year ago? During the past year, how have your ideas changed concerning the methods used by scientists? What important advances concerning his knowledge of the earth and space do you think man will make in the next decade? Prepare a report in which you answer these questions and in which you explain any changes that have occurred in your ideas about science or the work of scientists.

Checking Your Knowledge

IMPORTANT IDEAS

1. Scientists envision a Grand Tour of the outer planets of the solar system. Gravitational force would be used to supplement rocket propulsion in achieving high speeds.

2. Our knowledge of the earth's interior beyond the deepest hole yet drilled is based on indirect evidence. Project Mohole, an attempt to drill through the earth's crust, has been postponed indefinitely.

3. Quasars and pulsars are recently discovered sources of radio waves. These objects cannot be explained satisfactorily on the basis of our present knowledge.

4. Some recently obtained evidence suggests that a layer of nearly fluid material exists about 100 km below the earth's surface. Proving the existence of such a layer would have important implications concerning the development of mountains and continents.

5. The years ahead promise to be filled with achievement and adventure in all areas of the earth-space sciences.

USING NEW WORDS

Study the terms listed below. Each term is related to the term with which it is paired. Each pair of terms is related to frontiers of scientific research in the earth-space sciences. Write the letters *a* through *e* on your paper. After each letter write two brief statements. Tell how the words in the pair having the corresponding letter are related. Then, tell how the pair is related to frontiers in the earth-space sciences.

  a. Project Mohole — crust
  b. Grand Tour — *Mariner IV*
  c. quasar — pulsar
  d. continental drift — mantle
  e. space travel — time travel

TEST YOURSELF

Study the test below. Write the numerals *1-10* on your paper. Beside each numeral write the correct response to that part of the test having the corresponding numeral.

1. The Grand Tour described in Chapter 30 could be launched *(in the early 1970's, in the late 1970's, at any convenient time).*

2. The spacecraft *Mariner IV* is now *(orbiting the earth, traveling away from the solar system, orbiting the sun).*

3. Pulsars send out radio signals at regular intervals of about one each *(hour, minute, second).*

4. One aspect of quasars that is a subject of controversy among scientists is the quasars' *(extremely great red shift, extremely great apparent brightness, peculiar shape).*

5. In attempting to drill a hole to the earth's mantle, as in Project Mohole, scientists selected *(a deep valley, a sandy beach, the ocean floor)* as a drilling site.

6. The site of drilling operations for Project Mohole was selected because *(the drill would cut faster there, the crust is thinner there, it was the easiest place to set up a drilling platform).*

7. The possibility that intelligent life might exist at other places in the universe was raised by the discovery of *(continental drift, quasars, pulsars).*

8. According to Gödel, if man could travel at nearly the speed of light, he might be able to *(move backward in time, disprove the theory of gravitation, reach zero mass).*

9. Quasars and pulsars were discovered through the use of *(radio, optical, infrared)* telescopes.

10. Many theories of cosmology are based on Einstein's theory of _____.

Extending Your Knowledge

QUESTIONS TO EXPLORE

1. What reasons would you give to explain the fact that many scientists do not accept the hypothesis that pulsars are evidence of intelligent life in outer space?

2. Do you think it is more important for our government to spend money for space exploration or for research concerning the oceans? What reasons would you give to justify your answer? What other types of research do you consider important?

3. What observations concerning quasars are difficult to explain?

4. How do quasars differ from pulsars? How do these objects differ from our sun?

5. What, do you think, will occur first: (1) man's arrival on Mars or (2) the obtaining of a sample of material from the earth's core? How would you justify your answer?

6. Do you think the model of the universe described by Gödel and Einstein can be shown to be correct? If so, what are some problems that must be solved first? If not, what aspects of the model defy checking?

SOME THINGS TO DO

1. Find out all you can about the Mariner series of space probes. Try to answer questions such as the following. What was the objective of the Mariner series? What were the specific objectives of *Mariner I, Mariner II, Mariner III,* and *Mariner IV?* Were the Mariner spacecraft to be satellites of the earth? Was each flight a success? What information was gained that could be put to immediate, practical use for the benefit of mankind?

2. Find out about the most recent space probe that has been attempted. What was its main objective? What instruments were aboard the spacecraft? What experiments were to be performed? Was it a manned or an unmanned flight? Was the mission considered successful? Organize your findings into a report to be given to the class.

3. Make a study of Project Mohole. Find answers to these questions. What progress had been made before the project was discontinued? What were some factors that caused the project to be discontinued? Did the project provide any useful information before being halted?

CHALLENGES IN SCIENCE

1. Imagine that a drilling operation is in progress. An attempt is being made to drill through the earth's crust. The drilling is being done in the ocean floor at a place where the water is 10,000 feet deep. Imagine, too, that the drill bit breaks after drilling through 3,000 feet of rock. The bit must be replaced. Calculate the weight of the drill rod that must be lifted in order to change the drill bit, if the drill rod is steel pipe that weighs 31 pounds per foot. Find out how this pipe is lifted. Devise a procedure for lowering the bit into position so that the first 3,000 feet will not have to be drilled again. Make a list of difficulties encountered in deep-water drilling that are not encountered in drilling on land.

2. Devise a procedure that you would follow in order to determine whether or not the regularly spaced radio signals from pulsars are evidence of the existence of intelligent beings in outer space.

3. Write a paper describing how research in areas of the earth-space sciences might affect international relations. How might these relations be adversely affected by such research? What favorable effects might result from such research?

On December 7, 1872, H.M.S. *Challenger* sailed out of the mouth of the Thames River. From then until May 24, 1876, she sailed around the globe, logging 68,890 nautical miles. Scientists aboard gathered data and biological specimens from waters of various depths and at almost all latitudes. The end product was a vast collection of marine organisms such as the world had never seen and fifty new volumes of information, some of which are still useful as reference works today.

The voyage of the *Challenger* has the distinction of being the longest, continuous scientific expedition ever undertaken. The *Challenger* was a navy ship, but all her guns except two had been removed, and the main deck was set aside for scientific work. A small library and two laboratories—one for biology and one for chemistry —were installed. Equipment for the voyage was the best available at that time. All in all, the team of scientists aboard the *Challenger* had everything they needed to do their job, and the mission was an unqualified success. When the *Challenger* first set sail on the expedition, man's knowledge of the deep sea was almost nil. When *Challenger* returned, much still remained to be learned about the ocean, but at least the ocean's gross measurements had been taken. Data concerning depth, currents, temperature, and salinity had been recorded. Many new species and genera of marine organisms had been collected.

As important as the data were, the real importance of the *Challenger* expedition was not in the data gathered. After all, subsequent expeditions have been able to gather more accurate data because of advances in technology. Furthermore, the *Challenger* expedition was not the first to study some aspect of the ocean. What, then, was the importance of the work associated with the *Challenger's* voyage?

Previously, there had been some isolated attempts to study the ocean. Benjamin Franklin had charted the course of the Gulf Stream and had made observations of the temperature of its water. Matthew Fontaine Maury, an officer in the U.S. Navy, had made an intensive study of several major ocean currents. Samples of marine life had been taken from the ocean and studied. But such studies only whetted the curiosity of scientists. There had been no attempt to study the ocean in its entirety. Furthermore, the prospect of transoceanic telegraphy had aroused a practical interest in ocean-bottom conditions. The time was ripe for a thorough study of the ocean. Thus, when the British Admiralty made H.M.S. *Challenger* available to scientists, it marked the beginning of oceanography as an integrated science, rather than a hodgepodge of nonrelated studies.

Oceanographic research is vitally important. It may provide information about subjects of scientific interest, such as mountain development and the earth's origin. Furthermore, oceanographic research may provide man with sources of the food and minerals he needs. As time goes by, the science of oceanography will become increasingly important. Thus, the voyage that marked the beginning of modern oceanography is recognized as a breakthrough in science.

REVIEWING UNIT SEVEN

SUMMARY

1. The earth's upper atmosphere contains many ions produced by the interaction of high-energy radiation from the sun with the atoms and molecules found in the upper atmosphere.

2. A belt of charged particles exists in a certain region about the earth. Charged particles are trapped in this region as a result of their interaction with the magnetic field of the earth.

3. The moon has been a subject of scientific interest for more than three centuries. Today, the moon is being studied more intently than ever because scientists hope that man will soon be able to travel safely to the moon and back.

4. The space through which the earth moves is not empty. Countless bits of matter —some having great amounts of energy and mass—are "collected" by the earth each day.

5. Even after centuries of study and research, man has barely begun to solve the mysteries of the universe. Many frontiers are yet to be explored, both in space and on our own planet.

QUESTIONS TO DISCUSS

1. Are ions formed in the earth's atmosphere below an altitude of 90 km?

2. Do you think that belts of particles, similar to the Van Allen belt, exist about the moon? How would you justify your answer?

3. We always see the same side of the moon. Does this fact indicate that the other side of the moon is permanently dark? Why?

4. How can we be certain that the moon has no atmosphere? What are some effects of the lack of a lunar atmosphere?

5. How are pulsars and Cepheid variables alike? How do they differ?

UNIT TEST

Study the test below. Read the instructions for each portion of the test. Then, on your paper write the numerals *1-20*. Beside each numeral write the letter of the correct response to the part of the test having the corresponding numeral.

1-6. Indicate whether the mission of each type of spacecraft listed was to (a) study the earth's ionosphere, (b) study the closer planets, or (c) study the moon's surface.

1. Ranger   3. *Alouette*   5. Lunar Orbiter
2. Mariner   4. Surveyor   6. Explorer

7-10. Indicate which of the following— (a) magnetopause, (b) Van Allen belt, (c) ionosphere, or (d) cosmic rays—is most closely related to each statement below.

7. may originate in novae or supernovae
8. discovered by analyzing data from the satellite *Explorer I*
9. changes regularly from day to night
10. detected only in regions more than 20,000 km from the earth

11-14. Indicate the instrument or procedure—(a) Geiger counter, (b) falling-sphere method, (c) cloud chamber, or (d) ionosonde—used to study these properties.

11. the density of the upper atmosphere
12. the altitude of the E-layer
13. the shape of the Van Allen belt
14. the charge on a subatomic particle

15-20. Classify each term listed as (a) a property, (b) an instrument, or (c) an observable occurrence.

15. albedo   18. meteor shower
16. momentum   19. aurora borealis
17. ionosonde   20. electroscope

ENRICHING YOUR SCIENCE EXPERIENCES

INVESTIGATIONS TO CARRY OUT

1. Obtain the best photograph you can of a section of the moon's surface. Then, by cutting circular holes in 3 × 5 index cards, make a series of stencils. Make the largest hole as large as the largest crater on your photograph of the moon. Make the diameter of the next largest hole, half that of the largest hole. Continue making stencils having successively smaller holes. Make the diameter of each succeeding hole, half that of the previous one until you have made the smallest one you can make. Now, starting with the smallest stencil, count all the craters that fit inside the hole. Mark each crater as you count it. Then, use the stencil having the next larger size. Count the craters that fit within that hole, skipping the ones already counted. Repeat this procedure, using a larger stencil each time, until you have used all the stencils. Make a table of your results. How would you use such a table to support the meteorite impact theory of the origin of lunar craters? The volcanism theory?

2. Try to collect some meteoric dust particles. Collect about one-half cup of the debris from a rain gutter on your house or garage. Put the debris and about one quart of distilled water in a very clean container. Put a bar magnet in a waterproof plastic bag, and use the magnet in the bag to stir the mixture of water and rain-gutter debris. After thoroughly stirring the mixture, some particles will be adhering to the plastic bag. Place the plastic bag containing the magnet in a fresh cup of distilled water. Remove the magnet, but not the plastic, from this cup of distilled water. In this way, you can get any adhering particles free of the magnet, so they will settle to the bottom of the cup. Place some of the sediment from the cup of distilled water on a microscope slide. Examine the sediment under low power and then under high power. You may observe some particles similar to those in *Figure 29-10*. How would you distinguish between meteor dust and bits of other materials?

ADDITIONAL READING IN SCIENCE

Alter, Dinsmore, *Pictorial Guide to the Moon*. New York, Thomas Y. Crowell Company, 1963. 182 pp.

Cowen, Robert C., *Frontiers of the Sea*. Garden City, New York, Doubleday & Company, Inc., 1960. 307 pp.

Dietz, Robert S., "Astroblemes." *Scientific American* (August, 1961), pp. 50-58.

Hibbs, Albert R., "The Surface of the Moon." *Scientific American* (March, 1967), pp. 61-74.

Levin, E., Viele, Donald D., and Eldrenkamp, Lowell B., "The Lunar Orbiter Missions to the Moon." *Scientific American* (May, 1968), pp. 59-78.

Scott, Ronald F., "The Feel of the Moon." *Scientific American* (November, 1967), pp. 34-43.

Shklovskii, I. S., and Sagan, Carl, *Intelligent Life in the Universe*. San Francisco, Holden-Day, Inc., 1966. 509 pp.

APPENDIX

In this appendix are included some of the ideas and data necessary for developing an understanding of the universe as it is observed by man from his home on the planet earth. This appendix consists of five parts. In the first part, some of the standard units of measurement used in recording man's observations are described. Also, the use of scientific notation in recording data is discussed. In each of the other four parts, information and data relating to the earth, the solar system, the Milky Way Galaxy, and the universe are given.

UNITS OF MEASURE AND WAYS OF RECORDING THEM

In all fields of science, experimentation and observation are basic to learning about and understanding natural phenomena. Data obtained through observations made during an investigation are recorded. Thus, a record of the investigation is available for study, interpretation, and evaluation by the experimenter and by other persons interested in the particular field of investigation.

STANDARD UNITS

In science, many of the observations made are related to measurement. In these observations, measurements are made of length, mass, time, and volume. The standard units used in making such measurements are indicated below.

Measurement	Unit
length	meter
mass	gram
time	second
volume	liter

Divisions and multiples of these basic units are indicated by prefixes used with the names of the basic units. Some of the more commonly used prefixes and their meanings are listed below.

Prefix	Meaning	
mega	1,000,000	of the unit
kilo	1,000	of the unit
deca	10	of the unit
deci	0.1	of the unit
centi	0.01	of the unit
milli	0.001	of the unit
micro	0.000001	of the unit
nano	0.000000001	of the unit

In the recording of observations, the names of the units are often abbreviated. Listed below are the abbreviations used in recording the more common units.

Unit	Abbr.	Unit	Abbr.
meter	m	gram	g
kilometer	km	kilogram	kg
decimeter	dm	milligram	mg
centimeter	cm	metric ton	t
millimeter	mm	liter	l
second	sec	milliliter	ml

CONVERSION FACTORS

In science, measurements are usually made and the data recorded in terms of units of the metric system. It is sometimes necessary to change the expression of quantities from the metric to the English units, or vice versa. Below are listed equivalent values of various units.

Unit	Equivalent	Unit	Equivalent
1 km	0.6214 mile	1 mile	1.609 km
1 m	1.094 yards	1 yard	0.9144 m
1 m	3.281 feet	1 foot	0.3048 m
1 cm	0.3937 inch	1 inch	2.54 cm
1 l	1.057 quarts	1 quart	0.9463 l
1 l	33.81 fl. oz.	1 fl. oz.	0.02957 l
1 kg	2.205 pounds	1 pound	0.4536 kg
1 t	1.102 U.S. tons	1 U.S. ton	0.9072 t

OTHER UNITS OF IMPORTANCE

Observations in the earth-space sciences may involve units other than those of length, mass, time, and volume. Some of the additional units which may be involved are described below.

Angstrom, (A): a unit of length. One A is equivalent to 0.00000001 cm.

astronomical unit, (A.U.): a unit of distance equal to the average distance from the earth to the sun. (Approximately 150,000,000 km.)

calorie, (cal): the amount of heat necessary to raise the temperature of 1 gram of water at 15°C through 1°C.

degree, (°): a unit used in measuring temperature of materials. In the Celsius temperature scale, one degree is 1/100th the difference between the temperature of melting ice and that of boiling water under standard atmospheric pressure. One degree Celsius is equivalent to 1.8 degrees Fahrenheit.

degree, (°): a unit of measurement of angle. One degree is equal to 1/360th of a circle.

dyne, (d): a unit of force. One dyne, when applied to a one-gram mass, will cause an acceleration of 1 cm per second per second.

millibar, (mb): a unit of pressure. One millibar is equivalent to 1,000 dynes per sq. cm.

minute, ('): a unit of measurement of angle. One minute is equal to 1/60th of a degree.

second, ("): a unit of measurement of angle. One second is equal to 1/60th of a minute.

SCIENTIFIC NOTATION

In the sciences, it is often necessary to record very great numbers as well as very small numbers. One way of recording such numbers is to express them by using powers of ten. Recorded below are several examples of numbers expressed in scientific notation. Those enclosed in brackets are seldom used.

1,000,000,000	one billion	1×10^9
1,000,000	one million	1×10^6
1,000	one thousand	1×10^3
100	one hundred	1×10^2
10	ten	$[1 \times 10^1$
1	one	$1 \times 10^0]$
.1	one tenth	1×10^{-1}
.01	one hundredth	1×10^{-2}
.001	one thousandth	1×10^{-3}
.000001	one millionth	1×10^{-6}

In expressing a number in scientific notation, the number is expressed as a product of two factors. One factor is expressed as a power of ten. The other factor is expressed as the number, which, when multiplied by ten raised to the indicated power, will give a product equal to the original number. Thus, 1,800 is expressed as 1.8×10^3, and .018 is expressed as 1.8×10^{-2}. The number 1.8, however, represents an exception. It is expressed simply as 1.8.

THE EARTH

Man's home in space is the planet earth. It is with this object in space that man has been most concerned. It is with this object in space that man is most familiar. Included in this section of the appendix are data related to the planet earth.

Age. No definite figure can be given for the earth's age. The age of certain rock of the earth has been determined to be 3.5 billion years. Many scientists use the figure 4.5 billion years for the age of the earth.

Composition. The earth is often described as consisting of the lithosphere—soil and rock; the hydrosphere—water; and the atmosphere—gases of the air. Eight elements account for more than 95 per cent of the crust (by weight). Two of these, silicon and oxygen, account for nearly 75 per cent of the weight.

Density. The mean or average density of the planet is 5.522 g/cm³.

Formation. Various theories about the formation of the earth have been suggested. None has yet overcome all objections or answered all questions.

Mass. By various methods, the mass of the earth has been determined to be 5.983×10^{24} kg (6.595×10^{21} tons).

Movement. The earth moves in space with the galaxy and with the solar system. In the solar system, the earth revolves about the sun with an average speed of 29.77 km per sec or 18.5 miles per second.

The earth rotates on its axis at a rate of one rotation each 23 hours and 56 minutes. This rate at the equator is 0.4626 km per sec (1,035 miles per hour).

Shape. The earth is often described as a sphere. This is not technically correct. Measurements show that the diameter at the equator is 42.9 km (26.7 miles) greater than the diameter at the poles.

Structure. In general, the earth's structure can be thought of as a series of concentric spheres. At the center is the *core*. About an inner core is a fluid outer core. Surrounding the outer core is another layer, the *mantle*. About the mantle is the *crust*. Above the crust of over 70 per cent of the earth is the water of the ocean. About the earth's surface is the atmosphere.

Temperature. The mean temperature at the earth's surface is 14°C. Within the limits of man's observation, the temperature increases with depth at about 30°C per km. The temperature at the earth's core is estimated to be about 4,500°C.

Volume. The radius of a sphere having the same volume as that of the earth would be 6,371,221.3 m (3,958.89 miles).

THE SOLAR SYSTEM

The earth is part of a large system of materials and energy called the solar system. It includes the sun, nine planets, thirty-one satellites of planets, comets, asteroids, and different types of radiation. Data related to the system are listed below.

	Volume (Earth=1)	Mass (Earth=1)	Density (Average)	Gravity (Earth=1)	Orbital velocity (mi/sec)	Satellites (Natural)
Sun	1.3×10^6	3.32×10^5	1.41	28	—	—
Mercury	0.055	0.055	5.61	0.38	29.7	0
Venus	0.878	0.81	5.16	0.89	21.7	0
Earth	1.00	1.00	5.52	1.00	18.5	1
Moon	0.02	0.01	3.31	0.165	0.64	0
Mars	0.15	0.107	3.95	0.38	15.0	2
Jupiter	1320	317.4	1.34	2.64	8.1	12
Saturn	736	95.03	0.69	1.17	6.0	10
Uranus	51	14.5	1.36	1.03	4.2	5
Neptune	40	17.2	1.30	1.50	3.4	2
Pluto	?	?	?	?	3.0	0

THE MILKY WAY GALAXY

The solar system, although huge compared to the earth, is almost insignificant in the vastness of the Milky Way Galaxy. The sun, so important to the planets and its other satellites, is but one of a hundred billion stars in the galaxy. Listed below are some of the data and ideas used by astronomers in describing the Milky Way Galaxy.

COMPOSITION

The Milky Way Galaxy contains stars of many different sizes and colors. It contains star clusters and vast clouds of dust and gas. Scattered throughout are particles of hydrogen and all different types of radiation.

FORM

The galaxy, in general, is like a flat disk with a bulge in the center. The distance across the disk is about 100,000 light-years. The distance through the bulge at the center of the disk is about 10,000 light-years. The disk is not uniform, however.

Extending from the center and curving about the denser, inner portion are concentrated streamers of galactic material called spiral arms. Various types of stars and dust clouds are included in these spiral arms.

MOVEMENT

Observations of various galaxies indicate that the galaxies are moving through space. No doubt, the Milky Way Galaxy is also moving through space at a rapid rate. At the same time, the galaxy is rotating about its axis through the center bulge. The period of rotation is considered to be about 2.5×10^8 years.

THE UNIVERSE

The Milky Way Galaxy is one of millions of galaxies observed in space. Galaxies exist as far out from the Milky Way Galaxy as man is capable of observing. How far the galaxies extend beyond the limits of our observation is not known. Various theories suggest different ideas about the extent and form of the space and materials which, together, make up the universe. Many questions about the nature of the universe are still unanswered. Much remains to be determined.

GLOSSARY-INDEX

This glossary-index is like other indexes in that it lists in alphabetical order the topics, names, and science terms used in the book. But, in addition, it defines and shows the pronunciation of many of the words and terms of science. This makes it a special kind of dictionary as well as an index.

Use the glossary-index when you want to determine where to turn in the book to find out about a topic. Use it, too, when you want to find the meaning of a word or term used in science.

The following key to the pronunciation of words used in this book and in the glossary-index is from the Thorndike-Barnhart Dictionary Series.

a hat	ėr term	oi oil	ch child	ə represents:
ā age	i it	ou out	hw wheat	a in about
ã care	ī ice	u cup	ng long	e in taken
ä far	o hot	ù put	th thin	i in pencil
e let	ō open	ü rule	ŦH then	o in lemon
ē equal	ô order	ū use	zh measure	u in circus

Absolute magnitude: the brightness a star would appear to have if it were 32.6 light-years from the earth, 92, 96, 97, 111

Absolute temperature scale: scale of temperature that uses the lowest possible temperature—absolute zero—as its starting point, 70-71

Abyssal (ə bis′əl) **plain:** large, flat region of the ocean floor, 332, 333, 469, 470

Acceleration (ak sel′ə rā′shən): rate of change of velocity, 179, 189-190

Adiabatic (ad′i ə bat′ik) **cooling:** decrease in the temperature of a gas, occurring even though no heat is transferred between the gas and its surroundings, 358

Air

See Atmosphere

Albedo (al bē′dō): ratio of light reflected to light received by a celestial body, 513

Alluvial (ə lü′vi əl) **fan:** fan-shaped deposit of sediment, formed where a temporary stream empties onto a plain or other flat region, 316

Alouette, 485

Alpha Centauri, 85, 95, 559

Alpha particle: nucleus of a helium atom, composed of two neutrons and two protons, 375

Aluminum, 229, 280, 447, 456, 473
  abundance of, 229, 280
  production of, 473

Andromeda: a constellation of stars, 55

Andromeda galaxy: spiral galaxy seen in the area of the constellation Andromeda, 55, 57, 61, 66, 85
  appearance of, 55
  distance to, 85

Aphelion (ə fē′li ən): point in the orbit of a body moving about the sun that is farthest from the sun, 164

Apogee (ap′ə jē): point in the orbit of a body moving about the earth that is farthest from the earth, 497

Apparent magnitude: the brightness of a star, as viewed from the earth, 89-92, 96

Archimede's principle: principle which states that a floating object displaces an amount of fluid equal to its own mass, 270

Asteroids: group of solid objects, much smaller than planets, with orbits about the sun, 171-172, 536-537

Astronomical unit: the average distance between the centers of the earth and the sun, 95, 98, 558

Astronomy: the study of objects in space and phenomena taking place in space, 28

Astrophysicist (as'trō fiz'ə sist): scientist concerned with the makeup of objects in space and with the forces that affect them, 28, 29, 33

Atmosphere: the layer of gases that surrounds the earth, 25, 224-228, 342-361
characteristics of, 226
composition of, 343
density of, 343
heating of, 348
layers of, 344-347
mass of, 228
patterns of circulation in, 352-354
stability of, 357-358

Auroral displays, 505-507
causes of, 505
effects of, 507

Basalt: dark-colored, dense type of igneous rock, 268, 420, 464, 521-522
on the moon, 521-522

Batholith (bath'ə lith): mass of igneous rock often associated with a mountain range, 382

Bauxite: ore of aluminum, 415

Becquerel, A. H., 409

Beryllium (bə ril'i əm): chemical element found in some silicate rock, 456

Betelgeuse (bē'təl jüz): brightest star in the constellation Orion, 68, 111

Big-bang theory: theory which states that all the matter and energy in the universe were concentrated into one region which exploded, 133

Big Dipper, 77, 103

Binary star
See Double star

Biosphere (bī'ə sfir): thin zone at the surface of the earth wherein living creatures exist, 228

Bode's law: relationship, discovered by Titius, that exists between the planets' distances from the sun and a series of numbers, 197-198

Calcium carbonate: chemical compound found in limestone, 317

Cambrian (kam'bri ən) **Period,** 374, 437

Carbon 14: radioactive form of carbon used in radioactive dating, 439-441
in dating fossils, 441
decay products of, 440
half-life of, 439
production of, 440
See also Radioactive dating

Carbon-nitrogen cycle: nuclear reaction, involving a series of steps, in which hydrogen is converted to helium and energy is released, 118-120

Cassiopeia (kas'i ə pē'ə): constellation of stars, 48-49

Celestial sphere: sphere which, according to the ancients, surrounded the earth and upon which the stars were placed, 49

Celsius (sel'si əs) **temperature scale:** temperature scale in which the freezing point of water is zero degrees and the boiling point of water is one hundred degrees. This scale was formerly known as the centigrade scale. 71

Cenozoic (sē'nə zō'ik) **Era,** 374, 437

Center of mass: in astronomy, point about which the heavenly bodies of a system of heavenly bodies revolve, 77-78

Centrifugal (sen trif'ə gəl) **force:** the apparent force tending to cause a revolving object to move away from the center of revolution, 181

Centripetal (sen trip'ə təl) **force:** force tending to cause a revolving object to move toward the center of revolution, 181-183

Cepheid (sef'i id) **variable:** a star which varies in brightness at regular intervals, 61, 79, 96-98, 104
change in temperature of, 79
and distance measurement, 97

Ceres (sir'ēz): name of the largest asteroid discovered so far, 171

Chemosphere (kem'ə sfir): layer of the atmosphere in which chemical reactions take place and which is between the altitudes of about 20 km and 100 km, 345-347

Cleavage (klē'vij) **plane:** the plane along which a crystal or a rock splits, 425

Coal, 450-452
how formed, 451
types of, 452

Coal—*Continued*
uses of, 450
varieties of, 451
when formed, 450

Comet, 174-175, 540, 541

Conglomerate (kən glom′ər it): sedimentary rock consisting of stones of various sizes held together by some cementing material, 422, 461-470
cobble, 462
deposition of, 468
solidification of, 469

Constellation: group of stars forming a pattern or design, 47-49

Continental drift: theory which states that the continents were once bunched together, but that they split apart and drifted into their present positions, 405-406

Continental nucleus: area of a continent which was first to form, 399-403, 406
Grenville region of, 401-402
Keewatin region of, 401-402

Continental shelf: area adjacent to the shoreline of a continent. Although under water, this area is considered as part of the continent. 328-331
materials of, 329
slope of, 328
width of, 328

Continental shield, 315-316

Continental slope: sloping region of the ocean floor from the outer edge of the continental shelf to the deep ocean floor, 328

Contraction theory: theory of mountain development which states that mountains form as a result of the cooling and contracting of the outermost portions of the solid earth, 386-390
modern interpretation of, 388
and radioactivity, 386
shortcomings of, 390
strong points of, 389

Convection currents: currents generated by differences in temperature, 391-393, 397-398
in the mantle, 391
patterns of, 397
as a process in continent development, 397
surface effects of, 392

Convection theory: theory of mountain development which states that mountains form as a result of convection currents within the earth, 391-393
shortcomings of, 392
strong points of, 391

Copernicus, Nicholaus, 51, 94, 163

Copernican (kə pėr′nə kən) **system:** a sun-centered system, devised by Copernicus, to describe the motions of the planets, 163

Core: the innermost portion of the earth, 20, 252, 259-261, 278-279
composition of, 260, 278-279
density of, 259
structure of, 260

Core: a sample of material obtained by driving a hollow tube into the earth and then pushing the captured material out of the tube, 325

Coring device: a hollow tube that is driven into the earth to obtain samples of earth material, 325

Coriolis (kôr i ō′lis) **effect:** an effect, caused by the earth's rotation, that produces a deflection in the motion of objects moving on or near the earth's surface, 350-352, 357

Corona (kə rō′nə): a very rarefied, glowing region about the sun, sometimes referred to as a portion of the sun's atmosphere, 155

Correlation (kôr′ə lā′shən): in geology, the identification and matching up of rock layers in two separate regions, 368

Cosmic rays: high-energy rays or particles reaching the earth from outer space, 26, 529-534
effect on electroscope, 530
nature of, 531
origin of, 26
types of, 532

Cosmology: study of the nature and structure of the universe, 129, 551-552

Crab nebula: a rapidly expanding cloud of gas and dust that is believed to be the remnants of a supernova, 79, 533

Craters
causes of, 514-516
on earth, 172, 515, 535-536
on Mars, 173
on the moon, 512

Earth—*Continued*
structure of, 258-272
surface changes in, 226
surface materials of, 226, 228, 229
theories of origin of, 275, 292
volume of, 223

Earthquake(s): shaking motion of the outer part of the solid earth, 237-255, 384
and detecting instruments, 241-245
distribution of, 239
locating, 247
and relationship to mountain building, 384
under the ocean, 239

Eclipse (i klips'): darkening of a heavenly body when some other heavenly body is in a position that cuts off all or part of its light, 89, 513
lunar, 513
solar, 89

Einstein, Albert, 187-193, 551

Electromagnetic spectrum: the total known range of radiation, 169

Electron(s) (i lek'tron): a very small particle of matter, having the smallest possible negative electrical charge, 117-119, 489, 497, 502-506, 532
in atoms, 117
in the solar wind, 489
in the Van Allen belt, 497

Electroscope: apparatus for detecting the presence of an electrical charge, 530

Ellipse (i lips'): a plane curve shaped so that the sum of the distances between any point on the curve and two specified points, called foci, is constant, 164-165

Emerald: valuable, green-colored gemstone, 456

Epicycle (ep'ə sī'kəl): name given to a small circle, the center of which moves on the circumference of a larger circle called a deferent, 162-163

Equilibrium (ē'kwə lib'ri əm): stable condition in which opposing forces or processes balance each other, 120, 440

Equivalence (i kwiv'ə ləns), **principle of:** the statement that the effects of gravity are the same as those of a steady acceleration, 190

Era (ir'ə): a very extensive interval in the reckoning of geological time, 374

Erosion: wearing away of a material by moving air, water, or ice, 301, 308, 311, 366

Escape velocity: velocity needed to escape from a gravitational field, 136

Fahrenheit (far'ən hīt) **temperature scale:** temperature scale in which the freezing point of water is 32° and the boiling point of water is 212°, 71

Faraday, Michael, 479

Fault (fôlt): a crack in the earth's crust along which movement of adjacent portions of the crust occurs, 371, 388, 401

Feldspar, 418, 464

Fluorescence: the property of absorbing radiation of one wave length and emitting radiation of another wave length, 82

Focal length: the distance between a lens (or mirror) and the point at which the lens (or mirror) causes incoming parallel rays to come together, 58

Focus: (earthquake) the point at which an earthquake takes place within the earth, 384

Focus: (ellipse) one of two points used to determine an ellipse, 164

Fossils: evidences of earlier forms of life, 404, 430-443
building catalog of, 437
formation of, 431-433
See also Index fossils

Fraunhofer, Joseph von, 74

Fraunhofer (froun'hō fər) **lines:** the dark lines in an absorption spectrum, 75

Gabbro, 464

Galactic cluster: a group of hundreds of stars, all moving in the same direction and all believed to have been formed at the same time, 80

Galaxies: vast collections of stars, dust, and gas, 55, 60-63, 129, 131
classification of, 63
clusters of, 63
discovery of, 60
spectra of, 131
types of, 62

Galileo, 179-180, 187, 511

Gamma ray: a high-energy form of electromagnetic radiation, 532

Gauss, Karl Friedrich, 479

Geiger (gī′gər) **counter:** a device for detecting and counting ionizing particles, 495-497

Gemstones: materials—usually mineral crystals—that have great value because of their rarity and special properties, 455-457

Geochemistry (jē′ō kəm′ə stri): the study of the chemical composition of the earth's crust, 30, 32

Geologic time scale: history of the earth divided into units of time, 372-374

Geology (ji ol′ə ji): study of the earth, 29

Geophysics (jē′ō fiz′iks): the study of the earth's features and the forces which cause them, 29, 32

Geosyncline (jē′ō sin′klīn): a long, broad depression in the earth's crust, 381

Glaciers
    effects of, 312-313
    and glacial erratics, 366
    and glaciated valleys, 312
    nature of, 310

Globular cluster: a group of thousands of stars very close together in a spherical volume located outside the spiral arms of a galaxy, 53, 80

Gneiss, 267, 426

Gödel, Kurt, 551-552

Grand Canyon
    correlation of strata in, 369
    erosion in, 308-309, 366
    exposed layers of, 31, 318-319

Granite: the most common type of intrusive, igneous rock, 263, 267, 416, 420

Graphite, crystal structure of, 455

Gravitation: mutual attraction between masses, 178-193, 232, 466-467
    and erosion, 466-467
    and gravitational field of the earth, 232
    and gravitational mass, 189
    law of, 180

Gravitational constant: the term G in Newton's law of gravitation, $F = Gm_1m_2/r^2$, 180

Great circle: the intersection of the earth's surface and a plane through the earth's center, 192

Great Meteor Crater
    See Craters, on earth

Gulf Stream: an important surface current in the North Atlantic, 337

Guyot (gī′ət): a flat-topped seamount, the top of which is usually about 1,500 to 1,800 meters below sea level, 335

Half-life: the time required for half the total number of nuclei in a given mass of radioactive material to disintegrate, 375-376, 439, 442, 503
    concept of, 375
    of a neutron, 503
    of radioactive carbon, 439
    of radioactive potassium, 442
    of uranium, 376, 439

Hall, Charles, 473

Halley's comet: a comet that reappears about every 75 years. The first predicted reappearance (predicted by Edmund Halley) was made in 1758. 175

Helix: a spiral, or corkscrew-shaped, form—for example, the thread of a bolt, 498

Hematite, 448

Heroult, Paul, 473

Hertzsprung-Russell diagram: a graphic representation of the relationship between stellar luminosity and stellar temperature, 112-115, 124

Hornblende, 418

Horsehead nebula, 56, 81

Horse latitudes
    See Winds

Hurricane, 14, 355, 357, 361

Hutton, James, 295

Hydrosphere: waters of the earth, 25, 228, 288

Igneous rock: rock formed as molten material solidified, 266-268, 419-421
    formations of, 419-421
    types of, 266-268, 421

IGY: abbreviation for International Geophysical Year, an internationally sponsored project of scientific inquiry, 39

Impermeable rock: rock through which liquids and gases do not pass, 454

Incandescence: glow produced by high temperature, 535, 538

Index fossils
characteristics of, 435
definition of, 369
uses of, 373, 435-438

Inertia (in ér′shə): the tendency of an object to resist any change in its motion, 189

Inertial mass: the mass of an object as determined by observing its inertia, 189

Infrared radiation: electromagnetic radiation of a certain range of wave lengths, longer than visible light but shorter than radio waves, 169, 171, 281-282, 514
as a factor in differentiation, 281-282
from moon, 514
from planets, 169, 171

Inverse-square relationship: relationship between two variables in that one varies inversely with the square of the other, 90-91

Ion (ī′ən): atom or a group of atoms having an electrical charge, 153, 345, 479-488

Ionosonde (ī on′ə sond): radio transmitter and receiver designed to use in studies of the ionosphere, 480-481, 485

Ionosphere (ī on′ə sfir): layer of the earth's atmosphere extending from an altitude of 80 km to over 400 km, 345, 479-481
changes in, 481
discovery of, 479
and reflection of radio waves, 345
structure of, 481
studies of, 480

Island arc
See Mountain(s), primary arcs of

Jet streams: high-velocity, high-altitude winds circling the earth between the latitudes 30° and 40° in both the Northern Hemisphere and the Southern Hemisphere, 361

Jupiter, 52, 53, 160, 161, 169, 276

Jurassic (jủ ras′ik) **Period,** 374, 437

Kelvin temperature scale: an absolute temperature scale on which absolute zero is the starting point, the freezing point of water is about 273°K and the boiling point of water is about 373°K, 70, 71

Kepler, Johannes, 51, 164

Kepler's laws: statements describing the orbital motion of the planets, 164-165

Kilogram (kil′ə gram): a unit of mass measurement equal to 1,000 grams, or about 2.2 lbs, 558

Kilometer (kil′ə mē′ter): a unit of length measurement equal to 1,000 meters or about 0.62 miles, 16, 558

Land forms: surface features of the earth's continents, 300

Lapidary: one who cuts and polishes stones, 457

Laser (lā′zər): appartus used to produce narrow, intense beams of a special type of light, 457

Lava (lä′və): molten rock material flowing from a volcano, or from a crack in the earth, 419

Light scattering: process by which certain nebulae are made visible, 82

Light-year: a unit of length equal to the distance light travels in one year, 54, 96, 98, 558

Limestone: a type of sedimentary rock, 25, 267, 268, 317, 422, 464
composition of, 268, 317, 422
test for, 464

Lithosphere (lith′ə sfir): the solid portion of the earth, 25, 228

Local Group: a group of at least 17 galaxies consisting of those galaxies nearest the Milky Way Galaxy, 63

Love wave: a type of seismic wave, involving motion of the surface layer in a horizontal plane only, 246

Luminosity (lü′mə nos′ə ti): the brightness of a star, in terms of the amount of light being emitted by the star, 71, 72, 111

Lunar eclipse
See Eclipse

Lyell, Sir Charles, 435

Magellanic (maj′ə lan′ik) **clouds:** the small, irregular galaxies nearest the Milky Way Galaxy, 62

Magma (mag′mə): molten rock material beneath the surface of the earth, 419

Magnetic field: region about a magnet in which the effects of the magnet are observed, 231, 498-501
    and changed particles, 498-501
    direction of, 498
    lines of force of, 231
    and magnetic compass, 231

Magnetic field of the earth
    characteristics of, 231
    compared to gravitational field, 232
    effect of solar wind on, 233
    form of, 233, 498

Magnetopause (mag nē′tō pôz): boundary between the magnetosphere and outer space, 489-491

Magnetosphere (mag nē′tō sfir): the region of space about the earth in which the predominant magnetic field is that of the earth, 489-491

Magnitude: (stellar) term used to describe the brightness of a star, 67
    See also Absolute magnitude *and* Apparent magnitude

Main sequence: portion of an H-R diagram, running from the upper left corner to the lower right corner, in which most of the points representing stars are located, 113-114, 120-121, 124
    sizes of stars on, 114
    as a stage in stellar evolution, 124
    structure of stars on, 120

Mantle: portion of the earth between the core and the crust, 252, 261-265, 546-551
    and effects on earth's crust, 550
    fluid layer in, 550
    inner, 265
    intermediate, 265
    materials of, 262
    uncertainties concerning, 550
    upper, 265

Marble: type of metamorphic rock used for building and statuary, 267, 268, 425-426

Mare (mär′ē): area of the moon that appears relatively dark and smooth, 512

Mars, 20, 52, 160, 168, 169, 172-173, 277

Matrix (mā′triks): fine-grained material that holds the various stones together in a formation of conglomerate, 462

Mercury, 160, 161, 164, 169, 277

Mesopause: upper boundary of the mesosphere, 344-345

Mesosphere: a layer of the atmosphere between the altitudes of about 30 and 80 km, 344-345

Mesozoic (mes′ə zō′ik) **Era,** 374, 437

Metamorphic rock: a type of rock resulting from changes produced by high temperature and pressure on igneous or sedimentary rock, 267-268, 424-427
    laboratory studies of, 426
    types of, 425

Metamorphism (met′ə môr′fiz əm): change in the structure of a rock caused by pressure and/or heat, 424-425
    factors in, 424
    processes in, 424

Meteorites: masses of stone and/or iron that fall to the earth's surface from space, 33, 172-173, 211-212, 515, 534-537
    classes of, 535
    falls, 535
    finds, 535
    impact craters of, 515, 535-536
    origin of, 536
    sizes of, 534

Meteorology (mē′ti ə rol′ə ji): study of weather, 33, 347-348

Meteors: tiny, solid particles traveling through space that burn up, due to friction, as they encounter the earth's atmosphere, 537-541
    abundance of, 538, 541
    altitude of, 537
    nature of, 538
    size of, 537
    spectra of, 538
    speed of, 537

Meteor shower(s), 539-541
    and effects of gravitation on comets, 541
    of November 12, 1833, 539
    related to comets, 540

at great depth, 339
in the North Atlantic, 337
at the surface, 337-339
world map of, 338

Ocean floor
features of, 328-336
sampling of, 325
trenches in, 385-386

Oceanography, 326-327, 555
See also Oceanology

Oceanology: study of the ocean, 34-35
See also Oceanography

Oceans: the whole body of salt water that covers more than 70 per cent of the earth's surface, 225, 322-329, 398
deepest part of, 225
formation of, 398
and interaction with atmosphere, 323
and interaction with land, 323
nature of water in, 327

Olivine (ol′ə vēn): a green-colored mineral composed of magnesium silicate and iron silicate, 265

Olivine basalt: a material similar to basalt, but containing greater amounts of olivine, 269

Open cluster
See Galactic cluster

Orbit: the path followed by one body as it moves about another, 104-105, 181-186
elliptical, 185
and period of revolution, 104, 185

Ordovician (ôr′də vish′ən) **Period,** 374, 437, 453

Ore: a mixture of minerals from which it may be profitable to obtain a pure metal, 448

Ore deposits: regions in which the ore of a particular metal is concentrated, 448-450
formation of, 448-450
size of, 448

Orion (ô rī′ən): constellation of stars, 68, 82
brightest star in, 68
Great Nebula in, 82

Oscillating-universe theory: theory of the universe that states that the universe alternates between periods of expansion and contraction, 133

Ozone (ō′zōn): form of oxygen, in which each molecule contains three oxygen atoms, 346-347

Paleozoic (pā′li ə zō′ik) **Era,** 374, 404, 437

Parallax (par′ə laks): an apparent change in the position of an object when the object is viewed from two different locations, 93-96

Parsec (pär′sek): a unit of distance equivalent to 3.26 light-years, the distance to a star that has a parallax of one second, 96, 98

Pennsylvanian (pen′səl vā′ni ən) **Period,** 374, 437, 450-451

Perihelion (per′ə hē′li ən): point closest to the sun on an orbit about the sun, 164

Period: interval on the geologic time scale; a portion of an era, 374

Period of revolution
See Orbit

Permian (pėr′mi ən) **Period,** 374, 437

Perrin, Jean, 117

Petrifaction (pet′rə fak′shən): process of fossil formation in which the material of the original organism is replaced with minerals, 432-433

Petroleum: mixture of liquid hydrocarbons found in the earth, 453-454
formation of, 453
increasing use of, 453
locating, 454

Photoelectric cell: a light-sensitive device, useful in astronomy to measure the brightness of stars, 68, 482

Photo emission: emission of electrons as a result of being struck by electromagnetic radiation, 482

Photosphere (fō′tə sfir): the visible surface of the sun, 146

Plains: flat, or nearly flat, expanses of land, 314-316
formation of, 314
related to continental shields, 315
sediment on, 315

Planetary wind
See Winds

Planets: large, massive objects orbiting the sun, 50, 158-175, 207
atmospheres of, 166-168
determining the mass of, 161

Radioactive elements: elements with nuclei that are unstable and break apart, releasing energy and forming new elements, 19, 288, 398

Radioactivity: the radiation emitted as a result of being radioactive, 409

Radio telescope: device used for detecting and recording radio waves coming from objects in space, 42, 170-171, 549

Radius vector: line from the sun to a planet, 164

Real image: picture produced by light which has been focused by a lens or reflected from a mirror and which may be projected onto a screen, 58

Red giant: very large, relatively cool star, 113, 115, 121
    See also Star

Red shift: shift of spectral lines toward the red end of the spectrum, indicating that the object emitting the light and the observer are moving apart, 102, 548
    See also Doppler effect

Relativity, theories of, 187-190, 532
    general, 187, 190
    special, 189
    See also Cosmology

Retrograde motion: an apparent reversal in a planet's direction of motion, 50, 162-163, 165

River systems, 306-310

Ruby: gemstone composed of aluminum oxide with chromium oxide present as an impurity, 457

San Andreas fault: a major fault in the earth's crust located in California and noted for its horizontal displacement, 371

Sandstone: type of sedimentary rock composed of sand grains which have been compacted and cemented together, 267, 318, 454

Sapphire: gemstone composed of aluminum oxide with a small amount of titanium oxide present as an impurity, 457

Saturn: 53, 159-161, 169, 276, 545

Scoria, 421

Scuba: self-contained underwater breathing apparatus, 326, 327

Sedimentary rock: rock formed when materials deposited as sediment have become compacted and cemented together, 25, 266-268, 368, 377, 421-423
    dating of, 377
    forming of, 266-267, 421
    fossils in, 423
    as a source of geologic information, 368
    stratification of, 423
    types of, 267-268, 422

Sediments: materials which have been deposited by agents of erosion. Sediments may consist of rock particles, remains of living organisms, or chemicals. 314-319, 331
    in alluvial fans, 316
    consolidation of, 318, 331
    in deltas, 317
    formed by living organisms, 317
    resulting from chemical action, 317
    and sedimentary rock, 318

Seismic (sīz′mik) **waves:** vibrations which move through the earth as the result of a sudden disturbance, such as an earthquake, 245-254
    factors affecting, 249
    interpreting, 251-254
    reflection of, 250
    refraction of, 250
    speed of, 247
    types of, 245

Seismogram: the record of data obtained from a seismograph, 242, 264

Seismograph: instrument used to detect and measure motions of the earth's crust, 242

Seismology: study of earthquakes and the waves produced by earthquakes, 241, 330
    and the ocean floor, 330

Shadow zone: region on the earth's surface to which the seismic waves from a particular earthquake do not travel directly, 252-254

Shale: type of sedimentary rock composed of clay or silt which has been compacted and cemented together, 267, 318, 454

Sidereal (sī dir′i əl) **day:** the time it takes the stars to apparently go around the earth, 139

Sill: structure formed after magma forces its way between two layers of sedimentary rock and solidifies there, 420

Strata: layers of sedimentary rock, 368-371
  correlation of, 368-369
  and crustal movement, 370-371

Stratopause: upper boundary of the stratosphere, 344-345

Stratosphere: region of the atmosphere between the troposphere and the mesosphere, 344-347

Sun: the star about which the earth and several other planets revolve, 144-155, 210
  composition of, 147
  corona of, 155
  density of, 145
  interior temperature of, 147
  mass of, 145
  photosphere of, 146
  rotation of, 150, 210
  size of, 145
  as a star, 145
  surface temperature of, 145

Sunspots: areas on the sun's surface which appear dark compared with the rest of the sun's surface. These areas appear dark because they are cooler than the rest of the sun's surface. 151-153, 505

Supernova: a star which undergoes an extremely violent release of energy, becoming millions of times brighter in the process, 79, 533

Superposition, law of: law which states that within a series of layers of rock, an upper layer was deposited more recently than a layer below it, 436

Surface wave: type of seismic wave which travels along the surface of the earth, producing vertical motion, 246

S-wave: seismic wave which travels through the earth, vibrating perpendicularly to the direction in which the wave is traveling, 245-255

Talus (tā′ləs): rock fragments that form a sloping pile at the base of a cliff, 467

Telescope: instrument used to increase man's ability to observe his environment in space, 51-59, 73, 169-171, 511
  eyepiece of, 59
  invention of, 51
  objective of, 59

  radio, 42, 169-171
  reflector, 59-60, 73
  refractor, 57-59

Temperature: an indication of the average kinetic energy of the molecules of a substance, 70-71, 168-171
  of planets, 169
  scales of, 71
  of stars, 70

Tertiary (tĕr′shi er′i) **Period,** 374, 437, 453

Trace elements: chemical elements present in only very minute amounts in a given substance, 33

Trade winds
  See Winds

Translucent material: material through which some light can pass, but through which objects cannot be clearly seen, 51

Triassic (trī as′ik) **Period,** 347, 437

Tributaries (trib′yə ter′iz): streams that flow into a larger stream, 307

Trilobite (trī′lə bīt): animal, now extinct, commonly found as a fossil in rock of the Cambrian and Ordovician periods, 431

Tropopause: upper limit of the troposphere, 344

Troposphere: region of the atmosphere from sea level up to an altitude of 10 to 15 km, 344-347

Tsunami (tsü nä′mi): large ocean wave caused by an earthquake, 239-240

Turbidity current: flowing stream of mud and rock which moves across the sea floor, 333-334, 468

Unified field theory: theory which attempts to relate all the known forces and particles, 188

Universe, 43-141
  expansion of, 129-132
  galaxies of, 60-63
  man's observation of, 43-63
  theories of origin of, 133-136

Upper atmosphere: portion of the atmosphere above an altitude of 100 km, 478-491

Uranium (y u̇ rā′ni əm): a radioactive element found in some igneous and metamorphic rock, 375, 439